Healthy Foundations
in Early Childhood Settings

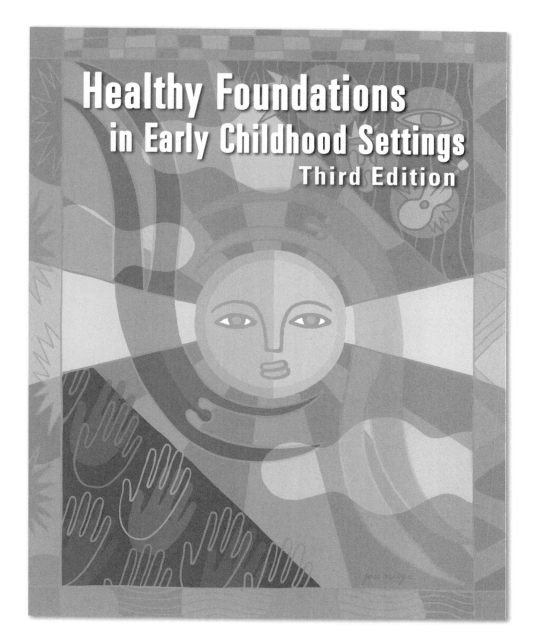

Healthy Foundations
in Early Childhood Settings
Third Edition

Barbara Pimento
George Brown College

Deborah Kernested
R.N.

THOMSON
NELSON

Australia   Canada   Mexico   Singapore   Spain   United Kingdom   United States

THOMSON

NELSON

Healthy Foundations in Early Childhood Settings, Third Edition

by Barbara Pimento and Deborah Kernested

Editorial Director and Publisher:
Evelyn Veitch

Executive Editor:
Joanna Cotton

Senior Marketing Manager:
Chantal Lanning

Developmental Editor:
Alwynn Pinard

Senior Production Editor:
Bob Kohlmeier

Copy-Editor:
Madeline Koch

Proofreader:
Margaret Crammond

Indexer:
Deborah Kernested

Senior Production Coordinator:
Hedy Sellers

Creative Director:
Angela Cluer

Interior Design:
Liz Harasymczuk

Cover Design:
Suzanne Peden

Cover Image:
José Ortega/The Stock Illustration Source

Compositor:
Alicja Jamorski

Printer:
Thomson/West

National Library of Canada Cataloguing in Publication

Pimento, Barbara
Healthy foundations in early childhood settings / Barbara Pimento and Deborah Kernested. — 3rd ed.

Previous ed. published under title: Healthy foundations in child care. Includes bibliographical references and index.

ISBN-13: 978-0-17-622481-3
ISBN-10: 0-17-622481-5

1. Day care centers—Health aspects—Canada—Textbooks.
2. Family day care—Health aspects—Canada—Textbooks.
3. Children—Health and hygiene—Canada—Textbooks. I. Kernested, Deborah, 1957– II. Pimento, Barbara. Healthy foundations in child care. III. Title.

HQ778.7.C3P55 2004   362.71'2
C2003-904364-9

CONTENTS

Before You Begin   xv
Acknowledgments   xix

UNIT 1   HEALTH PROMOTION

What Is Health?   3
Determinants of Health   4
    Individual and Community Roles   4
        Income/Social Status 5 / Healthy Child Development 9 /
        Freedom from Discrimination 10 / Communication and Life
        Skills 11
Canada's Health Care System   13
    Components of Canada's Health Care System   14
        Personal Health Care System 14 / Public Health Care System 15
Changing Attitudes toward Health Care   15
    An Emerging Collaborative Approach in Health Care   17
        Complementary Medicine Practitioners and Products   18
Prevention and Health Promotion   19
    What Is Prevention?   19
    What Is Health Promotion?   20
    Integrating Prevention into a Health Promotion Approach   20
Health Promotion Action Plan   22
    Action Plan   22
        Individual Problem Solving and Self-Reliance 23 / Collective
        Self-Help 23 / Community Action 24 / Societal Change 25
Health Promotion in Early Childhood Programs   26
    High-Quality Early Childhood Programs   26
        Advocating for Quality Early Childhood Programs 29 / Early
        Childhood Program Policies 30 / Parent–Educator Partnerships 32
        Cultural Diversity in Early Childhood Programs 34 / Networking with
        the Community 36
    Health Promotion Action Plan in the Early Childhood Program   36
Conclusion   38

What's Your Opinion? To Extend Eligibility or Not?   38
Assess Your Learning   39
Resource Materials   39
     Organizations 39 / Other Websites of Interest 40 / Printed Matter 40
Bibliography   40

UNIT 2   OCCUPATIONAL HEALTH

Promoting Your Physical Well-Being   50
     Achieving a Balance in Your Lifestyle   50
          Nutrition 50 / Physical Activity 54 / Leisure and Rest 56 /
          Reducing Other Risk Factors 57
     Infectious Diseases and You   59
     Preventing Musculoskeletal Injuries   61
     Furnishings and Layout   63
     Working with Art and Cleaning Products   66
          Workplace Hazardous Materials Information System   67
     Role of Public Health Agencies in Health Promotion   68
     Workplace Environmental Issues   68
     Injury Reports   69
Promoting Your Emotional and Social Well-Being   70
     Creating a Supportive Early Childhood Environment   70
          Role of Directors 71 / Role of Educators 72 / Men Working
          in Early Childhood Settings 74 / The Juggle Struggle: Stress 77
     Early Childhood Educational Experience: Setting the Stage   80
          Graduates: Starting the Job Search 82
Revisiting the Health Promotion Action Plan   83
Conclusion   84
What's Your Opinion? To Take a Break or Not to Break?   85
Assess Your Learning   85
Resource Materials   86
     Organizations 86 / Other Websites of Interest 86 / Printed Matter 86
Bibliography   87

UNIT 3   ILLNESS PREVENTION

Our Body's Natural Defence Mechanisms   101
     Immunity   102
How Infections Spread   102
     The Germ   103
     The Host   104
     The Vehicles of Transmission   104
          Through Direct or Indirect Contact   105
     The New Host   107
Breaking the Chain: Developing an Infection Control Strategy   108
     Immunization   109

Immunization Records 112 / Adverse Reactions 113 / Immune
  Globulin 113
Hygiene Practices   113
    Hand Washing 113 / Hygiene Practices for Infants and Toddlers 117
Cleaning and Sanitizing   123
    What Needs to Be Cleaned or Sanitized? 124 / Cleaning and
    Sanitizing Products and Techniques 125 / Implementing the
    Routines throughout the Day 127 / Protecting Yourself from
    Potentially Hazardous Substances 127
Revisiting the Health Promotion Action Plan   129
Conclusion   130
What's Your Opinion? To Glove or Not to Glove?   131
Assess Your Learning   131
Resource Materials   131
    Organizations 131 / Other Websites of Interest 132 / Printed Matter 132
Bibliography   132

UNIT 4   ILLNESS MANAGEMENT

Children's Health Care   136
    Children's Medical Examination at Enrollment   137
    Daily Observation of Children   138
        Daily Baseline Health Observations 138 / Health Observation
        throughout the Day 143
    Documenting Health Observations   143
        Documentation in Children's Files 144 / Early Childhood Program's
        Health Record 145 / Sharing Health Information with Physicians 146
    Excluding Children from Early Childhood Programs   146
        Alternative Care Arrangements 149 / Early Childhood Programs and
        Health Services for Ill Children 149
Childhood Infections: Just the Basics   156
    The Common Cold   156
    Ear Infections   157
    Gastrointestinal Infections: Diarrhea   158
    Pinkeye   159
    Chickenpox   160
    Head Lice   161
Antibiotic-Resistant Bacteria   162
Administering Medication   165
    Prescription and Over-the-Counter Medications   165
    Over-the-Counter Medications: Effective?   166
    Ensuring the Safe Administration of Medication   167
    Preventing Medication Errors   169
Allergies and Asthma   170
    Allergies   170
        Preventing Allergic Reactions 172
    Asthma   174

Revisiting the Health Promotion Action Plan   177
Conclusion   178
What's Your Opinion? To Collaborate or Not to Collaborate?   178
Assess Your Learning   179
Resource Materials   179
    Organizations 179 / Printed Matter 180
Bibliography   180

UNIT 5   NUTRITION

Factors That Shape Eating Habits   191
    Several Factors That Affect Eating Habits   191
        Physical 191 / Emotional 193 / Social and Cultural 195 / Body
        Image 196 / Economics 198
Nuts and Bolts of Nutrition   200
    Role of Nutrients   200
    The Foundation for Healthy Eating: *Canada's Food Guide to
    Healthy Eating*   201
        Relating *Canada's Food Guide to Healthy Eating* to Children 204 /
        Multicultural Foods and *Canada's Food Guide to Healthy Eating* 206 /
        Vegetarianism 207
Nutrition Labels and Food Processing   209
    Nutrition Labels   209
    Food Additives   211
        Nitrates and Nitrites 212 / Aspartame 212 / Pesticides 213 / Food
        Biotechnology: Genetically Modified Organisms and Food
        Irradiation 213
    Being Informed Consumers   215
Healthy Eating Habits   216
    Creating a Positive Eating Environment   216
    Infant Nutrition   220
        Breast Milk and Infant Formula 221 / First Foods 223 / The
        Process of Introducing Semisolid Foods 224
    Toddler Nutrition   227
    Preschool Nutrition   229
    School-Age Nutrition   230
    Concern about Amounts of Food Eaten   231
    Concern about Body Weight   233
Providing Foods and Menu Planning   235
    Providing Food in the Early Childhood Program   235
        Ways to Provide Enough Nutritious Food 237 / Child Nutrition
        Programs 238
    Menu Planning   239
        Advantages of Rotation Menus 240 / Getting Down to Writing
        Menus 240
Food Safety   242
    Reducing the Risk of Choking   243

Food Safety Practices   243
     Personal Hygiene 244 / Cooking Equipment and Surfaces 245 /
     Safe Food Handling 245 / Food Spoilage 246 / Safe Food Storage 247
     Controlling Insect and Rodent Infestation 247
Microwave Oven Safety   248
     Warming Bottles   249
Revisiting the Health Promotion Action Plan   250
Conclusion   250
What's Your Opinion? To Rise to the Challenge or Not?   251
Assess Your Learning   251
Resource Materials   252
    Organizations 252 / Other Websites of Interest 252 / Printed Matter 253
Bibliography   253

UNIT 6   SAFETY PROMOTION

The Five W's of Safety   266
    Who   266
    Why   267
    Where   269
    When   270
    What   271
     Motor Vehicle Collisions 272 / Drowning 272 / Burns 277 /
     Choking, Suffocating, and Strangling 277 / Falls 277 /
     Poisoning 278
How Can We Promote Children's Safety?   279
    Training   281
     Serious Occurrences   281
    Physical Environment   282
     Furniture 283 / Indoor Play Equipment 284 / Outdoor Play
     Equipment 286 / Conducting Safety Checks 297
    Supervision of Children   298
     During Indoor Play 299 / During Outdoor Play 300 / Prevention
     of Missing Children 301
    Safety Rules: A Learning Process   302
     Whose Need for Control? 303 / Guidelines for Safety Rules 304
What's the Rest of the Story?   308
    Being Outdoors Safely: Summer and Winter   308
     Summer 308 / Winter 314
    Walks and Field Trips   318
     Planning Successful Field Trips   319
    Environmental Contaminants   321
     Children's Vulnerability to Environmental Toxins 322 /
     Environmental Concerns and Children's Well-Being 323 / Possible
     Actions to Promote Environmental Health and Safety 326
    Being Prepared for Emergencies   326
     Injury Reports 327 / Children's Safety at Pickup Times 328

Revisiting the Health Promotion Action Plan   331
Conclusion   333
What's Your Opinion? To Climb or Not to Climb?   333
Assess Your Learning   333
Resource Materials   334
    Organizations 334 / Other Websites of Interest 334 / Printed Matter 335
Bibliography   335

UNIT 7   CHILD ABUSE PREVENTION

Exploring Your Feelings   350
    About Child Abuse   350
    About Family Diversity   351
Child Abuse   352
    Types of Abuse   352
        Physical Abuse 352 / Emotional Abuse 359 / Sexual Abuse 360 /
        Neglect 361
    Behavioural Indicators of Abuse   363
    Consequences of Abuse   364
    Causes of Child Abuse   367
Preventing Child Abuse   368
    Child Protection Agencies   368
    Primary Child Abuse Prevention   369
        The Educator's Role in Primary Prevention 369 / Preventing Child
        Abuse by Educators 374
    Secondary Child Abuse Prevention   377
        Identifying Suspected Child Abuse 377 / Do's and Don'ts When
        There Is a Disclosure 382 / Documenting Suspicions 384 /
        Reporting to the Child Protection Agency 386 / Preventing Abuse
        by Educators 390
    Tertiary Child Abuse Prevention   391
        Educator's Role in Tertiary Prevention 391 / Supporting Change
        in Parents 394
Revisiting the Health Promotion Action Plan   395
Conclusion   396
What's Your Opinion? To Report or Not to Report?   396
Assess Your Learning   397
Resource Materials   398
    Organizations 398 / Other Websites of Interest 398 / Printed Matter 398
Bibliography   399

UNIT 8   SUPPORTING CHILDREN'S DEVELOPMENT

Healthy Brain Development   404
    Self-Regulation   405
    Relating to Others   405

Helping Children Cope with Stress 408
        Children's Stress Factors 409 / Identifying Children Who Are
        Experiencing Stress 410 / Suggestions for Reducing Children's Stress
        410 / Helping Specific Children 412
    Sexuality   414
        Developing Human Sexuality 415 / Knowledge Promotes Healthy
        Attitudes 416 / Parents' Perspectives on Children's Sexuality 417 /
        Role of Educators as Sex Educators 419 / Children's Questions
        about Sex 420
Rhythm of the Program   421
    The Need for Rest and Relaxation   422
    The Need for Physical Activity   423
        Active Infants and Toddlers 425 / Active Preschoolers and School-
        Agers 426 / Physical Activity Checklist 427
Health Curriculum   428
    Children's Understanding of Health   428
        Cognitive Development 428 / Temperament 430 / The Family
        Connection 431 / Peers, Community, and the Media 432
    Developing and Implementing a Health Curriculum   433
    Health Needs and Interests of Children   433
        Infants and Toddlers 433 / Preschoolers 437 / School-Agers 438
    Getting Down to Health the Curriculum   438
        Environmental Health Education 439 / Nutrition Education 442 /
        Dental Health Education 449 / Hand Washing and Germs 452
Revisiting the Health Promotion Action Plan   454
Conclusion   456
What's Your Opinion? To Brush or Not to Brush?   457
Assess Your Learning   457
Resource Materials   458
    Organizations 458 / Other Websites of Interest 458 / Printed Matter 458
Bibliography   459

LIST OF EXHIBITS AND APPENDIXES

Tables

Table 1.1   Suggestions for Approaching Cultural Conflicts   35
Table 2.1   Dimensions of Personal Wellness   49
Table 2.2   Work Site Analysis of the Child Care Work Environment   64
Table 2.3   Making Your Own Cleaning Products   67
Table 2.4   The Ten Dimensions of Organizational Climate   71
Table 2.5   The Positives and Negatives of Working in Child Care   73
Table 2.6   Are You Listening?   75
Table 2.7   List of Statements about Organizational Climate   82
Table 3.1   Life of Viruses on Surfaces   104
Table 3.2   Summarizing the Links of the Chain   108
Table 3.3   Comparison of Cases of Disease in Canada before and after the Introduction of Immunization   110
Table 3.4   Routine Immunization Schedule for Infants and Children   111
Table 4.1   Exclusion Practices in Toronto Early Childhood Programs   164
Table 4.2   Common Allergic Substances and Reactions   171
Table 4.3   Signs of Managed and Poorly Managed Asthma   175
Table 5.1   What Food Can Mean   194
Table 5.2   Functions of Nutrients   200
Table 5.3   Recommended Daily Servings   202
Table 5.4   Key Nutrients in *Canada's Food Guide to Healthy Eating*   202
Table 5.5   Examples of Serving Sizes for Preschoolers   206
Table 5.6   Variety of Foods   207
Table 5.7   Developmental Characteristics Related to Eating   217
Table 5.8   Positive Eating Environment: Checklist   219
Table 5.9   Approximate Serving Sizes: 4 to 12 Months of Age   227
Table 5.10 Menu Planning Checklist   242
Table 6.1   Playground Equipment and Injury Rates   270
Table 6.2   Implementing Prevention Strategies   273
Table 6.3   Using Infant and Toddler Equipment Safely   285
Table 6.4   Suggested Facilities and Equipment for Play Activities   288
Table 6.5   Recommended Protective Surfacing   290
Table 6.6   Some Elements That May Appear in a Supervised Play Area   296
Table 6.7   What Does the UV Index Mean to Me?   313
Table 6.8   The UV Index: Typical Summer Midday Values   313
Table 7.1   Consequences of Abuse   365
Table 7.2   Strategies to Enhance Positive Relationships   375
Table 7.3   When a Parent Discloses an Abusive Domestic Situation: For Those Entering Early Childhood Education   380
Table 7.4   When a Parent Discloses an Abusive Domestic Situation: For Those with Experience in Early Childhood Education   380
Table 8.1   Cognitive Understanding of Health   429
Table 8.2   Developing a Health Curriculum: Guidelines   434
Table 8.3   Snacks Children Can Make   444

Figures

Figure 1.1   Child Poverty in Canada, 1989–2000   6
Figure 1.2   Groups and Individuals Who Interact with Child Care   37
Figure 2.1   Create Your Own *Canada's Food Guide* 52
Figure 3.1   The Links in the Chain   103
Figure 3.2   Breaking the Chain   109
Figure 5.1   Nutrition Facts Table: A Sample   210
Figure 7.1   Children's Bruises   353
Figure 8.1   Brushing Pattern   451

Forms

Form 4.1   Infant and Toddler Daily Care Record   150
Form 4.2   Early Childhood Program's Health Record   152
Form 4.3   Caregiver's Report on Illness   153
Form 4.4   Physician's Report on Illness   154

Appendixes

Appendix 1.1   Getting Started in Your Community: A Checklist   43
Appendix 2.1   The Financial Dimension   89
Appendix 2.2   *Canada's Physical Activity Guide to Healthy Active Living*   90
Appendix 2.3   Back Care   92
Appendix 2.4   Staff Exposed to Infectious Diseases   93
Appendix 2.5   Health Practices: You and Your Employer   95
Appendix 4.1   Management of Illness   182
Appendix 5.1   Nutrients: Their Functions and Food Sources   256
Appendix 5.2   *Canada's Food Guide to Healthy Eating*   259
Appendix 5.3   Lunch Program Menu   261
Appendix 5.4   Menu for Preschoolers and School-Agers   262
Appendix 6.1   Weekly Safety Checklist   338
Appendix 6.2   Injury Report   344
Appendix 8.1   *Canada's Physical Activity Guide for Children*   462
Appendix 8.2   Bread   464

BEFORE YOU BEGIN

Health is a complex subject that is interesting, challenging, thought-provoking, and sometimes complex. It includes a wide range of perspectives. We are confident that this edition of *Healthy Foundations in Early Childhood Settings*, like the previous ones, reflects all of these attributes and, in addition, addresses more fully those issues that are of greater concern today. As the title of this book implies, health is a cornerstone in ensuring high-quality early childhood education and care. Learning through play is fostered and supported when children are healthy and able to participate fully in child-centred curriculum. Health is integrated with children's development and cultural realities, and each of this book's units reflects this belief.

In collaboration with families, educators have an integral role in maintaining or improving children's overall health status. This role requires an anti-bias attitude, respect, and sensitivity to diverse ethno-cultural and family health beliefs and practices. Each of us has a responsibility for our own health, yet we can't dismiss the responsibility of our communities and society.

Healthy Foundations in Early Childhood Settings, Third Edition, reflects a national perspective while recognizing differences among the provinces' and territories' child care regulations. As a result, the authors have selected a number of terms that are used through the textbook.

Educator

Regardless of the term used officially in any particular province or territory, people working in the field use different titles for their profession. Here are a few:

- educator
- educarer
- facilitator
- child care worker
- child care provider
- child care practitioner

- teacher
- caregiver
- early childhood educator
- child care professional

At the national level there is ongoing discussion about selecting one term that can be used to designate a person who has formal early childhood education training, one term that reflects the complexity of roles in working with children and their families in child care programs. Two suggestions are "early childhood educator" and "early childhood care and education teacher." No consensus has been reached on this important issue. Complicating the discussion is the fact that in most literature the term "early childhood" applies to the ages between birth and 8 years, thus excluding school-agers between the ages of 9 and 12 and, by extension, those who work with them. We have chosen to use the term "educator." The authors recognize that trained, qualified professionals who work in early childhood education and care programs care, support, facilitate, and educate.

Director

The daily operation of an early childhood program is often determined by the number of children enrolled and the organization's management style. As a result, in some situations the director is responsible for the program's overall administration, is responsible for the supervision of staff, and sometimes works with children too. In other situations, the director oversees the finances and policy and staffing decisions and also takes primary responsibility for networking in the community and formally representing the program. In addition, one or more supervisors oversee the staff and work directly with children and families for all or part of each day. The term "director" refers to the individual who has primary responsibility for supervising educators and managing day-to-day operations. Programs that operate as cooperatives do not have directors. In these programs, "director" refers to the collective that makes decisions.

Program and Facility

In this edition, we use the terms "program" and "facility" rather than "centre."

The term "program" refers to the learning environment planned and implemented by educators, who base it on the children's emerging needs and interests. The term is also used to refer to the program in a more general sense, as an early childhood education and care program that is licensed by a province or territory. The use of "centre" is an exclusive rather than an inclusive term in its relation to educators. Educators work not only in child care centres but in a variety of programs, such as family resource centres, family day care homes, and nursery school programs.

The term "facility" refers to the physical space—the structure, the building—that houses the program.

Parent

The term "parent" refers to any adult who has primary responsibility for the child. The term encompasses legal guardians and foster parents. The authors recognize that the child's immediate family may comprise individuals other than simply biological or adoptive parents, and we hope that our use of the term "parent" reflects inclusiveness.

Child Care Office

The term "child care office" refers to the office or agency primarily responsible for licensing programs in individual provinces and territories. When we refer to child care regulations, we mean those that apply to your province or territory.

Age Groups of Children

Classifications for age groups vary with child care regulations. We use these definitions throughout the textbook:

- infants: birth to 12 months
- toddlers: 12 to 24 months
- preschoolers: 2 to 5 years
- school-agers: 6 to 12 years

The second edition of *Well Beings* (1996), by the Canadian Paediatric Society, provides the Canadian child care community with a comprehensive health resource manual. The book's audience extends beyond directors and educators to include child care office personnel, public health staff, physicians, and early childhood education instructors and students. It was important that this new edition of *Healthy Foundations in Early Childhood Settings* reflect the consensus reached in recommendations for standards of care and practice. Thus, we refer to *Well Beings* and use selected material from it throughout this textbook. *Healthy Foundations in Early Childhood Settings*, Third Edition, provides you with entry-level knowledge and skills and introduces you to *Well Beings*, Second Edition, which you will use as a resource manual on graduation to expand your knowledge and skills.

The emphasis in this textbook is on the overall health needs of all children. We have not included discussion of physical, cognitive, or socio-emotional challenges and long-term medical conditions such as epilepsy or diabetes. In most, if not all, early childhood education training programs, students are required to complete a course on working with children with special needs and working effectively with families and others involved in their care. Students then combine the knowledge, skills, and attitudes that they learn in their courses and program placements to meet the physical, emotional, and social needs of each child. Most training institutions also offer post-diploma education in this area.

New to the Third Edition

The new edition contains updated information and statistics in all units. Other significant changes are as follows:

- Unit 2 has an expanded discussion of educators' incorporating physical activity and informed food choices into their life styles.

- Unit 3 from the previous edition has been divided to create a new Unit 3 that covers the prevention of illness and a new Unit 4 that addresses the reality of ill children in early childhood education programs.

- The most recent immunization schedule for children, which includes the chicken pox vaccine, is included. It appears in Unit 3.

- The new food label is introduced in Unit 5.

- A greater emphasis is placed on health promotion and physical activity. Health Canada's *Canada's Physical Activity Guide for Children* is included in Unit 6.

- The up-to-date safety regulations for playground equipment and protective surfacing published by the Canadian Standards Association (2003) appear in Unit 6.

- The prevention of child abuse is dealt with in Unit 7, which includes discussion of the emotional abuse children suffer when they witness domestic violence.

- Throughout the textbook, an icon— www —is displayed to direct readers to further information available on the Internet. The reader is to refer to the Nelson ECE Resource Centre at **www.ece.nelson.com.** If the icon appears in the body of the text, it indicates that additional information on the surrounding material is available on the Web. The URLs for the relevant sites can be found in a list of Web resources or in the Nelson Resource Centre, and they can be useful either for study or instruction purposes. If the icon appears with a boxed feature, it indicates that the feature is available for download from the resources portion of the Nelson ECE Resource Centre. Students and instructors alike may access these forms, checklists, etc., in pdf form and print them for their own purposes, whether for instruction, for learning, or for study.

Learning Outcomes

Educational reform and initiatives across Canada—such as prior learning assessment, standards, and outcomes—are catalysts for some educational institutions to embark on the process of establishing learning outcomes. These are clear, broad statements that embody the necessary and significant knowledge, skills, and attitudes that learners are expected to demonstrate to successfully complete each course or program.

The authors have examined this textbook for significant learning statements. On completion of this textbook in conjunction with studies in health, it is expected that students will have demonstrated the ability to:

1. represent the holistic nature of health through examining its physical, emotional, and social dimensions
2. identify the scope and limits of the educator's roles with regard to health in early childhood education, recognizing the importance of sensitivity and respect for the primary role of parents and family

3. apply principles of a health promotion philosophy to their own lives as well as to their work with children
4. promote children's health based on knowledge of child development and observation
5. assimilate the importance of collaborating and networking with other professionals and agencies on an ongoing basis to enhance health in early childhood education and care programs
6. transfer the principles of essential health policies and practices to new situations in early childhood education

ACKNOWLEDGMENTS

The knowledge I gain continually through my relationships with family, friends, colleagues, and students is more meaningful to me than I can put to paper. Michael is wonderful, always there to listen, share ideas, and offer his wisdom and support in countless ways. Taryn's and Taylor's love for life and budding passion for health issues that affect all of us give me strength and make me proud.

Thanks to my colleagues, who are incredible individuals and are always so supportive. In addition to the George Brown College folks cited below, special thanks to Pam Doyle, Marie Goulet, Rachel Langford, Lynn Wilson, and Connie Winder, for their encouragement.

Deborah and I continue to work a province apart, as I marvel at her many strengths. When we work together, it's magic!

—Barbara Pimento

To Ali, thank you for your patience, support, and for taking care of me through all of those time crunches. To my mother, Rhoda, my sister Carla, and my niece and nephew Anastasia and Erik, along with my friends, thank you all for your love and encouragement. Barb and I have now written another edition while being separated geographically. Even with that experience we are still confronted with unique challenges, some of which were easier to meet with computers, the Internet, and e-mail. Thank you, Barb, for your commitment, dedication, and tenacity in making the third edition a reality. I've said this before, but I couldn't have asked for a better writing partner and friend.

—Deborah Kernested

There are many we would like to thank for sharing during the development of *Healthy Foundations in Early Childhood Settings*, Third Edition. Special thanks to Barb's colleagues at George Brown College who have continued to share their expertise, especially Rita Barron, Diane Bergeron, and Gail Hunter, who have also used the textbook, Patricia Chorney-Rubin, and the fabulous supervisors and staff at the George Brown College child care centres. What a team! Other affiliates, especially, Jill Harvey-Sellwood, Sue Hunter, and Theo Lax, have been so helpful. To our Production Editor at Nelson, Bob Kohlmeier, whose commitment and expertise to each of our editions is gratefully appreciated by both of us, thank you, Bob. To Alwynn Pinard, our Developmental Editor, whose enduring patience while moving us along the production schedule was very much appreciated. Your willingness to pitch in and assist us on the administrative tasks of writing a textbook was invaluable. Thanks also to the many others at Nelson, such as Joanna Cotton and Erica Smith, whose hard work helped make this book possible.

A textbook is not complete without its photographs. Thank you so much to the children, families, and staff at the five early childhood education programs who generously welcomed us into their wonderful programs. Some of the photographs in this book are courtesy of Lynn Wilson, Toronto; Carla Kernested, Winnipeg; the Patterson-Reynolds family, Toronto; Marie Goulet, Toronto; George Brown College, Child Care Programs, Toronto; Sister Celeste, Fort Norman, N.W.T.; the Manitoba Child Care Association, Winnipeg; FoodShare, Toronto; Joanna Cotton, Nelson; and Health Canada.

Finally, thank you to all who reviewed the second edition of this text in order to provide us with the direction required to develop the third edition. The information and insight provided by these reviewers proved invaluable in ensuring the quality of this resource, and, most of all, in keeping us abreast of the needs of our colleagues who bring this material to life. Special thanks therefore go to:

Leslie Kopf-Johnson, Algonquin College
Toni Lachance, Red Deer College
Heather Houston, Canadore College
Bonnie Rikkonen, Confederation College
Kathy Nielsen, Sault College
Dr. Malcolm Read, Medicine Hat College

Health Promotion

CONTENTS

What Is Health?   3

Determinants of Health   4
    INDIVIDUAL AND COMMUNITY ROLES   4

Canada's Health Care System   13
    COMPONENTS OF CANADA'S HEALTH CARE SYSTEM   14

Changing Attitudes toward Health Care   15
    AN EMERGING COLLABORATIVE APPROACH IN HEALTH CARE   17

Prevention and Health Promotion   19
    WHAT IS PREVENTION   19
    WHAT IS HEALTH PROMOTION?   20
    INTEGRATING PREVENTION INTO A HEALTH PROMOTION APPROACH   20

Health Promotion Action Plan   22
    ACTION PLAN   22

Health Promotion in Early Childhood Programs   26
    HIGH-QUALITY EARLY CHILDHOOD PROGRAMS   26
    HEALTH PROMOTION ACTION PLAN IN THE EARLY CHILDHOOD PROGRAM   36

Conclusion   38

What's Your Opinion? TO EXTEND ELIGIBILITY OR NOT?   *38*

Assess Your Learning   39

Resource Materials   39

Bibliography   40

TABLE

TABLE 1.1   SUGGESTIONS FOR APPROACHING CULTURAL CONFLICTS   35

FIGURES

FIGURE 1.1   CHILD POVERTY IN CANADA, 1989–2000   6
FIGURE 1.2   GROUPS AND INDIVIDUALS WHO INTERACT WITH CHILD CARE   37

APPENDIX

APPENDIX 1.1 GETTING STARTED IN YOUR COMMUNITY: A CHECKLIST   43

Promoting the health of children and families in early childhood programs is one of the most important roles of staff. So much of what educators do involves health. In this introductory unit, we explore what health is, and we look at what determines our health. We then provide you with a basis for understanding how Canada's health care system is organized. We explore health promotion and our changing attitudes toward health. The unit closes with an introduction to the health promotion action plan and how it can be incorporated into early childhood programs. The action plan is revisited in the subsequent units.

WHAT IS HEALTH?

OBJECTIVE

To learn the World Health Organization's definition of health.

The most influential definition of health in the 20th century was introduced by the World Health Organization (WHO) in 1947. Health, said the WHO, is "a state of complete physical, mental, and social well-being and not merely the absence of disease and infirmity." The definition has been criticized over the years because of, among other reasons, its use of the word "state" rather than "process" and for the impossibility of achieving a "complete" state of health. Yet there is no doubt that this definition paved the way for a social model of health and health promotion in Canada, broadening the concept of health from a medical one to one that encompasses quality of life. Quality of life refers to the degree to which an individual enjoys the important dimensions of her or his life, including the fulfillment of physical and emotional needs, social belonging, and the realization of goals, hopes, and aspirations. Quality of life is relevant to all humans, at any time and from their own perspectives (Brown et al. 1998, 4).

In 1984, the World Health Organization revised its definition of health to:

the extent to which an individual or group is able, on the one hand, to realize aspirations and satisfy needs; and, on the other hand, to change or cope with the environment. Health is therefore seen as a resource for everyday life, not the objective for living; it is a positive concept emphasizing social and personal resources, as well as physical capacity.

The ever-changing nature of our health means that our adaptability to change is an important lifelong attribute and influences our health. Also, health is enhanced by reasonable lifestyles and the equitable use of public and private resources that permit people to use their initiative individually and collectively to maintain and improve their own well-being, however they may define it (Rootman and Raeburn 1994, 69).

DETERMINANTS OF HEALTH

Health is a basic human right, so why are some of us more likely to enjoy good health than others? To answer this question, we first need to consider health determinants. There are no guarantees of good health and many aspects of our lives affect our health status. Maintaining our health is the combined responsibility of each of us, as members of our community and of society.

Individual and Community Roles

From the time we are conceived, heredity and environmental factors are always interacting. They affect all aspects of our health—physical, emotional, and social.

 The way we react to a life event (environment) such as losing a job is affected somewhat by our temperament (heredity).

Each of us is born with a unique genetic background that affects our strengths and challenges in the physical, emotional, and social self. Just as your genetic makeup determines your body type and eye colour, so it may predispose you to a particular medical condition (e.g., you may have a family history of allergies, heart disease, diabetes, or some other physical or emotional condition).

Heredity is only one determinant of health. Awareness of your family history, and an understanding of the risk factors that contribute to a particular disease, can help to prevent the disease or to reduce its effects.

 Frank has a family history of lung cancer but continues to smoke, which increases his likelihood of developing a serious and perhaps fatal lung disease.

People's attitudes and knowledge influence their behaviour. Yet individual decisions are not made in isolation from society. The community plays an equally important role in the health status of its members. Clean water, clean air, and an adequate sewage system are key factors in preventing widespread illness. A community also provides an economic infrastructure that supports employment opportunities and social, educational, emergency, and health services. Social attitudes, legislation, and policies affect our well-being and quality of life.

Many young girls believe that they must diet to achieve what they perceive as society's notion of the ideal female body image. They may also smoke—believing this will help reduce their appetite. Young girls are bombarded by unattainable images of women in television, magazines, and movies. A young girl's decision to diet is influenced by complex realities (e.g., family situations, media influences, issues relating to personal control).

Many aspects of our lives affect whether our basic physical, emotional, and social needs are being met. Each of these requirements includes a role for both individual and community (or societal) responsibility. Although Canadians focus attention on the health care system, in reality the most significant determinants of health are in fact social and economic. These include

- income/social status,
- healthy child development,
- freedom from discrimination, and
- communication and life skills.

Income/Social Status

We have known for some time that the better off people are in terms of income, social status, social networks, a sense of control over their lives, self-esteem, and education, the healthier they are likely to be. The wealthiest Canadians can expect to live four years longer than the poorest Canadians, and non-Aboriginal Canadians can expect to live seven years longer than Aboriginal Canadians (National Forum on Health 1997a, vol. I, 15).

The National Forum on Health acknowledges that health improves with each step up the income and social status ladders, and not only because of the obvious fact that the more income one makes, the better the services one can afford. It is also true that having choices and control over many of the decisions in one's life contributes to one's well-being, and a degree of control is enjoyed by most wealthier Canadians. It follows, then, that poverty, unemployment, and cuts in social supports have a dramatic impact on the health of many Canadians. A standard of living that fosters well-being is achieved when adults have the opportunity to work at meaningful jobs, have access to affordable housing, and have quality child care and education for their children.

Although Canada takes pride in its international reputation for fairness and compassion and is considered one of the best countries in the world in which to live, in 2002 the United Nations Human Poverty Index (HPI) ranked Canada twelfth in its treatment of the poor. The HPI measures levels of functional illiteracy, the number of poor people, and the level of social exclusion indicated by long-term unemployment (United Nations 2002, 160).

A significant measure of the health and strength of a society is the well-being of its children and families. By that measure, Canada is failing (Campaign 2000 2002b, 2). "Since 1989, when the House of Commons passed a unanimous resolution to '… seek to eliminate child poverty by the year 2000', poverty among children has increased by 21%. One in six children, or 1,139,000 children, still lives in poverty in Canada" (Campaign 2000 2002b, 2).

Campaign 2000 is a national, nonpartisan movement to build awareness and support for the 1989 all-party House of Commons resolution to eliminate child poverty in Canada.

A family's income determines whether a child lives in poverty. That an adult in a household is employed does not guarantee that the income earned provides the basic necessities or a standard of living above the poverty level. Many families depend on two wages to provide basic needs, and even the two combined may be insufficient. The gap between poor and well-off families in Canada has been widening steadily since 1973. This is mainly due to the lack of access to jobs that can support families. Most of the jobs that have been created are part-time, low-wage, contract, or seasonal, with few or no benefits. Furthermore, in recessionary times, people who have been gainfully employed for years may lose their jobs, putting them in short- or long-term poverty situations. Consequently, many families are excluded from participation in the economic and social fabric of their communities. This undermines the connectedness that communities need to maintain and build public support for social programs (Campaign 2000 2002b, 2, 3).

Research indicates that children have better health and do better in school when at least one parent works full-time (Canadian Council on Social

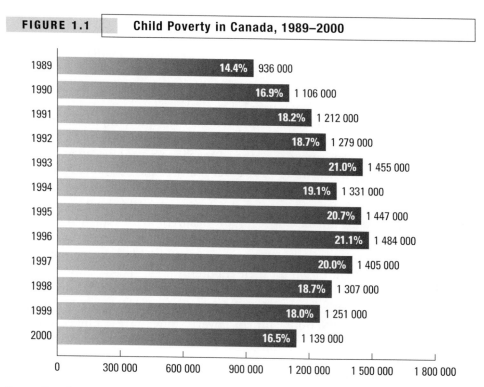

FIGURE 1.1 | **Child Poverty in Canada, 1989–2000**

Year	Percent	Number
1989	14.4%	936 000
1990	16.9%	1 106 000
1991	18.2%	1 212 000
1992	18.7%	1 279 000
1993	21.0%	1 455 000
1994	19.1%	1 331 000
1995	20.7%	1 447 000
1996	21.1%	1 484 000
1997	20.0%	1 405 000
1998	18.7%	1 307 000
1999	18.0%	1 251 000
2000	16.5%	1 139 000

0   300 000   600 000   900 000   1 200 000   1 500 000   1 800 000

Source: Data for 1989–1991 prepared by the Canadian Council on Social Development using Survey of Consumer Finances, Statistics Canada, microdata files; data for 1992–2000 prepared by the CCSD using Income Trends in Canada 1980–2000, Statistics Canada 13F0022XCB. Reprinted with permission from Campaign 2000, "Poverty Amidst Prosperity: Building a Canada for All Children," 2002 Report Card on Child Poverty (Toronto: Family Service Association of Toronto, 2002), 1.

Development 2002a, 1). The likelihood that families with dependent children have two incomes or one adequate income is not a reality for many. Consider:

- In 1997, the poverty rate for lone-parent mothers with dependent children was 56%. The facts show that most of those women were younger in age and had less formal education than the 44% who were not below the poverty line (Ross et al. 2000, 5). These two facts make finding a well-paid, stable job unlikely for most of these mothers.

- There are insufficient affordable good-quality early childhood programs. For parents who want to work, this fact results in one of the salaries barely or not even covering child care costs. "While 4.89 million children under 13 live in Canada and 68% of their mothers work outside the home, there are licensed child-care and nursery schools to accommodate only 12 per cent of those" (Phelp 2002, 2).

- In households where one of the adults is physically or emotionally challenged, that person may be unable to find employment that provides an adequate income—or to find any employment at all.

Evidence strongly suggests that poverty is the greatest barrier (or threat) to health—people living in poverty are much more likely to develop health problems, including chronic illnesses such as heart or lung disease, and to die at an earlier age than people living above the poverty level.

Poverty adversely affects children's well-being:

- "A low level of family income is associated with a higher rate of low birth weight and, potentially, with higher rates of adverse health effects stemming from the low birth weight, such as chronic illnesses, developmental delays and disabilities" (Canadian Institute of Child Health 2000, 179).

- There is a significantly greater number of deaths from injuries in boys from lower income families compared with higher income families, often stemming from the higher risks associated with unsafe neighbourhoods. Unsafe living conditions also make children in lower income families at higher risk for death from fires (Canadian Institute of Child Health 2000, 179).

- Education positively influences life chances, yet poor children often lose out. "In all countries, students from higher socio-economic backgrounds perform better in school than do students from lower socio-economic backgrounds" (Canadian Council on Social Development 2002a, 6). In Canada, only 19% of young people in the lowest income bracket attended university in 1998, compared with 39% of those in the highest (Canadian Council on Social Development 2002a, 6).

- "Children who live in persistent poverty are less likely to be included in aspects of society that are critical to their healthy growth and development. They were twice as likely to live in a 'dysfunctional' family, twice as likely to live with violence, and more than three times as likely to live with a depressed parent. Only half of the children who lived in persistent poverty participated in recreation at least once a week, compared to three-quarters of those who had never been poor" (Canadian Council on Social Development 2002a, 2).

Combine these facts with the ongoing stress that comes from living in poverty. It is not surprising that children who are poor are not likely to enjoy the same level of self-esteem or quality of life as their more financially stable peers (e.g., they are less likely to participate in sports or other physical activities because of high costs).

This poverty of opportunity speaks to the reality that, in Canada, we are not usually talking about absolute poverty, requiring the necessities of life. Nonetheless, this is the situation for many Aboriginal Canadians on reserves and homeless families in urban areas. However, a "poverty of opportunity" refers to the relative poverty experienced by more than a million children in Canada (Ross et al. 2000, 3).

> In a day and age when education, emotional maturity, leadership, and social and communication skills are prized as essential for prospering in an increasingly knowledge-based society, it is not promising that so many children are starting off with such disadvantage. The skills and attributes valued today require more than a start in life at a minimum subsistence level. (Ross et al. 2000, 3)

In order to build a stronger Canada, all levels of government need to act on their promises of a social investment strategy for children and families, so that "poverty amidst prosperity" doesn't continue to dramatically disadvantage people's lives (Campaign 2000 2002b, 1).

The situation of Canada's Aboriginal peoples highlights Canada's failure in addressing social and economic determinants of health. Aboriginal peoples have the poorest health status of all Canadians. The Royal Commission on Aboriginal Peoples (1996, 3–4) reported that

- Aboriginal peoples have higher unemployment rates;
- the incidence rates of violence, physical and sexual abuse, and suicide are higher among Aboriginal peoples;
- children in Aboriginal communities have the highest rates of injury and death of all Canadian children; and
- many Aboriginal communities have higher rates of infectious diseases (e.g., tuberculosis, AIDS) than non-Aboriginal communities.

The federal government holds primary responsibility to support Aboriginal communities in addressing the health gap. When basic needs such as safe water supplies and housing are not available to many communities, it is little wonder that health status is not significantly improving. To meet the challenge of administering and controlling their own health care, Aboriginal communities require adequate investment from the federal government to build their infrastructure. They also need continued support for initiatives that draw on traditional knowledge and culture to develop culturally relevant approaches to problems such as substance abuse and family violence. "Canada's Aboriginal people have contributed a rich heritage to the country, but they have not shared fully in its social and economic development" (Health and Welfare Canada 1992, 3).

In conclusion, poverty, particularly as it affects children and families, must be addressed in order to improve health. The Child Poverty Report Card, published by Campaign 2000 (2002a, 4), proposes the following policy options for the federal government to

- uphold its commitment to a 50% reduction in the depth and level of child poverty by 2007 through improved child benefits for all low-, modest-, and middle-income families

- commit to establishing the architecture for early childhood education and care that includes high-quality child care and is available to all families in every community across Canada; implementation requires a commitment of $1 billion in the first year and clearly defined targets and timetables for expansion
- commit to national investments of at least $1 billion per year until 2007, required to ensure an adequate supply of affordable housing throughout the country

Healthy Child Development

Healthy child development is now known to be a key determinant of long-term health (Hertzman 1998, S14). A healthy start in life has a great impact on the well-being of children and throughout life, providing opportunities to develop the attributes and resilience needed to mature into healthy adults in our complex society. A child's experiences during early childhood become embedded in the individual's biology. Early development sets in place essential conditions for lifelong growth and development (Keating and Miller 1999, 220). "Childhood is the most vulnerable period of human development, and by far the most influential. If the experiences of children support healthy development, they will be more likely to fulfil their potential as adults" (Guy 1997, xix). These experiences include a child's exposure to environmental contaminants. Although the complex processes involved in human growth and development are not fully understood, our history with toxic substances such as lead and pesticides makes it evident that even small amounts of some substances can have profound effects that may not appear until long after exposure. The Canadian Institute of Child Health is a known advocate working at all levels to limit unnecessary exposure to environmental contaminants (see Unit 6, "Environmental Contaminants," page 321).

Our Promise to Children (Guy 1997) is the culmination of a nationwide collaboration that brings together the findings of extensive research on the future of Canada's children. It explains clearly why and how to invest in children. It covers a wide range of research, from neuroscience, which tells us about brain development, to the social sciences, which are able to predict the kinds of environments that foster or hinder that development.

We are beginning to understand how social determinants affect the body through biological pathways. We now know that, although the brain has all its areas and neurons at birth, it is far from fully developed. Wiring essentially takes place during the first few years of life and ends around age 10. The neuron connections are made as a result of care and nurturing, and these depend on the quality of relationships with adults in the early years.

> During this investment phase, children develop language skills, the ability to learn, to cope with stress, to have healthy relationships with others, and to have a sense of self.... Failure to provide optimum conditions for a child's development during this time makes the developing brain physically different from the brain of children who have been well nurtured, and these differences can have lifelong consequences. (Hertzman 1997, 6)

Since the central nervous system communicates with all the systems in the body (e.g., immune, hormonal, gastrointestinal), it follows that brain development affects long-term functioning of the body, hence the incidence of disease (Hertzman 1998, S16).

Research shows that the following determinants of health help children to achieve optimal development:

1. protection (from harm and neglect)
2. relationships (children's developmental potential is supported or diminished by the care and attention received from parents, friends, relatives, neighbours, teachers, and other caring adults)
3. opportunity and hope (enabling children to build self-esteem and sustain hope for the future)
4. community (families need support networks around them, and in times of change the quality of the communities to which we belong is of tremendous importance)

When these determinants are in place for children, they are more likely to grow up healthy and happy. For many children in Canada, however, these needs are not met. Some are able to overcome the odds and flourish, but the more risks in a child's life, the less likely that child will be able to develop the flexibility and self-confidence to surmount the obstacles and live up to potential (Guy 1997, xvii). Childhood poverty, for example, has so many negative influences on lifelong development that "the preferred long-term strategy is not to build resilience in poor children, but to eliminate child poverty" (21).

The "family time famine" that is a reality in many homes due to economic pressures that require two working parents, or a full-time working lone parent, can also affect children's development. Parents are working long hours to make ends meet. This is problematic, because families need time together to nurture relationships and enhance members' sense of security, belonging, and competence. "In 2001, 74% of working women with children reported having too much to do, up from 67% in 1991. For working fathers, the rate was 55% in 2001, up from 45% in 1991" (Canadian Council on Social Development 2002a, 1). Schools, workplaces, and governments need to create family-friendly policies that support the changing demands, dynamics, and composition of families. "We have a collective responsibility to create the kinds of social and physical environments that enable children to thrive" (Guy 1997, 21).

Freedom from Discrimination

Another important contributor to well-being is freedom from discrimination as a result of an individual's race, religion, first language or ethno-culture, physical or emotional limitations, gender, age, social class, sexual orientation, physical size, or any other reason. For a victim of racism, classism, or any other form of discrimination, the effects on that individual's physical, emotional, and social well-being can be substantial.

Members of a minority group experience the frustration of being judged according to stereotypes and having limited options and opportunities. "In 2000, just over 51,000 children under age 15 immigrated to Canada — up 13% from 1990. More than half (56%) of recent immigrant children belong to visible minority groups — up from 32% among those who immigrated before 1986" (Canadian Council on Social Development 2002a, 1).

. . . .

e.g.

Students looking for housing may have experienced subtle or not-so-subtle prejudice from landlords who stereotype students as unreliable renters. Consequently, students may be limited to housing that doesn't feel as safe, is overpriced, or is farther from school. This situation may affect their physical, emotional, and social well-being:

■ Money that is spent on high rent is not available for food.

■ Emotional stress comes from feeling physically unsafe in the neighbourhood.

■ Students from a minority ethnic group or who are single parents may face even further discrimination.

. . . .

On the other hand, if you feel pride in who you are, and are accepted and respected by others, your health and quality of life are positively affected. Individuals have a responsibility to respect others. Society has a responsibility not to tolerate discrimination and to continue to find ways to educate people about the importance of tolerance and to include them in plans to improve their health and welfare.

Communication and Life Skills

Communication skills include the ability to speak and be understood as well as literacy. In Canada, literacy is defined as being able to read and write in one or both of our official languages, English and French. Twenty-two percent of adult Canadians have difficulty dealing with any printed materials in English or French and another 24% can only deal with simple reading tasks. It is interesting to note that Canadians with the lowest literacy skills have a 26% rate of unemployment compared to a 4% rate for those with the highest literacy skills (Statistics Canada 1996). Adults whose first language is English (or French) may have low literacy skills; so, too, may adults whose first language is another language. These individuals may be literate in their first language (e.g., Mandarin, Italian, Cree) but not in English or French; however, statistically they are not considered literate by Canadian standards and are at a disadvantage in the larger community. Almost two out of every three children who came to Canada between 1997 and 1999 could speak neither English nor French upon their arrival (Canadian Council on Social Development 2002a, 1).

Illiteracy often results in poor health because the individual cannot read printed information about health. People who do not speak or understand one of the official languages well are at a disadvantage, because they may not seek out information or must depend on someone else's interpretation. A person who is illiterate and has no access to an interpreter may be unable to make effective use of health or social services.

- A person may not adequately understand physician's or pharmacist's instructions.

- In an early childhood program, parents who are not sufficiently fluent in the same language as the educators may not understand when they are asked to bring in their child's immunization record.

- Parents who are illiterate may not disclose that they can't read the program's parent handbook outlining the health policies.

To improve readability, many public materials are now written in plain and simple language. In large cities, or areas where many people speak, read, and write in languages other than English or French, municipal governments often publish pamphlets and other documents in other languages. This service has had a positive effect on the well-being of people in the community.

Health, social services, and educational departments continue to find ways to increase the number of informational resources accessible to those who do not speak, read, and write English or French. As well, individuals and their cultural or ethnic communities have a responsibility to seek out language and literacy programs in English or French so they can use the available resources.

We depend on communication skills in all our daily activities—interpersonal skills, coping skills, problem-solving skills. People who are socially isolated are not likely living up to their potential. Individuals who adopt a problem-solving approach to life, and who interact effectively with family and community, become responsible in a social context. All communication skills play a significant role in the individual's level of participation in the labour force, training opportunities, and social and community activities.

Knowledge and skills in personal hygiene, sanitation, nutrition, food preparation and storage, basic health care, budgeting, and so on have positive effects on healthy behaviour. Learning life skills enables individuals to participate in society. Community resources must be available to answer individual questions.

What determines how healthy an individual is, then, is a complex combination of biological, hereditary, and environmental factors.

. . . .

A parent recognized that her family's current eating habits were not as healthy as they could be and contacted the public health nurse for information on buying and preparing food. The parent is more likely to buy a variety of fresh vegetables and grains when she knows how to cook and serve them.

. . . .

CANADA'S HEALTH CARE SYSTEM

Where does Canada's health care system fit in this picture? As discussed earlier, social and economic factors have a greater impact on our health than does health care, and improvement in health for populations is strongly linked to policies and programs that address inequities. However, the quality of that health care also influences our health, in both prevention and management of disease and injury.

> Medicine is better than ever. And we live longer than ever before. But there's a problem. People put these two facts together and wind up assuming a cause-and-effect relationship between them that simply doesn't exist.... How we live—how we eat, how we work, how we love, and how we take our minds off our troubles—has far more impact on our health than the efforts of hospitals and doctors. (Rachlis and Kushner 1992, 162–63)

In Canada, we are fortunate to have a system of universal medical and hospital insurance, one that tries, although does not always succeed, to provide all citizens with equal access to health care. Canada has made the right to health care one of the priorities on its political agenda. We are treated by doctors and are hospitalized when necessary.

➤ THE FIVE PRINCIPLES OF MEDICARE

- Universality—Medicare is available to all Canadians.
- Comprehensiveness—Medicare covers all necessary medical procedures.
- Portability—Medical coverage in one province/territory is accepted in the others and pays for a limited number of medical costs outside Canada.
- Publicly administered—A public authority is accountable to its provincial/territorial government.
- Accessibility—All Canadians have an equal opportunity to obtain necessary medical services.

Over the past decade, the health care system has reached a crisis point. Every few days you hear a news story about balancing the budget, spiraling health care costs, hospital closures, staff layoffs, cuts to health care services, and reductions in the quality of care. Canada and the provinces and territories are paying more than they can afford in health services but they are not seeing the anticipated return in overall health. Health care reform has proved to be an immense task in Canada. Health care reform—rethinking and restructuring—is being taken on worldwide.

The somewhat rigid structure of the health care system has not provided the flexibility needed to meet the diverse needs of a rapidly changing society. For example, technological and therapeutic improvements should have made it possible to shift away from institutional-based health care (National Forum on Health 1997a, vol. I, 12).

If our health care system were being established today, the system would rely less on hospitals and doctors and provide a broader range of community-based services (National Forum on Health 1997b, vol. II, 12). A high standard of care remains essential, but simply doing more of the same with less won't work.

All levels of government in Canada are calling for a more community- and home-based approach to health care, yet some of these governments are also cutting social services that are needed in an infrastructure for an integrated and comprehensive system. Simply sending patients home from hospital earlier without adequate support for care at home doesn't address the problem and certainly doesn't contribute to modernizing medicare for the 21st century (Kirkey 1998, 11).

In 2002, the Commission on the Future of Health Care in Canada published a report that emphatically supports the core values of equity, fairness, and solidarity that have defined the health care system in the past and must guide future reforms. This report, commonly known as the Romanow Report

- recognizes that close collaboration by all levels of governments in Canada is essential;
- calls on the federal government to create an accountable and sustainable system, one that says no to private care and user fees and yes to accountability;
- acknowledges the importance of prevention and health promotion (e.g., regarding smoking, obesity, physical activity);
- recognizes linking reform to a social equality agenda (Canadian Council on Social Development 2002b, 1–2).

Despite the criticisms, there is little doubt that most people living in Canada have benefited from our medicare system. *Quality of Life in Canada: A Citizen's Report Card* reported that even with concerns about the viability and access problems with our health care system, Canadians continue to rate it reasonably high on many issues (Michalski 2002, 74).

Components of Canada's Health Care System

There are two components of the health care system: personal health and public health.

Personal Health Care System

Although health care reform is affecting change, the personal health care system essentially includes conventional medical services available to people who want to maintain their health and seek cures for illness. General practitioners, family physicians, and pediatricians are the physicians that we first contact when seeking medical care or advice. In certain situations, these physicians consult with specialists (e.g., gastroenterologists, cardiologists) and other medical professionals such as physiotherapists, dietitian-nutritionists, and audiologists. We are seeing a movement toward including complementary medical practices in the medical services available through medicare, such as chiropractic services. Social workers and other relevant professionals are often brought into patients' medical care when non-physical factors affect health (e.g., housing, poverty, substance abuse, child abuse).

Public Health Care System

"The goal of the public health system is to improve the health status of the whole population; it focuses on groups rather than individuals" (Canadian Paediatric Society 1996, 21). In Canada, public health services are provided regionally within each province and territory. Each public health department serves a specific geographic area.

> Usually, each agency is headed by a medical officer of health, who is a physician with specialty training in community medicine. The medical officer of health is given legal powers to prevent health hazards through provincial/territorial public health legislation. (Canadian Paediatric Society 1996, 21)

The public health agency usually provides a variety of services when budgets permit. The medical officer of health designates services to address the public health needs in that geographic area. Large urban communities, for example, have a higher concentration of individuals addicted to drugs or living with AIDS than do rural communities. When a region has a number of early childhood programs, ideally the public health agency responds to each program's unique needs for information, consultation, and education.

As an early childhood educator, you will be involved with the public health system. Public health agencies are responsible for inspecting and approving health standards in early childhood programs, particularly licensed child care centres. Many centres, however, also actively seek an ongoing relationship with their public health professionals, to maximize the potential for health promotion. Directors commonly seek guidance for infectious disease control, immunization, safety, nutrition, and dental health.

Financial restraints have meant larger workloads for public health personnel. Often the agency's priority for health promotion makes a relationship with an early childhood program mutually beneficial. Directors or educators may need to initiate contacts with the designated public health nurse or inspector due to great demands on the official's time.

CHANGING ATTITUDES TOWARD HEALTH CARE

More people today are questioning the curative approach to conventional medicine and are considering the merits of a holistic approach to health care. The holistic approach encompasses health promotion as a way of reducing health risks to individuals and the community at large. Reduced health risks would mean less money would be needed for curative treatments and more money could be re-allocated to health promotion measures, which include prevention. Many in the medical establishment resist this change in ideology, as the balance of power in decision making over the health of individuals shifts and the health care delivery system is restructured.

Conventional medical care has become established in Western countries only in the past 200 years. Medical care primarily focuses on treating people after they become sick and on health maintenance rather than on health care based on promotion. Most people seek medical advice only after experiencing symptoms of illness. Physicians evaluate the symptoms, look for a cause, and decide on a treatment. The recommendations can be narrow in focus. Usually they treat the physical symptoms rather than consider the connections among the patient's dimensions of well-being. Treatments commonly include surgery, medication, physical or occupational therapy, or a change in nutritional habits—or any combination, all of which relate to the patient's physical health. This style of medical care is one in which the doctor is in charge and the patient asks few questions. When a patient is hospitalized, other health care professionals, such as dietitian-nutritionists, occupational therapists, and respiratory technicians, see the patient when the doctor requests a consultation.

Conventional medicine is extremely expensive, because of its reliance on highly specialized professionals and institutions (hospitals and clinics). Moreover, it does not care for the patient as a whole. It does not routinely use the expertise and skills of a variety of health professionals within a collaborative team approach; rather, it uses them as consultants if the doctor deems their input necessary. Health promotion costs less than curing or treating illness, especially in the management of long-term medical conditions. For both the individual and the community, avoiding illness altogether makes the most sense.

This curative or health recovery approach was, and still is to some degree, widely held among many in the medical community and society. Many patients expect doctors to be miracle workers—to cure all their ills without patients accepting any responsibility for their unhealthy lifestyles. But another health care delivery system is gaining support, one that takes a holistic or broader view of health. We are becoming more informed consumers, asking our physicians questions and viewing ourselves as partners or advocates in our health care. Many Canadians are taking more individual control over accessing health professionals—chiropractors, physiotherapists, naturopaths—rather than waiting for a doctor's referral.

Traditionally, health care providers have been the main source of information and advice for patients. While this is still largely true, there are patients using the Internet who believe they know more about their conditions than does their physician. However, without the background health knowledge and experience of a physician, the average Canadian is not prepared to make decisions based on publicly accessible information, since so much of this information is unreliable. Nevertheless, the demand by patients for greater involvement in decision making has made it essential that the public have access to user-friendly information. It also suggests that the role of health care providers will become more interpretative, with a greater focus on the vast amount of information available to the public (National Forum on Health 1997a, vol. I, 19).

An Emerging Collaborative Approach in Health Care

Medicine is a business and doctors are having to adapt to the changing attitudes and expectations of consumers. Examples of the changing direction in Canada's health care system include a revamping, on the part of some medical schools, of teaching programs to a community-based model, a movement toward community medicine (e.g., community health centres), and the licensing of midwives.

- Midwifery has been a legal and legitimate profession in England for over 500 years, but the publication of the *Midwifery Act* in Ontario on January 1, 1994, was the first legal acknowledgment in Canada of the legitimacy of birthing babies beyond the medical model approach. Pregnancy and childbirth are natural and low-risk processes for most women. Midwives provide continuity of care by supporting the woman and her family throughout the pregnancy, during the birth, and for six weeks after delivery.

- Midwifery care reduces the incidence of interventions such as cesarean sections, epidural anaesthetic, and episiotomies, resulting in savings to Ontario's health care system and hospitals through lower operating room time and drug costs. These savings offer opportunities to reinvest health care resources at the community level (Association of Ontario Midwives 2001, 1).

- Women who use midwives can choose a home or hospital birth.

- Currently in Ontario, approximately 35% of midwife-assisted deliveries take place in the home, representing the lowest cost option for healthy deliveries (Association of Ontario Midwives 2001, 1).

- For midwife-attended hospital births, the mother's hospital stay decreases dramatically.

e.g.

Community health centres are another example of this direction. Under one roof they provide the services of professionals such as physicians, nurses, public health nurses, nurse practitioners, dietitian-nutritionists, social workers, physical and occupational therapists, health advocates, counsellors, interpreters, massage therapists, and pharmacists. These professionals work together to meet the diverse needs of individuals and their families. The health care centres refer patients to, and work with, other community services such as job retraining, English-as-a-second-language (ESL) lessons, housing and income agencies, legal aid, and so on.

These and other measures benefit patients and the public by reducing overuse and misuse of the system and by providing alternatives that may be more appropriate for the health and well-being of some individuals. Obviously, the expertise of doctors remains important to Canada's health care system, but a team approach uses the expertise of many health and health-related professionals effectively.

This change moves away from the doctor's office and hospitals to clinics that provide a variety of services in collaboration. Community health centres also make a statement that health and social services should not be separated. Many people, such as those who live in poverty or on the street, who are not fully literate, or who have recently immigrated to Canada, are unable to obtain the level or quality of health care that others can in the conventional medical care system.

Ideally, community health centres are designed and administered by the community to meet its unique needs.

Complementary Medicine Practitioners and Products

Historically, complementary (or traditional) medicine practitioners such as homeopaths and naturopaths have been excluded from the conventional medical model in Canada. Many alternative practices and products have not been scientifically proven to be effective or safe, so they are unregulated and not covered by medical insurance plans or drug benefit plans. Conversely, critics of conventional medicine question whether some treatments covered by medicare are medically necessary or effective, or at least they question those that are overused (e.g., the high number of ultrasounds done during healthy pregnancies). One may assume that using a complementary practitioner is a step toward holistic health; however, that may not always be the case. An individual who chooses to consult a complementary practitioner—or a physician, for that matter—must be a very conscientious consumer. Urgent attention on the part of governmental authorities is needed to ensure the safety and effectiveness of complementary interventions.

Natural health products (NHP) such as vitamins, herbs, minerals, and supplements are now the most popular form of complementary health care in North America. In May 2000, an average of two out of three Canadians surveyed had used an NHP in the past month. But natural doesn't always mean safe. For example, some NHPs are toxic in large doses, some can cause side effects, allergic reactions, or interact with other medications, and some may be harmful for people in certain circumstances (e.g., with heart disease, during pregnancy). It is therefore important to consult your doctor, naturopath, or pharmacist before trying a product (Tzu Chi Institute 2002, 1).

The intent of the federal government's Natural Health Products Regulations is to ensure that the products are safe, effective, and of high quality. The regulations include

- labelling requirements that place more information about individual products in the hands of consumers and practitioners,
- a pre-market approval process to ensure that what is described on the label is actually in the bottle, and
- a requirement that appropriate levels of scientific evidence support any claims on the label about the product's effects (Tzu Chi Institute 2002, 3).

Some families in early childhood programs use complementary practitioners and medicines. Remedies and medicines may come either from cultural or traditional backgrounds or from a philosophy that differs from the established medical model. It is important to respect health practices different from your own and to be aware of your role in promoting the health of each child in your care. If you question an aspect of the family's health practices, find out more about it before taking action.

In Canada, some practitioners unregulated in the past now receive provincial/territorial government funding under medicare; osteopaths and chiropractors are two examples. Some medical doctors are incorporating complementary practices into their patients' care. These doctors are under increasing scrutiny from their licensing body. In contrast, some European countries have progressed further in recognizing the effectiveness of combining conventional and complementary medical practices. The cost of complementary practices is covered by their medical insurance plans.

PREVENTION AND HEALTH PROMOTION

Prevention and health promotion activities have been practised for centuries. In the 1970s a more committed and conscious movement toward healthy living began in Canada.

What Is Prevention?

As one component of health promotion, "prevention involves identifying the factors which cause a condition and then reducing or eliminating them" (Epp 1986, 4). The goal is to have individuals adopt preventive strategies in their daily lives that may lower the risk of occurrence or recurrence of a particular illness or injury. Although lowering a risk doesn't guarantee that a disease is prevented, most people recognize the positive elements of this change.

Here are some examples of prevention strategies:

- Stop-smoking programs and no-smoking policies for preventing lung cancer and lowering the risk of heart disease and other major diseases.
- Monthly breast self-exams and regular Pap smears for women for early identification of disease.
- Regular dental checkups.
- Hand-washing and immunization programs for children to reduce the spread of infectious diseases.
- The design of play equipment for safety and appropriateness for the ages and number of children using it.
- The use of seat belts in cars and bike helmets on bicycles and scooters.

There is not always evidence to support cause-and-effect relationships between health behaviour and disease. In fact, the many interrelated factors involved in disease make prevention complex. Also, popular opinion often promotes certain preventive lifestyle behaviour. These situations highlight the importance of the informed consumer, who weighs the pros and cons of specific behaviour. In particular, we cannot assume that every preventive practice recommended for adults can be applied to children.

Promoting a high-fibre diet is believed to help prevent colon cancer in adults. However, "high intakes of dietary fibre may not be well tolerated by youngsters" (Network of the Federal/Provincial/Territorial Group on Nutrition and National Institute of Nutrition 1989, 43). There is concern that a lot of fibre for children

- causes very loose stools in young children,
- does not allow foods to remain in the digestive system long enough for the needed vitamins and minerals to be absorbed from the food, and
- does not provide enough of their caloric needs.

To learn the World Health Organization's definition of health promotion.

To define prevention.

To describe how prevention fits into the health promotion approach.

This example highlights the importance of consulting with the appropriate health professional, in this case a dietitian-nutritionist, before making decisions that affect someone else's health.

What Is Health Promotion?

Health promotion is "the process of enabling people to increase control over, and to improve their health" (World Health Organization, Health and Welfare Canada, and Canadian Public Health Association 1986, 1).

> Health promotion is concerned with creating living conditions in which people's experience of "health" (well-being) is increased. To an extent, this also requires decreasing their risk of disease. But disease prevention is not the primary goal of health promotion; it is a secondary goal. A health promotion program can improve health (well-being) without necessarily reducing the prevalence of disease, or of specific disease risk factors such as smoking, high fat intake or lack of fitness. (Labonté 1993, 6)

Areas in which the federal government has implemented healthy public policy are restrictions on the sale and advertising of tobacco, publicity to reduce impaired driving, and the recent ban on PVC use in plastic mouthing/teething toys. Over time our understanding of the factors that contribute to better health has deepened. At first, government policies focused on lifestyle choices and on healthy public policy. Now, largely because of research on the non-medical determinants of health and on health promotion, the focus has shifted to the societal level, beyond factors that are within the immediate control of individuals and communities (e.g., safe and affordable housing, enhanced maternity/parental leave, reduction of environmental contaminants).

With a holistic view of health, everyone can be involved in promoting health. It is becoming increasingly apparent that people who believe they can control aspects of their lives and have choices are more likely to be action-oriented and self-confident. It is easy to lose hope or view ourselves as ineffective when we believe we have no control over our destiny. In your work with children, you will model and foster feelings of self-confidence and belief in oneself within a realistic framework of what we may or may not be able to control.

Integrating Prevention into a Health Promotion Approach

You may be saying to yourself, "I have control over most aspects of my life," and that is true to a degree. Many of us didn't succumb to outside influences and start smoking. Perhaps we made other lifestyle decisions based on positive or negative influences. No one can claim, for example, "Cigarette advertising and peer pressure made me smoke." To focus solely on individual lifestyle decisions is to ignore the complex aspects of health behaviour. Nor can society simply blame the victim, absolving itself of its responsibility for coordinating healthy public policy, fostering public participation, and strengthening community health services (Epp 1986, 8). An individual's ability to implement specific prevention strategies and the likelihood of success or failure are directly related to other factors that affect that person's life. To think otherwise is to blame the victim (e.g., "It is the teenage girl's fault that she has anorexia," or "If he had been stronger willed and stopped smoking, he wouldn't have lung cancer," or "She's fat because she eats too much"). This attitude toward prevention is unacceptable and does nothing to enhance our understanding of health and improve our well-being.

Tobacco use is Canada's number one public health enemy. Smoking accounts for 55% and 51% of premature death among males and females, respectively. Tobacco kills approximately nine times as many Canadians prematurely as suicide, traffic collisions, HIV/AIDS, and homicide combined (Villeneuve and Morrison 1994, 102).

. . . .

e.g.

Sarah quit smoking to reduce her health risks. She can't understand why everyone else can't do the same. For others, quitting smoking is more than withdrawal from addiction to nicotine. Malcolm has tried to quit a few times, but he recently lost his job and smoking helps to reduce his overwhelming feelings of stress. Sarah is probably right when she says Malcolm should find a healthy alternative for relieving his stress, but it is a more complicated issue. Most of Malcolm's friends smoke and their social activities permit them to smoke. Moreover, his father and uncles smoked and lived long lives without developing lung cancer, so he has no firsthand evidence in support of claims made by experts.

A health promotion perspective takes into account the challenges of reducing inequities in Malcolm's life and enhancing his capacity to quit smoking. He enters a job-retraining program that results in meaningful employment. His standard of living improves, as do his self-esteem and outlook on his future. With lowered stress levels, Malcolm is better able to cope with everyday stress by walking to and from work. He now works in a no-smoking workplace. His new friends at work happen to be nonsmokers and he is involved in different social activities. And when you add the high cost of cigarettes, no-smoking legislation in public places, and concerns about secondhand smoke, smokers are feeling society's pressure to stop smoking. Malcolm now has a much better chance of success because so many other factors are in place to support his decision.

. . . .

e.g.

By society's standards, Marsha is obese. She has spent years yo-yo dieting and trying to attain a body size that is acceptable to those around her. Whenever she loses weight, even under a physician's care, she quickly regains it. She feels like a failure because she realizes she will never be able to lose the weight that she wants to. Family and strangers joke about Marsha's size, which is hurtful and disrespectful, and diminishes her self-esteem (e.g., "You would be so pretty if you would only lose weight"). Marsha's anger is understandable—prejudice against fat people is one of the last forms of discrimination in which disparaging attitudes and comments remain socially acceptable.

Hercilia, a friend of Marsha's, is a large woman yet is much more self-assured. She suggested that Marsha consult with her dietitian-nutritionist, who follows a health promotion model. This was the turning point for Marsha. Two years later, Marsha's body size still does not fit society's standard. However, she has become much more aware of what is important to her and has a quality of life that far surpasses that of her past, when she was always on hold until she lost weight. She consistently makes healthy food choices and incorporates physical activity into her daily routine. For the past year, Marsha and her counsellor have worked through her feelings of failure, and that work has improved her self-esteem. The self-help group that she attends provides mutual support in coping with society's prejudice against people who are fat, their putdowns, and intrusive questions (e.g., a taxi driver asks his passenger, "So how much do you weigh?"). Since Marsha has stopped focusing on weight loss and has incorporated a health promotion model into her approach, she has more energy than ever before and is slowly losing weight.

. . . .

The fashion industry creates powerful images of beauty and desirability that particularly affect society's view of women. However, changes in societal attitudes are gradually taking place. Today, there is some recognition of a wide range of healthy body sizes. Fashionable and affordable clothes are more readily available in a range of sizes. Even fast-food restaurants have started to offer foods that help people make healthier choices. A physically active lifestyle is essential for the long-term well-being of all Canadians (see Appendix 2.2, page 90). Some physical activity programs are designed for larger people, which may help them feel less self-conscious about exercising in front of others.

In summary, health promotion involves all aspects of a person's life that affect his or her well-being, and prevention focuses on particular risks or behaviour believed to be causal factors in disease or injury.

OBJECTIVE

To identify the four components of a health promotion action plan and describe how they can be implemented.

HEALTH PROMOTION ACTION PLAN

Health promotion in a broad sense enables individuals and the community to identify health risks and make positive changes at the individual, community, and societal levels.

Action Plan

Health promotion activities enable us to take action to improve our own health and that of all Canadians. An action plan establishes a set of strategies that can be divided into four components:

- individual problem-solving and self-reliance
- collective self-help
- community action
- societal change

Optimally, when all four components are at work, the likelihood of significant change is high. Realistically, though, we are not always successful in achieving our original goals. During the process we may need to adjust the vision. Barriers may be impossible to overcome. But even these situations usually have outcomes that contribute to good health, such as developing coping skills, increased social supports, networking, and a long-term commitment to work for change.

Individual Problem Solving and Self-Reliance

As individuals, we solve problems all the time, and many of our behavioural changes occur when we put our mind to it. However, changing our behaviour is easier when we do not have to overcome barriers or when we have the resources to effect change.

- Because Alyssa's parents provide a variety of nutritious foods, she has learned to make healthy food choices. They guide their daughter's development of healthy eating habits by modelling. By the time she is of school age, she will have developed the knowledge and decision-making skills to make choices. Then when she becomes influenced by peers and the media and may not always make the healthiest choices, she will at least be aware when she is eating less nutritious foods and can therefore balance her choices.
- You decide to add more physical activity to your life by regularly walking to work or school.

Societal barriers or influences can affect our ability to make healthy lifestyle decisions either positively or negatively. In the past, smoking was accepted by society. The media depicted it as fun, sophisticated, and elegant. Smokers could smoke almost anywhere, and no one was concerned about secondhand smoke or about pregnant women smoking. There were no barriers; in fact, society encouraged people to smoke. Today, smoking is recognized as one of the most serious public health concerns, and this has resulted in public education on the risks of smoking, support and products to help stop smoking, legislation on smokefree environments, taxes on tobacco, strict limitations on advertising, and limitations on availability (e.g., pharmacies do not sell tobacco, and cigarette vending machines have been banned). Long-time smokers are quitting, supported and encouraged by society. People are more comfortable in asking smokers not to smoke in their cars or homes, and many smokers ask permission before lighting up. Smoking in public has been severely restricted. Public health officials remain concerned, however, about the number of teenagers (more girls than boys) who are first-time smokers. From a developmental perspective, it's not surprising that adolescents are exerting control over their lives and may in fact make decisions counter to parental or public opinion. This is complicated by the fact that teenagers and young adults view themselves as invincible.

Collective Self-Help

When individuals come together as a collective, they pool skills, knowledge, and resources to support one another and work toward change.

e.g.

A group of tenants in an apartment building has recognized that grocery shopping is difficult because of issues such as

- their low income,
- the lack of public transportation to affordable stores,
- the many single-parent families who have no one to care for their children while the parents are grocery shopping.

As a collective, the tenants organize a food depot that is open once a week and sells fresh fruit and vegetables. A food produce supplier provides the produce at a reasonable cost.

. . . .

Collectives don't always have to be large groups of people.

. . . .

 Several neighbours organize an informal baby-sitting system that lets one parent do grocery shopping while another cares for the children. This allows the parents to shop without taking tired, bored, or hungry children with them, which often results in impulse buying and angry parents or frustrated children.

. . . .

Although this example reflects cooperation, the group is somewhat self-reliant. Often, once groups have worked together in this way, they begin to identify broader social and health issues or concerns (e.g., causes of ill health) and may move toward more of a community action model.

. . . .

 A group of directors that meets regularly as a network shares a concern about the food that parents are providing for their school-age children. The directors organize a parent meeting, invite a dietitian-nutritionist and social worker, and provide child care and dinner. At the meeting, participants identify a number of issues:

- lack of affordable food
- lack of nutrition resources that fit the literacy and interest levels of a number of the parents
- time constraints for parents and their need for ideas for nutritious lunches that can be easily prepared
- children's practice of trading lunch items with peers and a concern that nutritious foods won't be desirable
- children's beliefs that foods from their ethno-cultural backgrounds will not be accepted by their peers

. . . .

These issues call on the resources and agencies in the community. They highlight the importance of looking beyond self-help to a much broader health promotion action.

Community Action

A health promotion strategy oriented toward community action is increasingly viewed as an effective way to make change to meet the health needs of the community, particularly where barriers are present. It aims for changes that will affect the whole group. Those changes can happen when groups of people

- work together to identify issues and priorities that reflect their needs,

- develop and implement an action plan, which usually involves communication with a number of agencies and resources, and

- evaluate the strengths and deficiencies of their actions and the extent to which they have realized their goals.

In the example about nutrition for school-aged children, the collective's work led the participants to develop an action plan that included reaching out into the community for resources. This had benefits not only for the immediate issue but also for long-term well-being. Regular links with the broader community tend to foster an active problem-solving approach to life.

All participants involved have some role in the process, including evaluating whether goals have been met. Parents and staff may have different responsibilities and perspectives, but everyone works toward the same goal. Depending on the ages of the children and the actions being taken, some or all of the children may be involved in the process (e.g., if a community vegetable garden is part of the solution).

- -

A few people in a neighbourhood are concerned about the quality of the air due to smokestack emissions at a local factory. Together, they go door to door to gain citizen support and they meet with public health officials, governmental officials, and the factory management. Then they develop a plan of action to reduce the emissions.

e.g.

- -

Depending on the extent of the issue and who is involved, community action can lead to legislative changes—locally, provincially, or federally—that affect everyone. If we take this example a step further, stricter government regulations for companies to reduce air pollution levels may emerge from what began as a small community action (see Appendix 1.1, page 43).

Societal Change

Issues can have a very broad impact on everyone through the work of community and lobby groups, agencies, and so on. Societal changes often result from changes in legislation or public health policy. Here are some examples:

- air pollution controls
- no-smoking policies in public places
- drinking-and-driving legislation
- changes in advertising guidelines for the tobacco and liquor industries
- legislative bans on manufacturing and selling equipment that doesn't conform to safety regulations

Let's take one last look at the example of staff and parents and their concerns about children's nutrition. As a group, they recognize that their experience is not isolated, that the issue and solutions go beyond their own community and into the society at large. Consequently, some participants join a lobby group that is trying to ban television advertising of junk food aimed at children, while others work with a national antipoverty group. As discussed earlier in this unit, a focus on the bigger issue of reducing and eliminating poverty is, ultimately, the most effective health promotion approach. A collective vote is a powerful tool for effecting change. Find out where political candidates stand on various issues and cast your vote accordingly.

OBJECTIVE

To discuss student and educator strategies to advocate for high-quality early childhood programs.

HEALTH PROMOTION IN EARLY CHILDHOOD PROGRAMS

Promoting health is something we can do to improve the quality of our life and the lives of those around us. How can early childhood programs be part of this movement?

High-Quality Early Childhood Programs

Tens of thousands of children in Canada are enrolled in licensed early childhood programs, and many more thousands of children would benefit from the opportunity. High-quality programs support children's lifelong learning and families' social needs. Consequently, society must acknowledge that early childhood education and care are essential services for families, recognize the indicators of high-quality programs, and support the delivery of service through legislative and financial changes. If parents have access to high-quality early childhood programs, they can participate fully in their work or education, which enhances the quality of their lives and the lives of their children.

Early childhood programs support parents in their role as their children's primary educators. High-quality early childhood programs have positive long-term health effects for children. "The positive relationship between child care quality and virtually every facet of children's development … is one of the most consistent findings in developmental science" (Shonkoff and Phillips 2001, 313).

Legislation in each province and territory establishes regulations for licensed early childhood programs, including specifications for the following matters, among others:

- early childhood education training requirements
- group size
- staff–child ratios
- space requirements
- program planning
- nutrition requirements
- management of ill children

Every licensed early childhood program has a copy of its provincial/territorial regulations. It is important to understand that these regulations ensure a minimum standard. A minimum level of care is not high-quality early childhood education and care. Because licensing early childhood settings is a provincial/territorial responsibility, regulations vary greatly across Canada. An area of particular concern is the wide variation in levels of early childhood education training required for staff working in the field.

➤ CHILD CARE SECTOR STUDY ON QUALITY

Elements of Quality

The elements of quality include both the ways in which child care environments are organized and the nature of interactions supported by that environment—in other words, the structure and process elements. A high-quality child care environment incorporates the following principles:

- Responsible, stable caregiver–child interactions that are sensitive to children's needs, provide support and encouragement, and set consistent behavioural expectations are of primary importance in both home- and centre-based child care.

- Caregiver knowledge of child development (usually indicated by postsecondary education credentials) supports positive adult–child interactions both in family child care and in child care centres.

- The caregiver–child ratio and group size, which allow the caregiver to be aware and involved, are important to adult–child interactions in child care centres.

- Low staff turnover creates a stable and consistent caregiver–child relationship. High turnover reduces stability.

- Daily routines, including planned activities and free play, with health and safety provisions, support children's learning and protect their well-being in family care homes and child care centres.

- A child-appropriate physical environment allows children to take part in learning opportunities and encourages increased positive interactions with caregivers.

- A positive organizational climate, which includes opportunities for caregivers to be involved in decision making, creates a coherent administrative framework to support caregivers in centres. In family child care, support and contact with other caregivers are part of a positive organizational climate.

- In family child care settings, caregiver "intentionality" is associated with better outcomes for children. Intentionality is the conscious commitment to caring for children and the provision of nurturing, stimulating child care.

Ensuring Quality

The elements of quality and the quality of the care provided are affected by factors outside the immediate program setting. The following principles ensure quality:

- In centre-based programs, adult–child interactions are influenced by the caregiver's job satisfaction level, which, in part, is determined by the work environment, including wages and benefits, general working conditions, and administration. Low job satisfaction is associated with higher staff turnover, which reduces the stability of relationships between caregivers and children. Compensation levels and other aspects of the work environment are determined by the level of available funding.

- High-quality child care is more likely to be found in nonprofit than in commercial child care settings. However, there are both low-quality nonprofit centres and high-quality commercial centres.

continued

- The level of government regulation, particularly for caregiver education, caregiver–child ratios, and group size, does influence the quality of care in centre-based settings.
- Quality may be encouraged through professional standards of practice for individual caregivers and for child care settings.

Source: Adapted from Beach, Bertrand, and Cleveland (1998), 32–34.

Your role as a student and entry-level educator in providing quality care is crucial in promoting the physical, emotional, and social well-being of the children and families you serve.

Advocating for Quality Early Childhood Programs

Although many regard licensed early childhood programs as a social welfare program rather than a health promotion program, early childhood education and care have significant implications for children's health. In 1988, the federal government announced a child care support program for working mothers. In the 1980s, advocates for a national child care plan agreed on three fundamental principles for a child care system: universal accessibility, comprehensiveness, and high quality. Their continued advocacy for child care indirectly promotes children's health. The legislation was not enacted and was abandoned in 1991; the advocacy movement wasn't. In 2002, the federal government renewed its promise "to increase access to early learning opportunities and to quality child-care" (Campaign 2000 2002a, 1). Early childhood education and care (ECEC) benefits all children. "There is much to support the premise that a universally accessible set of ECEC services should be available for all children rather than a fragmented set of targeted services for special populations" (Doherty 2001, 1–2).

Advocacy doesn't occur only at the national level. Advocates for high-quality early childhood education are working to improve standards of care in each province and territory by ensuring that revisions made to legislation reflect the indicators of quality early childhood education and care.

How can early childhood program staff and early childhood education students deliver high-quality early childhood education and care that support health promotion? Your training provides you with the entry-level knowledge and skills to provide a level of care higher than the minimum set out in the legislation. Your training also helps you recognize the importance of delivering a high-quality early childhood program. This commitment to ongoing learning and professional behaviour makes you a "personal" advocate. To be a public policy advocate, you can be involved in local, provincial/territorial, or federal early childhood education organizations that advocate for access to high-quality early childhood education and care for families and professional recognition for educators. We need to speak with one voice in order to safeguard accomplishments and move forward (Gestwicki and Bertrand 1999, 230–31).

Early Childhood Program Policies

An early childhood program can ensure that high-quality early childhood education and care are implemented by having

- a written philosophy that states its ideology about children's care and learning;
- policies and procedures that answer the who, what, when, where, and why for each policy; and
- educators who consistently implement the policies and procedures. Educators and parents need to understand the rationale behind the policies before they can see the big picture in procedures.

Early childhood education and care is a cooperative effort shared by the staff and parents. Preparing a policy manual is one way to demonstrate that shared commitment. Writing, reviewing, and revising it annually draws on the expertise of the staff, parents, and professionals in the community (e.g., public health, child abuse prevention, social services). The reviewers evaluate the effectiveness and relevance of the policies and procedures. Health information, circumstances, and priorities change. Staff or parents may raise new issues and concerns.

Health Policies

Policy manuals are legal documents that outline the program's philosophy, its goals and objectives, and how the educators intend to meet the regulations and implement the procedures. Well-written policies combine the child care regulations, early childhood education training, the expertise of other professionals and parents, and the most current health information available, in addition to drawing upon what staff have learned from managing previous health and safety issues. However, regulations are only minimum requirements based on legislation. High-quality early childhood programs build on that foundation to develop fuller, broader, inclusive policies that reflect their knowledge and skills in caring for children daily. When a policy is well written, its rationale is clearly understood and the stated procedures obviously promote the well-being of children, staff, and families.

Policy manuals are living documents. Our knowledge of children's well-being, including health, nutrition, hygiene, safety, growth and development, illness, medical conditions, and physical or emotional challenges evolves faster than legislators make or change regulations. Furthermore, educators use past experiences to identify additional policy issues. Policy manuals incorporate the unexpected—"What will we do if this happens?" (The manual outlines the steps to follow if, for example, a child's non-custodial parent arrives to take the child from the centre, as well as what to do when a child vomits medication.) An effective policy manual adapts to the changing needs of individual early childhood settings.

· ·

An infant program has an outbreak of diarrhea. Hand-washing and diapering routines should be suspected of causing the spread of the virus or bacteria responsible for the gastrointestinal infection. Without the policy manual setting out the steps for diapering and hand washing, staff are not able to evaluate the educators' compliance to the routines that would have prevented the spread. Perhaps the policy and procedures are not effective. Perhaps educators need retraining in the routines and closer supervision.

e.g.

· ·

Beyond the legal licensing requirement for having a manual, policies have a variety of purposes. They can explain how to

- conduct staff orientation, in-service training, and job performance appraisals;
- extract the most relevant policies to be developed into parent handbooks; and
- define lines of communication and confidentiality.

They also
- contain the administrative and medical/health forms, and specify who has access to that information;
- contain information sheets and handouts, and routines that can be used for posters on such topics as diapering, toileting, hand washing, and exclusion criteria; and
- identify the names and associations related to early childhood programs so staff stay current with related research.

Each regulation provides directors, educators, their boards, and parents with the basis for developing policies and procedures for the individual day-to-day program, the ages of the children, and their location. The following illustrates a few of the issues that may be included in discussions about policies and procedures.

- The medication policy indicates what medications are permitted and why. Procedures are clearly spelled out and cover administration, storage, and record keeping; identification and reporting of side effects and medication errors; and the management of emergency situations. The program's expectations of parents regarding medications would also be included. In the event of a medication incident, comparing the procedures with the actions of the educator will determine whether precautions were in place and carried out to the best of the person's ability to prevent the error. Perhaps such a review would determine that the current medication procedures require revision.

- A child falls from a climbing structure in the winter and breaks his arm. On examination, the impact-absorbing surface is found to be covered with a sheet of ice. Does the program have an outdoor play policy and procedures in place that, when implemented, would prevent children from using a climber when the surface does not meet safety requirements?

- A school-age program located in an elementary school establishes clear lines of communication with the principal and the children's teachers to ensure the consistent coordination of health policies.

- When a child gets sick during the day, does the school notify the parents, or is doing so the program's responsibility?

- Are the regular safety checks of the playground and equipment a shared responsibility of the early childhood program staff and the school, or are they solely the school's responsibility? Are the expectations about the use of the playground equipment consistent between the program and school? When issues arise, how are they reported and recorded? Who is responsible for record keeping?

- Do the educators and teachers consistently teach and model healthy habits?

- When concerns are raised about a child or family by either the educators or a teacher, do both parties work together to address the concerns?

HIV is cloaked in emotion, fear, and discrimination. A small number of children and educators in early childhood settings are HIV-positive. Consequently, some programs have developed an HIV/AIDS policy. Programs that have comprehensive policies and procedures have already integrated the issues relating to HIV/AIDS. Policy statements relating to confidentiality, freedom from discrimination, universal precautions, and the management of all blood-borne diseases encompass HIV/AIDS. The most effective instrument in changing the attitudes and behaviour of educators, parents, and the general public is HIV/AIDS education, not policy. The ECEC community sends an inappropriate message to staff, parents, and the community when a policy is developed for a specific infection that is not spread through casual contact and has never been reported to have been transmitted in an early childhood setting.

Parent–Educator Partnerships

You share a partnership with parents and other family members in enabling the child to be the best that he or she can be—physically, emotionally, socially. Parents know their child best, and it is important that you respect their values and parenting practices. After all, the child is part of that family for a lifetime but is part of your early childhood program for only a limited time. Parents are the decision makers about their child's health. Educators, however, may be able to provide information such as referrals to agencies, books, articles, and other individuals who help parents consider new information or another perspective in their decisions. Building relationships with parents on a daily basis benefits everyone involved.

After you graduate as an early childhood educator, you may at times be concerned about the effects of a family's health values, or practices, on the child's well-being. You must determine whether your concern stems from a value or practice that is different from any that you are accustomed to. This difference may reflect socio-cultural differences, a term that refers to ethnicity, race, class, religion, or any other aspect of a social group that shapes values and practices. This value or practice may be very different from, or even in conflict with, one that you grew up with. If it is, you must decide whether this value or practice is simply another way of looking at something or is potentially harmful to the child's physical, emotional, or social well-being. You broaden your awareness by learning about other perspectives. You may or may not decide to adopt this value or practice, but it is important that you not judge others solely on the basis of your limited view. Competent educators strive to communicate with families and support each family's values as much as possible while maintaining standards of high-quality early childhood education and care.

If, on the other hand, you are unsure about the parents' values or practices because of the potential for physical, emotional, or social harm to the child, you have a responsibility to investigate. Effective communication with parents ensures that you understand the value or practice. Ineffective communication frequently results in assumptions and judgments based on incomplete information. It is possible, often with the help of community resources, to make a more informed decision on the issue and decide, likely with the director, on a plan of action. Keep in mind that most parents care about their children and believe that their parenting reflects this care. This principle can be very helpful in deciding what to do next.

. . . .

You are concerned about Karim's eating habits. You talk with his parents about his total nutritional intake and any food restrictions. Perhaps a dietitian-nutritionist from the public health department can provide you and the parents with educational material.

. . . .

In addition to pre-enrollment interviews, parents and educators find out more about each other through day-to-day communication, regular parent–educator interviews, the parent handbook, bulletin boards, and other communication vehicles. If differences exist between the program's philosophy and policies and the parents' values and practices, the parents might consider using an early childhood program that better reflects their attitudes. In most situations, however, educators and the director will have tried to negotiate a mutually acceptable situation before that happens.

Cultural Diversity in Early Childhood Programs

"Culture" is a very complex term. What is culture? It is probably best defined by each individual. "Inherited" culture includes one's race, ethnicity, language, religion, and social class. "Personal" culture, on the other hand, is acquired.

You may have become interested in environmental issues, and the way you live is based on a philosophy of care for the environment. Your philosophy may affect the way you eat, the clothes you wear, the way you travel, and so on.

You may define your personal culture primarily by your family structure, your race or ethnic background, the language you speak (e.g., deaf culture), your religion, your sexual orientation (e.g., lesbian), and so on. People usually define their culture by the aspects of their lives that most affect their day-to-day living.

Assessing the situation:

Your program's philosophy places a high value on helping children develop independence. However, one family in the program places a high value on interdependence (i.e., a long-term commitment to depending on one another, remaining close to family). How do the staff and parents compromise in the best interest of the child?

"One way, especially if it is your own, may feel [more right] to you" (Gonzalez-Mena 1997, 87). By asking parents informal questions such as "How do you handle this type of situation at home?" you can gain insight into why a child doesn't respond well to the educators' strategy, and you can also acquire another way of looking at the issue. In a program that has an open view to diversity, this would simply be viewed as a different way—a way to be respected. Children can be caught between two value systems. When issues about value differences arise, it is a priority to negotiate a cultural conflict so that neither way is devalued (see Table 1.1).

Educators have a responsibility to find out as much as possible about the child and family's culture and to be sensitive and responsive to differences. It is certainly possible for children to move comfortably between the early childhood setting and the home culture, where roles, expectations, and interactions may differ considerably, if there is mutual respect and interest by educators and parents. A climate of acceptance paves the way for understanding and learning for everyone involved.

If a child and his or her parents believe that the early childhood environment supports the child's individuality and cultural values, beliefs, and practices, they will feel emotionally secure and comfortable contributing to others' awareness of their values and practices. Children are profoundly influenced by the attitudes of their adult community.

So far, we have defined culture very broadly. The term "ethno-culture" commonly refers to specific ethnic groups—that is, a group of people identified by themselves and others as sharing racial or national origins sometimes called common heritage or ancestry. People from common ethnic backgrounds may have shared traits (e.g., skin colour, language), customs, and behaviour. How people view health and illness, doctors, medicine, and approaches to healing may be influenced by their ethnicity. In addition to finding out about these beliefs directly from parents, you

TABLE 1.1	Suggestions for Approaching Cultural Conflicts

Here is a summary of hints to help you deal with the cultural conflicts that can arise in a child care setting:

1. *Take it slow.* Don't expect to resolve each conflict immediately. Building understanding and relationships takes time. Some conflicts won't be resolved; they'll just be managed. You have to learn to cope with differences when there is no common meeting ground or resolution. This coping sounds hard, but it's possible, if you're willing to accept the fact that resolution is not always the outcome of disputes.

2. *Understand yourself.* Become clear about your own values and goals. Know what you believe in. Have a bottom line, but leave space above it to be flexible.

3. *Become sensitive to your own discomfort.* Tune in on those times when something bothers you instead of just ignoring it and hoping it will go away. Work to identify what specific behaviours of others make you uncomfortable. Try to discover exactly what in yourself created this discomfort.

4. *Learn about other cultures.* Books, classes, and workshops help, but watch out for stereotypes and biased information. Your best source of information comes from the parents in your program. Check out what they believe about their cultures, and see if it fits with other information you receive. However, don't ever make one person a representative of his or her culture. Listen to individuals, take in the information they give you, but don't generalize to whole cultures. Keep your mind open as you learn. Check out your point of view. There's a difference between finding and celebrating diversity and explaining deficiencies.

5. *Find out what the parents in your program, individually, want for their children.* What are their goals? What are their caregiving practices? What concerns do they have about their child in your program? Encourage them to talk to you. Encourage them to ask questions. You may find out about cultures this way, or you may just find out about individual or familial differences. All are important.

6. *Be a risk taker.* If you are secure enough, you may feel you can afford to make mistakes. Mistakes are a part of cross-cultural communication. It helps to have a good support system behind you when you take risks and make mistakes.

7. *Communicate, dialogue, negotiate.* If you have a chance to build a relationship before getting into negotiations, you're more likely eventually to reach a mutually satisfying point.

8. *Share power.* Empowerment is an important factor in the dialogue-negotiation process. Although some see empowerment (allowing others to experience their own personal power) as threatening, in reality empowerment creates new forms of power. Some teachers and educators fear that empowerment means giving away their own power, but this is not true! No one can give personal power, and no one can take it away. We all have our personal power, though we can be discouraged or prevented from recognizing or using it. Sharing power, or empowerment, enhances everyone's power.

In conclusion, hard as it may be to take the risks involved in cross-cultural encounters, to learn what is needed to understand culturally different people, to gain skills in communication, and to cope when conflicts arise, exposure to more than one culture is a definite asset. As you care for children from various cultural backgrounds, everyone gains. You, the children, and the parents have the opportunity to learn more about and appreciate human diversity.

Source: Reprinted with permission from J. Gonzalez-Mena, *Multicultural Issues in Child Care* (Mountain View, CA: Mayfield Publishing, 1997), 33–34.

can contact agencies that are aware of an ethno-culture's health beliefs and practices. We can't assume from general information, however, that a family has particular health beliefs or practices. Individuals and families are unique in their situations and beliefs—ethnicity is just one aspect of many that shape people's lives.

Networking with the Community

Networking within the community contributes to the well-being of children, families, educators, and the overall early childhood program. Educators working effectively as a team contribute significantly to the level of quality provided by the program. No one works in isolation, and early childhood settings are no exception. Staff cannot and should not try to be all things to all people. Staff must establish a network with professionals, agencies, and associations in their community (see Figure 1.2). This network allows the staff to grow both personally and professionally, resulting in higher-quality early childhood programs. Your early childhood education training and skills equip you to work as an effective member of the network of professionals concerned with the growth, development, and health of children (e.g., public health departments, child abuse prevention teams, school boards, community health centres). Collaboration with others should have the additional benefit of drawing a number of services together, thus reducing duplication, improving the delivery of service, and lowering costs.

As students in an early childhood education program, you may be overwhelmed when you think about developing relationships with individuals and groups, but be assured that it doesn't happen overnight. It is important that you see the benefits of working cooperatively, learning from others, and also sharing your expertise. In early childhood settings where staff and the director do not work cooperatively, children, families, and staff are at a real disadvantage. No one person or agency can do it all or know it all. Networking increases resources and decreases educator stress levels (see Figure 1.2).

As you can see from our discussion on health promotion, your approach to your work can affect the health and well-being of children and families. For those educators who are committed to their profession, what you think (attitude), what you know (knowledge), and what you do (behaviour) are evolving positively through education and experience. We must recognize our strengths and limitations throughout this lifelong learning process and make responsible decisions accordingly. All educators and directors need access to resources; a student or recent graduate of an early childhood education program needs to have increased support that is readily available.

Health Promotion Action Plan in the Early Childhood Program

An action approach to promoting health in programs is positive for a number of reasons:

1. *It fosters partnerships with parents and other family members.* Working together for common goals recognizes and builds on people's knowledge and strengths. In addition to getting the job done, you develop relationships with the families—a benefit to everyone involved.

2. *An action approach helps people learn to solve problems and experience the value of working cooperatively.* When individuals see results, they are more

FIGURE 1.2 | **Groups and Individuals Who Interact with Child Care**

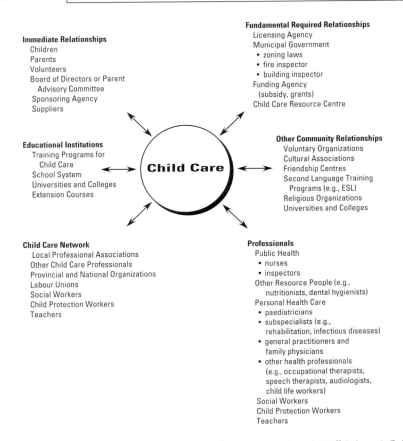

Immediate Relationships
Children
Parents
Volunteers
Board of Directors or Parent
  Advisory Committee
Sponsoring Agency
Suppliers

Fundamental Required Relationships
Licensing Agency
Municipal Government
  • zoning laws
  • fire inspector
  • building inspector
Funding Agency
  (subsidy, grants)
Child Care Resource Centre

Educational Institutions
Training Programs for
  Child Care
School System
Universities and Colleges
Extension Courses

Other Community Relationships
Voluntary Organizations
Cultural Associations
Friendship Centres
Second Language Training
  Programs (e.g., ESL)
Religious Organizations
Universities and Colleges

Child Care Network
Local Professional Associations
Other Child Care Professionals
Provincial and National Organizations
Labour Unions
Social Workers
Child Protection Workers
Teachers

Professionals
Public Health
  • nurses
  • inspectors
Other Resource People (e.g.,
  nutritionists, dental hygienists)
Personal Health Care
  • paediatricians
  • subspecialists (e.g.,
    rehabilitation, infectious diseases)
  • general practitioners and
    family physicians
  • other health professionals
    (e.g., occupational therapists,
    speech therapists, audiologists,
    child life workers)
Social Workers
Child Protection Workers
Teachers

Source: Reprinted with permission from Canadian Paediatric Society (1996), *Well Beings: A Guide to Promote the Physical Health, Safety and Emotional Well-Being of Children in Child Care Centres and Family Day Care Homes* (Ottawa: Canadian Paediatric Society), 37.

likely to view themselves as having enough personal and collective power to effect change. When all the players are committed to the issue, there are fewer barriers. Of course, there are times when interactions among employers, administrators, and boards, or budget restraints, result in insurmountable obstacles. Although this will be disappointing, it is helpful to view what has been gained through the process. Obviously, in addition to the benefits from the action itself, working cooperatively also models a cooperative approach for children that is crucial for adapting in our ever-changing world.

3. *An action approach increases the individual's and group's awareness of community resources as well as community agencies' knowledge of community needs.* An action plan will probably include communication with the public health and other municipal departments, community health centres, social service agencies, doctors, and so on. An active approach to promoting health in early childhood settings can lead to improved accessibility for children and families to the larger community, as information is shared through family and friends.

CONCLUSION

As educators, we can contribute to the health promotion plan. In our daily work with children and families, we can put into practice a health promotion philosophy by

- developing and following healthy policies and procedures;
- modelling healthy habits ourselves;
- communicating in an ongoing way with the families, demonstrating sensitivity and openness to their health beliefs and practices; and
- networking with the community, realizing that we all benefit through sharing resources.

Each of the following units in this book will discuss the health-related practices in the early childhood program.

Healthy lifestyles, the physical environment, and genetics are significant determinants of health. In order to improve the quality of life for all Canadians, however, action needs to be taken on the social and economic determinants of health in particular, giving priority to the serious problem of income inequity. Generally, the wider the gap in population income, the poorer the population health. "Those with the lowest incomes have the worst health outcomes, but the negative impact of inequity is felt among all Canadians" (Canadian Institute of Child Health 2000, 178).

As Nelson Mandela, former president of the Republic of South Africa, put it: "Security for a few is insecurity for us all" (Campaign 2000 2000b, 11).

What's Your Opinion?

TO EXTEND ELIGIBILITY OR NOT?

The federal government's parental leave benefits enable eligible parents to spend up to 50 weeks at home with their newborn. A mother or father can be at home for the entire time, or the parents can split the time between them. There are numerous short- and long-term benefits for both the infant and the family, including the potential for longer duration of breast-feeding and the opportunity for parents to build a strong relationship with their child from the start, which also supports early brain development with lifelong effects.

Not all parents are eligible for this benefit (e.g., those who are self-employed or are not gainfully employed during pregnancy). This reality can put their children at a disadvantage for optimal well-being.

Do you believe that more parents should be eligible for this benefit? Why and how? Consider the potential impact of this benefit on early childhood education and care in Canada.

ASSESS YOUR LEARNING

Define terms or describe concepts used in this unit.

- health
- health status
- determinants of health
- principles of medicare
- personal health care system
- public health system
- community health centres
- complementary medicine

- health promotion
- prevention
- health promotion action plan
- quality early childhood education and care
- early childhood program policies
- cultural diversity
- networking

Evaluate your options in each situation.

1. You and your housemate are bored with eating pasta and sauce, burgers, and hot dogs. You're both intrigued by a number of the fruits, vegetables, and grains you've noticed in a new grocery store. You would like to try some, but you don't know where to start.

2. Your doctor hands you a prescription. When you ask him what it's for and whether there are side effects, he replies, "Don't worry about it. Just take these pills and you'll feel better."

3. Classes have been cancelled for the day to allow students to attend a child care rally at the legislature. You are tempted to skip it because you have to study for a test.

4. A parent is angry at pickup time because his daughter's sleeves are damp from water play even though she was wearing a smock. He believes that this is how someone gets a cold. He asks that his daughter never play at the water table again.

5. A safety issue arises at the centre. None of the staff can think of a suitable response, and you suggest that consulting with another centre may provide options. The director insists, "We can work this out ourselves," and does not want outside interference.

RESOURCE MATERIALS

Organizations

Campaign 2000, c/o Family Service Association of Toronto, 355 Church Street, Toronto, ON M5B 1Z8. Tel. (416) 595-9230, ext. 244; fax (416) 595-0242. www.campaign2000.ca

Canadian Child Care Federation, 201–383 Parkdale Avenue, Ottawa, ON K1Y 4R4. Tel. (613) 729-5289 or 1-800-858-1412; fax (613) 729-3159. www.cccf-fcsge.ca

Canadian Institute of Child Health, 384 Bank Street, Suite 300, Ottawa, ON K2P 1Y4. Tel. (613) 230-8838; fax (613) 230-6654. www.cich.ca

Child Care Advocacy Association of Canada, 323 Chapel Street, Ottawa, ON K1N 7Z2. Tel. (613) 594-3196; fax (613) 594-9375. www.childcareadvocacy.ca

Family Service Canada, 404–383 Parkdale Avenue, Ottawa, ON K1Y 4R4. Tel. (613) 772-9006 or 1-800-668-7808; fax (613) 722-8610. www.familyservicecanada.org

Other Websites of Interest

Canadian Association of Health, Physical Education, Recreation, and Dance (CAHPERD): www.cahperd.ca

Canadian Health Network (Health Canada): www.canadian-health-network.ca

Childcare Resource and Research Unit: www.childcarecanada.org

Coalition for Active Living: www.activeliving.ca

The Lung Association: www.lung.ca

National Institute of Environmental Health Sciences (United States): www.niehs.nih.gov

Printed Matter

Alternative Health Care: The Canadian Directory (1997), by B.L. Harden and C.R. Harden (Noble Ages Publishing).

Child Care Policy in Canada: Putting the Pieces Together (1994), by M. Friendly (Addison-Wesley).

Complete Canadian Health Guide (1993), by J.V. Engel (Key Porter).

Health Promotion in Canada: Provincial, National, and International Perspectives (1994), by A. Pederson, M. O'Neill, and I. Rootman, eds. (W.B. Saunders Canada).

BIBLIOGRAPHY

Association of Ontario Midwives (2001). "Cost-Effective Care" (Information Sheet). <www.aom.on.ca/facts/costofcare.html> (July 2003).

Beach, J., J. Bertrand, and G. Cleveland (1998). "Our Child Care Workforce—From Recognition to Remuneration: More Than a Labour of Love." A Human Resource Study of Child Care in Canada. Ottawa: Human Resources Development Canada.

Brown, I., D. Raphael, and R. Renwick (1998). *Quality of Life Profile.* Toronto: Centre for Health Promotion, University of Toronto.

Campaign 2000 (2002a). "Diversity or Disparity? Early Childhood Education and Care in Canada." Toronto: Family Service Association of Canada.

——— (2002b). "Poverty Amidst Prosperity: Building a Canada for All Children." Toronto: Family Service Association of Canada.

Canadian Council on Social Development (2002a). "The Progress of Canada's Children: 2002 Highlights." Ottawa: CCSD.

——— (2002b). "Response of the CCSD to the Final Report by the Commission on the Future of Health Care in Canada." November 28. Ottawa: CCSD.

Canadian Institute of Child Health (2000). *The Health of Canada's Children: A CICH Profile*, 3rd ed. Ottawa: Canadian Institute of Child Health.

Canadian Paediatric Society (1996). *Well Beings: A Guide to Promote the Physical Health, Safety and Emotional Well-Being of Children in Child Care Centres and Family Day Care Homes.* Toronto: Canadian Paediatric Society.

Doherty, G. (2001). "Targeting Early Childhood Care and Education: Myths and Realities." Occasional Paper No. 15. Toronto: Childcare Resource and Research Unit.

Epp, J. (1986). *Achieving Health for All: A Framework for Health Promotion.* Ottawa: Supply and Services Canada.

Gestwicki, C., and J. Bertrand (1999). *The Essentials of Early Education,* 1st Canadian ed. Toronto: ITP Nelson.

Gonzalez-Mena, J. (1997). *Multicultural Issues in Child Care,* 2nd ed. Mountain View, CA: Mayfield Publishing.

Guy, K., ed. (1997). *Our Promise to Children.* Ottawa: Health Canada.

Health and Welfare Canada (1992). *Brighter Futures: Canada's Action Plan for Children.* Ottawa: Supply and Services Canada.

Hertzman, C. (1998). "The Case for Child Development as a Determinant of Health." *Canadian Journal of Public Health* 89, Suppl. 1:S14–S19.

——— (1997). In K. Guy (ed.), *Our Promise to Children.* Ottawa: Health Canada.

Keating, D.P., and C. Hertzman, eds. (1999). *Developmental Health and the Wealth of Nations: Social, Biological, and Educational Dynamics.* New York: Guilford Press.

Keating, D.P., and F.K. Miller (1999). "Individual Pathways in Competence and Coping: From Regulatory Systems to Habits of Mind." In D.P. Keating and C. Hertzmann (eds.), *Developmental Health and the Wealth of Nations: Social, Biological, and Educational Dynamics.* New York: Guilford Press.

Kirkey, M. (1998). "One-on-One with Dr. Michael Rachlis: 1998 Review/1999 Forecast." *Hospital News* (12): 11, 18.

Labonté, R. (1993). *Health Promotion: Theory and Practice Background Material 1.* Toronto: Centre for Health Promotion, University of Toronto.

Michalski, J.H. (2002). "Quality of Life in Canada: A Citizens' Report Card" (Background Report). Ottawa: Canadian Policy Research Networks.

National Forum on Health (1997a). *Canada Health Action: Building on the Legacy, vol. I (Final Report).* Ottawa: Minister of Public Works and Government Services.

——— (1997b). *Canada Health Action: Building on the Legacy, vol. II (Synthesis Reports and Issue Papers).* Ottawa: Minister of Public Works and Government Services.

Network of the Federal/Provincial/Territorial Group on Nutrition and National Institute of Nutrition (1989). *Promoting Nutritional Health during the Preschool Years: Canadian Guidelines.* Ottawa: The Network.

Phelp, M. (2002). "National Daycare Plan Being Hammered Out." *The Globe and Mail,* 12 December.

Rachlis, M., and C. Kushner (1992). *Second Opinion: What's Wrong with Canada's Health Care System.* Toronto: Collins Publishers.

Rootman, I., and J. Raeburn (1994). "The concept of health." In A. Pederson, M. O'Neill, and I. Rootman (eds.), *Health Promotion in Canada: Provincial, National and International Perspectives.* Toronto: W.B. Saunders Canada.

Ross, D.P., K.J. Scott, and P.J. Smith (2000). *The Canadian Fact Book on Poverty 2000.* Ottawa: Canadian Council on Social Development.

Royal Commission on Aboriginal Peoples (1996). *National Forum on Health, vol. VII: The Need for an Aboriginal Health Institute in Canada.* Ottawa: Supply and Services Canada.

Shonkoff, J., and D. Phillips (2001). *From Neurons to Neighbourhoods: The Science of Early Childhood Development*. Ottawa: National Academy of Sciences.

Statistics Canada (1996). *Reading the Future: A Portrait of Literacy in Canada*. Ottawa: Statistics Canada.

Tzu Chi Institute for Complementary and Alternative Medicine (Canadian Health Network Affiliate) (2002). "Natural Doesn't Mean Safe." <www.canadian-health-network.ca/html/newnotable/jan1a_2002e.html> (July 2003).

United Nations (2002). *Human Development Report 2002: Deepening Democracy in a Fragmented World*. New York: Oxford University Press.

Villeneuve, P., and H. Morrison (1994). "Health Consequences of Smoking in Canada: An Update." *Chronic Diseases in Canada* 15(3): 102–4.

World Health Organization, Health and Welfare Canada, and Canadian Public Health Association (1986). *Ottawa Charter for Health Promotion*. Ottawa: Health and Welfare Canada.

Getting Started in Your Community: A Checklist

1.1

Those communities that try to identify the needs of their children and develop comprehensive plans to address those needs are more likely to find effective solutions. But there is no one blueprint for successful community action. Each community has its own particular needs and its unique combination of resources.

Building on community-based success stories and the latest research and best practices can help lead the way, but in the end the needs of the children in your community, your community's collective assets, and the possibilities for community-wide collaboration help define your community's particular goals and implementation strategies.

Here are a few questions to keep in mind:

❑ Who are the key people in the community concerned about the well-being of children, the community's social environment, and the local economy? For example, this would include individuals who are

- currently involved in caring for, educating, and providing services for children
- researchers and experts in child development and social policy
- leaders in local politics, business, labour, and the media
- young people, community activists, members of parent organizations, and volunteers

❑ What is the best forum for bringing these partners together? For example:

- a task force set up by the mayor's office, by municipal leaders, or by a planning association
- a coalition of community-based organizations that serve children, youths, and families
- a dedicated group of community members who have potential access to resources, research, and expertise
- a "child-friendly" community effort

❑ How can you use information effectively to guide your efforts? In other words, how do you measure how well your community's children are doing and assess the community assets at your disposal?

- Who in the community collects data on children—a district health council, school boards, a child care association, a university, municipal or regional government, etc.?
- Whom can you recruit to help pull this information together or to look at developing new indicators to help measure the well-being and competence of children in your community?
- What are some of the assets within your community, such as voluntary networks, service systems that are open to change and collaboration, equity of opportunities and outcomes for children, and financial and in-kind sources of support?

❏ How can your group develop an action plan that lays out steps to improve the outcomes for your community's children? Based on the assessment of both the key strengths and weakness in your community:

- What do you want to achieve or, in other words, what problems do you want to address?

- How can you make the best use of the expertise that exists in your community?

- What are the most practical next steps? What are some of the issues that require more long-term planning?

- What indicators can you use that will show whether you achieved your objectives? For example, what is the percentage of low-birth-weight babies, and how many children are assessed to be ready to learn when they arrive in grade 1?

❏ How can you build broad-based support for your action plan?

- What are the key messages you would like to convey to the community as a whole?

- What practical steps can you recommend to people who might be interested in getting involved in the community? For example, you might target individual members of neighbourhoods, labour, business, government, non-governmental organizations, charities, religious congregations, and professional organizations.

- Who can help you develop and implement a public relations and media strategy?

Source: Adapted with permission from K. Guy (ed.), *Our Promise to Children* (Ottawa: Health Canada, 1997), 132–33.

UNIT 2

Occupational Health

CONTENTS

Promoting Your Physical Well-Being   50
   ACHIEVING A BALANCE IN YOUR LIFESTYLE   50
   INFECTIOUS DISEASES AND YOU   59
   PREVENTING MUSCULOSKELETAL INJURIES   61
   FURNISHINGS AND LAYOUT   63
   WORKING WITH ART AND CLEANING PRODUCTS   66
   ROLE OF PUBLIC HEALTH AGENCIES IN HEALTH PROMOTION   68
   WORKPLACE ENVIRONMENTAL ISSUES   68
   INJURY REPORTS   69

Promoting Your Emotional and Social Well-Being   70
   CREATING A SUPPORTIVE EARLY CHILDHOOD ENVIRONMENT   70
   EARLY CHILDHOOD EDUCATIONAL EXPERIENCE: SETTING THE STAGE   80

Revisiting the Health Promotion Action Plan   83

Conclusion   84

What's Your Opinion? TO TAKE A BREAK OR NOT TO BREAK?   85

Assess Your Learning   85

Resource Materials   86

Bibliography   87

TABLES

TABLE 2.1   DIMENSIONS OF PERSONAL WELLNESS   49
TABLE 2.2   WORK SITE ANALYSIS OF THE CHILD CARE WORK ENVIRONMENT   64
TABLE 2.3   MAKING YOUR OWN CLEANING PRODUCTS   67
TABLE 2.4   THE TEN DIMENSIONS OF ORGANIZATIONAL CLIMATE   71
TABLE 2.5   THE POSITIVES AND NEGATIVES OF WORKING IN CHILD CARE   73
TABLE 2.6   ARE YOU LISTENING?   75
TABLE 2.7   LIST OF STATEMENTS ABOUT ORGANIZATIONAL CLIMATE   82

FIGURE

FIGURE 2.1   CANADA'S FOOD GUIDE SUGGESTS...   52

APPENDIX 2.1 THE FINANCIAL DIMENSION 89

APPENDIX 2.2 *CANADA'S PHYSICAL ACTIVITY GUIDE TO HEALTHY ACTIVE LIVING* 90

APPENDIX 2.3 BACK CARE 92

APPENDIX 2.4 STAFF EXPOSED TO INFECTIOUS DISEASES 93

APPENDIX 2.5 HEALTH PRACTICES: YOU AND YOUR EMPLOYER 95

Students in community colleges and universities are not a homogeneous group but reflect the communities in which they live. Many students are right out of high school, others are mature students returning to school after time spent in the work force. Some are parents. Some are in their first educational program since arriving in Canada. Many are juggling school and part-time jobs or other commitments. You, too, are entering the early childhood education program with experiences different from those of your classmates, and you have responsibilities beyond the classroom and placements in early childhood settings.

Even at the best of times, school is stressful. It is a period of transition: establishing new friendships and study habits, trying to budget your time and money. There can be additional adjustments to make, such as moving away from home for the first time or to a new community. It's not surprising if you are experiencing stressors, suffering emotional ups and downs, feeling tired and at times discouraged, feeling pulled in different directions. Recognizing and managing stress in your life are essential now and on graduation, when you will be working in an early childhood program.

There is growing recognition that employees' overall health plays a significant role in job satisfaction, productivity, and turnover rates. Occupations that we tend to think of as stressful are those that are inherently dangerous, such as mining, operating heavy machinery, firefighting, and police work. Yet every occupation presents potential risks to its employees' physical and emotional health. Store clerks who repeatedly drag groceries over the scanner at the checkout counter can develop severe wrist pain as well as sore legs or varicose veins from standing. People who work at computer terminals all day may suffer from eyestrain, lower back pain, and carpal tunnel syndrome. Employees who perform repetitive tasks and work that permits them little control over their jobs experience a low level of autonomy, which leads to low job satisfaction.

Early childhood education and care is *not* babysitting! Many still believe that working in early childhood is just an extension of minding other people's children. In addition, the fact that early childhood education is a predominantly female profession has historically accorded it low status, and many people believe that women naturally have the aptitude, knowledge, and skills needed to care for groups of children. In other words, the popular myth is that anyone can look after children. Many people also don't believe that early childhood education and care (unlike education and health care) constitutes an essential service to families. These attitudes contribute to the low status, low salaries, and lack of respect accorded to educators. A variety of sources indicate that centre-based educators with a college diploma or certificate working full-time earned approximately 75% of what average full-time female workers with the same education earned (Beach et al. 1998, 77). In addition, there is a wide discrepancy in wage rates for centre-based staff, even within the same province or territory (79).

Fortunately, change is happening, however slowly. More people are recognizing what quality early childhood education and care is. Other professions are identifying the important impact of early childhood programs on children's lives (e.g., preventing child abuse). The early childhood community and its professional associations tirelessly advocate at all levels of government. Most parents recognize that early childhood programs are an essential service, and that children's early experiences are critical to their overall development.

The You Bet I Care! study compared results with the Caring for a Living Survey on wages and working conditions in early childhood workplaces conducted in 1991. The study's findings are based on almost 5000 staff members (including 848 centre directors) in non-profit and for-profit settings, and point to an urgent need to address five issues:

1. the current method of funding of child care
2. the current low levels of remuneration, which relates directly to the current method of financing child care
3. provincial/territorial regulations pertaining to staff education and the current limited accessibility and affordability of training in many jurisdictions
4. the lack of respect from the public perceived by staff and directors
5. the lack of coordinated policies that ensure that high-quality child care is available to all children in Canada, regardless of where they live or their family income (Doherty et al. 2000, 177)

As in any other occupation, not everyone is suited to the work. Yes, children are amazing, energetic, curious, active learners. Yes, it can be exciting and rewarding to be involved in their lives and development. But contrary to the stereotype addressed earlier, educators must develop the attitudes, knowledge, and skills necessary to be competent in their career. In addition, early childhood education and care is physical and emotional work. Always having to be "on" with children can be emotionally tiring. Combine this with the working dynamics of co-workers, administration, and management styles of supervisors and directors, and educators can experience job stress and, possibly, burnout.

Low salaries and limited opportunities for advancement are two factors that contribute to staff turnover. Neither is likely to change to educators' advantage in the near future. However, you can control other aspects of the work to increase your job satisfaction. In recent decades, a holistic approach to health has often been translated into dimensions of wellness to facilitate self-awareness and enhance individual goal setting. Although dimensions are listed separately in the accompanying table, there is recognition that all aspects of wellness are interrelated (Hoeger and Hoeger 2000, 4). Table 2.1 provides descriptions of eight commonly identified dimensions of wellness.

TABLE 2.1   Dimensions of Personal Wellness

Physical: awareness of and respect for body—nutrition, physical activity, relaxation, sleep, use of tobacco, health habits

Emotional: level of self-esteem, security, flexibility, ability to express feelings, recognition of strengths and weaknesses

Social: level of involvement with others; sense of belonging, membership, or affiliation

Intellectual: active mind, inquiring, curious, seeking new information and ideas

Occupational: clarity of direction; satisfaction with development of skills and potential, as well as autonomy; motivation to investigate options

Spiritual: ability to achieve a sense of renewal, see purpose in life, find things that nourish the soul

Environmental: level to which external environment contributes to or detracts from wellness; commitment to improving the environment

Financial: becoming financially literate; learning to take control over money; ability to meet basic needs

---

Goals can be short-term (usually accomplished within a year), long-term, or ongoing (e.g., lifelong inclusion of daily physical activity). You're more likely to achieve success in lifestyle changes if your goals are

- specific—Identify in exact terms what you hope to achieve and set out a detailed action plan.

- personalized—Set your own goals rather than having someone set them for you.

- written—Write down your goals and keep a journal of your progress and setbacks; make a contract with yourself.

- realistic—Be realistic. Unattainable goals will discourage you.

- measurable—Ensure that you can measure your goals, for example "To be able to climb stairs to my apartment (six floors) without being out of breath within eight weeks." Goals like "I'm going to get fit" or "I'm going to lose weight" are not measurable.

- time-specific—Establish target dates for your goals. Deadlines are motivational; however, keep in mind adjustments may be necessary.

- evaluated—Monitor your progress. This will help you to keep on track and determine when a goal may be unrealistic or too easy. Make the necessary goal adjustments to support you in moving forward (Hoeger and Hoeger 2000, 35–37).

Appendix 2.1 (page 89) provides you with a sample of financial criteria. Completing such a checklist can help you decide on goals and an action plan.

This unit begins with an exploration of the physical dimension of early childhood work for educators and ECE students. The second section explores the social and emotional dimensions. Although the topics are organized in sections, they are all interrelated. To explore other dimensions (e.g., spiritual, environmental) more specifically, you may want to refer to wellness manuals such as the one by Donatelle et al. (2003). (See also Resource Materials, page 86.)

PROMOTING YOUR PHYSICAL WELL-BEING

What are your health concerns about working with children? When instructors ask new ECE students this question, many students worry about catching chickenpox, head lice, colds, and the flu. We know that when children are first enrolled in programs, they get sick more often; but as time passes, the rate of illness declines. This pattern applies to students as well. Adults benefit from a mature immune system; they are fully immunized, one hopes, and most have already experienced the common childhood diseases (e.g., chickenpox). Adults can also implement hygiene practices that protect them and reduce the opportunities for illness to spread among children and adults. Even so, you may experience a few viral infections when you begin your early childhood program placements.

It probably will take only a couple of days of work in a program to experience firsthand how physically demanding work with children can be. It's a strain for educators to lift and carry infants and toddlers, move play equipment, sit on the floor, lean over child-sized tables, sinks, and toilets, and be constantly on the move in the playground to supervise children or take part in a physical activity. The positive side is that this constant and varied movement, when performed correctly, contributes to physical fitness.

Achieving a Balance in Your Lifestyle

As adults we make individual lifestyle choices that can have positive or negative effects on our health.

Nutrition

One of our basic needs is food. However, the amount of emphasis placed on food and our health varies among individuals and throughout society. The bottom line—nutrition has a significant impact on our health. The principles of nutrition discussed in Unit 5 apply to children's nutritional status as well as to your own. As well, factors that shape eating habits are discussed; these can assist you in developing insight into why, what, and when you eat. Some people's habits fall far short of the recommended principles of nutrition. Others know what good nutrition includes and put these principles into practice every day. Of course, there are times when nutrition is less of a priority—especially to someone experiencing a great deal of stress. There is concern, however, that this becomes a pattern of behaviour or a vicious circle, because our bodies have increased nutrient needs at times of emotional or physical stress.

w w w

Lynn, an ECE student, is studying frantically for midterm tests and is trying to stay awake by drinking lots of coffee. Not surprisingly, the coffee keeps her awake even when she wants to sleep. Lynn doesn't believe she has time for sit-down meals and instead eats doughnuts in the cafeteria. By week's end, Lynn is snapping at everyone and can't imagine how she'll ever survive her weekend job at the mall.

This example highlights the interplay between nutrition and physical, social, and emotional well-being. Lynn's nutritional habits have raised her stress level rather than lowered it. How can she use nutrition in her favour when she is stressed out during test week? Recognizing the problem, Lynn makes it a point to learn more about nutrition and how nutrients (especially B and C vitamins) nourish the nervous system. As test week approaches, Lynn eats a variety of foods high in these vitamins—whole-grain breads and cereals, milk and yogurt, dark-green leafy vegetables, broccoli, tomatoes, oranges, and bananas. During that week she brings in nutritious snacks like whole-grain crackers with cheese or hummus and fruit that she can refuel on. She limits her coffee to a couple of cups during the morning. She is pleasantly surprised that by the end of the week she isn't a bear! Let us hope that this experience has a positive impact on Lynn, and that she makes some permanent changes to her eating patterns that help her in the long term.

Eating nutritiously confers benefits daily and over time for all of us. Foods that are high in nutrients keep our minds and bodies in good working order, providing ongoing energy. Eating patterns that maximize the intake of wholesome foods while minimizing the intake of processing and additives contribute to the prevention of serious chronic diseases (e.g., a diet that is low in fat is thought to help prevent heart disease and some forms of cancer). In addition to feeling good and preventing disease, we also provide healthy role models for children. *Canada's Food Guide* (2007a) is based on two principles, eat well and be active today and everyday.

Health Canada does not recommend dieting, which is recognized as counterproductive. Canadians are urged to reject the popular myth that healthy body size is narrowly defined. Realistically, a healthy body size is achieved and maintained through nutritious eating, without dieting, and through incorporating regular physical activity into one's lifestyle. Age, gender, body type, and other factors influence our body size. It is noteworthy, though, that the dramatic increase in the rate of obesity in Canada is of concern to our mortality and morbidity. Statistics Canada (2002) reported that 47.9% of Canadians were overweight in 1998. Currently, the World Health Organization's guidelines for Body Mass Index (BMI) and measures of fat distribution (waist-to-hip ratio) are used to define obesity. With regard to BMI,

- adults with less than 18.5% body fat may have risks associated with being underweight;
- 18.5–25% body fat is optimal for adults;
- adults with more than 25% body fat may have increased risks associated with being overweight.

The risk of metabolic complications increases with a waist-to-hip ratio greater than 94 for men and over 80 for women (World Health Organization 1998, 9).

Following *Canada's Food Guide* and putting consistent effort into normalizing routine physical activity will help adults who are considered overweight move into a healthier range. Individuals who may be considered obese will probably require guidance and supervision by a physician and dietitian.

How does your eating pattern rate? Try recording what you eat for the next few days or, even better, for a week. Then use the *Make Your Choices Count!* checklist to see how your choices compared with *Canada's Food Guide* recommendations (see Figure 2.1).

FIGURE 2.1

CANADA'S FOOD GUIDE SUGGESTS...

☑ Eat the recommended **amount** and **type** of food each day.

☑ Eat at least one dark green and one orange vegetable each day.

☑ Choose vegetables and fruit prepared with little or no added fat, sugar or salt.

☑ Have vegetables and fruit more often than juice.

☑ Make at least half of your grain products whole grain each day.

☑ Choose grain products that are lower in fat, sugar or salt.

☑ Drink skim, 1% or 2% milk each day.

☑ Select lower fat milk alternatives.

☑ Have meat alternatives such as beans, lentils and tofu often.

☑ Eat at least two Food Guide Servings of fish each week.

☑ Select lean meat and alternatives prepared with little or no added fat or salt.

☑ Include a small amount of unsaturated fat each day.

☑ Satisfy your thirst with water.

☑ Limit foods and beverages high in calories, fat, sugar or salt.

☑ Be active every day.

Source: (Eating Well with Canada's Food Guide: Resource for Educators and Communicators), Health Canada, (2007). Reproduced with the permission of the Minister of Public Works and Government Services Canada, 2007.

- You are doing everything right and this review confirms and supports your healthy lifestyle.

- You have a low energy level and feel that your overall health (e.g., complexion, dullness of hair, frequency of colds, headaches) can be improved.

- If you are a woman, perhaps you have chronic premenstrual syndrome (PMS) and have heard that changes in diet, such as eliminating caffeine and alcohol, may help reduce the symptoms.

- You know that you overeat when you're bored or that you crave salty food when you study.

Any habit is hard to break or adjust, so don't expect change to happen overnight. The first step is to find out what influences your eating. As children, we develop positive and negative associations with food. Using examples, Table 5.1 illustrates what food can mean to someone (see page 194). Sometimes you eat food because you feel like it, whether it is nutritious or not! If we feel deprived of food we enjoy, we are more likely to abandon our progress in making changes. Here are a few additional suggestions:

- If you are not currently a breakfast eater, try gradually to make changes. Eating from at least three of the four food groups in the morning has short- and long-term benefits.

- Reduce the percentage of animal foods in your diet, and eat some fish and soy foods (e.g., tofu). More specifically, the "unhealthy" fats are saturated (e.g., from meats and cheese) and trans fats (created when liquid oils are transformed into shortening and margarine) (Liebman 2002, 3–4). These raise our LDL ("bad" cholesterol). Better fats (which don't raise cholesterol) are mono- and polyunsaturated fats (e.g., olive, canola, soy, and sunflower oils). The best fats are the omega-3 fats (e.g., fish oils, particularly salmon, trout, and sardines, but there are some omega-3 fats in all fish). It seems that there is something in omega-3 and omega-6 fats that raise our HDL ("good" cholesterol) and protects the heart. Eating seafood at least two a week or taking a supplement is recommended.

- Follow the age and stage recommendations in Health Canada's *Canada Food Guide*. For example: Women who could become pregnant, are pregnant or breastfeeding should take a multivitamin daily containing 400 micrograms of folic acid (Health Canada, 2007b, 42). Folic acid is a B vitamin that is known to reduce the risk of a fetus developing a neural tube defect, and also supports the growth of maternal and fetal tissue. Men and women over the age of 50 need more vitamin D than can be obtained from food, in order to reduce the risk of osteoporosis and fractures. A supplement containing 400 IU of vitamin D in addition to consuming 500 mL of milk each day is recommended (Health Canada, 2007b, 43).

- Gradually reduce the number of processed foods you buy, though some convenience foods may be too convenient to give up! Most, but not all, processed foods have a lot of saturated or trans fat, salt, sugar, and additives. Read labels to determine nutrition content.

- Bring your own food to school or work as often as possible, or bring at least part of the meal, or bring snacks to ensure some high-nutrient foods.
- Share ideas with your friends. Potluck lunches or two or three friends taking turns bringing lunch may be enjoyable and time-saving. This idea can promote openness to try new foods.
- My *Food Guide* (2007c) is an interactive tool that helps you to personalize the information found in *Canada's Food Guide*.

Physical Activity

Generally, physical activity includes any bodily movement caused by muscle contraction that results in using energy. Balancing healthy eating with daily physical activity is a winning combination. Health Canada's (2007a) proclamation to "Eat well and be active today and every day!" includes benefits such as: better overall health, lower risk of disease, a healthy body weight, feeling and looking better, more energy, and stronger bones and muscles. These benefits have a positive impact on one's sense of well-being, and they enhance one's physical and intellectual abilities, now and as we get older.

The fitter you are, the better your body is able to deal with the everyday demands you put on it and to recover from any injury. Further reasons why physical activity is healthy for us are listed in *Canada's Physical Activity Guide to Healthy Active Living* (Appendix 2.2), which sets out Health Canada's physical activity guidelines for all Canadians.

Some people don't give exercise a second thought because being active is just part of their lifestyle (e.g., they walk or ride a bicycle to work rather than drive). Those of us who have not incorporated regular physical activity into our lives may find it easier to start by taking small steps rather than big leaps. A drastic change can be motivating at first but soon becomes discouraging if the work and effort don't bring quick results. It may be difficult to fit one more thing into an already crowded schedule, and exercise may seem to be expendable. Single parents of young children, for example, may not see how it is possible. Maybe riding a stationary bike while watching television with the children would be workable, or taking the stairs rather than an escalator whenever possible. Often making a conscious effort to be more active while at work or school is a possibility. While supervising on the playground, educators can keep moving as much as possible, or they can go for a brisk walk during the coffee break.

Four components of physical fitness are universally recognized as promoting good health: aerobic fitness, flexibility, strength, and endurance.

Aerobic (or cardiovascular) fitness is considered the most important component, and refers to how well your heart is able to pump oxygen-rich blood to your cells and carry waste out of your cells. The term aerobic means "with oxygen." In aerobic activity, the body performs low- to moderate-intensity tasks over an extended period of time. By working our heart muscle at 60–80% of its capacity for a minimum of 10 minutes (progressing to 30 minutes) four days a week, we increase and maintain our aerobic fitness level. Walking, hiking, cross-country skiing, cycling, dance aerobics or water aerobics, rope skipping, in-line skating, rowing, and stair climbing are some possibilities.

Individuals need to choose activities and times that suit their life situations. Busy people often try to fit aerobic activity into their workday by walking or climbing stairs at lunch, or getting off public transit a few kilometres from work or home and walking the rest of the way. A bonus is that we get outside and have a change of scenery, which is also good for stress management.

Flexibility refers to the ability of your joints to move through the full range of their motion. Proper stretching is the best way to increase flexibility. Good back health and the prevention of pulls and other muscle damage are important benefits of flexibility (see Preventing Musculoskeletal Injuries, page 61). Stretching each major muscle group after a few minutes of warm-up and before you begin vigorous aerobic or strength training is an important way to prevent strains and sprains. Some stretching exercises can be incorporated into your day, such as head tilts, side stretches, arm circles, and sit/reach stretches. Even stretching in the morning before getting out of bed can contribute to your flexibility and back health. You may also enjoy yoga or tai chi classes for many benefits, including flexibility.

Strength refers to the ability of one of your muscle groups to exert force in one motion (e.g., lifting a toddler or moving a table). Strength training in a gym usually involves a range of machines with weights, focusing on strengthening different muscles. To a certain extent, this can also be done with free weights. A *set* is the number of repetitions performed for a given exercise lifting a certain weight. It is important to build strength and endurance gradually, to prevent muscle fatigue and injury. Strength training exercises without weights and using body resistance to build strength include activities such as pushups, sit-ups, step-ups, pull-ups, arm curls, and abdominal curl-ups.

Endurance refers to the ability of one of your muscle groups to perform muscular contractions of moderate force over an extended period (e.g., lifting half of your maximum capacity a few times a minute over five minutes). If you walk, ride a bike, or climb a hill, you are working on your aerobic fitness, strength, and muscular endurance all at the same time. In the work environment, muscular endurance may translate into putting all the cots away after nap time or being able to lift 10 toddlers—one at a time—off the change table.

Both strength and endurance increase through activity involving resistance training because your muscles get stronger when you condition them to lift more weight and gain endurance when you gradually increase repetitions. It is essential that you learn and practise the proper techniques to prevent injury.

An active lifestyle should include all four fitness components, but your goals and the level of activity you want in your life will help to determine how much of each component will be included. For example, someone who wants to improve overall well-being but doesn't have the time or interest in focusing a lot of attention on a program may place more emphasis on aerobic activities and some gentle stretching to improve flexibility. Regardless of the aerobic activity chosen, strength and endurance should be relatively easy to incorporate. Although programs such as yoga, Pilates, and tai chi do not focus on aerobic activity, they improve flexibility, strength, and endurance.

Recognizing the short- and long-term benefits of moderate physical activity for one's personal and professional lives is the first step toward fitness. Remember:

- Start your program gradually and choose activities you enjoy.
- Make sure you have the right equipment and clothing for the activity. If cost is a factor, choose an activity that has lower equipment costs.
- Learn and use the proper techniques to prevent injury and maximize fitness benefits.
- Stop if it hurts! Listen to your body. Pain means there is something your body is not ready for and you can injure yourself if you continue.

Provincial or local chapters of the Heart and Stroke Foundation of Canada and many other agencies and resources are available to help you get started with suggestions for fitness activities.

Leisure and Rest

Balancing our need for meaningful work with our need for leisure contributes to well-being. Leisure means different things to different people. For example, most individuals have a need for solitude that can be fulfilled through a variety of activities such as completing puzzles, doing crafts or artwork, or meditating. Many people use meditation to relax and manage stress. Although different techniques and philosophies are advocated, in general meditation uses deep breathing, allowing tension to leave the body. Most forms of meditation involve sitting quietly for 15 to 20 minutes, focusing on a particular word or symbol (a mantra), controlling breathing, and becoming more in tune with the inner self. With meditation, as with other forms of coping with or managing stress, it is the individual who determines how effective it is as a tool. To satisfy our need to relate to others, we may like going to a movie with a friend, talking on the phone, entertaining at home, fishing with others, or going camping. Religious or political meetings may also fulfil this need. We might satisfy our need to participate through organized sports or physical activity, a gardening club, or an ethnocultural group. Most individuals also need to observe at times. They may satisfy that need by visiting amusement parks, watching parades, sitting on the porch and watching passersby, or browsing in a bookstore.

These are but a few examples, but they highlight the fact that for most of us there is an overlap between physical activity and relaxation, because going to the gym or taking a brisk walk may achieve both ends. In the discussion on stress later in this unit, the topic of leisure activities—whether physically active and social or quiet and solitary—appears again as a means to cope with stress. Being aware of what is relaxing for you and finding regular opportunities to unwind are part of everyday health promotion.

Our bodies need time to rest and sleep in order to revitalize and to provide time for the bodily functions and organs to slow down. The duration of sleep that adults need varies, but most of us need seven to eight hours a night. Illness, pregnancy, or other factors may increase the amount of sleep needed.

Stress factors such as financial or personal problems, exam-time worry, or a colicky baby can affect the amount or quality of our sleep. Here are some common-sense suggestions for having a better sleep:

- Avoid alcohol (which can disrupt sleep patterns) or smoke (because nicotine makes you wakeful) before going to bed.

- Eliminate or reduce consumption of caffeinated drinks (e.g., coffee, cola drinks) starting in late afternoon.
- Do something relaxing before going to bed.
- Maintain a regular schedule and routine for going to bed and getting up.
- Get out of bed and do something (e.g., read a relaxing book, write a list to reduce worries) rather than watching the clock when you are unable to sleep.
- Stress coupled with sleep deprivation is very taxing on one's emotional and physical health, and talking with a friend or counsellor can help to find short- or long-term solutions.

Especially when we are young, and often as students, socializing in the evenings may take precedence over getting enough sleep every night. When lack of sleep affects our health or work/school performance, we are faced with making some decisions and establishing priorities. And when we work with children, we must be especially alert to our surroundings from the standpoint of safety. As well, sleep deprivation often makes us irritable—not an appropriate frame of mind when working with children and coworkers. These decisions are sometimes difficult, especially for young adults who are training for a career, but responsibility does involve setting priorities. Balancing our need to socialize (e.g., on the weekend) with our responsibilities is essential to becoming a professional.

Reducing Other Risk Factors

Health behaviour either promotes your health or undermines it. Here are important examples of health behaviour that contribute positively to our health:

- quitting smoking and avoiding passive (secondhand) smoking
- limiting your consumption of alcohol, and refraining from drinking alcohol during pregnancy and breastfeeding
- avoiding illegal drugs and being careful about medication use
- practising safer sex to prevent sexually transmitted diseases (STDs), including HIV infection and hepatitis B
- maintaining a regular schedule of physical and dental checkups, and monthly self-exams of breasts or testicles for early detection of breast or testicular cancer

In keeping with the health promotion philosophy discussed in Unit 1, the continuum of responsibility between individual and society depends very much on your circumstances.

Selecting health care professionals who best suit our health needs can play a significant role in health promotion. If you live in an area where there is more than one choice, choose the health professional or agency that

- answers your questions clearly and directly,
- gives you access to your medical file, should you choose to see it, and
- is linguistically and culturally relevant to you.

You may have additional criteria, and it is important that you feel like a partner in your health care. It's in your best interest to take an active role in decision making about your medical treatments. This is our individual responsibility. When in doubt, ask for a second or third opinion. Women in particular often feel uncomfortable with or even intimidated by physicians and do not ask them questions about their own health care. Even today, some physicians prescribe tranquilizers for women with complaints like PMS or symptoms of menopause.

One of the best ways that people who smoke can improve their long-term health is by quitting, but that's not easy. It's especially difficult when other stress factors are present and beyond the smoker's control. Smoking may be relaxing or a stress reliever for that person in that situation. Pursuing ways to quit smoking, though, is well worth the effort, and many communities have support systems that can help. At a time when so many Canadians are quitting smoking, it is discouraging that teens and young women are the fastest-growing groups starting to smoke. Young people who have been smoking only a short time are strongly encouraged to quit before the addiction becomes stronger. What messages are educators and ECE students sending to children who see them smoking outside the building on breaks, who smell the smoke on their clothes and hair, who see them smoking in the mall or on the street?

The issue of partner abuse is included to raise awareness and sensitize readers to the possibility that fellow students, future coworkers, children's parents, or even you yourself may be a victim. Violence can take many forms, including physical, sexual, emotional, social, and financial. You will need to expand your knowledge in this area, since we are only touching the surface of abuse.

. . . .

Lidia was a victim of spousal abuse. She felt powerless to escape. She believed that if she left her husband, he would find and possibly kill her. Her coworkers talked among themselves about how weak Lidia was for not leaving her husband. Yet it's too simple to say, "Just leave him!" Family violence is a very complicated situation. Lidia eventually found the support and legal assistance she needed at the local women's shelter, but not before years of violence had taken a great toll on her well-being.

. . . .

According to the Canadian Centre for Justice Statistics (2002):

- Since 1974, nearly 2600 spousal homicides have been recorded in Canada, the majority of which have been against women (1).
- Twenty-four percent of adults living in violent relationships during the five-year period preceding the survey feared that their lives were in danger (14).
- Twenty-six percent of women in violent relationships reported being assaulted 10 or more times by a spousal partner within the five years preceding the survey (14–15).
- When victims confide in someone, it is generally (54%) family members, friends, and neighbours. More than one in five (23%) confided in a coworker. Others confided in doctors, nurses, lawyers, and spiritual advisors (16).
- Shelters exist in every province/territory and provide services to women and child victims of various types of abuse (18).

Women stay in abusive relationships for a number of reasons: fear, low self-esteem, a lack of economic and social supports, cultural taboos, religion, obligation, and oppression. When a woman discloses abuse to you, listen and believe her. This is the first step for her, and the emotional support you provide may encourage her to take action, although the decisions should be her own. In the future, possibly with your support, she may seek options (e.g., shelters, legal advice, services sensitive to women's needs) and make a safety plan.

Familiarize yourself with your community's emergency shelters and the telephone hot line as well as any available long-term services. Partner abuse, date rape, and other forms of violence, particularly against women, are known to be prevalent in our society. With support, many women can escape the vicious circle of violent relationships. Stopping the violence is a complex task and requires a multifaceted societal response. Training programs for early childhood educators are important tools to support women and children in these difficult circumstances.

Infectious Diseases and You

When you start working in programs, you'll probably find that you get sick more often than usual. Although this is to be expected, there are things you can do to prevent being ill so frequently, including being immunized, implementing hygiene practices, and maintaining a well-balanced lifestyle.

Early childhood education training programs should require students to have up-to-date immunizations before they do their first placement in a program. The training institution's health personnel collect and review students' immunization records and other related medical information. In addition to the vaccines we get as children, adults should receive a booster shot for diphtheria and tetanus every 10 years. Depending on the community, the public health agency may recommend that educators be tested for tuberculosis.

To reduce the spread of infectious diseases in programs, educators are responsible for implementing hygiene practices. Steps taken to reduce the spread of germs among children will have a positive effect on educators' health. On a daily basis, educators must pay particular attention to how and when they wash their hands. Unit 3 outlines what you need to know, including the ins and outs of hand washing and information on hygiene practices.

There will be times when educators who are ill should be excluded from work (see Appendix 2.4, page 93). Much of what we know about childhood infections applies also to adults, who can get the same infections. The more common childhood illnesses are discussed in Unit 4, which includes a table that summarizes the management of children's illnesses in the program (see Childhood Infections: Just the Basics, page 156).

Hepatitis B is a virus that causes infection of the liver and is spread by direct contact with blood or bloody body fluid. It has so rarely been reported in early childhood settings that routine screening of children or staff is not recommended (Canadian Paediatric Society 1996, 182, 690). The hepatitis B virus immunization is part of the routine childhood immunization schedule in Canada. Vaccinations for educators are not routinely recommended on account of their line of work (Health Canada 2002, 56–57, 105), although they may be beneficial because of educators' own personal health behaviour (e.g. sexual practices). There is no documented risk in allowing an educator who has recovered from hepatitis B to care for children (Canadian Paediatric Society 1996, 691). Hepatitis C, like hepatitis B, is a virus that causes infection of the liver and is spread by direct contact with blood or bloody body fluid. The routine screening of children for hepatitis C is not recommended, nor is the exclusion of children with hepatitis C from early childhood programs (American Academy of Pediatrics 2000, 115, 305). Universal precautions are always important when cleaning blood and bodily fluids (see Universal Precautions, page 127).

Pregnancies are not always planned. Working with children increases your exposure to infections. Female ECE students and educators may have peace of mind if they talk with their physician. Three infections are particularly important to pregnant women: chickenpox, rubella, and cytomegalovirus (CMV).

Chickenpox

Fortunately, most people have chickenpox when they are children. Although it is usually mild in children, it can cause severe illness in adults. Students and educators who can't recall whether they had chickenpox as children may wish to ask their doctor to do an antibody test, which will tell them whether they have had the disease. Working in programs puts you at risk of caring for children with chickenpox. Susceptible adults exposed to chickenpox or shingles should receive varicella-zoster immune globulin (VZIG) within 72 hours of exposure. The chickenpox vaccine is available in Canada. The immunization of susceptible adults is recommended (Health Canada 2002, 225). For more information about it, contact your physician.

For women who are susceptible to chickenpox and become infected during the first half of pregnancy, the fetus is at high risk of malformation. As soon as a woman knows that she has been exposed to chickenpox or shingles, she must contact her physician or the public health agency. When an infant is born to a mother who developed chickenpox a few days before or after delivery, the baby will likely develop a severe case of chickenpox.

Rubella (German Measles)

If your immunization schedule is up to date, you will know if you received your rubella vaccine. If not, ask your physician about the antibody test. If a pregnant woman is susceptible and has been exposed to rubella, she should talk to her physician immediately. Susceptible pregnant women who are infected with rubella during the first four months of pregnancy are at high risk of a miscarriage or, if the fetus goes to term, of delivering a baby with malformations.

Cytomegalovirus

A person who is infected with CMV may not have any symptoms or may develop ones that are similar to those of mononucleosis (i.e., swollen glands, fatigue, fever). Usually we aren't aware that we have been exposed to CMV because our bodies produce antibodies to protect us. In fact, we may have had CMV as children. Women pass their CMV antibodies to the fetus. After birth, children excrete the virus in the urine and saliva for a year or two and intermittently throughout life. Because of the relatively close contact between educators and children, some susceptible educators will probably become infected with CMV. Educators' best protection is effective hand washing, effective diapering and toileting routines, and cleaning and sanitizing surfaces that have been contaminated with body secretions (e.g., saliva, vomit, urine, or stool).

The only real concern about CMV is when women who are susceptible to CMV become infected during their pregnancy. When this happens, a very small percentage of newborns have physical or developmental challenges (e.g., deafness, cerebral palsy, visual impairment). A vaccine or immune globulin for CMV is not available (Canadian Paediatric Society 1996).

Preventing Musculoskeletal Injuries

Research on 54 Quebec early childhood settings concluded that the most common injury experienced by educators is back injury (Markon and Le Beau 1994, 1–3, 12). The injuries were due to excessive lifting, pulling, pushing, or carrying, although the layout and design of the building, its furniture, the number of people, and available floor space all play a role in the likelihood of injury. Fortunately, more than half of the educators who were injured did not have to leave work as a result. Most of the injuries were strains and sprains—a muscle pulled when lifting a child awkwardly, for example, or an ankle sprained when tripping on a toy (Maxwell and Huot 1994, 29). This study has not been replicated over the past decade in Canada, but the reality of muscular-skeletal injury risk is still true for educators.

You don't have to go very far to find someone who has or is experiencing back pain. You may have had back pain too. Not all back pain or injury is preventable, but certainly there are ways to reduce the risk of back injury, and also to manage back pain when it does occur:

- Maintain the three natural curves of your spine, to take undue pressure off your spine.
- Change posture, even slightly, every few minutes, because the disks, like the rest of the body, take in nutrients and get rid of waste products. When we remain in one position for too long, that process can't happen efficiently.
- Take part in regular physical activity, which helps increase the muscles' ability to support the back.
- Do stretching exercises to increase flexibility, decrease risk of injury, and correct posture.
- Use proper lifting techniques, as described below.

When back pain does occur, individuals should

- consult with their family physician;
- resume routines gradually but as soon as possible—it is now widely believed that bed rest for more than two or three days usually does more harm than good;
- pursue physiotherapy, chiropractic, acupuncture, massage, and yoga as more conservative therapy options. Surgery is not recommended as a therapeutic option in the vast majority of back problems.

In particular, improper lifting and carrying can result in back injuries, which may lead to long-term back problems, loss of wages, and even the need for a career change. Awareness of the potential problem and proper lifting techniques can help to prevent back problems. Whether you are standing, walking, sitting on a chair or floor, or lifting or carrying something, your goal is to maintain the natural curves of your spine.

Some readers may think that the following list of preventive steps applies only to people who lift boxes in a warehouse, not to educators who lift infants off the floor. Granted, lifting a baby off the floor in the same way as you might bend to touch your toes may not hurt your back the first time, but using this technique repeatedly almost guarantees eventual back injury. You may lean over a table or reach down to pick up a piece of paper and then find you can't straighten up. A baby may not look as heavy as a large box or suitcase, but a nine-month-old could easily weigh 8 kilograms (18 lbs.) or more. When we lift something by using our back (by bending over) rather than our legs, that 8-kilogram baby puts 82 kilograms (180 lbs.) of pressure on our back. To prevent injury, follow these steps (from Markon and Le Beau 1994, 131–48) when you are lifting something or someone from the floor:

- Keep your back straight. This maintains the curves of your spine.
- Stand in front of what you are going to lift and as close to it as possible.
- Keep your feet about hip-width apart, with one foot slightly behind the other for stability. This reduces the risk of falling, twisting the spine, or putting more weight on one side of the body.
- Bend your knees, but not so much that you are sitting on your heels, which makes getting back up much more difficult.
- Keep the arms as straight as possible, which prevents you from lifting with your arms and straining your shoulders and back. Obviously, when you lift a child you hold the child against your chest and your elbows are bent.
- Look ahead before straightening your knees, to avoid turning at the waist.

The following are other important rules to live by to prevent lower back problems (Back Association of Canada 1999).

- Never lift or move heavy furniture by yourself.
- Avoid sudden overloading of muscles or sudden movements.
- Learn to keep your head in line with your spine, no matter what your activity.
- Avoid straining to open windows or doors.
- Don't pack more than 15% of your body weight in bags or backpacks, and ensure that you use both shoulder straps when carrying.
- Do these easy exercises, which will ease tension and help tone muscle groups, whenever you have a chance during the day:
  - Turn head slowly side to side.
  - Rotate shoulders forward and back.
  - Slowly touch left ear to left shoulder. Repeat on right side.
  - Shrug shoulders toward ears and then down.

- Pull in abdominal muscles, tighten, and hold to count of eight, then relax slowly.
- Lie on your back, bring both knees slowly to the chest, tighten abdominal muscles, hold for 20 seconds, then lower knees slowly. Relax. Repeat five times.

Learning how to lift properly and ensuring that you actually follow the steps each time helps to prevent back injuries (see Appendix 2.3, page 92).

Furnishings and Layout

The physical environment's design and the actual layout of space, including the height of counters and storage shelves, contribute to our health status. The equipment and furnishings in early childhood settings are designed for children's (not adults') comfort and accessibility. Many activities happen on the floor. In addition, educators always put the children's safety before their own (Maxwell and Huot 1994). Of course this is necessary, but it may mean that unforeseen twists and turns are a reality. From a list of 24 factors that create stress for educators (Markon and Le Beau 1994, 18–20), five relate to the physical workspace: noise, temperature, lack of rest areas, inadequate furnishings, and lack of equipment. As students, you have little or no control over the physical aspects of the space where you do placements. However, if you observe questionable or unsafe situations, you are obliged to report them to staff. Table 2.2 outlines some activities that educators are constantly involved in and provides suggestions for avoiding injury.

Fewer than two-thirds of centres provided a separate staff room (Markon and Le Beau 1994, 83). Most centres did not provide an adult-sized table, chair, or sofa to be used in rooms with children or adult-sized seating outside. Educators, like other employees, need to get away from their work for breaks and to do

TABLE 2.2	Work Site Analysis of the Child Care Work Environment
PROBLEM	**RECOMMENDATIONS**
1. Incorrect lifting of children, toys, supplies, equipment, etc.	1. Educate staff on proper lifting and carrying techniques 2. Promote task rotation where possible 3. Encourage independence in children whenever feasible
2. Inadequate work heights (e.g., child-sized tables and chairs)	1. Create a chair that allows the staff to slide their legs under the table 2. Use sit/kneel chairs 3. Educate staff on using proper body mechanics 4. Provide the staff with adult-sized chairs for occasional use
3. Difficulty lowering and lifting infants in and out of cribs	1. Modify crib sides to enable them to slide down or modify the legs of the cribs to accommodate the staff 2. Educate staff on using proper body mechanics 3. Have step stool available in sleep room
4. Frequent sitting on the floor with back unsupported	1. When possible, have staff sit up against a wall or furniture for back support 2. Perform stretching exercises 3. Educate staff on using proper body mechanics
5. Excessive reaching above shoulder height to obtain stored supplies	1. Redesign kitchen area, placing heaviest items at waist height, lightest above 2. Reorganize snacks and supplies to simplify snack preparation procedures 3. Use step stools when retrieving items that are above cupboard height
6. Frequent lifting of infants and toddlers on and off diapers changing tables	1. Educate staff on using proper body mechanics 2. Encourage toddlers to use steps in order to decrease distance staff are lifting
7. Forceful motions combined with awkward posture required to open windows	1. Use step stool to allow for better leverage and reduce awkward posture 2. Have maintenance staff improve quality of window slide
8. Carrying garbage and diaper bags to dumpster	1. Provide staff with cart to transport garbage 2. Relocate garbage cart closer to work area 3. Reduce size and weight of loads 4. Educate staff on using proper body mechanics

Source: Adapted with permission from C.P.H. Vary et al. (1996), "The Ergonomics of Child Care: Conducting Worksite Analyses," *Work: A Journal of Prevention, Assessment, and Rehabilitation* 6(1): 25–32.

administrative work. A staff room provides an area in which educators can relax and socialize.

The layout of centres can impede the movement of educators and children.

e.g.

- The layout does not provide easy access to all areas. While heights keep objects out of children's reach, educators often have to stretch to reach across or up high on shelves and in cupboards.

- The layout lacks storage space. Educators resort to piling boxes on the floor, which not only reduces walking space but forces educators to do more lifting.

- Rooms have limited space. In preschool centres, the same space is used for playing, eating, and napping. Therefore staff must lift and move equipment and furniture daily. The limited space increases the likelihood of tripping, falling, and running into one another (Markon and Le Beau 1994, 87–90).

In the long term, ergonomic research will provide architects and early childhood licensing offices with vital information on designing settings that meet the physical needs of adults as well as children. Lack of funding and resources impedes needed improvements for adults in the early childhood environment. In the meantime, how can we improve workplace conditions? The most obvious answer is to purchase more adult-sized furniture and relatively inexpensive equipment to prevent musculoskeletal problems. For example, legless chairs are available that provide the educator with the necessary back support while sitting on the floor with the children. New tables and chairs purchased should be light and easy to move; mats and cots should be easy to store by the staff (Markon 1999, 3). When replacing worn equipment such as cribs, look for ones that meet Canadian Standards Association (CSA) safety standards and that have rails that can be lowered to mattress level.

A couch in a play area provides a comfortable spot for adults and children to sit and talk or read and for staff to bottle-feed infants. Perhaps a set of steps can be built that slide in and out under the diaper counter to give toddlers the opportunity to climb onto or down from the table rather than being lifted—an activity that most toddlers would prefer.

Educators should gather all the necessary diapering supplies before they bring the child to the change area. This eliminates the educator's having to keep one hand on the child while reaching or turning to get supplies during the change.

Educators looking at their own workspace, talking about the issues, and referring to resources will undoubtedly come up with many more ideas. Directors and employers need to assess how work is organized to avoid excessive demands on staff. Work tasks should also be evaluated on the basis of physical demands (Canadian Paediatric Society 1996, 657). Of course, the primary obstacle in implementing improvements is accessing funds.

Working with Art and Cleaning Products

Art supplies and cleaning products can be hazardous to educators and children. Educators must select play materials that are non-toxic and read labels for any special handling instructions. Pay particular attention to solvents, glues, dyes, and pottery products.

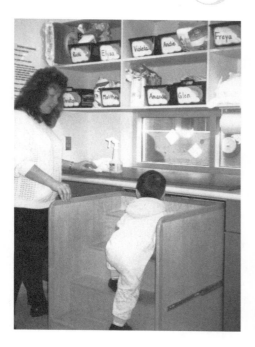

Painting is a desirable ongoing experience for children. Rather than buying ready-to-use paints, staff often purchase powder paint and then mix colours as needed. Educators need to exercise caution when handling the powder. If inhaled, the powder can harm the lungs' airways. To protect themselves, educators should mix paint in a well-ventilated area away from children (Canadian Paediatric Society 1996, 670). Educators with asthma may need to avoid mixing powdered paint or wear a filter over their nose and mouth.

In terms of cleaning products, many programs choose soap and water for cleaning surfaces and objects. Many use a dilute solution of bleach and water for sanitizing. Facilities with automatic dishwashers will use the detergent recommended for the machine. All kinds of commercial products are on the market that we can use in our homes and in programs. Many companies advertise the product's sanitizing qualities and claim it makes things sparkling and fresh. For the most part, however, soap and water and good old elbow grease, which creates friction, remove most of the germs. Bleach kills any germs that may remain after cleaning. When one part bleach is diluted with 100 parts water, the bleach is strong

TABLE 2.3	Making Your Own Cleaning Products

PRODUCTS	SAFER ALTERNATIVES
Carpet Stain Remover	• mix 60 mL (1/4 cup) borax and 500 mL (2 cups) cold water
Drain Cleaner	• put 60 mL (1/4 cup) baking soda and 125 mL (1/2 cup) vinegar in the drain, put in the plug, wait, and rinse with water
Glass and Mirror Cleaner	• mix 1 part vinegar and 100 parts water in a spray bottle
Laundry Detergent	• mix 1.25 L (5 cups) soap flakes and 250 mL (1 cup) washing soda; use 60 mL (1/4 cup) per load
Oven Cleaner	• cover spills with table salt while the oven is still hot, and then scrape them off once the oven has cooled; or • warm oven and then turn it off; mix 60 mL (1/4 cup) ammonia and warm water in a glass bowl, leave it overnight in the oven, and then wipe clean
Toilet Cleaner	• use baking soda and a toilet brush

enough to be effective yet dilute enough that it won't ruin clothes or make everything smell like bleach. And it is safe to use around children. An environmentally friendly alternative to bleach—one that falls within public health guidelines—will be welcomed when it arrives. Table 2.3 outlines other household products that can be used for cleaning.

To protect themselves and others when using products, educators need to take precautions.

■ Read and follow the product's instructions.

■ Wear household rubber gloves to protect your hands from drying, if you prefer.

■ Never mix two products (e.g., when ammonia and bleach are mixed, a poisonous gas is produced).

■ Keep solutions in their original container and locked out of reach of children.

■ Choose cleaners that are safe for our environment.

Workplace Hazardous Materials Information System

The legislation for the Workplace Hazardous Materials Information System (WHMIS) applies to all workplaces, which include early childhood settings. Employers are obliged to provide employees with information on the products they use at work. Certain controlled products have been defined as hazardous because they are compressed gas, flammable and combustible, oxidizing, poisonous, or infectious. These products must have labels that list their ingredients, their toxic effects, instructions on safe handling, and first-aid treatments. This legislation applies mainly to industries that use these types of products. Public health inspectors (PHIs) may be consulted to verify whether any of the cleaning and sanitizing products are controlled products. ECE programs frequently buy their cleaning products at grocery stores, and products for sale there would not be controlled.

Read the label for directions and the first-aid treatment on the container (e.g., "If splashed in eyes, flush thoroughly with water. If swallowed, give water or milk. Call a physician"). The first-aid treatment also includes the name of the hazardous ingredient (e.g., "contains sodium hypochlorite"). This information will be very helpful to your poison control centre, whose number is listed in the front of your phone book, if someone ingests the product.

Role of Public Health Agencies in Health Promotion

 Public health nurses (PHNs) and public health inspectors work in public health agencies. PHNs may be available for consultation on staff illnesses, immunizations, and other concerns. PHIs conduct environmental sanitation inspections of early childhood settings. At least annually, PHIs inspect the building—its lighting, ventilation, kitchen facilities, garbage disposal, and so on. They submit a report to the licensing office (with a copy to the program) that includes any concerns and recommendations for improvement. As well, they may consult with the staff and answer questions about cleaning and sanitizing procedures and products. If the role of public health personnel in your community has been curtailed due to cutbacks, it is important for directors and staff to seek other consultants to perform this role. Keeping the physical environment up-to-date with current information and changes is essential for children's and adults' health in the early childhood program.

Workplace Environmental Issues

Heating/air conditioning, ventilation, noise, and light levels all contribute to educators' and children's emotional and physical well-being. If it's too hot inside, we get drowsy and irritable, and are more prone to making mistakes. Inadequate lighting causes eyestrain and headaches. The building's architectural design should allow as much natural light into the space as possible.

A well-ventilated space helps to remove indoor air contamination. Indoor air is tainted by hair sprays, perfumes, cleaning products, and dust; by odours from photocopiers and computer laser printers; by formaldehyde (e.g., from unsealed plywood or particleboard, urea-formaldehyde insulation, fabrics, glues, carpets); by germs from people's respiratory tracts; and by outdoor pollutants. These pollutants are particularly irritating to people with asthma, respiratory illnesses, and contact lenses. Staff should suspect the quality of the air in the building when people are frequently experiencing symptoms such as headaches, fatigue, dizziness, or irritation in eyes, nose, or throat. Children and educators may be suffering from "building-related illness" (Clarke and Nikkel 1994, 7–8).

Ideally, there are windows in every room that staff open every day for some time, year round. However, for programs located within larger buildings (e.g., in an office tower), the air is part of the building's ventilation system. Programs located in workplaces (e.g., in a manufacturing plant) should have a separate ventilation system to ensure that the children and staff are not breathing air from the plant. If staff or children frequently experience symptoms of illness, the ventilation system must be evaluated.

Finally, the noise level can be an issue, considering the number of children and adults in the same place for extended periods. Although the noise level is never in a range that could potentially damage someone's hearing, a constant noise level can make people feel tired and irritable. Couches, curtains, carpets, pillows, carpeted areas, acoustic ceiling tiles, dress-up clothes, etc., all absorb sounds within the room.

Educators can manage noise by

- alternating quiet and active programs,
- guiding children to use their "indoor voice" indoors,
- alternating educators who supervise the playground, and
- taking staff breaks in a separate room.

In a broader environmental perspective, as citizens and professionals we have much to be concerned about with regard to our own health and the health of our planet. North Americans are on a binge of consumption, at a rate that is clearly unsustainable for the planet. Many individuals have recognized the importance of taking action at all health promotion levels in order to reduce their own feelings of powerlessness and, of course, to make a difference. In particular for women, the increase in breast cancer rates is alarming and environmental risks must be considered. For example, among other causes, radiation, pesticides, and some plastics have been linked to breast cancer. Although radiation and pesticides have long been an issue as powerful carcinogens, there is growing concern (and controversy) about the ingredients (nonylphenols) in some plastic wraps used to cover food, added to make the wraps more flexible. Nonylphenols, known carcinogens, are not chemically bound and can leach out of the plastic fairly easily. Other ingredients in plastics (e.g., phthalates) are hormone disruptors. For more information on the environment, your health, and actions you can take to lessen your exposure to potentially hazardous products, refer to *Taking Action for a Healthy Future* (1997), a publication of the Women's Network on Health and the Environment (see Resource Materials, page 86).

Injury Reports

When educators are injured at work, they must complete an injury report. Sometimes they are tempted to avoid the extra paperwork, especially if they believe that the injury is minor. However, a report is important for a number of reasons:

- to maintain adequate workplace injury records for liability
- to document any injury that seems minor at first but becomes serious later (e.g., a cut that becomes infected)
- to prevent further injuries, potentially

When staff can assess the conditions that caused or contributed to an injury, they can implement preventive practices, review or provide training (e.g., in proper lifting), or modify the physical space to make it safer (e.g., by installing a handrail by the stairs or improving the lighting of the staff parking lot), which benefits everyone. Often the same injury report can be used for the children and educators (see Appendix 6.2, pages 344).

OBJECTIVES

To discuss the major role that communication plays in educators' emotional and social well-being.

To identify the sources of stress and their impact on our well-being.

To understand the role and benefits of networking with community professionals and agencies.

PROMOTING YOUR EMOTIONAL AND SOCIAL WELL-BEING

Workplaces don't present only physical risks and benefits; there are also emotional and social factors that can have positive and negative effects on employees' health. Although working with children and families is rewarding, no job is without elements that can create feelings of stress for employees. By recognizing potential stress factors, students take the first step in preventing or reducing the negative impact, resulting in richer professional and personal lives.

Creating a Supportive Early Childhood Environment

The single most important component of high-quality early childhood education and care, in terms of promoting healthy child development, is the nature of the daily relationship and interactions between educator and child. This relationship is, of course, affected by other quality factors. Although educators are the key component of quality, there is little recognition of the value of early childhood education as a profession. Most educators are relatively poorly paid, and many have few traditional occupational benefits and lack adequate professional development opportunities (Beach et al. 1998, 13). For these issues to change, we need a coordinated policy approach and a new method of funding child care (Doherty et al. 2000, 172). These changes will take time and political will, but in the meantime, the Doherty study found that approximately 95% of educators and directors stated that it is the satisfaction of working with children and helping families that keeps them in their jobs.

Educators who are content with their work conditions are much more likely to develop self-confidence and competence, and are less likely to be dissatisfied and resign. Lower turnover rates mean more consistent care for children. Table 2.4 identifies 10 dimensions of the work climate that support professionalism. As you review those dimensions, you'll see the implied partnership between employee and employer.

A program emphasizes the personal and professional growth of the employees. The employer (e.g., director, board of directors, agency, college, or university) provides support and access to professional development activities (e.g., conferences, workshops). However, educators need to be motivated to attend, learn, and incorporate their learning into their work with children.

TABLE 2.4	The Ten Dimensions of Organizational Climate
DIMENSION	**DEFINITION**
Collegiality	the extent to which staff are friendly, supportive, and trust one another
Professional Growth	the degree of emphasis placed on personal and professional growth
Supervisor Support	the degree of facilitative leadership that provides encouragement, support, and clear expectations
Clarity	the extent to which policies, procedures, and responsibilities are clearly defined and communicated
Reward System	the degree of fairness and equity in the distribution of pay, fringe benefits, and opportunities for advancement
Decision Making	the degree of autonomy given to the staff and the extent to which they are involved in program-wide decisions
Goal Consensus	the degree to which staff agree on the goals and objectives of the program
Task Orientation	the emphasis placed on good planning, efficiency, and getting the job done
Physical Setting	the extent to which the spatial arrangement of the physical environment helps or hinders staff in carrying out their responsibilities
Innovativeness	the extent to which the organization adapts to change and encourages staff to find creative ways to solve problems

Source: Adapted with permission from P.J. Bloom et al., *Blueprint for Action: Achieving Center-Based Change through Staff Development* (New Horizons, 1991), 178.

Role of Directors

How can directors promote staff health? Directors' philosophies and management styles play an integral role in supporting a healthy work environment. First, directors often set the tone in the program—if they are committed to employee health and ongoing training, their commitment will likely have a positive effect on educators. These directors will advocate for proactive employee health policies that are clearly outlined in their policy manuals. These policies may include

- an interview and selection process that assists in hiring individuals that fit their specific program;
- job descriptions for all staff members;
- an orientation program and job performance appraisals;
- lines of communication and conflict resolution;
- an immunization schedule to ensure that all staff are up-to-date;
- techniques for staff to implement that reduce the physical hazards of the work, such as proper lifting techniques, methods for safely handling potentially hazardous products, and methods for cleaning up spills of those products and bloody body fluids;
- exclusion criteria for educators and pregnant women in relation to infectious diseases;

- reporting of workplace injuries and compensation for illness or injury;
- opportunities for professional development and in-service training; and
- role of substitutes, students, and volunteers in the program.

Regular job evaluations (at least annually) are acknowledged as a learning tool rather than a punitive device. A health-promoting director supports educators in goal setting and in achieving those goals. She implements measures to decrease stress for staff whenever possible. She serves as an advocate for educators with the board of directors and the outside community.

Directors also have the following responsibilities for educators' health:

- They conduct regular inspections of early childhood settings (see Appendix 6.1, page 338).
- They ensure that educator–child ratios and group sizes are maintained throughout each day.
- They regularly review the work assignments to assess whether the work is too demanding and how tasks can be modified.
- They review and discuss work-related injuries and determine what preventive steps are required.

Probably the director's most important role in promoting educators' emotional and social well-being is to establish clear lines of communication. Most of the dimensions in Table 2.4 are directly related to communication. Educators who receive effective administrative support, encouragement, and clear expectations tend to experience job satisfaction. Directors can also provide opportunities for educators to participate in decision making and professional growth. The purpose of health promotion is to increase the amount of control that individuals and groups have over their lives. It makes sense that the more autonomy educators have at work, the more they feel in control. With the director's support, they feel free to express themselves on the job, especially when they view the director as an advocate. Directors help to solve problems when they arise, such as inadequate opportunities for regular breaks, or issues about communication with a parent. A director's role is also paramount in difficult issues such as suspected child abuse. Educators often need to relieve feelings of stress by talking frankly with the director without fear of repercussion. Effective directors expect professional confidentiality from educators and also model this behaviour.

Role of Educators

It goes without saying that working with children has many rewards. It's probably the main reason you chose to enroll in an early childhood education program. The You Bet I Care! study asked educators and directors to list the most positive and most negative aspects of working in the early childhood education field. The results are summarized in Table 2.5.

Many educators prefer to work with a particular age group because their experience tells them that their aptitudes and interests fit best there; they usually find

TABLE 2.5   The Positives and Negatives of Working in Child Care

	% OF STAFF IDENTIFYING THIS AMONG THEIR TOP 3 CHOICES	% OF DIRECTORS IDENTIFYING THIS AMONG THEIR TOP 3 CHOICES
ON THE POSITIVE SIDE		
Nature of the work	94.6	93.7
For example: a people-orientated job; love from children; freedom to be creative; having my own group of children; a varied, stimulating job		
Fulfillment	32.6	37.6
For example: feel I am having an impact/helping; gives me a feeling of competence; enjoy the challenge		
Coworkers	20.1	22.7
For example: teamwork; working with other child care professionals; support from other staff		
Parents	11.9	23.8
For example: helping parents		
ON THE NEGATIVE SIDE		
Pay and promotion opportunities	75.5	73.5
For example: low salary; lack of wage increases; lack of benefits; unpaid overtime		
Lack of respect	45.8	43.1
For example: public's perception of the status of child care staff		
Working conditions	32.4	26.7
For example: hours; staffing ratio; lack of supplies; difficulty finding qualified substitutes		
Nature of the work	25.0	23.3
For example: doing cleaning and maintenance; lack of adult contact; insufficient planning time; collecting fees		
Dealing with society and government	20.7	25.2
For example: the attitude of government officials		
Note: Responses are not mutually exclusive.		

Source: Adapted with permission from Doherty, G., et al. (2000), "You Bet I Care! Study 1: A Canada-Wide Study on Wages, Working Conditions, and Practices in Child Care," University of Guelph: The Centre for Families, Work, and Well Being.

the stress factors manageable. Yet some educators may work with a particular age group because they have no choice. Others may have lacked prior experience or ECE training and assumed that they would fit well and didn't. Educators who don't have a "fit" with their work or the age group may find the nature of the work overwhelming. Working with infants is quite different from working with preschoolers, which is quite different from working with school-agers. During your placements, you will have opportunities to work with various age groups, gain realistic perceptions of working with children, and talk with educators about how they feel about their work and what they find rewarding and challenging (or stressful). You may have assumed, for example, that working with infants would not match your personality, but after your placement were pleasantly surprised that you preferred this age group and that you have decided to begin your career there.

One thing is certain about work stress in early childhood settings: educators who develop and practise effective communication skills have lower stress levels. We have discussed the director's role in creating a supportive environment—let us not overlook the educators' attitudes, knowledge, and behaviour. Much of educators' work involves communicating with children, coworkers, and parents. Educators who demonstrate collegiality with coworkers are likely to have it reciprocated.

Directors who are appreciated for their efforts find it easier to support staff. The opportunity for autonomy assumes that the educator has the ability and motivation to make responsible decisions. In other words, communication is not a one-way street! A checklist such as the one in Table 2.6 provides feedback on listening skills. However, communication skills are complex and require work, practice, and a willingness to learn. Cross-cultural communication, for example, assumes that you recognize that your usual way of communicating is only one way, not the best way.

Men Working in Early Childhood Settings

Historically, the overwhelming majority of educators in early childhood education have been female. For example, 95% of the staff and supervisors surveyed in the You Bet I Care! study were women (Doherty et al. 2000). If you are a male student, you probably have accepted that you will be working mainly with female

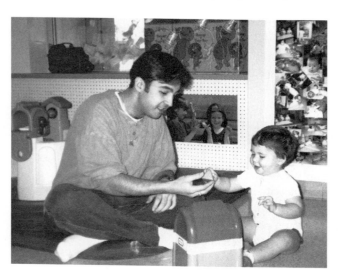

colleagues. Although the following three criteria apply to all educators, they are discussed specifically as they relate to men: accountability, reciprocal support, and establishing positive working relationships.

Accountability

Male educators demonstrate professional behaviour such as open communication with parents and awareness of the need to be visible to another adult whenever possible when they are with any one child. In this way, they find that they are not likely to be considered suspect. Male educators may find it stressful that parents (and sometimes female educators) place them under scrutiny. However, most men understand that this fear results from

TABLE 2.6   **Are You Listening?**

WHEN YOU AND I ARE TALKING TOGETHER ...	OFTEN	SELDOM
• you make me feel as if this is the most important thing you could be doing right now and that your time is truly mine.		
• your attention is divided. You interrupt our conversation by answering the phone or addressing the needs of others who come by your door.		
• you begin shaking your head or saying "no" before I finish.		
• you make references to other conversations; there is a history to communication.		
• you fidget and squirm and look at the clock as though you cannot wait to get on to other, more important, projects and conversations.		
• you begin asking questions before I finish my message.		
• you look me in the eye and really focus your attention.*		
• you ask questions that let me know you were not really listening.		
• you finish my sentences for me as though nothing I have to say could be new to you.		
• you express interest by asking thoughtful questions and by contributing your insights.		
• you change the agenda by taking over and changing the content of the conversation.		
• you follow up on what we discussed and keep me posted on what is happening.		
• you are sensitive to the tone of what I have to say and respond respectfully.		
• you give me credit for ideas and projects that grow out of our communications.		
• you try to speed things up and leap ahead with ideas or conclusions as though we are in a rush.		
• you smile at me and make me feel comfortable and valued.		
• you make jokes about things that are serious to me and thereby belittle my concerns.		
• you get defensive and argue before I can fully explain my point.		
• you seem to assume I have something worthwhile to say.		
• you ask questions that demonstrate your efforts to understand what I have to say.		
• whether or not you agree with me, you make me feel that my opinions and feelings are respected.		

*Making direct eye contact during conversation is considered disrespectful in some cultures. This practice alone doesn't indicate poor communication.

Source: Reprinted with permission from "Are You Listening?" *Child Care Information Exchange*, P.O. Box 2890, Redmond, WA 98073, 1-800-221-2864.

the fact that men commit the vast majority of crimes of sexual abuse. As each educator demonstrates his commitment and care for the children, these suspicions usually disappear.

    Educators who take an active role in speaking with parents about the child's day help parents realize that educators are knowledgeable and care about their child. Parents can then get to know and trust the educators rather than simply view them as "male." Male educators who demonstrate professional behaviour avoid subtle and overt sexist remarks, jokes, and other such slights. One hopes that female educators also refrain from this type of behaviour so that working relationships are not tainted with sexist overtones.

Men find ways to nurture children without placing themselves under suspicion. Early childhood staff should not, however, attempt to avoid suspicious circumstances for male educators by creating separate job responsibilities for males and females.

. . . .

 All educators are involved in diapering or toileting. A division of different responsibilities only serves to increase suspicion and animosity among educators.

. . . .

Reciprocal Support

Men who connect with and support other male educators reduce their feelings of isolation, which is one of the most significant stressors for males in early childhood education and care (Bloom 1989, 47). Often a male educator is the only male staff member and he rarely, if ever, has the opportunity to talk with adult males at work other than with fathers at drop-off or pickup times. He will feel added stress from female educators or parents if he is stereotyped in particular roles.

- He may be expected to do all the heavy lifting or repairs, or to take a lead role in disciplining children. Obviously, the assumption of roles or abilities on the basis of gender is inappropriate.
- Male educators often have to deal with the stereotype that they are not as masculine as other men. The stereotype is based on the traditional view of women taking responsibility for caring for children.

This stereotype is stressful to male educators, so it is beneficial to them if they can informally or formally network with others. It may be challenging to find out where other male educators work (your local ECE college faculty may know), but when you do there are a number of ways to establish networks: a telephone buddy system, online chat or email discussions, monthly meetings of a support group, or biannual sessions or workshops through the local ECE association. Opportunities to talk about issues that arise, and possible ways to handle them, can be helpful in managing stress and preventing problems. Male ECE students may be interested in pursuing some kind of support while in training, either informally, by talking with a male educator in placement, or by finding out if there is (or could be) a support system in which male educators serve as mentors to students and new graduates.

Establishing Positive Working Relationships

Emphasizing effective communication with the other educators reduces or avoids the "them and me" attitude.

Some female educators believe that men receive special treatment because of gender and are offered opportunities that female educators are not offered.

A key factor in reducing negative views is the experience of working with a male colleague in the early childhood setting. Obviously, then, energy put into communication is worth the effort. Male educators feel less isolated when they have positive working relationships. Camaraderie is fostered when all staff are included in social events after work or in lunchroom discussions.

The Juggle Struggle: Stress

Statistics Canada (2002) reported that 25% of adult Canadians aged 18 or older are experiencing high life stress and 36% moderate life stress. A higher percentage of women than men in all age groups (except 18-to-19-year-olds) experience high life stress.

Students and educators are no exception and have very busy lives—juggling a number of roles that contribute to a time crunch and ultimately stress.

Stress is a fact of life. Both positive and negative events in our lives create stress. Stress is defined as "the wear and tear on our bodies that is produced by the very process of living" (Elkind 1981, 142). Stress affects the mind and emotions as well as the physical self. In moderation, stress is positive: it motivates us to learn, to develop, to cope with life's frustrations. But the way that it is perceived and managed depends on the individual and the environment (e.g., family, work, school, socioeconomic class, community).

Coping refers to the ways that a person tries to decrease or eliminate a stress factor—a person's response to it. Stress management plays a major role in our wellness. If the individual is able to find ways to cope with stress, this has a positive impact on health. We all have had days when one thing after another goes wrong, usually minor things, and we feel "stressed out." We may stomp our feet, shout, slam a door, cry, or feel defeated. Eventually those feelings pass. But when stress is severe or long-term, the body and mind are weakened, making the person vulnerable to a number of physical and emotional conditions. This is especially true in individuals who have inadequate coping strategies or whose environment contains insurmountable barriers. These people may experience symptoms of stress overload, including headaches, insomnia, back or neck pain, repeated cold or canker sores, higher than usual susceptibility to illness, ulcers, addictions, anxiety, or depression. Stress overload is also a factor in heart disease and other chronic conditions.

Stress factors can result from a number of sources: our personal and professional lives, and societal pressures.

Personal Stress Factors

Stress factors can be short-term (e.g., an argument with a family member or friend, a minor injury, a busy week). Some stress factors are long-term (e.g., separation or divorce, financial difficulties, death of a loved one).

How we perceive and cope with personal stress depends on our temperament, tolerance level, and experience. Our temperament plays a part in how we perceive the stress in our lives. People who prefer (innately) stability and pre-dictability experience change as stressful.

. . . .

The idea of moving to another city and beginning a new job is quite exciting and positive for some people. Yet for others that change is perceived as anxiety-producing and negative.

. . . .

We all have individual tolerance levels for stress. When our tolerance level is reached and surpassed, we can experience feelings of distress. Past experiences with stress and the types of coping mechanisms that we have developed either help or hinder our ability to manage stress. An individual whose childhood was fraught with insecurity is likely to react differently to stressful events as an adult than a person whose childhood was happy and secure.

Our personal lifestyles can either magnify our feelings of stress or help us manage them. A balanced lifestyle contributes to our health; part of that lifestyle is helping our mind and body manage stress. Adequate sleep and leisure, physical activity, and healthy eating are effective body defences against stress. We can help our body by avoiding certain substances that can trigger stress responses, such as caffeine and nicotine.

Professional Stress Factors

Every profession and workplace has inherent stress factors; even people working from their homes experience stress. Identifying stress factors and eliminating them, or at least reducing them, fall into the domain of occupational health. Working with children and staff is not a calm and tranquil experience. Although the majority of educators express high job satisfaction while working with young children and making a difference in their lives, the following stress factors are commonly experienced by educators (Beach et al. 1998, 91–93):

- The increasing demands on, and expectations of, early childhood education and care. The sector is trying to respond to the needs of parents while providing high-quality programs. Parents are becoming increasingly aware of the importance of quality early childhood education and care and early experiences to their child's development, and are expecting more of educators.

- The need for more skills in guiding children with behaviour challenges, in culturally sensitive practice, and in inclusive care for children with special needs.

- The constant attention needed to ensure the safety and security of young children.

- Low compensation rates, which fail to reflect the responsibilities and skills involved in the work. This reality is, obviously, due to the lack of government commitment to public funding for early childhood education and care—families are expected to pay the lion's share of the cost.

- The lack of benefits, typical in other workplaces, such as paid sick leave, extended health care, or long-term disability. These are not available to many in the early education field.

- The lack of resources needed to maintain a good environment.
- The isolation from other adults.
- The lack of opportunities for career advancement.

In addition, communication issues with coworkers, directors, and parents can be stressful.

Individuals may be managing their personal life very well but may experience feelings of stress at work. Without a resolution of, or at least a reduction in, the stress factors, their personal life is affected. There are ways to manage some workplace stress (e.g., limiting coffee, going for a walk at lunch), but often stress is the result of issues that need to be addressed by the organization (e.g., division of workloads, improving lines of communication, evaluation of ventilation, ergonomically correct furniture). Making changes involves identifying stress factors and, with the commitment of staff and management, working toward that change. Educators in all settings express considerable interest in additional training, education, and professional development (Beach et al. 1998). Evidence suggests that educators do take advantage of training opportunities available to them. Increased skills improve the quality of care that children experience and improve educators' work environments and recognition.

Societal Pressures

The quality of early childhood education and care across Canada and the issues of affordability, accessibility, and comprehensiveness for parents are national concerns. Many families are affected by government's lack of commitment to early childhood education and care, and educators across Canada experience every day the effects of these societal attitudes. Other societal pressures affect everyone, educator and non-educator alike, such as

- the expectation, especially for women, to have multiple roles and to perform them all well (e.g., to have two full-time jobs: one inside and one outside the home);
- issues of discrimination;
- the fast-paced, ever-changing world, particularly its technology, which makes many of us feel that we are being left behind;
- growing concern about violence in our communities and around the world; and
- serious concerns about other national and global issues such as the economy and the environment.

Identifying sources of stress in our lives is the first step in managing them and avoiding stress overload. Some stress factors may be impossible to change. Fortunately, many can be addressed, with problem solving and commitment. The Heart and Stroke Foundation of Canada's website is an excellent resource that provides you with numerous tools to identify stressors in your life and ways to manage them. Try asking yourself three questions before deciding which coping skill to use in a situation (Canadian Mental Health Association and Heart and Stroke Foundation 1997):

1. Is this an appropriate thing to do in this situation? (e.g., chanting during a job interview may not be advisable)

2. Is this a positive way of coping? (e.g., excessive alcohol or even excessive exercise may not be positive)

3. Is this going to help in the long run? (e.g., a short-term solution may not be enough)

In our professional lives, possible approaches include improving relationships with coworkers, management, or parents; seeking further training in a specific area (e.g., child guidance; see *Meeting the Challenge* in Resource Materials, page 87); and addressing occupational hazards (e.g., noise levels, the risk of back injury). Specific problems or more general stress factors are more likely to change when we collaborate with others (i.e., practise teamwork).

- An early childhood program institutes a family responsibility leave for its staff, allowing educators whose own children are ill to be at home with them. This significantly reduces their overall stress level as working parents.

- All educators who belong to their provincial/territorial ECE association benefit from lower premiums for disability insurance.

Societal pressures are more difficult and complicated. Anxiety is often reduced through education—taking courses to enhance our understanding of issues or to build skills (e.g., computer, self-defence). Get involved in national, regional, or local organizations advocating for change in areas such as early childhood education and care and the environment. Participating in and working for positive change, even if it seems daunting, is one of the best ways to gain a sense of control over the world around you.

Early Childhood Educational Experience: Setting the Stage

The process of becoming a professional begins the day you start your ECE training. You have chosen a career that requires a vast range of attitudes, knowledge, and skills. ECE students are on the road to lifelong learning that begins with recognizing their individual and social responsibilities and taking ownership of their responsibilities. Here are some examples of the professional behaviour that you can take ownership of now:

- Promptness for classes and placements—behaviour that is not only expected throughout your professional life but is also appreciated in your personal life.

- Good personal hygiene.

- Communication skills that demonstrate respect for others' opinions, such as listening respectfully in class when the instructor or a classmate is speaking (as a matter not of authority but of respect) and using body language that conveys interest and learning (while recognizing a range of ways of communicating that reflect ethno-cultural diversity). Communication is a lifelong learning process and is obviously a critical skill for professionals. It is important to become aware of how you, as a student, communicate, and to be open to learning new skills (see Table 2.6, page 75).

Assessing the situation:

As a student, you are frustrated by a clique of three students who sit together and regularly disrupt the class. What do you do?

Placements in early childhood settings provide you with opportunities to observe and analyze, which help you to formulate your personal philosophy of education, which is in turn based on an integration of theory and practice. Placements also offer the advantage of starting your professional career with some experience working with educators already behind you. This experience helps you identify some of the attitudes, knowledge, and skills that either contribute to quality care or detract from it. Some examples of human qualities that are beneficial for educators include warmth, patience, high energy, openness to new ideas, flexibility, curiosity, and maturity. Educators who possess these qualities are positive role models for students and graduates. With every placement experience, you meet a variety of educators who have their own styles yet fulfil these criteria. However, some educators demonstrate physical and emotional exhaustion through behaviour such as impatience and sarcasm with children, tension with others at work, and apathy toward their job. Unfortunately, these educators are modelling as much for students as are their positive coworkers.

Placements allow you to experience different management styles. The working environment is created by the educators' personal styles and the levels of education, how well they work together, the types of policies, and the style of the director. Some individuals like to work in an environment that is more laid-back; others like a structure with rules clearly laid out. Whatever the administrative style you prefer, remember the 10 dimensions of organizational climate in Table 2.4 (see page 71). As a student, you probably will not see the inner workings of the organization (e.g., salaries and fringe benefits, how promotions are handled, how the program implements change). Yet you can get a sense of how staff work together, the level and effectiveness of the supervision, and staff morale. A list of statements accompanies the 10 dimensions of the organizational climate (see Table 2.7). As you work through the list, check off one of the three choices for each statement. You will see how healthy that work climate is and whether you would like to work in that environment on graduation.

Among the most important training opportunities that placements offer you as a student are self-evaluation and, of course, an evaluation of your progress by experienced professionals. Ongoing feedback of your demonstrated skills assists you in identifying areas of strength and areas in which you need to make immediate or long-term changes. Students who view evaluation positively as a valuable learning tool can incorporate constructive criticism into their learning and make consistent progress in their skill levels. Self-evaluation and evaluation by others will be essential aspects of your career.

TABLE 2.7	List of Statements about Organizational Climate			
		SELDOM	SOMETIMES	ALMOST ALWAYS
Staff are friendly and trust one another.				
Morale is high. There is a good team spirit.				
Staff are encouraged to learn new skills and competencies.				
The program provides guidance for professional advancement.				
Supervisors are knowledgeable and competent.				
Supervisors provide helpful feedback.				
Communication on policies and procedures is clear.				
Teachers help make decisions about things that directly affect them.				
People feel free to express their opinions.				
Staff share a common vision of what the program should be like.				
The program is well planned and efficiently run.				
The work environment is attractive and well organized.				
There are sufficient supplies and equipment for staff to do their jobs.				
Staff are encouraged to be creative and innovative in their work.				

Source: Adapted with permission from P.J. Bloom et al., *Blueprint for Action: Achieving Center-Based Change through Staff Development* (New Horizons, 1991), 179.

Graduates: Starting the Job Search

Your first position in an early childhood setting will probably leave a lasting impression on you. Starting in a program where you are treated with respect by educators who remember what it's like to be the new kid on the block, and who provide you with guidance and support, helps to build your confidence and self-esteem. New graduates are influenced significantly by their first director. The kind of assistance, support, opportunities, and guidance that graduates receive contributes greatly to their ability to move forward (Taylor 1993, 7). Therefore, during job interviews it's in your best interest to consider the qualities of the director—will they fit with yours?

Graduates often bring a breath of fresh air, new ideas, and enthusiasm into programs. Graduates who demonstrate openness to learning from others—not an "I've learned everything I need to know" attitude—will start off on the right foot with their coworkers. A commitment to lifelong learning means that you recognize that your ECE training has set the stage for future learning rather than being the final curtain.

REVISITING THE HEALTH PROMOTION ACTION PLAN

With reference to the Action Plan for Health Promotion introduced in Unit 1, the following discussion illustrates this plan put into practice in terms of occupational health.

Individual Problem Solving and Self-Reliance
With the awareness of health issues that affect educators, each of us is able to identify our own health concerns, and can be proactive in preventing or reducing the impact of our choices on our health. You, for example, may be making changes to include more whole foods and less fat in your diet, and gradually becoming more physically active. You may also be cutting down on your smoking and getting support during this difficult transition. As a result of these changes, you're probably beginning to notice that you have more energy in working with the children. You feel like a better role model. You are practising sensible lifting and bending techniques. Your commitment to lifelong learning through reading and attending workshops, seminars, and conferences on health issues enhances your ability to make choices in your personal life and professionally. All education plays a role in your ability to advance in your career.

Collective Self-Help
Together, the director and staff support each other, parents, and families. Staff meetings are based on the premise that you can learn from one another through sharing resources and acknowledging each educator's expertise, experiences, and contribution. Stress relief comes in part from the knowledge that you can share concerns with a coworker or director and trust their professional confidentiality—and this contributes to a positive working environment. Conferring with professionals and agencies with expertise in occupational health, management, communication, and other areas also helps staff reduce stress and increase educators' knowledge and skills.

Community Action
Becoming involved in local organizations related to work with children and families (e.g., local breakfast clubs, joint health and safety committees) can enhance educators' understanding of issues and help to effect change. As the early childhood profession is enhanced, so too are educators' feelings of self-worth and status as professionals.

Societal Change
Advocacy at the provincial/territorial and federal levels can create change that affects occupational health on a broader level, such as a national early childhood education and care plan, family responsibility leave, or positive, supportive changes in legislation.

As educators develop skills in the process of thinking about and addressing problems, they also develop increased pride in their work and growing confidence in their ability to communicate outside of the classroom. Passive acceptance of disheartening conditions in schools or programs, which leads to cynicism and burnout, can be replaced with optimistic attempts to improve situations whenever possible (Fennimore 1989, 195–96).

CONCLUSION

A proactive way to achieve job satisfaction and avoid burnout is to be aware of how well you are implementing healthy physical, emotional, and social practices. It is also important to examine your workplace—are the policies and practices contributing to staff well-being or to burnout? Appendix 2.5 (page 95) provides a checklist for this purpose. Can you identify practices that could be improved? Can you identify supports and barriers and possible solutions? Look back to the eight dimensions of wellness. Achieving balance in your life through setting achievable goals and action plans will contribute to your sense of control.

Where are we going in the future? The career ladder integrates education with career advancement, each a step further along in growth. Each step—based on training, job skills, and experience—broadens your role and responsibilities. With career advancement come increases in salary and job status.

Career advancement shouldn't mean that once you have worked with children for a certain period, the only place to go is the position of supervisor or director. Community colleges and some universities offer post-diploma training to ECE graduates. Educators may want to continue working with children and their families within a program but have more specialized skills and knowledge, such as infant and toddler care, special needs, child assessment, program evaluation, or health promotion advocacy. Here again, salaries must reflect the level of education and roles. Increased career opportunities in early childhood education and care depend in part on better bridges between levels of education and training and between different types of early childhood settings and related early childhood services (Beach et al. 1998). Recognizing that educators are the key component of quality early childhood education and care, the steering committee from Our Child Care Work Force made 23 recommendations to all levels of government (Beach et al. 1998, 134–43). Some of the commitments that underlie these recommendations include

- affordable, accessible quality care and acceptance of the value of a well-paid, competent, and stable workforce;
- equitable wages, benefit levels, and working conditions;
- an educated and competent workforce; and
- opportunities for career mobility.

Government action and inaction have always been of key importance in shaping the direction of development of the early childhood education and care sector. Governments need to begin acting more progressively on behalf of children, families, and this workforce in Canada.

TO TAKE A BREAK OR NOT TO BREAK?

Annie, a very enthusiastic student in her placement, insisted that she didn't need breaks during the day. Although the staff in the room pointed out opportune times to leave the floor for 10 or 15 minutes, Annie said she was fine and didn't want to miss a minute of learning opportunity. The educators appreciated her eagerness but were concerned that this was not a physically, emotionally, or socially healthy pattern to get into. What is your opinion?

ASSESS YOUR LEARNING

Define terms or describe concepts used in this unit.

- balanced lifestyle
- aerobic (cardiovascular) fitness level
- flexibility fitness level
- strength fitness level
- endurance fitness level
- workplace injuries
- public health agencies
- workplace environmental issues
- WHMIS
- supportive early childhood environment
- stress factors
- stress reduction
- professional conduct

Evaluate your options in each situation.

1. A colleague buys her lunch from the nearby fast-food restaurant almost every day. You can't resist having her pick up something for you too, even though you often feel full after eating the nourishing hot lunch with the children before you have your lunch break. The fries or burger tastes great, but you feel sluggish all afternoon.

2. You and a coworker rarely agree on program-related issues. As a result, your relationship deteriorates to the point where you speak as little as possible and the tension is felt by the other staff, children, and parents.

3. After 18 months of working with toddlers, you find that the lifting, bending, and reaching are taking their toll on your physical health. You are coming home exhausted every evening and collapsing in front of the television. You pulled a muscle last month, and you are starting to notice lower back pain.

4. You enjoy talking with parents but are not confident trying to communicate with parents whose first language is not English. You feel that you are being patronizing, speaking loudly and very slowly, and making hand gestures.

5. To the best of your parents' and your own knowledge, you never had chickenpox as a child. You are now pregnant and there are three children who have chickenpox in the program.

RESOURCE MATERIALS

Organizations

Canadian Centre for Occupational Health and Safety, 135 Hunter Street E., Hamilton, ON L8N 1M5. Tel. (905) 572-4400; fax (905) 572-4500, for inquiries 1-800-263-8466, for ordering publications 1-800-263-5466. www.ccohs.ca

Canadian Child Care Federation, 201–383 Parkdale Avenue, Ottawa, ON K1Y 4R4. Tel. (613) 729-5289 or 1-800-858-1412; fax (613) 729-3159. www.cccf-fcsge.ca

Canadian Mental Health Association, 2160 Yonge Street, 3rd Floor, Toronto, ON M4S 2Z3. Tel. (416) 484-7750; fax (416) 484-4617. www.cmha.ca

Child Care Advocacy Association of Canada, 323 Chapel Street, Ottawa, ON K1N 7Z2. Tel. (613) 594-3196; fax (613) 594-9375. www.childcareadvocacy.ca

Heart and Stroke Foundation of Canada, 222 Queen Street, Suite 1402, Ottawa, ON K1P 5V9. Tel. (613) 569-4361; fax (613) 569-3278. www.heartandstroke.ca

Women's Network on Health and the Environment, 517 College Street, Suite 233, Toronto, ON M6G 4A2. Tel. (416) 928-0880. www.web.net/~wnhe

Other Websites of Interest

Sports Canada: www.pch.gc.ca/sportcanada

Canadian Institute for Health Information: www.cihi.ca

Centre for Children and Families in the Justice System of the London Family Court Clinic: www.lfcc.on.ca

Health Canada: www.hc-sc.gc.ca

Internet Mental Health: www.mentalhealth.com

National Forum on Health: wwwnfh.hc-sc.gc.ca

National Institute on Nutrition: www.nin.ca

Shelternet: shelternet.ca

Statistics Canada: www.statcan.ca

World Health Organization: www.who.int

Printed Matter

Blueprint for Action: Achieving Center-Based Change through Staff Development (1998), by P.J. Bloom et al. (New Horizons).

"The Caregiver's Physical Health" and "The Caregiver's Emotional Health," in *Well Beings: A Guide to Promote the Physical Health, Safety and Emotional Well-Being of Children in Child Care Centres and Family Day Care Homes* (1992), by the Canadian Paediatric Society (Canadian Paediatric Society).

For Your Back: Self-Help Manual (1992), by H.D. Saunders (Saunders Group Inc., 4250 Norex Drive, Chaska, MN 55318-3047. Tel. [612] 368-9214).

Handbook for Canada's Physical Activity Guide to Healthy Active Living (1998), by Health Canada, Ottawa. (For copies contact Health Canada, national toll-free 1-888-334-9769 or www.paguide.com.)

Health and Safety at Work for Day-Care Educators (1994), by P. Markon and D. Le Beau (National Library of Quebec).

Health—The Basics (2004), by Rebecca Donatelle et al. (Prentice-Hall/Allyn and Bacon Canada).

Making the Most of Meetings (2002), by Paula Jorde Bloom (New Horizons).

Meeting the Challenge: Effective Strategies for Challenging Behaviours in Early Childhood Environments (1999), by B. Kaiser and J.S. Rasminsky (Justice Canada, Health Canada, and Human Resources Development Canada). (For information or copies, contact Canadian Child Care Federation, 30 Rosemount Avenue, Suite 100, Ottawa, ON K1Y 1P4. Tel. 1-800-858-1412; fax [613] 729-3159; www.cfc-efc.ca/cccf.)

Our Bodies, Ourselves for the New Century (1998), by Boston Women's Health Book Collective (Simon & Schuster).

The New Ourselves, Growing Older: Women Aging with Knowledge and Power (A Book for Women Over Forty) (1994), by P.B. Doress-Worters and D.L. Siegal (Simon & Schuster).

Taking Action for a Healthy Future (1997), by the Women's Network on Health and the Environment (Women and Environment Education and Development Foundation).

"Working with Children of Different Ages," in *Well Beings: A Guide to Promote the Physical Health, Safety and Emotional Well-Being of Children in Child Care Centres and Family Day Care Homes* (1996), by the Canadian Paediatric Society (Canadian Paediatric Society, 744–52).

BIBLIOGRAPHY

American Academy of Pediatrics (2000). *Red Book 2000: Report of the Committee on Infectious Diseases.* Elk Grove Village, IL: American Academy of Pediatrics.

"Are You Listening?" *Child Care Information Exchange,* Sept.–Oct. 1990, 62.

Back Association of Canada (1999). "Did You Know?" <www.backassociation.ca/home.html> (April 1999).

Beach, J., J. Bertrand, and G. Cleveland (1998). "Our Child Care Workforce—From Recognition to Remuneration: More Than a Labour of Love." A Human Resource Study of Child Care in Canada. Ottawa: Human Resources Development Canada.

Bloom, P.J. (1989). *Avoiding Burnout: Strategies for Managing Time, Space, and People in Early Childhood Education.* Illinois: Gryphon House.

Bloom, P.J., M. Sheerer, and J. Britz (1991). *Blueprint for Action: Achieving Center-Based Change through Staff Development.* Lake Forest, IL: New Horizons.

Canadian Centre for Justice Statistics (2002). "Family Violence in Canada: A Statistical Profile 2002." Report. Catalogue no. 85-224-XIE. Ottawa: Statistics Canada.

Canadian Mental Health Association and Heart and Stroke Foundation (1997). *Coping with Stress.* Toronto: CMHA.

Canadian Paediatric Society (1996). *Well Beings: A Guide to Promote the Physical Health, Safety and Emotional Well-Being of Children in Child Care Centres and Family Day Care Homes.* Ottawa: Canadian Paediatric Society.

Clarke, D., and D. Nikkel (1994). *Office Air: A Worker's Guide to Air Quality in Offices, Schools, and Hospitals.* Ottawa: Minister of National Health and Welfare.

Doherty, G., M. Friendly, and B. Forer. (2000). "You Bet I Care! Study 1: A Canada-Wide Study on Wages, Working Conditions, and Practices in Child Care." Guelph, ON: University of Guelph, Centre for Families, Work, and Well Being.

Donatelle, R.J., and L.G. Davis (2003). *Health: The Basics,* 3rd Canadian ed. Scarborough, ON: Prentice Hall/Allyn and Bacon Canada.

Elkind, D. (1981). *The Hurried Child*. Don Mills, ON: Addison-Wesley Publishers.

Fennimore, B.S. (1989). *Child Advocacy for Early Childhood Educators*. New York: Teachers College Press.

Health and Welfare Canada (1992). *Using the Food Guide*. Ottawa: Minister of Supply and Services.

Health Canada (2007a). *Eating Well with Canada's Food Guide*.

——— (2007b). *Eating Well with Canada's Food Guide: A Resource for Educators and Communicators*.

——— (2007c). My Food Guide.http://www.hc-sc.gc.ca/fn-an/food-guide-aliment/myguide-monguide/index_e.html > (March 2007).

——— (2002). *Canadian Immunization Guide*. Ottawa: Canadian Medical Association.

Hoeger, W.K., and S.A. Hoeger (2000). *Lifetime Physical Fitness and Wellness*, 6th ed. Englewood, CO: Morton Publishing.

Liebman, Bonnie (2002). "Face the Fats," *Nutrition Action Health Letter* 29(6) (July–August): 3–12. Toronto: Centre for Science in the Public Interest.

Markon, Philippe (1999). "Safety in the Child Care Center Is Also for the Early Childhood Staff." *Child Care Connection*, Issue 2.3.

Markon, P., and D. Le Beau (1994). *Health and Safety at Work for Day-Care Educators*. Chicoutimi: Université du Québec à Chicoutimi.

Maxwell, A., and G. Huot (1994). "Health and Occupational Safety for Child Care Educators." *FOCUS*, January: 29–34.

Saunders, H.D. (1994). *For Your Back: Self-Help Manual*. Chaska, MN: Saunders Group.

Statistics Canada (2002). *Health Indicators Highlights: Life Stress*, vol. 2002, no. 2. Ottawa: Ministry of Health.

Taylor, A. (1993). "So They're Trained...What Now?" *Interaction*, Summer: 7–9.

Vanier Institute of the Family (2000). *Profiling Canada's Families*. Ottawa: Vanier Institute of the Family.

Vary, C.P.H., M. Carmody, R. LeBlanc, et al. (1996). "The Ergonomics of Child Care: Connecting Worksite Analyses." *Work: A Journal of Prevention, Assessment, and Rehabilitation* 6(1): 25–32.

World Health Organization (1998). "Obesity: Preventing and Managing the Global Epidemic. Report of a WHO Consultation on Obesity." Geneva: World Health Organization.

Women's Network on Health and the Environment (1997). *Taking Action for a Healthy Future*. Toronto: Women and Environment Education and Development Foundation.

The Financial Dimension

_____	I have written down my dreams and have a clear view of my priorities.
_____	I know my net worth (assets minus liabilities) and what my debt equity ratio is.
_____	I have calculated my monthly cash flow (in/out).
_____	I recognize my spending patterns and am able to take control of them to work for me rather than against me. I know that I can work toward financial wellness if I live within my means.
_____	If I have one, I use a credit card for convenience only, and I pay the balance when the monthly statement comes in. I do not view the credit card as an effective method of long-term payment.
_____	I pay down my debts, giving priority to those with the highest interest rates (e.g., credit cards).
_____	I consistently use a budget, allocating funds for specific items. I don't see borrowing as an option. Instead, I use a savings plan to afford desired items or vacations.
_____	I know how to get what I need and want from my banking institution (e.g., the best bank fees, the account type that suits my needs).
_____	If my situation allows it, I have an emergency fund and a regular savings plan in place, routinely putting aside a reasonable amount.
_____	I save for my retirement every year (e.g., RRSP).
_____	I take advantage of all tax deductions to which I am entitled and file my annual taxes.
_____	I use tax refunds to pay down debt or to invest (e.g., RRSP), rather than spending them on consumer items or vacations.
_____	I understand the programs that are mandatory and optional with my employer (e.g., vacation, sick leave, extended health, life insurance, pension).
_____	I am financially literate, keep up-to-date in understanding basic financial information, and can communicate with investors in my best interest.
_____	I am working toward having control over money rather than having it control me.

Canada's Physical Activity Guide to Healthy Active Living

CANADA'S
Physical Activity Guide
to Healthy Active Living

Physical activity improves health.

Every little bit counts, but more is even better – everyone can do it!

Get active your way – build physical activity into your daily life...
• at home
• at school
• at work
• at play
• on the way
...that's active living!

TAKE THE STAIRS

Increase Endurance Activities

Increase Flexibility Activities

Increase Strength Activities

Reduce Sitting for long periods

 Health Canada   Santé Canada

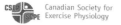 Canadian Society for Exercise Physiology

Choose a variety of activities from these three groups:

Endurance

4-7 days a week
Continuous activities for your heart, lungs and circulatory system.

Flexibility

4-7 days a week
Gentle reaching, bending and stretching activities to keep your muscles relaxed and joints mobile.

Strength

2-4 days a week
Activities against resistance to strengthen muscles and bones and improve posture.

Starting slowly is very safe for most people. Not sure? Consult your health professional.

For a copy of the *Guide Handbook* and more information: **1-888-334-9769**, or **www.paguide.com**

Eating well is also important. Follow *Canada's Food Guide to Healthy Eating* to make wise food choices.

Get Active Your Way, Every Day – For Life!

Scientists say accumulate 60 minutes of physical activity every day to stay healthy or improve your health. As you progress to moderate activities you can cut down to 30 minutes, 4 days a week. Add-up your activities in periods of at least 10 minutes each. Start slowly... and build up.

Time needed depends on effort

Very Light Effort	Light Effort *60 minutes*	Moderate Effort *30-60 minutes*	Vigorous Effort *20-30 minutes*	Maximum Effort
• Strolling • Dusting	• Light walking • Volleyball • Easy gardening • Stretching	• Brisk walking • Biking • Raking leaves • Swimming • Dancing • Water aerobics	• Aerobics • Jogging • Hockey • Basketball • Fast swimming • Fast dancing	• Sprinting • Racing

Range needed to stay healthy

You Can Do It – Getting started is easier than you think

Physical activity doesn't have to be very hard. Build physical activities into your daily routine.

- Walk whenever you can – get off the bus early, use the stairs instead of the elevator.
- Reduce inactivity for long periods, like watching TV.
- Get up from the couch and stretch and bend for a few minutes every hour.
- Play actively with your kids.
- Choose to walk, wheel or cycle for short trips.

- Start with a 10 minute walk – gradually increase the time.
- Find out about walking and cycling paths nearby and use them.
- Observe a physical activity class to see if you want to try it.
- Try one class to start – you don't have to make a long-term commitment.
- Do the activities you are doing now, more often.

Benefits of regular activity:

- better health
- improved fitness
- better posture and balance
- better self-esteem
- weight control
- stronger muscles and bones
- feeling more energetic
- relaxation and reduced stress
- continued independent living in later life

Health risks of inactivity:

- premature death
- heart disease
- obesity
- high blood pressure
- adult-onset diabetes
- osteoporosis
- stroke
- depression
- colon cancer

No changes permitted. Permission to photocopy this document in its entirety not required.
Cat. No. H39-429/1998-1E ISBN 0-662-86627-7

Source: *Canada's Physical Activity Guide to Healthy Active Living*, Health Canada. Reproduced with the permission of the Minister of Public Works and Government Services Canada, 2003.

Back Care

4.5 kg (10 lbs)
45 kg (100 lbs)

4.5 kg (10 lbs)   45 kg (100 lbs)

4.5 kg (10 lbs)   4.5 kg (10 lbs)

Keep weight close to body.

Partial Squat Lift

The Power Lift

Kneel when working in a low position.

The Golfer's Lift

Straight Leg Lift: Bend at the hips, not the back.

Source: Adapted with permission from H. Duane Saunders, *For Your Back: Self-Help Manual* (Chaska, MN: Saunders Group, 1994), 31–32. Tel. (612) 368-9214.

Staff Exposed to Infectious Diseases

INFECTION	MANAGEMENT OF STAFF EXPOSED TO INFECTION	MANAGEMENT OF STAFF DIAGNOSED WITH AN INFECTION
Respiratory Infections		
Colds	Observe for illness. Ensure hand-washing.	Exclude if too ill to work. Ensure hand-washing.
Influenza (Flu)	Observe for illness. Caregivers with cardiac disease, respiratory disease, or diabetes should contact their physician about a vaccination.	Exclude if too ill to work. Ensure hand-washing.
Pinkeye (Conjunctivitis)	Observe for illness. Ensure hand-washing.	Exclude only if discharge is pus (thick, yellow) and until the antibiotic has been taken for 1 full day.
Tuberculosis	Contact LPHA.[1]	Contact LPHA.[1] Exclude until treated and non-infectious.
Whooping Cough (Pertussis)	Contact LPHA.[1] Observe for illness.	Contact LPHA.[1] Exclude until 5 days after start of antibiotics. If not treated, exclude for 2 weeks.
Gastrointestinal Infections		
Diarrhea	Observe for illness. Ensure hand-washing.	Exclude if too ill to work. Ensure hand-washing. Ensure person does not prepare or serve food.
Hepatitis A	Contact LPHA.[1] Obtain immune globulin. Contact physician if pregnant.	Exclude for 1 week after onset of jaundice.

Vomiting Illness	Observe for illness. Ensure hand-washing.	Exclude if too ill to work. Ensure hand-washing. Ensure person does not prepare or serve food.

Infections with Rash

Chickenpox (Varicella)	Contact LPHA.[1] Check if susceptible and in need of VZIG.[2] Contact physician if pregnant.	Contact LPHA.[1] Exclude until 5 days after onset of rash or until all blisters have crusted, whichever is shorter. May return sooner if illness is mild and able to return to work.
Fifth Disease (Parvovirus B19)	Contact physician if pregnant.	Contact physician. No exclusion required.
Measles	Contact LPHA.[1] Exclude if susceptible and unvaccinated until 2 weeks after onset of last case in the child care facility.	Contact LPHA immediately.[1] Exclude until at least 4 days after onset of rash.
Rash with Fever	Contact LPHA.[1]	Contact LPHA.[1] Exclude until diagnosis has been made by physician.
Rubella (German Measles)	Contact physician if pregnant.	Exclude until 7 days after onset of rash.
Shingles (Zoster)	Contact physician if susceptible, especially if pregnant.	Exclude until lesions have crusted only if lesions cannot be covered by clothing or a dressing.

Infections Spread by Contact with Blood

Hepatitis B	Contact LPHA.[1] HBIG[3] may be indicated for certain exposures to infected children, e.g., bites or contact with blood. Contact physician.	No exclusion required.

Other Infections

Boils	Ensure hand-washing.	No exclusion required. Ensure hand-washing.
Cytomegalovirus (CMV)	Ensure hand-washing. Contact physician if pregnant.	No exclusion required. Ensure hand-washing.
Infectious Mononucleosis	Ensure hand-washing	Exclude if too ill to work.

[1]LPHA: Local public health agency
[2]VZIG: Varicella-Zoster Immune Globulin
[3]HBIG: Hepatitis B Immune Globulin

Source: Reprinted with permission from Canadian Paediatric Society (1996), *Well Beings: A Guide to Promote the Physical Health, Safety and Emotional Well-Being of Children in Child Care Centres and Family Day Care Homes* (Ottawa: Canadian Paediatric Society), 696–97.

Health Practices: You and Your Employer

2.5

The following checklist summarizes the aspects of occupational health discussed in this unit. How do you rate yourself and a centre where you've done a placement? You may find it enlightening to check again after you've been working in an early childhood program for a year.

DO YOU . . .	YES	NO	SOMETIMES
maintain healthy eating habits by			
• being aware of your eating pattern	❏	❏	❏
• lowering fat intake	❏	❏	❏
• drinking water every day	❏	❏	❏
• increasing fibre	❏	❏	❏
• decreasing processed foods	❏	❏	❏
balance work, rest, and exercise by			
• making time for regular physical activity	❏	❏	❏
• ensuring you get adequate sleep	❏	❏	❏
• finding ways for leisure daily	❏	❏	❏
• spending time with friends and family	❏	❏	❏
prevent the spread of illness by			
• keeping your immunization up to date	❏	❏	❏
• washing your hands effectively	❏	❏	❏
• implementing cleaning and sanitizing routines	❏	❏	❏
prevent workplace injuries by			
• using proper lifting techniques	❏	❏	❏
• identifying and reporting required adjustments to workspace, equipment, and furnishings	❏	❏	❏
• following products' safety recommendations	❏	❏	❏
• using environmentally friendly products	❏	❏	❏
• implementing the principles of WHMIS	❏	❏	❏
• reporting workplace injuries	❏	❏	❏
• keeping your first-aid and CPR certificates up-to-date	❏	❏	❏

(continues on next page)

DO YOU . . .

	YES	NO	SOMETIMES

promote your social and emotional well-being by

	YES	NO	SOMETIMES
• demonstrating respect for self and others through professional behaviour such as promptness and confidentiality	❏	❏	❏
• developing and practising effective communication skills	❏	❏	❏
• knowing and using designated lines of communication to share concerns	❏	❏	❏
• being actively involved in your self-evaluation and evaluation by others	❏	❏	❏
• being flexible and open to learning new ideas	❏	❏	❏
• identifying your stress factors and developing coping mechanisms that eliminate or reduce them	❏	❏	❏
• seeking further professional development	❏	❏	❏
• being a member of an early childhood association	❏	❏	❏

lower other risk factors by

	YES	NO	SOMETIMES
• stopping smoking	❏	❏	❏
• conducting monthly breast self-examinations or testicular self-examinations	❏	❏	❏
• limiting regular consumption of alcohol	❏	❏	❏
• practising safer sex	❏	❏	❏
• feeling good about your health care professional	❏	❏	❏
• keeping up-to-date on health issues	❏	❏	❏

CAN YOU . . .

evaluate balance in your life through awareness of wellness dimensions:

	YES	NO	SOMETIMES
• physical	❏	❏	❏
• emotional	❏	❏	❏
• social	❏	❏	❏
• intellectual	❏	❏	❏
• occupational	❏	❏	❏
• spiritual	❏	❏	❏
• environmental	❏	❏	❏
• financial	❏	❏	❏

CAN YOU ARTICULATE YOUR . . .

goal statement (specific and measurable)
action steps: 1.
          2.
          3.
          4.
target date:
Resources available to help you:
Barriers and how to deal with them:

DOES YOUR EMPLOYER . . .

	YES	NO	SOMETIMES

support educators' healthy eating habits by

	YES	NO	SOMETIMES
• ensuring adequate break times	❏	❏	❏
• providing a relaxing place to eat and relax	❏	❏	❏

recognize the importance of staff balancing work, rest, and exercise by

	YES	NO	SOMETIMES
• maintaining adequate educator–child ratios	❏	❏	❏
• ensuring all staff take regular breaks each day	❏	❏	❏

(continues on next page)

DOES YOUR EMPLOYER . . .	YES	NO	SOMETIMES
• incorporating sufficient time in the daily schedule for program planning and documenting	❑	❑	❑
• curtailing overtime and discouraging staff from taking work home	❑	❑	❑
prevent the spread of illness by			
• keeping track of staff's immunization records	❑	❑	❑
• providing orientation and regular in-service training in			
– infection control strategy	❑	❑	❑
– food handling and preparation	❑	❑	❑
• providing adequate supplies and posters for hand washing, diapering, toileting	❑	❑	❑
• developing and posting cleaning and sanitizing routines	❑	❑	❑
prevent workplace injuries by			
• providing orientation and regular in-service training in			
– proper lifting techniques	❑	❑	❑
– WHMIS and product safety	❑	❑	❑
• responding to inadequacies in workspaces, equipment, and furnishings	❑	❑	❑
• purchasing environmentally friendly products	❑	❑	❑
• completing workplace injury reports and responding to injuries	❑	❑	❑
• requiring evidence that staff's first-aid and CPR certificates are up-to-date and arranging for staff to renew as a group	❑	❑	❑
promote staff's collegiality and emotional well-being by			
• providing job descriptions for each position and ensuring that all understand one another's role	❑	❑	❑
• outlining lines of communication	❑	❑	❑
• providing adequate supervision	❑	❑	❑
• conducting regular performance evaluations	❑	❑	❑
• organizing staff meetings and in-services on communication, conflict resolution, etc.	❑	❑	❑
• providing a comprehensive employee benefit package that includes family responsibility leave	❑	❑	❑
• providing time and possibly financial support for professional development	❑	❑	❑
• actively participating as a centre member in a regional or national child care association	❑	❑	❑
• encouraging opportunities for staff to socialize	❑	❑	❑

DOES YOUR EARLY CHILDHOOD PROGRAM . . .

	YES	NO	SOMETIMES
lower other risk factors by			
• networking with community health resources	❑	❑	❑
• providing current health literature for staff (e.g., public health pamphlets)	❑	❑	❑

CAN YOU ARTICULATE YOUR PROGRAM'S

goal statement (specific and measurable)
action steps: 1.
         2.
         3.
         4.
target date:
Resources available to help you:
Barriers and how to deal with them:

Illness Prevention

CONTENTS

Our Body's Natural Defence Mechanisms   *101*
     IMMUNITY   102

How Infections Spread   *102*
     THE GERM   103
     THE HOST   104
     THE VEHICLES OF TRANSMISSION   104
     THE NEW HOST   107

Breaking the Chain: Developing an Infection Control Strategy   *108*
     IMMUNIZATION   109
     HYGIENE PRACTICES   113
     CLEANING AND SANITIZING   123

Revisiting the Health Promotion Action Plan   *129*

Conclusion   *130*

What's Your Opinion? TO GLOVE OR NOT TO GLOVE?   *131*

Assess Your Learning   *131*

Resource Materials   *131*

Bibliography   *132*

TABLES

TABLE 3.1   LIFE OF VIRUSES ON SURFACES   104
TABLE 3.2   SUMMARIZING THE LINKS OF THE CHAIN   108
TABLE 3.3   COMPARISON OF CASES OF DISEASE IN CANADA BEFORE AND AFTER THE INTRODUCTION OF IMMUNIZATION   110
TABLE 3.4   ROUTINE IMMUNIZATION SCHEDULE FOR INFANTS AND CHILDREN   111

FIGURES

FIGURE 3.1   THE LINKS IN THE CHAIN   103
FIGURE 3.2   BREAKING THE CHAIN   109

Young children get sick whether they are cared for at home or in an early childhood program, but the rates of common illness are two to three times higher for children enrolled in centres (Canadian Paediatric Society 1996, 50–51). One study of groups of children over a three-year period found that children in centres with seven or more children had an average of 7.1 illnesses per year, compared with 4.7 per year for children in family daycare (Wald et al. 1988, 542). Over the next two years of the study, the difference in the rate of infections between the types of early childhood settings became smaller. Therefore, the longer that children are in a centre's care, the less often they are sick, and in fact they aren't sick much more often than children in family daycare. This information is reassuring for parents who choose centre care.

Among the reasons for higher rates of childhood infections are the following:

- The children enrolled in an early childhood program are from different families, which increases the number of infections that could be spread. Each child may be exposed to germs or infections from his or her parents, siblings, friends, or even from strangers riding on the bus in the morning. So every day it is likely that children spread germs among themselves and staff.
- Preschool children are still learning good personal hygiene habits.
- Infants and young children are more susceptible to illness because their immune systems are still developing.

In the past, most infants, toddlers, and preschoolers remained at home with their mothers. It was not until the children were in kindergarten or grade 1 that they frequently experienced common childhood illnesses during the first few months of starting school, for the reasons outlined above. But by the time children are five or six years old, they are better able to fight infections. Their immune system has matured and they have almost completed their series of immunizations. Obviously, every child must eventually become part of a group, so the concerns lie in the age at which this occurs and in what can be done to reduce the number of infections that each child experiences as a result of that participation.

The opportunities for illnesses to spread are even higher among infants and toddlers than among preschoolers. Young children wear diapers, may be learning to use the toilet, require a great deal of hands-on care, crawl on the floor, and put hands, toys, and objects in their mouths and then share these wet objects with others. They are only beginning to learn how to wash their hands. They are also quite affectionate with each other (e.g., kissing, hugging, touching). Although this physical contact can contribute to the spread of respiratory infections, the emotional and social benefits of physical affection far outweigh the risk of illness. Rather than discourage this social behaviour, educators implement hygiene practices that reduce the spread of germs among infants and toddlers (e.g., hand washing, cleaning and sanitizing mouthing toys, diapering and toileting routines).

Early childhood educators' understanding of how infections are spread and the ability to implement health practices reduce the incidence of infections in children. The less often children are ill, the less often parents and staff need to manage illness. In other words, the discomfort and stress experienced by children, parents, and staff are reduced. Also, the fewer visits that children make to their physicians, the less money government is obliged to spend on physicians' fees, laboratory tests, and prescriptions, thus reducing health costs.

Most common childhood illnesses are minor and don't last more than a few days. The most typical childhood illnesses are the common cold, ear infections, other respiratory infections, and diarrhea. There are also several more serious communicable diseases that children and adults are susceptible to if they have not developed immunity either through immunizations or by having had the disease (see Immunity, page 102, and Immunization, page 109).

OUR BODY'S NATURAL DEFENCE MECHANISMS

OBJECTIVE

To identify and describe our body's natural defence mechanisms.

Because germs are everywhere, we are fortunate that our body has a built-in defence system; otherwise we would have some kind of infection all the time. Our skin is our body's first defence, and one of the most important defence mechanisms, against the germs that we contact every day. The oily substance excreted by glands in the walls of the hair follicles is acidic; it kills germs that would otherwise grow on our skin. Normal intact skin is impermeable to germs and to fluids like water and blood. Where the skin is non-intact (because of cuts, scrapes, sores, burns, for example), germs can enter. Some chemical agents such as some pesticides can enter our body through the hair follicles.

Many germs enter our body through the nose. The nasal hair that you can see and the cilia that cover the mucous membranes in our nose and throat filter and collect air particles such as dust and germs. The mucus produced by the mucous membranes traps the particles, which are then swallowed and destroyed by gastric and acidic secretions in the stomach. We also expel mucus by coughing or sneezing, which rids our body of germs. As well, the mucous membranes in the gastrointestinal and urinary tracts can inactivate or destroy germs, which the bloodstream then clears out of our body. The urine's bacteriostatic (bacteria-destroying) action keeps the urinary tract sterile. Tear secretions destroy bacteria in our eyes. Wax protects our ears.

You have probably heard the sayings "You'll catch a cold if you go outside with wet hair" and "If you sit in a draft, you'll get a cold." In fact, the only way to catch a cold is through exposure to a cold virus that infects our body. Therefore, neither saying is true. But both remind us to think about vulnerability to viruses and bacteria. For example, when you are rundown or "running on empty" your body will be more vulnerable to a virus or bacteria. Every day we can provide our body with the nutrients and energy to fight off an infection or to get better. Our body needs these essential elements:

- nutritious food and a well-balanced diet
- adequate sleep
- adequate physical activity
- fresh air
- coping strategies to keep stress under control

And, of course, we need to live in a home that provides us with the basic needs of clean water, sewage disposal, and comfortable temperature, and we need warm clothes, coats, shoes, and boots in the winter. If we were always using our energy to keep warm in the winter, our body wouldn't have energy left for everything else we must do to keep healthy.

Immunity

Immunity provides us with protection from specific infections. Each time a germ enters your body, your immunity increases. When a specific germ multiplies in your body, it produces large numbers of its specific protein (antigen), which enter the bloodstream. The immune system responds by producing specific antibodies. Even when an infection is over, your body may continue to make antibodies for long periods, sometimes even for life.

But after many infections, the antibodies disappear from your body over time. Despite this disappearance, cells in your immune system remember the germ so that if it is contracted again, the immune system makes antibodies very rapidly. Most people who have had chickenpox have a lifelong immunity to it. It is rare to get it again, even after being exposed to a person who has it. The body has a harder time warding off the common cold, however. There are approximately 200 different viruses that cause the common cold.

> Being infected by a virus which causes a cold may not lead to immunity to that virus. In fact, infection by the same cold virus can occur many times over. The many different cold viruses, plus the failure of infections to produce immunity, explain why people get so many colds. (Canadian Paediatric Society 1996, 135)

We develop immunity to a disease in one of two ways:

- naturally or actively
- passively (see Immune Globulin, page 113).

For the first few months of life, infants are resistant to some diseases. This naturally acquired immunity is passed on to babies from their mother before birth. Breast milk contains antibodies, which help to protect infants from some bowel, ear, and respiratory infections. However, this natural immunity is short-lived. The immune systems of infants and young children mature through actively acquired immunity. Children develop different antibodies in two ways: either by actually having an infection or through immunizations (see Immunization, page 109).

OBJECTIVE

To explain how germs are spread.

HOW INFECTIONS SPREAD

Germs are everywhere. By understanding how germs are spread, you can break the chain of transmission and ultimately reduce or stop the spread of germs that cause illness.

The chain of transmission has four links, as illustrated in Figure 3.1:

- the germ
- the host (person who is ill)
- the vehicles of transmission
- the new host (next person who becomes ill)

FIGURE 3.1 The Links in the Chain

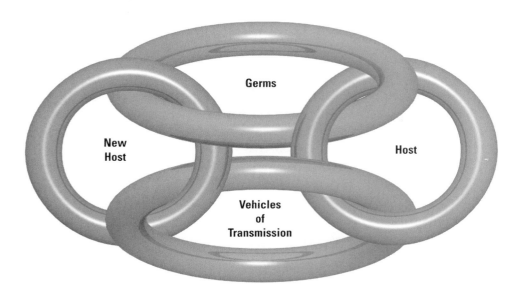

The Germ

The term "germ" is used generically to include viruses, bacteria, parasites, and fungi. Though most germs can't be seen by the naked eye (they are microscopic), they are capable of causing infections that range in severity from minor to fatal. The type of germ usually determines which part of the body develops the infection. This explains why we develop different infections such as colds, strep throat, ear or chest infections, impetigo, urinary-tract (bladder) infections, or diarrhea.

We all have germs that live in our body and play an important role in keeping us healthy. Women, for example, have small numbers of bacteria and a fungus known as *Candida* living in the intestinal tract and the vagina. Let's use this example to see how the germs normally found in the body can cause infections in the following two scenarios.

In the first scenario, women may experience vaginal yeast infections while they are taking an antibiotic for a bacterial infection. While the antibiotic is destroying the bacteria that have caused the infection, it may also destroy the bacteria normally found in the vagina. Consequently, the fungus in the vagina multiplies, causing a yeast infection, because the natural balance of the vaginal bacteria and fungus has been altered by the antibiotic. *Candida* diaper rash can develop in young children in a similar way. An antibiotic given to an infant or toddler to treat a bacterial infection may also destroy bacteria normally found in the bowel, which then permits the fungus to multiply.

In the second scenario, you don't have to have diarrhea yourself to cause someone else to get diarrhea. We all have bacteria that live in our bowels and help to keep us healthy. But when those bacteria contaminate an environment and someone else comes in contact with them, that person may develop diarrhea.

Effective hand washing is the key to preventing the stool from contaminating an environment.

Some germs, surprisingly enough, can live outside our body for several hours or even weeks and can still cause infection (see Table 3.1). Rotavirus and hepatitis A can live for weeks on objects such as toys, and germs that cause respiratory infections can live for several hours. This longevity contributes to the spread of infection. Germs thrive and multiply in food, causing intestinal infections that can, in rare cases, be fatal (see Through Food, page 106).

Furthermore, children and adults who have an infection are often infectious (or contagious) for a period of time, which fluctuates depending on the type of germ. Children with the common cold may be infectious for a day or two before the cold symptoms start and may remain so for the next seven days (see Appendix 4.1, page 182).

TABLE 3.1	Life of Viruses on Surfaces		
VIRUS	**COUNTERTOPS/TOYS**	**CLOTH**	**SKIN**
Respiratory Syncytial (common cause of bronchiolitis and pneumonia)	8 hrs.	1 to 2 hrs.	25 min.
Influenzae A and B	24 to 48 hrs.	8 to 12 hrs.	5 min.
Rotavirus (common cause of diarrhea)	8 days to wks.		
Cytomegalovirus (CMV)	8 hrs.		
Hepatitis A	2 wks.		

Source: Reprinted with permission from Canadian Paediatric Society (1996), *Well Beings: A Guide to Promote the Physical Health, Safety and Emotional Well-Being of Children in Child Care Centres and Family Day Care Homes* (Ottawa: Canadian Paediatric Society), 53.

The Host

Health and medical professionals use the term "host" to describe the person with the infection. Think of the infected person as the host of a dinner party. The infected person's body provides the germs with the nourishment and warmth that they need to thrive. Germs may be spread to others during the three stages of an infection: before we know we are ill, while we are ill, and in some cases even after we have recovered. A "carrier" is a host who does not actually have symptoms of an infection but has the germ living dormant in his or her body. Carriers can spread germs (e.g., hepatitis B) to others, and sometimes the germs may reactivate and cause an infection (e.g., shingles) in the carrier.

The Vehicles of Transmission

Hosts have germs in their body secretions (such as stool, saliva, blood) that can be transmitted (or spread) in a number of ways. The germs contaminate our environment and are spread directly from person to person through the air or by direct contact (e.g., touching, kissing, biting), or indirectly on vehicles (e.g., toys, hands, food, objects).

Through Direct or Indirect Contact

Infections are spread directly and indirectly from one host to another. The direct spread of infection takes place when we breathe in the germs that cause infections such as colds, chickenpox, and flu. Another way we come into contact with germs that cause skin infections is by touching the host's infected skin (e.g., impetigo, cold sores, scabies, the fluid in the blisters of chickenpox, the rash of shingles). Another example is when someone becomes infested with head lice after coming in contact with head lice.

Germs are spread indirectly on contaminated vehicles. Vehicles can be anything around us that germs can contaminate. The vehicles in early childhood programs that we need to pay particular attention to are hands, food and food-related objects, facial tissues, diapers, potties, mouthing toys, hairbrushes, toothbrushes, and blow toys/pipes/straws used in water tables. The germs on these vehicles can easily and frequently find their way into our body.

Educators of toddlers and young preschoolers are often concerned about children biting. From the standpoint of infection control, the risk of children transmitting hepatitis B or C or human immunodeficiency virus (HIV) through biting is extremely unlikely (Canadian Paediatric Society 2002, 2). In fact, there has not been a single reported case of HIV transmitted in any program. However, there has been at least one case of hepatitis B in an American centre. It is unusual for a child's bite to actually break (cut) the victim's skin and cause bleeding. Saliva has not been shown to spread HIV (Canadian Paediatric Society 1996, 55–56, 182–85; American Academy of Pediatrics 2000, 303; Aronson 1991, 143).

> A human bite will rarely transmit a bacterial infection. Usually, the transmission of bacterial infections is associated with fighting incidents among adults. Severe bites are unusual in a day care setting and almost never lead to bacterial infections. (Canadian Paediatric Society 2002, 2)

If a bite mark does bleed, the Canadian Paediatric Society (2002, 2) recommends the following:

- the wound should be allowed to bleed gently
- the wound should be cleaned carefully with soap and water
- a mild antiseptic should be applied
- the child's tetanus immunization should be reviewed and updated
- the parents should be notified
- an official report should be written and filed
- the wound should be observed over the next few days
- if redness or swelling develops, the child's parents should consult a health professional

In terms of the victim's potential exposure to blood-borne infections, the physician and public health staff will advise whether treatment is required. The medical officer of health (MOH) may determine that the child or adult be given hepatitis B immune globulin (HBIG).

Keep in mind that biting is a guidance issue for educators. Consideration may need to be given to children who are known to be biting and to the pain they inflict on others in the program. Biting is usually a short-term behaviour. Parents and educators will need to discuss a consistent way to manage the biting.

Through the Air

Young children frequently experience colds and eye, nose, and throat infections. It is easy to understand why. The germs, both viruses and bacteria, that cause minor or serious infections are in the host's saliva and nasal secretions. The germs are spread by droplets of secretions that move through the air when we cough or sneeze. We can breathe in the droplets or they can land in our eyes, nose, or mouth. Or the droplets, saliva, or nasal discharge land on an object or our hands and the germs find their way into our mouth.

Through Contact with Stool

Diarrhea can be caused by bacteria, parasites, or viruses found in the host's stool. As we have discussed, there are bacteria in our bowels that help to keep us healthy. However, if those bacteria contaminate our environment, they can cause an intestinal infection in someone else. Whenever stool contaminates our hands, food, water, cooking surfaces, toys, taps on sinks, and other objects, the germs spread very easily among us. Germs enter our mouth from our hands and from toys or through food or water. This means of transmission is also known as the fecal-oral route.

Through Food

Food is an ideal medium for germs to grow on and multiply. Typically, food is contaminated in one of two ways: germs may be in or on the food before we buy it, or we can contaminate food when we handle or prepare it. Regardless of the way germs get into food, the way we prepare, cook, serve, and store food determines whether the germs multiply or are destroyed.

Although most food will have some germs in it, you don't get sick every time you eat because your body's defence mechanisms can destroy many germs. Only when germs multiply in numbers before you eat the food can they cause mild, serious, or, rarely, fatal infections. The severity of the infection depends on the type of germ or the number of germs that have entered the body. Breaking the chain of food transmission involves several safe food-handling practices: handwashing, purchasing, storing, preparing, cooking, and serving (see Food Safety Practices, page 243).

Through Contact with Blood and Bloody Body Fluids

Two serious infections, hepatitis B and human immunodeficiency virus (HIV), are blood-borne diseases and in most cases spread to others through direct contact with blood or semen. These viruses are spread three ways:

- by sexual intercourse
- by sharing needles used for illegal intravenous drug use
- by an infected woman to her fetus and, in the case of HIV, during breast-feeding

The HIV virus creates anxiety in schools, early childhood programs, and hospitals, but routine screening of patients, students, employees, or children in early childhood programs, schools, and hospitals is not permitted under human rights legislation. Nor is it recommended or necessary under the guiding principle of universal precautions in infection control. Following possible exposure to the virus, there is a "window period" during which your body either will or will not develop antibodies to HIV, which will then be detected in the blood. This period varies from a few weeks to about six months. When someone is concerned that she or he may have been exposed to HIV and is tested during this period, the result could be negative. Testing after this window period confirms whether she or he is HIV-negative or HIV-positive. If these later tests are positive, the initial test was false-negative. False-negative tests are one of the important reasons why routine screening for HIV is not conducted. The HIV blood test tests individuals only for a moment in time.

It is important to understand that someone's HIV status is confidential medical information and that it is against human rights legislation either to insist on HIV testing or to demand that someone disclose her or his HIV status to program staff or to anyone else. If parents disclose their child's HIV-positive status to one educator, that educator must maintain confidentiality by not telling her or his co-workers, director, or other parents. This information can be shared only by the parents. Many people who are HIV-positive fear discrimination, rejection, and isolation after disclosing their HIV status, so they keep it a secret. Through education and public awareness, sensitivity, and respect, perhaps the social climate will change and we will embrace and support people living with HIV/AIDS.

Neither HIV nor hepatitis B is spread by casual contact. The work that is done in early childhood programs is defined as casual, and the risk of transmitting HIV and hepatitis B within programs must be put into perspective. Working with children and coworkers does not put educators at risk of HIV transmission. We must focus instead on our personal lives to reduce our risks. Educators, like the general population, put themselves at risk if they participate in unprotected sexual intercourse or share needles and syringes. To learn more about HIV and hepatitis B transmission and about reducing your risk, contact your college/university resource or health centre, the public health agency, physicians, or the AIDS committee in your province or territory (see *HIV/AIDS and Child Care* in Resource Materials, page 132).

Hepatitis C is another blood-borne disease that has a very low infection rate among the general public. Its profile was raised, however, in recent years by those infected from tainted blood transfusions before 1989. But like HIV and hepatitis B, those at risk for the infection are intravenous drug users and those who participate in unprotected sexual intercourse.

The New Host

The term "new host" refers to the next person who gets the infection after the germs enter the body, whether through the mouth, eyes, nose, an open cut, a rash or sore on the skin, or by way of the genito-urinary or gastrointestinal tract. The type of germ usually determines which part of the body develops the infection. This explains why we develop different infections such as colds, strep throat, ear or chest infections, impetigo, urinary-tract (bladder) infections, or diarrhea.

The incubation period begins when the germ first enters the new host's body. Then the germ multiplies in number. The body's natural defences try to destroy the germs, and if they are successful we don't get sick. But if they are unsuccessful, we experience symptoms within hours, days, or weeks, depending on the germ and how much time it needs to multiply before it causes infection. By the time you feel that cold coming on, however, you have already been spreading the cold virus among others. This is relatively common for infections, including chickenpox, which makes controlling the spread of infection very difficult. Therefore, the control of infections is an ongoing job; you don't do it just when you know someone is ill.

TABLE 3.2	Summarizing the Links of the Chain
The Germ	• viruses
	• bacteria
	• parasites
	• fungi
The Host	• person who is ill (germs found in saliva, stool, and blood, on skin or hair, etc.)
The Vehicles of Transmission	• directly from person to person (e.g., through air, by touching, kissing, biting)
	• indirectly from person to person (e.g., on hands, toys, food, objects)
The New Host	• new person who is ill

BREAKING THE CHAIN: DEVELOPING AN INFECTION CONTROL STRATEGY

Our initial defence against germs is understanding that although germs are everywhere, we neither want to, nor are we able to, produce a sterile environment (as in an operating room). Early childhood environments are designed to be friendly, nurturing, interesting, and child-centred. Although children do become ill, our underlying assumption is that most people are healthy most of the time. Thus, we carefully choose where to focus our energy to prevent or reduce environmental contamination and the spread of germs. Maintaining our own health and that of the children in our care prevents the germs normally found in our bodies from causing infection, and in many cases helps us resist germs from other sources. Thus, a program's infection control strategy demonstrates the staff's understanding of the chain of transmission by developing and implementing specific policies and procedures. To break the chain of transmission, programs' policy manuals will include infection control policies and procedures on the following:

- immunization
- hygiene practices
- cleaning and sanitizing routines
- daily observation of children

- documentation of health observations and sharing observations with parents and physicians
- exclusion criteria
- effective communication with parents

OBJECTIVES

To understand why certain items must be cleaned and sanitized before and after use, or on a daily or regular schedule.

To understand the goal of universal precautions and how to put them into practice.

FIGURE 3.2	Breaking the Chain

Hygiene Practices
Health Policies

Germs   Host   Vehicles of Transmission   New Host

Cleaning and Sanitizing

Immunization, Daily Observation, Communication with Parents and Health Professionals, Documentation, Exclusion

Immunization

Before vaccines were developed, epidemics occurred causing thousands of people to die or, in the case of polio, to be left physically challenged. Table 3.3 illustrates the effectiveness of immunization here in Canada. Currently, there are 12 serious infections—communicable diseases—that can be prevented through routine immunization, which can begin in infancy (see Table 3.4). The National Advisory Committee on Immunization (2002) also has schedules for children who were not immunized during infancy. The schedules vary depending on whether the vaccination program begins before or after the child is seven years old.

Immunization is one of the most important ways of promoting the health of children. Vaccines, however, have not eliminated these viruses. Without immunizations, children are susceptible to these infections. Canadian children are fortunate that routine vaccination costs are covered by medicare, but this is not the case for millions of other children around the world.

Some parents in Canada, however, choose not to immunize their children for personal reasons. And we live in a country that welcomes people from around the world. Consequently, many immigrant children may not have been vaccinated and could be carrying the virus for polio or diphtheria, which would put unimmunized persons at risk. To ensure the health of Canadian children and those arriving in Canada, public health agencies must work toward 100% immunization.

TABLE 3.3 — Comparison of Cases of Disease in Canada before and after the Introduction of Immunization

ESTIMATED NUMBER OF CASES AND DEATHS PER YEAR

Disease	Before Vaccination		1991–2000	
	Cases	Deaths	Cases	Deaths
Diphtheria	12,000	1,000	0–5	0
Tetanus	60–75	40–50	0–2	0
Pertussis	40,000	50–100	3,000	1–5
Polio	2,000		0	
Haemophilus b	3,000	15–25	20–30	1–2
Measles	300,000	300	25	0
Mumps	30,000	80		
Rubella	255,000		25	
Congenital Rubella Syndrome (CRS)	200		2–5	

Source: E.L. Ford-Jones and R. Gold (2002), "Pediatric Immunization Update," *Patient Care in Canada* 13(4): 57.

Your body responds to a vaccination by forming antibodies against specific diseases. The vaccination almost always results in lifelong immunity. In other words, the antibodies remain in your body ready to destroy the virus every time it enters, whether you know you were exposed to it or not.

Did you know:

- For measles, mumps, and rubella, we require two doses of each vaccine?
- For the other diseases, we need a series of vaccinations to achieve immunity?
- For lifelong immunity against tetanus and diphtheria, adults require booster shots every 10 years?

An exception is pertussis (whooping cough), whose vaccine protection wears off over time. As a result, previously immunized children and adults can develop pertussis, though the infection would not be as severe. Vaccinations against pertussis are not given to people over age 7 because the risk of severe complications from pertussis is low in older children and adults. Moreover, adverse reactions from the vaccine, such as fever and pain, are common.

- A series of three doses of vaccine for hepatitis B is recommended for children in infancy or two doses for children between 9 and 13. This protects them before they might become sexually active or use intravenous drugs.
- Since 1999, Health Canada has recommended that children over 12 months of age be immunized against chickenpox.

TABLE 3.4 | **Routine Immunization Schedule for Infants and Children**

AGE AT VACCINATION	DTAP[1]	IPV	HIB[2]	MMR	TD[3] OR DTAP[10]	HEP B[4] (3 DOSES)	V	PC	MC
Birth						Infancy or preadolescence (9–13 years)		Infancy	
2 months	x	x	x					x^8	x^9
4 months	x	x	x					x	x
6 months	x	$(x)^5$	x					x	x
12 months				x			x^7	x	
18 months	x	x	x	$(x)^6$ or					or
4–6 years	x	x		$(x)^6$					
14–16 years					x^{10}				x^9

DTaP   Diphtheria, tetanus, pertussis (acellular) vaccine
IPV   Inactivated poliovirus vaccine
Hib   *Haemophilus influenzae* type b conjugate vaccine
MMR   Measles, mumps, and rubella vaccine
Td   Tetanus and diphtheria toxoid, adult type with reduced diphtheria toxoid
dTap   Tetanus and diphtheria toxoid, acellular pertussis, adolescent/adult type with reduced diphtheria and
           pertussis components
Hep B   Hepatitis B vaccine
V   Varicella
PC   Pneumococcal conjugate vaccine
MC   Meningococcal C conjugate vaccine

Notes:

1. DTaP (diphtheria, tetanus, acellular or component pertussis) vaccine is the preferred vaccine for all doses in the vaccination series, including completion of the series in children who have received >1 dose of DPT (whole cell) vaccine.
2. Hib schedule shown is for PRP-T or HbOC vaccine. If PRP-OMP is used, give at 2, 4, and 12 months of age.
3. Td (tetanus and diphtheria toxoid), a combined adsorbed adult-type preparation for use in people > 7 years of age, contains less diphtheria toxoid than preparations given to younger children and is less likely to cause reactions in older people.
4. Hepatitis B vaccine can be routinely given to infants or preadolescents, depending on the provincial/territorial policy; three doses at 0-, 1-, and 6-month intervals are preferred. The second dose should be administered at least 1 month after the first dose, and the third at least 2 months after the second dose. A two-dose schedule for adolescents is also possible.
5. This dose is not needed routinely, but can be included for convenience.
6. A second dose of MMR is recommended, at least 1 month after the first dose for the purpose of better measles protection. For convenience, options include giving it with the next scheduled vaccination at 18 months of age or with school-entry (4–6 years) vaccinations (depending on the provincial/territorial policy), or at any intervening age that is practicable. The need for a second dose of mumps and rubella vaccine is not established but may benefit (given for convenience as MMR). The second dose of MMR should be given at the same visit as DTaP IPV (+ Hib) to ensure high uptake rates.
7. Children aged 12 months to 12 years should receive one dose of varicella vaccine. Individuals > 13 years of age should receive two doses at least 28 days apart.
8. Recommended schedule, number of doses, and subsequent use of 23 valent polysaccharide pneumococcal vaccine depend on the age of the child when vaccination is begun.
9. Recommended schedule and number of doses of meningococcal vaccine depends on the age of the child.
10. DTaP adult formulation with reduced diphtheria toxoid and pertussis component.
11. Recommended schedule and number of doses depend on the product used and age of the child when vaccination is begun. Not required past age 5.
12. Delay until subsequent visit if child is < 12 months of age.
13. Omit these doses if the previous doses of DTaP and polio were given after the fourth birthday.

Source: National Advisory Committee on Immunization, *Canadian Immunization Guide*, 6th ed., Health Canada (2002), 56–57. Reproduced with the permission of the Minister of Public Works and Government Services Canada, 2003.

There are three vaccines against the three types of meningitis: *Haemophilus influenza* type b, pneumococcal, and meningococcal.

The polio vaccine is available in two forms: oral and injection. Other vaccines can be given as individual injections. Fortunately, they are commonly given in a combined solution, so children are given just one shot.

Immunization Records

Considering the importance of immunization, you may be surprised to learn that early childhood regulations on immunization at enrollment vary across Canada. But even in regions where immunization is not mandatory in the regulations, many programs require children to be immunized on enrollment and document it in their policy manual.

Although most parents agree that immunizing their children is important, many children's immunization schedules are not kept up-to-date. Depending on where children live, either individual physicians or a local public health clinic are responsible for immunizing them. As a result, there is often no systematic way of notifying parents of an upcoming appointment.

The physician or public health nurse usually gives parents an immunization record card for each child. The card is updated whenever the child is vaccinated. At the time of enrollment, parents provide the director with a copy of their child's record. Directors compare the information on these cards with the standard immunization schedule. If any discrepancy is found, the director asks the parents to discuss it with their physician or the director contacts the public health agency (see Children's Medical Examination at Enrollment, page 137).

Children's immunizations may not be up-to-date for many reasons, including

- families' hectic schedules,
- children of different ages in a family needing immunizations at different times, or
- the family's lack of a regular physician.

For most parents, a simple reminder that their child is due for an immunization prompts them to make an appointment with the doctor or clinic. Programs play an important role in ensuring that children are immunized at enrollment and by regularly reviewing these records to ensure that children don't miss a booster shot.

Some parents have decided not to immunize their children for religious, moral, or other reasons. Children cannot be denied access to programs if they are not immunized. In these cases, directors should have the parents provide a letter from the child's physician. If a child or educator develops a communicable disease, the public health agency then excludes all non-immunized children and staff from the program for a certain period. This eliminates further contact with the infected child and attempts to protect the non-immunized individuals (see Appendix 4.1, page 182).

If a child develops a serious disease, all susceptible children must be identified quickly and the illness managed properly. Consequently, the director and the public health staff must have immediate access to the current immunization record for every child and staff in the program.

Adverse Reactions

Before children are immunized, the physician or public health nurse discusses the possible adverse reactions and contraindications of the vaccines with the parents. A day or two after a vaccination, children commonly experience mild side effects, ranging from redness, slight swelling, and tenderness at the injection site to a low-grade fever and irritability. Directors may suggest that parents arrange to have the vaccination appointment on a Friday. This way children can spend the weekend getting the extra care they might need at home.

Children rarely experience serious allergic reactions following a vaccination. If one does occur, the child's physician and public health officials will determine whether the child receives further vaccinations.

Immune Globulin

Passively acquired immunity results when a susceptible individual is exposed to a certain disease and then given the immune globulin for it. Immune globulins are injections of antibodies that temporarily protect the individual from the disease or at least reduce the symptoms. In the case of chickenpox, within 72 hours of exposure susceptible educators are given the varicella-zoster immune globulin (VZIG). Immune globulins are available for only a few diseases.

Hygiene Practices

You may initially feel overwhelmed by the number of health practices that you are expected to perform in a program. You may wonder, for example, why so many steps are involved in changing a diaper. Over time, effective hand washing and diapering routines become second nature. And you will see that the time spent learning these steps reduces the number of ill children and educators. Remember: Infection control is an essential component of programs' disease prevention strategies.

Let's begin by examining the vital role hand washing plays in reducing the spread of infections in programs. This practice is important for everyone in the program: children, educators, and parents. The physical care of infants and toddlers poses challenges for infection control for educators. Without stringent adherence to diapering and toileting routines, outbreaks of diarrhea are inevitable.

Hand Washing

The most common and efficient way for germs to enter our body is through our mouth. Take a moment to think of everything that our hands touch each day: the number is staggering. Combine that with the number of times we put our hands or objects (e.g., pencils, toys, eating utensils) into our mouth.

Hand washing is the most important health practice that educators and children must implement to reduce the spread of infections. From the moment we wash our hands, we begin to collect germs all over again. Yet we can't spend the day with our hands in running water and soap. But if we pay particular attention to when and how we wash our hands, we accomplish the most significant practice in infection control.

When Do We Wash Our Hands?

While we care for children and carry out tasks in the program, we collect germs on our hands. By washing off germs before we begin particular activities, we greatly reduce the opportunity to spread germs to others. Washing our hands is important

- before preparing, serving, or eating food;
- before feeding infants and children;
- before giving a medication;
- before playing in the water table; and
- before carrying out first aid.

Certain activities expose our hands to large numbers of germs. To prevent contamination, it is important that we wash our hands immediately after completing the following activities. Washing our hands is important

- after using the toilet or helping children at the toilet;
- after changing a diaper;
- after caring for ill children;
- after cleaning up spills of blood and body fluids;
- after wiping a child's nose (if possible);
- after cleaning or sanitizing routines, even if you wore disposable or rubber gloves;
- after handling animals;
- after playing outside or in sand tables; and
- after handling garbage.

What We Use for Effective Hand Washing

The five important components in the hand-washing routine are running water, soap, friction, drying the hands, and turning off the taps.

Running water is essential to rinse the germs off the hands and down the drain. A comfortable water temperature allows you to keep your hands in the running water for 10 seconds. Take disposable alcohol-based hand wipes with you on field trips when you don't have access to running water.

Using running water may raise concerns over water conservation and our environment, but washing in a full sink or basin of water is *not* the solution. You defeat the purpose of hand washing by rinsing off the soap and germs in a pool of water. This practice re-contaminates your hands with all the germs that are now in that pool of water. To conserve water, don't turn on the tap full blast.

All you need is plain, mild hand soap for hand washing, regardless of the activity you have just completed. Soaps with germ-killing ingredients are expensive and unnecessary and may kill "friendly" protective bacteria as well. Soaps with an alcohol base dry the skin. It is actually the friction that is created by rubbing hands and soap together that removes the germs from our skin.

Liquid hand soap is recommended for two reasons: the soap pump is convenient and it's easier for children to use than a slippery bar of soap, which often falls on the floor. Also, germs, dirt, paint, and sand collect on the soap bar and in the soapy water at the bottom of the soap dish.

Educators wash their hands frequently, which may dry and chap their skin. Using mild soap and hand lotion helps to prevent this. And, as discussed earlier, germs can enter our body through non-intact skin. As you'll see in step two of the hand-washing routine, you wet your hands before adding the soap. This reduces soap's drying effect on your skin.

You have most likely seen advertisements for products that you can use to "wash" your hands without running water. Alcohol is the cleaning ingredient. You can purchase them in pump form or in containers small enough to keep in a purse or backpack. But are they replacement for soap and water in an early childhood program? The available research doesn't tell us how effective these products are in illness prevention nor have there been any studies published on the use of these products in early childhood programs (Aronson 2003, 61). They are more expensive than soap, which is a consideration for programs operating on tight budgets. Following the instructions properly requires applying an adequate amount on hands for 15 seconds, which is not much of a timesaver compared to the recommended hand-washing routine (see How We and Children Wash Our Hands, page 116). Because of the alcohol base in these products, they should be kept out of children's reach. They are convenient when activities such as field trips do not provide easy access to running water.

Soap and water are available everywhere in Canada. The single most important infection control practice that children learn is proper hand washing. During the course of the day, children observe educators washing their hands effectively. In addition, when the children's hand washing is supervised, this essential health practice is reinforced, which has a significant impact on the rates of infection in the program.

Many programs refill rather than replace empty soap pumps and hand lotion containers. Before you refill them, however, clean out the containers with soap and water and rinse them with water to remove the remnants and any germs that may have travelled down the pump during use. If the insides of the containers are not properly cleaned, these germs will contaminate the fresh liquid that is added.

Occasionally, educators' and children's fingernails need to be cleaned. Nailbrushes should not be used, for two reasons. First, the brushing action can cause very small cuts on the cuticles and under the nails, which can trap germs. Second, a communal nailbrush accumulates and transmits germs from everyone who has used it. Instead, use a disposable manicure stick to clean under fingernails (Canadian Paediatric Society 1996, 69).

Drying our hands and turning off the taps are the final steps in hand washing. These steps can either remove further germs or re-contaminate our hands before we leave the sink.

Towels can be either cloth or paper. Programs base their decision on cost, access to laundry facilities, storage space, and the number of staff and children. Rolling towel dispensers and electric hand dryers are not used in programs. We've all used rolling cloth towel dispensers that wouldn't let us pull out clean towel or had run out of towelling, and we've all seen someone use a section of towel that someone else has used already. Electric hand dryers are not used for two reasons: they can break down, and they take a long time to dry hands thoroughly. It is not practical to expect groups of children and staff to wait in line to dry their hands.

Since we turn on taps with dirty hands, we don't want to wash and dry our hands and then turn off the taps with our clean hands. Some programs' sinks may have elbow taps, foot pedals, or sensors, which eliminate the need to use hands to turn the water on and off.

The scrubbing and rinsing during hand washing remove most of the germs. The drying action may remove even more. But reusing a wet or dry cloth towel increases the likelihood of re-contaminating our hands with the germs that were left on the towel from the previous use. Single-use towels, however, whether cloth or paper, ensure that we dry our hands with a fresh towel each time. Then the towel can be used to turn off the taps before it is put into the laundry or the garbage.

Some programs may choose to use individual cloth towels, each one clearly marked with the child's or educator's name, hung to dry without touching, and changed at least daily. Individual cloth towels have disadvantages, however. They should not be used to turn off the water, because the taps then contaminate the towels used throughout the day. As well, it is likely that the same towel will be used by more than one person during the day.

How We and Children Wash Our Hands

How, when, and what we use to wash our hands help to ensure effective hand washing. The eight steps in the hand washing routine ensure that as many germs as possible are removed. Remember, you are not trying to sterilize your hands, which is impossible, but rather to remove as many germs as you can.

Just as it is important for us to wash our hands, it is equally important for all children to wash their hands. Effective hand washing is one of the health habits we need to develop for a lifetime. Learning this habit begins in infancy (see Hand Washing for Infants and Toddlers, page 117).

For preschool and school-age children, the educator's role evolves from one of physically washing their hands to one of encouraging, supervising, and modeling effective hand washing. In school-age programs, children often need to be reminded to wash their hands, since their attention turns easily to more exciting activities. Basically, children should wash their hands before and after the same activities that were listed for educators. But children must be encouraged to focus

---

Here are the eight essential steps (Canadian Paediatric Society 1996, 957) in an effective hand washing technique:

1. Use warm running water.
2. Wet your hands and add soap.
3. Rub your hands vigorously for 5 to 10 seconds.
4. Wash all surfaces, including the backs of hands and between fingers.
5. Rinse your hands well under running water for 5 to 10 seconds.
6. Dry your hands well with a towel. Turn off the taps with a single-use towel.
7. Dispose of the cloth or paper towel.
8. Apply hand lotion as needed.

especially on washing their hands after they use the toilet and before they eat or handle food (see Hand Washing and Germs, page 452).

Monitoring Hand Washing

We have all been in public washrooms that didn't have soap or towels, have seen the tail end of the rolling towel lying on the floor, or have experienced electric hand dryers that don't blow hot air. The next time you are in a public washroom, compare the number of people who wash their hands thoroughly to the number who simply run one hand under the water or don't wash at all. How would you feel about sharing a box of popcorn at the theatre, being served at a restaurant, or having as a coworker someone whose hand washing was so perfunctory?

Though we know the importance of the eight hand washing steps, we may tend to skip steps or cut down on the time we spend at the sink because we are in a hurry. A poster close to the sink will act as a reminder to educators and parents. Regular monitoring of educators' hand washing compliance is very important in order to maintain a high level of hygiene. Remember, this simple, inexpensive, low-tech routine is the most important health practice in the program's infection-control strategy.

Hygiene Practices for Infants and Toddlers

The rate of gastrointestinal infection is highest for infants and toddlers. The responsibility for infection control rests squarely on the educators' shoulders. This section highlights the hygiene practices that should be in place to reduce the opportunity for infection.

Hand Washing for Infants and Toddlers

Have you ever wondered why babies would need to have their hands washed during the day? Watch them to see what their hands touch as they explore and you will know the answer to this question. And remember, germs can be almost anywhere. Washing their hands is important

- after they have a diaper change or use the toilet/potty,
- before they eat or are bottle-fed, and
- after they play outside or with materials such as sand or paint.

To wash an infant's hands, use a warm, wet, soapy single-use towel; rinse with a second, wet towel; and dry with a third. When toddlers are able to stand at a sink, with careful supervision and help they will follow the same steps for hand washing as the older children and educators.

Caring for Children in Diapers

Before we discuss the steps involved in changing a diaper, we will examine other hygiene practices related to diapers. Either cloth or disposable diapers are used in programs. To prevent stool from contaminating the environment, diapers must

- absorb the urine and stool,
- fit snugly around the thighs and waist to contain the urine and stool,
- have a waterproof cover, and
- be covered with clothing.

Researchers continue to compare the amount of fecal contamination in programs from disposable diapers to that from cloth diapers. Generally, disposable diapers are more absorbent and leak less than cloth diapers. However, the Canadian Paediatric Society and many public health officials do not recommend one type of diaper over another in programs. Programs and parents can choose the type of diaper that best meets their needs, based on financial considerations, environmental issues, access to a commercial diaper service, and laundry facilities.

If cloth diapers are chosen, care must be taken to ensure that the diaper covers ("pants") are laundered properly to ensure that urine and stool are

removed. Many programs use a fresh diaper cover at each diaper change. The use of diaper covers that are pulled up and down the legs is discouraged. Problems arise if the leg elastics have stool on them, because stool contaminates the child's legs when the pants are pulled off. Instead, diaper covers that fasten at the waist permit the educator to remove the cover and diaper in one step, reducing the risk of contaminating the program's environment. Obviously, if stool has leaked out of the diaper onto the legs, it will be washed off with soap and water during the change.

Studies have shown that the amount of fecal contamination is significantly reduced when children wear clothes over their cloth or disposable diapers. Clothing is an additional barrier between the diaper, its contents, and the room (Van et al. 1991). Permitting children to wear just a T-shirt and diaper, or to eat in just a diaper and bib, to make cleanup easier is not acceptable practice for infection control. Babies soon figure out how to open a diaper, and will learn even more quickly when there aren't any clothes to slow them down. Sitting beside another child provides another opportunity to gain easy access into another's diaper if that other child is wearing no outer clothing.

Second in importance only to hand washing, a strict diapering routine is essential in infant and toddler programs to control the incidence of gastrointestinal infection. Regardless of the type of diaper used, the educator's actions are crucial in determining the level of fecal contamination. Children learn to use the toilet at different ages; for many this occurs after age two. Preschool programs may have children in diapers and, if so, the diapering routine applies to preschool staff and parents.

The diaper change surface, the surrounding area, and diapering supplies should always be considered contaminated. The area should never be used for anything else, including putting a baby bottle down on the counter even for a minute.

Posting a diapering routine by the changing area acts as a reminder for educators and parents. However, regular monitoring of the educator's diapering technique helps to ensure that the routine is properly implemented all the time.

You may be thinking, "I've changed a lot of diapers and it didn't take me 14 steps—or 10 minutes to change a single diaper," or "There must be a ton of diapers to change during a day's work in an infant program!" However, if you were to write down everything you did during a diaper change, you may be surprised at just how many steps you did take. Furthermore, parents and others who change one child's diapers at home do not need to follow the same stringent guidelines,

---

Effective diapering involves the following steps:

1. Assemble all the necessary supplies.
2. Place the child on the changing surface and remove the soiled diaper. Fold the soiled surface inward and set it aside. If safety pins have been used to fasten the diaper, close them and put them out of the child's reach. Never put the pins in your mouth.
3. Clean and dry the child's skin.
4. When necessary, use a facial tissue to apply ointments or creams.
5. Put a fresh diaper on the child.
6. Wash the child's hands. Return the child to a supervised area.
7. Formed stool can be flushed down the toilet. Do not rinse the diaper.
8. Dispose of the cloth or disposable diaper and, if used, the disposable paper covering.
9. Spray the sanitizing solution onto the entire surface of the changing surface. Leave for 30 seconds.
10. Put away all diapering supplies.
11. Wash your hands.
12. Dry the changing surface with a single-use towel. Dispose of the cloth or paper towel.
13. Wash your hands thoroughly.
14. Record skin condition and bowel movements, as necessary.

Source: Courtesy of the Canadian Paediatric Society. From *Well Beings: A Guide to Promote the Physical Health, Safety and Emotional Well-Being of Children in Child Care Centres and Family Day Care Homes* (Ottawa: Canadian Paediatric Society, 1996), 958.

because one baby at home is quite different from 8 or 12 infants and toddlers in a group setting. At home, every family member gets used to each other's germs. Older siblings are past the developmental stage at which they put everything in their mouth, and their own personal hygiene habits are improving.

Educators' compliance depends on their understanding of the importance of and the rationale for the routine. The list below provides the rationale for a number of steps from the diapering routine.

Step 1: It is not necessary to wash your hands before starting. We assume that educators have been washing their hands whenever necessary during the day. As well, the diapering area and supplies are always considered to be contaminated. So it doesn't make sense to wash your hands and then contaminate them immediately after taking off the soiled diaper or picking up a tube of ointment. After you take off the diaper and wash the child's skin, your hands are covered with germs.

Step 4: Using a facial tissue to scoop ointment out of the jar or to squeeze it from a tube onto the tissue has two purposes. First, the tissue provides a barrier between your hands and the ointment, which keeps the ointment in the jar or at the end of the tube from being contaminated by your hands. Second, the tissue is then used to spread the ointment onto the skin. This keeps the germs that are already on your hands off the child's washed skin. If you need more ointment, use a new tissue to get more from the jar or tube. This rule applies regardless of whether each child has her or his own jar of diaper cream or a communal container is used. From what you've read so far, you should be able to come up with the rationale for this last requirement.

The routine use of diaper creams and ointments on children's healthy skin is discouraged. Changing diapers frequently and cleaning the skin at each change prevents urine, stool, or ammonia from contacting the skin long enough to cause irritation. These preparations are also difficult to wash off thoroughly with every change, so urine and stool can be trapped under the cream and irritate the skin. When you do use these products, apply them sparingly. Do not use baby powders or talc because the infant's airways can be damaged by inhaling powder in the air when the container is shaken.

Step 6: Before children arrive at the diaper table, they may have already had their hands in their diaper. During diaper changes, children will likely touch the wet or soiled diapers, the changing surface, and the educator's hands. If children don't have their hands washed after the diaper change, they will immediately begin contaminating the environment with their hands.

Step 7: To reduce the amount of stool going to landfills or to commercial diaper services, use toilet paper to pick up formed stool or roll it off the diaper into the toilet. At home, parents who use cloth diapers often soak soiled diapers in the toilet, but educators must not do this in programs. The number of times the diaper is then handled increases by at least three times, and it is difficult not to splash and drip the water in the diaper over the toilet and onto the floor. The amount of fecal contamination would be excessive.

Step 8: During a diaper change, stool or urine can end up on the changing surface. Diapering surfaces need to be smooth, durable, and easy to clean, which allows educators to wipe up any visible urine or stool with toilet paper and then sanitize the surface. Cleaning first with soap and water is not necessary except in cases where a large quantity of stool or urine is left on the diapering surface. Some programs use disposable change-table paper (the kind used in doctors' offices), which provides a barrier between the baby and the surface. Yet when urine or watery stool touches the paper, the liquid leaks through, which defeats the paper's purpose. Remember, even if the paper is still dry following a diaper change, the paper must be discarded and the surface sanitized. This, along with the cost and the extra garbage created by the paper, is why change paper is not recommended.

Step 11: Educators must wash their hands to prevent them from re-contaminating the surface while they are drying off the sanitizing solution and remaining germs. But by drying the surface and then discarding the towel, they have now re-contaminated their hands and need to wash their hands again (Step 13).

The routine use of disposable gloves is not recommended for changing diapers, even with stool. Gloves provide little protection in this situation beyond the natural protection of your skin. The toilet paper or facial tissue used to wipe stool off the skin and the disposable or cloth towel to wash and dry the child's skin provide the barrier between the stool and your hands. If stool gets on your hands, germs can't get into your body through your skin. If you are concerned about a cut or scrape, use a bandage and replace it when it is soiled or wet. If you have dermatitis or a cut or other broken skin and you must change diapers, use disposable gloves as a temporary means to keep stool off your open skin. Sometimes diapers are filled with loose or watery stools, which may have covered the child front and back or run down the legs. Some educators find these diapers to be particularly difficult to stomach, and using disposable gloves makes them feel more comfortable.

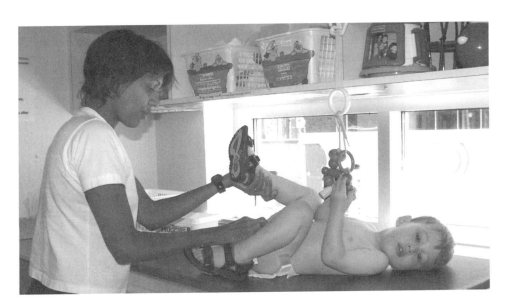

Diaper changes provide ideal opportunities in your busy day for one-to-one interaction with the child. Wearing gloves puts plastic between your skin and the child's skin, which can't be comfortable for the child. And are we inadvertently sending children the message that bowel movements are somehow not a natural function of their body and that they are "dirty"?

The only time that disposable gloves are recommended is when blood is visible in the child's stool. Choosing disposable plastic gloves over latex gloves affords the program the same kind of protection without the increased cost. In addition, reducing exposure to latex (e.g., gloves and balloons) is a safer alternative for staff and children who are allergic to latex. Regardless of the reasons for wearing gloves, you must wash your hands after removing the gloves. If you don't wash your hands well after every diaper change, you contaminate objects, food, and the environment, and the germs can then enter children's and educators' body through the mouth.

Toileting Routine

The toileting routine is made up of the following 15 steps:

1. If the child wears a diaper, remove it. If the diaper is soiled, clean and dry the child's skin. Dispose of the cloth or disposable diaper.
2. Place the child on the toilet or potty. Stay with the child for a specific period of time. Five minutes is usually long enough.
3. Wipe the child.
4. Flush the toilet or let the child flush it. If a potty was used, empty its contents into the toilet and flush.
5. If necessary, diaper the child and help the child get dressed.
6. Assist the child in hand washing. Return the child to a supervised area.
7. Rinse out the potty and flush the water down the toilet. If there is any remaining stool in the potty, wear household rubber gloves and remove all the stool with toilet paper. Rinse the potty and flush the water.
8. If wearing rubber gloves, remove them. Spray the sanitizing solution onto the potty and the diaper-changing surface (if used). Leave for 30 seconds.
9. Put away all diapering supplies.
10. Wash your hands.
11. Dry the potty with a single-use towel. Dispose of the cloth or paper towel.
12. Dry the diaper-changing surface with a different towel. Dispose of the cloth or paper towel.
13. Return the potty to the storage area.
14. Wash your hands thoroughly.
15. Record the child's use of the potty, any bowel movements, and any skin condition, as necessary.

Source: Courtesy of the Canadian Paediatric Society. From *Well Beings: A Guide to Promote the Physical Health, Safety and Emotional Well-Being of Children in Child Care Centres and Family Day Care Homes* (Ottawa: Canadian Paediatric Society, 1996), 959.

For many of the same reasons that apply to the diapering routine, educators need to take extra steps when cleaning a potty to prevent contamination of the surrounding area:

- Utility sinks should be available for staff to use for cleaning, including potties. The utility sink must be cleaned and sanitized after every use. hand washing sinks should not be used to rinse or clean potties.

- You may prefer to wear rubber gloves while you remove stool stuck to the potty. However, wearing gloves does not eliminate the need to wash your hands. After all, you are not the only person to wear those gloves. Your hands had germs on them before you put on the gloves and so did the hands of the person who used the gloves before you. Therefore these germs may have gotten inside the gloves and may end up on the next person's hands. In addition, you get more germs on your hands when you put on and take off the gloves.

- Before taking off the gloves, rinse them with water and hang them to dry. You do not have to sanitize the rubber gloves. Wash your hands after you remove the gloves. These gloves may also be used for cleaning washrooms and larger amounts of stool, urine, and vomit. Labeling the rubber gloves prevents their being used for any other purpose, such as washing dishes or cleaning and sanitizing mouthing toys.

Cleaning and Sanitizing

You know that germs are everywhere. You know that germs can live on surfaces for hours, days, even weeks. You've read about the vehicles of transmission and the important role they play in spreading infections. The rationale for the cleaning and sanitizing routines in programs is to have staff focus on objects and surfaces that pose the greatest risk to children and staff.

It can be overwhelming to think about all the objects and surfaces that children and staff come into contact with every day, as well as everything and everyone who has come into contact with germs that are spread through the air from coughing, sneezing, and talking. Where do I start? How often do I clean this and that? What do I clean with? How do I know that I am cleaning this object properly? These are just some of the questions that are answered in this section.

One of the infection control practices carried out by staff to break the chain of transmission is regular cleaning and sanitizing of objects, surfaces, and areas within programs. To implement this, educators need to

- identify what needs to be cleaned or sanitized, or both;
- use effective cleaning and sanitizing products and techniques; and
- understand how to protect themselves from potentially hazardous substances.

The purpose of *cleaning* is to remove dirt (organic material) and germs from objects and surfaces. But, as in hand washing, the cleaning solution must be combined with a scrubbing action to create the friction needed to remove dirt and germs. This is followed by rinsing with water and air-drying.

The purpose of *sanitizing* an object or surface is to ensure that as many germs as possible are eliminated. In most cases, objects and surfaces are cleaned and rinsed, then sanitized, and left to air-dry.

What Needs to Be Cleaned or Sanitized?

By establishing priorities, you can identify the items to be cleaned or sanitized, or both, and how frequently. With the publication of *Well Beings*, much of the organizational work has been done for program staff. Rather than repeating those recommendations, let's explore the rationale behind two of them.

Toys

Toys that have been in infants' and toddlers' mouths are obvious vehicles of germ transmission. Many toys for infants are designed to be safe for them to put in the mouth (e.g., plastic stacking rings on a cone, squeak toys, rattles). These toys are often referred to as mouthing toys. Of course young children can put almost anything into their mouth (e.g., corners of books, puzzle pieces, plastic fruit and vegetables). For clarity, we will refer to any toy that children have chewed or sucked on as a mouthing toy. After one child has finished playing with a mouthing toy, it should be picked up by staff before a second child chews on it.

Toys that are mouthed should be cleaned and sanitized daily. Cleaning washes off organic materials, such as the children's saliva and any stool that may

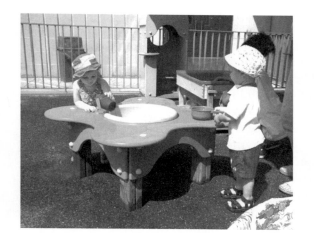

have been on a child's hands and transferred to the toys. Sanitizing is an added precaution that removes germs that may remain after cleaning, before the toys are air-dried and returned to the children. Plastic books can be cleaned and sanitized by hand; cloth ones can be put in the laundry.

The potential for spreading germs via toys used by preschoolers or school-agers is much lower than via mouthing toys, for three main reasons. Older children are not constantly putting their toys and hands into their mouth; they aren't touching, hugging, and kissing each other as frequently as babies and toddlers do; and their personal hygiene is improving. For these reasons, these toys can be cleaned weekly and when they are obviously soiled, but sanitizing is not necessary.

Water Tables

Although the water table is an important medium for learning, a pool of water can be easily contaminated and spread germs among the children using it. Germs enter the water from the children's hands and from everything they put in the water, such as toys, soap, and food colouring. Additional germs enter the water from blow toys and straws, as well as air-borne germs that land in the water from laughing, talking, and coughing. Adding bleach or other sanitizing solutions is not necessary—saliva, soap, and sand in the water will reduce the bleach solution's effectiveness.

The Canadian Paediatric Society (1996, 99–100) recommends the following hygiene practices for communal water tables:

- Fill the table with fresh water each morning.
- Empty the table at the end of every day, sanitize, and leave to air-dry overnight.
- Sanitize and air-dry the water toys.
- Clean and sanitize blow toys, pipes, and straws after use. These toys, like mouthing toys, should not be shared among children.
- Encourage children and educators to wash their hands before playing in the table.
- Discourage children who are not feeling well (e.g., cold, diarrhea), or who have a skin infection, from using the table.
- Close the table when the program has an outbreak of diarrhea.

Given how much infants and toddlers love to explore, not to mention their willingness to share toys, their affectionate nature, and their vulnerability to infections, it makes sense that infants and toddlers not use communal water tables. Instead, each child should have his or her own basin of water. The basins can be placed on the floor or on a table in a way that encourages social play. Individual basins permit children to use toys that can go between their own basin of water and their mouth and to splash and drool in the water and even drink it. In this way, the children do not share toys or come into direct contact with the contents of one another's basins. *Children must never be left alone* with the basins of water, even for a second. Children have drowned in as little as 4 cm ($1\frac{1}{2}$ in.) of water.

Cleaning and Sanitizing Products and Techniques

Household cleaning products and detergents that are safer for the environment are also effective cleaning products in programs. Cloth towels can be used for all cleaning and can be laundered after each use. When cleaning up blood and large amounts of stool, urine, and vomit, paper toweling is preferred because it can be safely discarded.

Household bleach is recommended for a number of reasons: it is highly effective, inexpensive, easy to use, readily available, and safe to use around children. When bleach is not used, programs usually consult their public health inspector before choosing sanitizing products. Other products are effective and directors consider each product's cost and its safety around children and staff, as well as its environmental friendliness.

Using bleach may raise a few questions about chlorine in the environment, ruined clothes, and the smell of bleach in the air. You need add only a small amount of bleach to water to sanitize. The recommended dilution is 1 part bleach in 100 parts water—for example, 2.5 mL ($\frac{1}{2}$ tsp.) of bleach in 250 mL (1 cup) of water. When this proportion is used, the bleach solution is so diluted that problems with bleach odour and ruined clothing are eliminated. But the solution is still strong enough to be effective.

Remember the following points when you use bleach:

- Objects and surfaces are usually cleaned first to remove visible organic material (e.g., dirt, food, saliva), because organic materials reduce the effectiveness of the bleach solution.

- The bleach solution is mixed fresh each morning for spray bottles used for diaper-change surfaces. When the bleach solution is mixed in open containers and sinks, it should be prepared just before use. Otherwise, the bleach solution evaporates throughout the day and anything that falls into the pail could reduce its effectiveness. From a safety perspective, containers of water should never be left within reach of children.

- The bleach solution needs to remain on the object or surface for 30 seconds to allow time for it to work.

- To protect your hands from the dryness that comes with using cleaning or sanitizing solution, you may wish to wear rubber gloves. Remember, take off your rings, watches, and bracelets to protect them from bleach.

Four Steps for Cleaning and Sanitizing

Having effective cleaning and sanitizing products, cloths, and rubber gloves—and being organized—takes some of the work out of cleaning.

Educators follow these four steps:
1. Fill one container (or sink) with soap (detergent) and water to scrub toys or objects and to wash surfaces.
2. Fill a second container with water to rinse what has been washed. (Soap needs to be rinsed off to ensure that sanitizing is effective.)
3. Fill a third container with the bleach solution. Bleach and water should be measured accurately. (To save time, the water level can be marked on the inside of plastic containers, then only the corresponding amount of bleach needs to be measured.)
4. The objects or surfaces are left to air-dry. The diaper-change surface is the one exception. After the solution has been on the surface for 30 seconds, dry it off with a fresh towel.

Some objects, such as books and puzzles in infant and toddler programs, need to be sanitized only. Obviously, these and other objects are not placed in a container of bleach and water. Instead, they are wiped with a cloth that has been rinsed and wrung out in the bleach solution.

The dishwasher can be a timesaving device for cleaning and sanitizing smaller plastic toys. Make sure the toys can withstand the water temperature and the detergent.

Implementing the Routines throughout the Day

The number of times that educators wash their hands and the time spent on the routines discussed in this unit depend on the following factors: the size of the program, the number of children and staff, the ages of the children, and whether meals and snacks are prepared in the program or provided by parents.

Some programs, because of their location (e.g., workplace, office buildings, colleges, universities) have cleaning services that maintain bathrooms, floors, carpets, etc. In these programs, staff have more time for the remaining routines. However, it is important that staff monitor the external cleaning services to ensure that the quality is satisfactory, that the cleaning is done with the recommended frequency, and that the products used are safe around children.

A day in any program is busy, and fitting in all the routines takes some finesse. But the importance of implementing routines to break the chain of transmission means that there can't be shortcuts. We must ensure that the time spent on implementing routines is protected, because the work reduces the frequency of infection.

A written schedule for all routines is essential to ensure that they are implemented consistently. Programs may design a schedule based on the frequency of the routines (e.g., daily, twice a week, weekly) or by room. The schedule breaks down what can seem like an overwhelming task into more manageable routines. It includes instructions on how each item is to be cleaned or sanitized so that educators aren't left questioning the effectiveness of their work.

When there is an outbreak of an infection, a review of these written schedules can provide insight into the effectiveness of the cleaning and sanitizing routines and whether the schedule should be revised on a short- or long-term basis.

· ·

During an outbreak of diarrhea, it is advisable to close the water table. At the same time, staff's hand washing, diapering routines, and food-safety practices need to be evaluated.

e.g.

· ·

Protecting Yourself from Potentially Hazardous Substances

In this section, we discuss the potential risks and steps to reduce educators' exposure to hazardous products related to infection control. These include the concept of universal precautions, the safe use of cleaning and sanitizing products, and the appropriate use of gloves.

Universal Precautions
Under normal conditions, when patients are admitted to a hospital, they are not routinely tested for any number of diseases. This practice would be expensive and time-consuming, as we have learned with the outbreak of Severe Acute Respiratory Syndrome (SARS) in Ontario in 2003. In addition, such tests may not provide the hospital's infectious disease experts with reliable information. You have already read that a person can spread germs to others before she or he develops symptoms and that some of us carry infections even though we are not ill.

Universal precautions constitute the fundamental principle in protecting staff from the potential risks in the workplace. Hospital staff assume that everyone has the potential to expose them to germs, so safe medical and nursing procedures are developed specifically for the task or medical technique being implemented. Universal precautions in turn protect patients from the hospital staff.

You may be wondering how anything in a hospital has any relevance to programs. Educators aren't changing bandages with blood, giving needles, routinely being exposed to blood, or caring for seriously ill patients. The fundamental principle on which hospitals build their infection control strategy is the same one as for programs. To reduce the spread of germs and to protect themselves from unnecessary exposure to potentially harmful organisms, educators must implement universal precautions in their daily work with children. All the procedures covered in this unit are based on universal precautions and, when implemented, protect not only the educators but also the children.

Cleaning and Sanitizing Products and Gloves

Cleaning products used in programs should be safe to use around children and staff and preferably be friendly to the environment. This does not eliminate the need for the products to be stored out of reach of children. Most products used in programs are household products purchased in grocery stores. It is advisable to read all product labels for safe handling directions and any first-aid information (see Workplace Hazardous Materials Information System, page 67).

Just as water and soap can dry our skin, cleaning and sanitizing products can be abrasive. Using rubber gloves while dishwashing and during cleaning and sanitizing routines helps protect our hands. There may be times when disposable rather than rubber gloves should be used.

Disposable gloves are used when educators are at risk of exposure to blood or bloody body fluids. Once the gloves have been used, they can be disposed of carefully. Carefully remove one disposable glove at a time. While you are slowly peeling off a glove (starting at the wrist), turn the glove inside out. This method protects you from the germs on the gloves and it also protects the immediate area. Wash your hands after disposing safely of the gloves.

Disposable gloves are just one way of providing a barrier between your hands and the blood. Facial tissue used to stop a nosebleed provides a barrier between your hand and the child's nose. Cotton balls or sterile gauze in first-aid kits, when used appropriately to clean cuts and scrapes, can be effective barriers between your hands and the source of the blood. It is not necessary for staff to keep disposable gloves in their pockets in case a child is injured or gets a nosebleed. Our skin's natural ability to protect us from germs—along with effective hand washing—is our best protection.

The routine use of disposable gloves for diaper changing is not recommended. The routine use of gloves is an unnecessary expense; it also needlessly adds plastic to our landfill sites (see Caring for Children in Diapers, page 118).

Regardless of which type of glove is used, there are two points to keep in mind:

- "Gloves can provide a protective barrier against germs that cause infection, but they offer little protection beyond that achieved by good hand washing" (Canadian Paediatric Society 1996, 104).
- You must always wash your hands after you remove the gloves.

REVISITING THE HEALTH PROMOTION ACTION PLAN

Recall the Health Promotion Action Plan introduced in Unit 1. The following example illustrates this plan in practice in terms of preventing childhood illnesses, using immunization as the point of reference.

Individual Problem Solving and Self-Reliance

Due to the dynamic nature of immunization research, the list of diseases for which immunization is available is increasing. This reality makes it important for educators and parents to keep current through their family physician or local public health agency. As individuals, we are encouraged by public health agencies to recognize the importance of complying with recommended immunization schedules (see Table 3.4, page 111). Parents are encouraged to follow through with their children's immunization in order to contribute to their health and the public's health. An annual checkup with a family physician includes a review of each child's immunization history and future needs. As adults, you will want to keep track of when you are due for your diphtheria and tetanus boosters, recommended every 10 years. Parents who have made a decision for religious or other reasons not to follow through with immunization guidelines have an ethical responsibility to the early childhood program to submit a physician's letter for documentation. They must also follow public health guidelines in the event that these children are exposed to certain illnesses (see Appendix 4.1, page 182).

Collective Self-Help

Directors and educators can support the goal of 100% immunization by posting reminders for families on a parent bulletin board and by providing pamphlets that clarify the availability and benefits of specific immunizations. Directors need to keep immunization records up-to-date and contact parents if their child's immunization records have not yet been submitted. Directors can also help parents find a family physician by knowing which doctors in the community are taking new patients, as well as having information about community health clinics and drop-in clinics. An annual parent–staff meeting facilitated by a public health nurse could also promote awareness and education about immunization and other public health initiatives.

Community Action

In promoting 100% immunization in the community, it is important to know the issues that pose challenges or barriers to full participation in immunization compliance. For example:

- In some remote communities, families may not have ongoing access to family physicians.
- In communities where few or no infectious disease outbreaks have occurred for over a generation, families may be more complacent and not see the need for immunization.

- Recent immigrants who have come from countries that do not have a universal immunization program, particularly those whose first language is neither English or French, may not have the experience or access to our immunization information in their first language.

We all must realize that immunization plays a significant role in continuing to prevent outbreaks. It is important to respond to the specific community issues through effective action (see Appendix 1.1, page 43). Perhaps a community forum access to culturally relevant information, or other plans to build broad-based education and support, may lead to effective action.

Societal Change

A number of public challenges may present roadblocks to attaining the goal of 100% immunization. Provinces and territories may not make all immunizations recommended in the schedule available to everyone through medicare. In these situations, some children are possibly at a disadvantage if their families cannot afford to pay or have the costs covered through extended health benefits. Another barrier may be the lack of access to family physicians in non-urban areas. Government priorities placed on prevention involves advocacy, as stated earlier in this textbook. Hopefully, changes resulting from the Romanow Report (2002) will improve some of these realities—funds put into universally accessible preventive health care, incentives for physicians to practice in non-urban areas (and in Canada generally), and citizen advocacy groups.

CONCLUSION

One of the primary goals of high-quality early childhood programs is to maintain or improve the health status of children, which contributes to their growth and development and to their participation in the programs' program and activities. Indicators of good quality include adequate educator–child ratios, small group sizes, staff trained in early childhood education, the provision of orientation and regular in-service training, and low staff turnover rates. These all need to be in place to control infectious diseases.

The consistent implementation of an infection control strategy is one of the best ways to prevent infections or at least reduce their spread in programs. Such a strategy includes effective hand washing as a priority for both educators and children to break the chain of transmission. Adherence to a strict diapering and toileting policy (and procedures), regular cleaning and sanitizing, and of course hand washing are all essential to promote children's physical health in the early childhood setting. In addition, informal but routine daily health observations, beginning with a baseline conducted when the child arrives at the program, ensure that staff connect with child and usually the parent. This process, which will be discussed in more detail in Unit 4, ensures that adults take note of each child's health status so that changes in physical or behavioural status are recognized and responded to appropriately.

TO GLOVE OR NOT TO GLOVE?

Scenario: You are in your first program placement. You are feeling nervous and, understandably, unsure of yourself. During your first few days at the program, you observe that all the educators wear disposable gloves whenever a child has stool in the diaper. When one of the educators runs through the diapering routine with you, she makes it clear that you are expected to wear gloves.

Would you simply comply with the program's practice? If not, how would you proceed in this situation?

ASSESS YOUR LEARNING

Define terms or describe concepts used in this unit.

- immunity
- germs
- host
- vehicles of transmission
- new host
- immunization

- hygiene practices
- hand washing
- cleaning and sanitizing routines
- potentially hazardous substances
- universal precautions

Evaluate your options in each situation.

1. In the program where you have recently started working, the routine hand washing practice before lunch is to dunk the infants' and toddlers' hands into a communal basin of water and dry them with individual paper towels.

2. You have a close working relationship with a parent who discloses to you that her child is HIV-positive. You are the only person in the program she has told and she has asked you not to tell anyone else, including the director.

3. One of the daily sanitizing routines in the program is to add a capful of bleach to the water table each morning. This practice saves water and time because staff empty the water only once a week.

4. While demonstrating the diaper change procedure, one of the educators tells you not to bother washing the infant's hands after diapering. She says it is a time-waster; instead, she wants you to ensure that the baby's hands are busy with a toy to prevent then from becoming contaminated during diapering.

RESOURCE MATERIALS

Organizations

Canadian Institute of Child Health, 384 Bank Street, Suite 300, Ottawa, ON K2P 1Y4. Tel. (613) 230-8838; fax (613) 230-6654. www.cich.ca

Canadian Paediatric Society, 100–2204 Walkley Road, Ottawa, ON K1G 4G8. Tel. (613) 526-9397; fax (613) 526-3332. www.cps.ca

Hospital for Sick Children, Centre for Health Information and Promotion, 555
University Avenue, Toronto, ON M5G 1X8. Tel. (416) 813-5819.
www.sickkids.on.ca/CHIP

Other Websites of Interest

Canadian Immunization Awareness Program: www.immunize.cpha.ca

Health Canada, Division of Immunization and Respiratory Diseases:
www.hc-sc.gc.ca/pphb-dgspsp/dird-dimr

Hospital for Sick Children, Toronto: www.sickkids.ca

Printed Matter

HIV/AIDS and Child Care: Fact Book and Facilitator's Guide (1995), by B. Kaiser and J.S.
Rasminsky. For copies, contact Canadian HIV/AIDS Clearinghouse, Canadian Public
Health Association, 400–1565 Carling Avenue, Ottawa, ON K1Z 8R1. Tel. (613) 725-
3434 or 1-877-999-7740; fax (613) 725-9826.

Your Child's Best Shot: A Parent's Guide to Vaccination (2002), by Ronald Gold, MD. 2nd
ed. (Ottawa: Canadian Paediatric Society). For copies, contact the Canadian
Paediatric Society. (For contact information, see under Organizations.)

BIBLIOGRAPHY

American Academy of Pediatrics (2000). *Red Book 2000: Report of the Committee on
Infectious Diseases.* Elk Grove Village, IL: American Academy of Pediatrics.

American Academy of Pediatrics and American Public Health Association (2002).
*Caring for Our Children: National Health and Safety Performance Standards:
Guidelines for Out-of-Home Child Care Programs.* 2nd ed. Washington, DC: American
Public Health Association and American Academy of Pediatrics.

Aronson, S.S. (2003). "Ask Dr. Sue Your Health and Safety Questions: 2002 Update on
Hand Hygiene in Child (Day) Care Settings." *Child Care Information Exchange* 3:
58–62.

———— (1991). *Health and Safety in Child Care.* New York: HarperCollins.

Black, S.M. (1999). "HIV/AIDS in Early Childhood Centres: The Ethical Dilemma of
Confidentiality versus Disclosure." *Young Children* March: 39–45.

Canadian Paediatric Society (2002). *A Bite in the Playroom: Managing Human Bites in
Day Care Settings.* Position Statement from the Infectious Diseases and
Immunization Committee. Reaffirmed April 2002.

———— (1996). *Well Beings: A Guide to Promote the Physical Health, Safety and
Emotional Well-Being of Children in Child Care Centres and Family Day Care Homes.*
Ottawa: Canadian Paediatric Society.

Ford-Jones, E.L., and R. Gold (2002). "Pediatric Immunization Update." *Patient Care in
Canada* 13(4): 54–74.

National Advisory Committee on Immunization (2002). *Canadian Immunization Guide.*
6th ed. Ottawa: Public Works and Government Services Canada.

Renaud, A., et al. (1997). "Knowledge and Attitude Assessment of Quebec Daycare
Workers and Parents Regarding HIV/AIDS and Hepatitis B." *Canadian Journal of
Public Health,* January–February: 23–27.

Romanow, R. (2002). "Building on Values: The Future of Health Care in Canada." Ottawa: Commission on the Future of Health Care in Canada.

Van, R., et al. (1991). "The Effect of Diaper Type and Overclothing on Fecal Contamination in Day-Care Centers." *Journal of the American Medical Association* 265(14): 1840–44.

Wald, E.R., et al. (1988). "Frequency and Severity of Infections in Day Care." *Journal of Pediatrics* 112: 540–46.

Wong, D.L., et al. (1992). "Diapering Choices: A Critical Review of the Issues." *Pediatric Nursing* 18(1): 41–54.

Illness Management

CONTENTS

Children's Health Care *136*
  CHILDREN'S MEDICAL EXAMINATION AT ENROLLMENT 137
  DAILY OBSERVATION OF CHILDREN 138
  DOCUMENTING HEALTH OBSERVATIONS 143
  EXCLUDING CHILDREN FROM EARLY CHILDHOOD PROGRAMS 146

Childhood Infections: Just the Basics *156*
  THE COMMON COLD 156
  EAR INFECTIONS 157
  GASTROINTESTINAL INFECTIONS: DIARRHEA 158
  PINKEYE 159
  CHICKENPOX 160
  HEAD LICE 161

Antibiotic-Resistant Bacteria *162*

Administering Medication *165*
  PRESCRIPTION AND OVER-THE-COUNTER MEDICATIONS 165
  OVER-THE-COUNTER MEDICATIONS: EFFECTIVE? 166
  ENSURING THE SAFE ADMINISTRATION OF MEDICATION 167
  PREVENTING MEDICATION ERRORS 169

Allergies and Asthma *170*
  ALLERGIES 170
  ASTHMA 174

Revisiting the Health Promotion Action Plan *177*

Conclusion *178*

What's Your Opinion? TO COLLABORATE OR NOT TO COLLABORATE? *178*

Assess Your Learning *179*

Resource Materials *179*

Bibliography *180*

TABLES

TABLE 4.1   EXCLUSION PRACTICES IN TORONTO EARLY CHILDHOOD
            PROGRAMS 164
TABLE 4.2   COMMON ALLERGIC SUBSTANCES AND REACTIONS 171
TABLE 4.3   SIGNS OF MANAGED AND POORLY MANAGED ASTHMA 175

FORMS		
FORM 4.1	INFANT AND TODDLER DAILY CARE RECORD	150
FORM 4.2	EARLY CHILDHOOD PROGRAM'S HEALTH RECORD	152
FORM 4.3	CAREGIVER'S REPORT ON ILLNESS	153
FORM 4.4	PHYSICIAN'S REPORT ON ILLNESS	154

APPENDIX	
APPENDIX 4.1	MANAGEMENT OF ILLNESS 182

OBJECTIVES

To describe the why, how, and what of daily health observations.

To identify the signs and symptoms of illness and describe how to proceed with concerns.

To explain the principle of exclusion and consider the issues surrounding exclusion from the child care program.

To describe how to respond to the most common childhood infections.

To describe the safe administration of medication to children.

CHILDREN'S HEALTH CARE

This section focuses on the appropriate role that educators play in caring for children who are ill. In addition to implementing an infection control strategy, the educators' role includes

- working in partnership with parents;
- identifying possible signs and symptoms;
- implementing the early childhood program's policy for ill children, including
  - documenting observations in children's files and reports,
  - sharing relevant health information with parents,
  - communicating with health professionals, and
  - implementing the physician's recommendations;
- helping children feel better, including
  - excluding children,
  - TLC (tender loving care), and
  - administering medication, if necessary.

Educators observe children throughout their daily activities. With experience, educators gain the expertise to differentiate between behaviour that is developmentally appropriate for children, behaviour that should be watched more closely, and behaviour that is cause for concern. If an educator is concerned about a child's behaviour or state of health, action is required on the part of educators and parents.

Educators' ability to articulate health concerns about children is an essential skill. As with any skill, experience and motivation on the part of the individual to continue learning assist educators in fine-tuning their skills for observation and documentation. The methods used for documenting health observations vary among early childhood programs. Regardless of the method, the key to effective documentation is that it is objective, systematic, and concise. Educators are trained professionals communicating with other educators, with parents, and with health or social service professionals in the community.

The quality of the relationships that staff have with parents in managing illness is paramount, since parents are the decision makers regarding their child's health. Establishing effective relationships with a child's parents begins at the time of enrollment, not the first time educators have concerns about the child. Because children will get sick and be unable to attend the program, the enrollment interview is the time for the director and parents to discuss the following issues: information sharing, program policies on health observations, childhood illnesses, communications with their physician, criteria for excluding children from the program, and administration of medication.

If the program's health policies and practices are realistic, logical, practical, and based on current health information, parents will likely understand their purpose and work cooperatively with staff. If, however, policies and practices seem unrealistic or unrelated to current health information, parents may be less willing to cooperate.

- -

■ Early childhood education and care programs that take children's temperatures at the hint of a warm forehead and then use only the temperature's value to exclude children and send them to the doctor.

e.g.

■ Early childhood education and care programs that exclude children with colds when the nasal discharge is yellow or green in colour.

- -

Neither example requires children to be excluded, nor do actions like these contribute to parents' viewing the program and educators positively. Partnerships with parents in managing children's illnesses mean that staff

■ ensure that exclusion policies and practices are parent-positive—respectful, realistic, non-punitive;

■ demonstrate empathy for the parents' situation, balancing this with the needs of the ill child, other children in the group, and staff; and

■ are supportive with regard to health information and resources, but do *not* diagnose illness. Instead, educators document signs and symptoms that the parent can communicate to the physician.

Children's Medical Examination at Enrollment

Most early childhood education and care programs in Canada require parents to have their children examined by a physician within a certain time period after starting in the program. These examinations result in a number of health promotion benefits:

■ They provide the parents, physician, and educators with an overview of the child's current health status, which can be used as a measure in the future.

■ They ensure that the child's immunizations are up-to-date.

- They advise doctors that one of their patients is starting in group care, which gives doctors the opportunity to talk with parents about the frequency of childhood illnesses.
- they include educators as participants in the care plan for children with specific health care needs by encouraging the physician and parents to share relevant information with the staff.

Daily Observation of Children

As educators get to know the infants and toddlers in their care, they become increasingly aware of behavioural changes and other signs and symptoms that may indicate possible infections. Preschool and school-age children are generally better able to tell educators if they aren't feeling well and answer questions that the educator asks for clarification. This assists educators in determining whether the parents should pick up their child early or whether the child is able to participate in the activities and can remain in the program. There are times when children are excluded because of a specific infection.

When it comes to observing children for possible signs of illness, educators must first acknowledge the importance of daily health observations to identify ill children. Decisions regarding the care of children are based on the educators' observations, subsequent conversations with the parents, and physicians' diagnoses.

Daily Baseline Health Observations

Programs that recognize the importance of baseline (starting point) health observations schedule enough staff at the start of the day to conduct them. Educators conduct baseline health observations of each child when he or she is dropped off so that educators can talk with the child and the parent. Staff encourage parents to take a few minutes at drop-off to ensure that parent, child, and educator have enough time to talk about

- how their child felt overnight and this morning,
- whether he or she ate breakfast,
- how well she or he slept, and
- whether they have any concerns about their child (e.g., "She had a sore tummy when she went to bed but seems to be feeling better this morning").

These conversations with parents, and the educator's familiarity with the children, establish a daily baseline to identify behavioural changes in a particular child for the rest of the day. The most reliable indicator of possible infection in children is a change in behaviour.

. . . .

During the morning, there are times when the child just doesn't seem to be herself: she wants to lie down, turns down her snack, wants to be held a lot. Educators watch her more closely, taking into account the time of day and whether there are other sick children. The director calls the parent to let him know that his daughter is feeling under the weather. Jointly they decide whether she can remain in the program for the rest of the day or whether other steps should be taken.

e.g.

. . . .

Physical and Behavioural Signs and Symptoms
Using a checklist to evaluate children's signs of illness systematically assists educators in checking children. With practice, using the checklist quickly becomes second nature. Start at the child's head and move down to the toes and in just a few moments educators have completed a baseline health observation.

Observing children calls on your senses of sight, hearing, touch, and smell. Educators should look for the following physical signs:

- Face: sad, tired, angry, upset, flushed
- Eyes: eyelids are puffy, whites of the eyes are red or yellow; eyes themselves are watery and clear or show thick (pus) discharge; sores or sties present; child rubs eyes
- Ears: child rubs or pulls at ears; drainage seen in the outer ear
- Nose: runny; red or chafed from wiping or rubbing; child sneezes
- Mouth: bleeding; swollen gums; cold sores
- Neck: swelling along the jawline
- Breathing and/or voice: wheezing, congestion, coughing; child sounds stuffed up (nasal) or hoarse
- Skin: rashes or patches of irritated skin; cuts, scrapes or abrasions, bruises, bumps; skin has a yellow colour; child scratches the skin; skin, feels hot, cold, sweaty, clammy, etc.

It is not only unnecessary but inappropriate for educators to examine children physically by using a flashlight to look into children's mouth and throat, or by examining the skin for rashes or marks (e.g., bruises) on parts of the body that are covered by clothing. Even if a child complains of a sore throat, you are not responsible for examining the throat to determine whether the tissue is red or swollen or for concluding that he or she should be seen by a physician. Medical examinations are just that—medical—and can be intrusive to patients. Keep in mind that you are not expected or trained to be a doctor or nurse.

During the day, educators will naturally see the bodies of infants and children while changing diapers, helping them on the toilet, or helping them change into swimsuits. These occasions provide opportunities to note the presence of skin rashes, bruises, and so on.

In most situations where a child is injured or complains of itchiness or pain, it is appropriate for the educator to look at the child's skin and proceed accordingly. An exception is with preschoolers and school-agers, when the genitals or buttocks are involved. In such cases, the child's physician or parents examine the child. However, in cases where sexual abuse is suspected, educators should follow their suspected child abuse protocol.

The baseline health observation includes assessing children's hygiene, emotional health, and growth and developmental milestones. Early childhood courses in child development thoroughly cover the observation and documentation of children's milestone achievements. Concerns about the emotional, physical, or sexual abuse of children and issues of neglect are examined in Unit 7.

The terms "personal hygiene" and "cleanliness" are often used interchangeably. However, personal hygiene is a broader term. It includes hand washing, toileting practices, and dental care along with the cleanliness of one's skin, hair, and clothing. In hygiene, as in many other things, there is a range of what each person finds to be an acceptable level. The food we eat (e.g., spices), the way foods are prepared (e.g., fried), the laundry products we use (e.g., scented or unscented), and whether we smoke, as well as whether we use perfumes or colognes, what shampoo or conditioners and deodorants or even incense we use, and whether we have pets—and so on—all contribute to our individual scent and the aroma in our homes. You may be aware of children's individual scents (e.g., the smell of fabric softener on a child's clothes). Some scents may be different from your own and you may find particular scents unpleasant. In other cases, the scents may just be unfamiliar. Yet just because the scent is different doesn't mean the child is unclean. As in any other situation, educators' sensitivity to children and parents and respect for personal preferences are important to children's emotional well-being. Educators model appropriate comments and behaviour to children. There may be times when children have a distinctive odour because their skin, hair, or clothing is dirty from infrequent bathing or soiled clothes. Again, educators use their discretion in determining whether this is a common or infrequent occurrence. If it happens frequently, the child may be neglected.

If an educator observes more significant behavioural changes, the child should be seen by a physician as soon as possible. Parents or educators must seek medical attention for the child if the child shows any of the following behavioural changes, or a combination of them:

- lethargy (or lacks energy)
- much sleepier than usual
- not alert

- uninterested in their environment (other children, toys, activities)
- unusually cranky, fussy, or irritable
- inconsolable
- refusal to eat or drink

Parents or educators must seek medical attention for the child if the child shows any of the following physical symptom:

- change in breathing (rapid, shallow, or shortness of breath)
- pain or difficulty swallowing
- stiff neck
- rash with a fever
- rash with a change in behaviour

Fevers

A fever is just one of a number of signs of illness, like a runny nose, sore throat, cough, diarrhea, or vomiting. Fever by itself is not dangerous. In fact, it is one of our body's defence mechanisms that helps us fight infection. But when a child feels warm, many adults reach for the thermometer, give the child medication, and call the physician. Fever is unreliable as a sign in determining how sick a child is or whether to call the parents to pick up their child.

Even though children can be seriously ill and not have a fever, many people believe that a child with a fever is sicker than a child without a fever. But this is not necessarily the case. Infants are generally less likely to have a fever with a serious illness than are older children with a serious illness (American Academy of Pediatrics et al. 1992, 81). Children can have a very serious illness (e.g., meningitis) and have a normal or below-normal body temperature. A mild viral infection can cause a fever as high as 40°C (104°F). Most infections accompanied by a fever in children are minor (e.g., upper respiratory infections). These are often caused by a virus and the child usually gets better without medical treatment.

Another reason why parents become concerned about their child having a fever is the possibility of a febrile seizure. About 3% to 5% of children with a fever have one febrile seizure in their childhood. Febrile seizures are not harmful to children (Canadian Paediatric Society 1996, 132; Warden et al. 2003). However, witnessing a seizure can be traumatic for parents, educators, and other children because of the thrashing movements, drooling, difficulty breathing, and other involuntary behaviour by the child. Febrile seizures occur when the body's temperature rises rapidly and are often the first sign that the child has a fever at all (Canadian Paediatric Society 1996, 132). There is no treatment or preventive care for children with a history of febrile seizures (Freeman 1992). But if staff know that a child may have febrile seizures, that knowledge itself can alleviate some of the anxiety if one does occur.

A fever is not caused by teething. There are a number of factors that cause our body temperature to rise:

- overdressing
- strenuous exercise/play

- time of day (our normal temperature varies during the day, being highest in late afternoon)
- a vaccination
- an infection

By definition, a fever is a rise in body temperature, to 38.5°C (101.3°F) or higher as a rectal temperature, or 38°C (100.4°F) or higher as an oral temperature. Axillary (armpit) temperatures are not reliable and are discouraged (Canadian Paediatric Society 1996, 131).

Staff often feel that they are in a Catch-22 situation—they observe a change in a child's behaviour and know that he or she is not feeling well. But when they call the parents, the parents want to know the child's temperature. And if the child does not have a fever, the parents may be reluctant or refuse to leave work. This situation causes the greatest concern. It could be dangerous to assume that because there is no fever, the child is not ill enough to be seen by a physician.

Observing a child's behaviour is much more important than taking a child's temperature. The child's behaviour helps you tell how sick the child is (Canadian Paediatric Society 1996). Generally speaking, "how sick the child appears is more important in establishing the severity of underlying illness … than the height of fever" (Tulk and Ipp 1992, 26).

As educators become familiar with each child, they can identify behaviour changes. When children feel warm to the touch, you can first rule out the other possible reasons for the fever. If you think a child is ill and that is why she or he feels warm, watch closely for changes in behaviour. If the child feels warm but is playing and smiling, there is little to worry about. But if the behaviour changes, you must be concerned and take appropriate steps.

A child with any of the following symptoms (Canadian Paediatric Society 1996, 132–33) must be seen by a physician as soon as possible, regardless of whether the child has a fever or feels warm to the touch:

- unusual sleepiness, drowsiness
- lack of interest in toys, books, other children
- irritability, fussiness
- persistent crying, weak cry, inconsolable
- difficult or rapid breathing
- rash with a fever
- poor skin colour
- excessive drooling
- diminished appetite

Suggestions for managing children's fevers:

1. Share with parents information on fever and the importance of responding to children's behaviour. Encourage parents to discuss the issue of fever with their child's physician, or invite a physician or public health nurse to speak to the staff and parents.

2. Post the list of signs and symptoms of illness that the staff will watch for in children at drop-off and throughout the day. Discuss this issue with each parent at the time of enrollment.

3. Taking children's temperature in early childhood programs is not recommended (Canadian Paediatric Society 1996, 809). Parents should understand this policy and the rationale for it. If the educator does take children's temperatures, the steps should be outlined in the program's policy manual. Guidelines will ensure that taking temperatures is done safely and correctly.

4. It is not recommended that acetaminophen (e.g., Tylenol, Tempra) be given to children for the treatment of fevers. Although this medication does lower the temperature, its main purpose is to relieve aches and pains due to illness (Canadian Paediatric Society 1996; Freeman 1992; Kluger 1992). Children should never be given acetylsalicylic acid (aspirin) for fevers without consulting the child's physician. Children who ingest this medication when they have the flu or chickenpox may develop Reye's syndrome. Although this disease is rare, it is often fatal.

5. Your program's exclusion policy should include the following (Canadian Paediatric Society 1996, 134):

   ■ Children with a fever or who feel warm to the touch can continue to attend the program if they feel well enough to participate in the program.

   ■ Infants under six months who feel warm to the touch, look flushed, or have a fever should be seen by a physician as soon as possible. This should be done regardless of whether the infant shows behavioural changes.

   ■ Notify parents immediately if their child has a febrile seizure. The child should be seen promptly by a physician to determine whether the seizure is part of a more serious infection, such as meningitis.

Health Observation throughout the Day

The health observations made when children begin their day provide educators and parents with a baseline against which to compare children throughout the remainder of the day. This baseline is particularly important when educators note a specific sign or symptom and monitor its progress. In other words, they watch to see if the sign or symptom gets worse, is resolving itself, or remains the same. Documenting health observations also assists educators and parents to identify patterns in types of illnesses. Educators who observe the following early signs of allergies in children can assist parents and physician in the diagnosis: recurring colds and ear infections, nosebleeds, headaches, stomachaches, dark circles under the eyes, irritability (see Allergies, page 170).

Documenting Health Observations

Educators and parents of infants and toddlers in child care keep daily written records for each child. Form 4.1 provides a section for parents to share relevant health information with their child's educators. Educators complete the remainder of the form during the day. Parents are interested in reading this information at pickup time. "Anecdotal" notes elaborate on children's activities and their overall well-being. "Health Notes" is an ideal space for the educators to record their daily health observations (e.g., "Beginning to sound stuffed up" or "He didn't seem to be himself after his nap this afternoon").

Fewer educators are working with more children in preschool and school-age programs than in infant and toddler programs. Staff may not make daily entries in each child's file because children are older and because of time constraints. If nothing unusual happens, it may be unproductive for educators to write reports for the sake of it or for parents to read what they already know.

Documentation in Children's Files

Educators' careful and accurate documentation of each child's health provides parents and, ultimately, health professionals with valuable medical information in making diagnoses. For example, an educator would not phone a parent and simply say, "Max is not feeling well and you need to pick him up right away." Rather, educators formulate their thoughts about their health observations before they write in a child's file or phone the parents. Their experience and training equip them with the skills needed to ask themselves the same questions that the parents will ask of them. The answers to these questions guide educators in determining what to do for the child.

- How has the child's behaviour changed to lead you to believe that the child may be ill?
- What are the signs and symptoms that the child is experiencing? Describe the symptoms as clearly as possible.

In the case of a tummy ache:

- Where is the pain in the abdomen, and does the pain move? (Depending on the child's age, the child may be able to point to where the pain is.)
- What kind of pain is it (sharp, throbbing, comes and goes, etc.)? (The answer will depend on the child's verbal ability.)
- Is the child feeling nauseated? Has he or she vomited or had diarrhea?
- What has the child eaten that day? Does he or she have allergies?
- When were the signs and symptoms first noticed, and how long have they lasted?
- Have the signs and symptoms changed? If so, how? Are they getting worse? Have they stayed constant or are they coming and going (intermittent)?
- How is the child's appetite? Is he or she experiencing difficulty urinating or having a bowel movement?
- Has the child started eating a new food, taken a medication, been immunized in the past two weeks, or been recently injured?
- Does the child have any long-term medical conditions?
- Has the child had similar symptoms before?
- What have you done for the child so far? For example, have you continued to watch the child, administered a medication, or isolated him or her from the other children?
- What time was the parent called? What was said by both parties, and what is to be done next?

■ Did you call the child's physician or an ambulance?

If one child is ill, educators take into account what has happened in the program over the past few days to consider factors that might be relevant to this child:

■ Are any other children ill in the program? What are their signs and symptoms? What was the diagnosis (if they were seen by a physician)?

■ What activities have the children been involved in over the past couple of days? Have they been on a field trip?

Coworkers or parents often say that their child always seems to be sick with something. Rather than searching through daily entries to find the ones that concern illness, educators may find it useful to maintain a flow sheet that lists each child's illnesses or symptoms. It takes only a couple of moments to complete and it could be conveniently kept in the front of each child's file. Such a sheet enables educators and parents to review the frequency and types of illness that the child experiences or to refer back to a specific entry within the body of the child's file. Directors may also wish to include a photocopy of the child's immunization schedule.

Early Childhood Program's Health Record

The frequency of illnesses is of concern to educators and parents. So in addition to maintaining the flow sheet for each child, staff are encouraged to keep an ongoing health record that includes the suspected and diagnosed illnesses of all the children in the program on one form (see Form 4.2). Staff should include the following information in each notation:

■ date

■ child's first and last names

■ brief description of the symptoms

■ physician's diagnosis (if the child was seen)

■ whether the child was excluded and, if so, for how many days

At the very minimum, use initials on the daily attendance form to indicate trends in absenteeism. For example, use "D" for diarrhea, "R" for respiratory illnesses, and "O" for other health reasons (Ying et al. 1998, 312).

Reviewing this form provides educators with valuable information:

■ the frequency of specific illnesses

■ which children are ill more often

■ patterns in illnesses, because similarities begin to emerge in terms of the time of year, the age group of the children, and any one group of children experiencing more illnesses than other groups

Patterns in illnesses can help staff identify factors that might contribute to the spread of illness and what they can do to reduce that spread, such as improving the children's and educators' hygiene, cleaning and sanitizing routines, and food preparation practices.

Sharing Health Information with Physicians

Staff network with a variety of professionals in their community and share information verbally and in written reports. Because of the frequency of young children's illnesses, educators may regularly communicate indirectly with physicians through the child's parents. To protect confidentiality, educators do not communicate directly with physicians. Before they do so, parents must give the educators permission to speak with their doctor and let the doctor know that an educator may call.

Educators' health observations are essential to assist physicians or other health professionals in caring for children. As professionals, educators are encouraged to document their health observations on a report form, which the parents take to their child's physician (see Form 4.3). For the staff, this form is a direct line of communication with the physician. In addition, parents benefit from this documentation because it saves them from having to remember all of the details conveyed verbally by the educator.

Obviously, effective communication results when all parties share accurate information. Educators rely on the parents to share relevant medical information with them after the visit to the doctor's office. The Canadian Paediatric Society recommends that physicians share relevant medical information directly with the staff. To arrange this, staff provide the parents with a form that they ask the physician to complete. Parents return the completed form to the staff when their child returns to the program. This document provides staff with pertinent care information and provides the physicians with the program's exclusion criteria. Many directors experience situations in which the doctor's recommendations are not consistent with those of their program. This inconsistency often results in unnecessary conflicts between staff, parents, and doctor (see Form 4.4).

Work experience familiarizes educators with the more common childhood illnesses. Educators may feel they know quite a bit about illness, especially if they are parents themselves. Once they have seen a few children with chickenpox or head lice, they are able to identify pox marks or lice eggs. Parents in the program, particularly those with infants or toddlers, often view individual educators as consultants on a range of topics, including their child's health. Of course, educators want to be helpful and can answer some health questions for parents. However, giving out medical information is overstepping their professional boundaries. Diagnosing illnesses and offering medical consultation are the roles of health professionals, not educators.

Excluding Children from Early Childhood Programs

If you ask educators to list the issues that they find to be the most challenging, ill children will probably be among the top three, perhaps even the first. If you are not a parent, you may have a hard time putting yourself into a parent's position. As discussed earlier, parents are in work or school situations and face a vast range of reactions and expectations from employers or teachers. Imagine yourself sitting in a board meeting, working on an assembly line, or writing an exam, and you are called away to take a phone call. Your child's educator tells you that your daughter is ill and you must pick her up as soon as possible to see the doctor. Not only are you going to be worried about your child but you are also faced with rescheduling your workday or class work, making a doctor's appointment, and returning to work. As a student, are you able to concentrate on your exam when you know that your daughter may be ill?

Most employers do not provide family responsibility leave for their employees. This benefit entitles parents with paid leave to attend to a child who is ill or other family emergencies. Currently, most parents either use their personal sick-leave benefits, if eligible, or leave work without pay. Others may risk losing their job if they leave work. Few parents have jobs that afford them the flexibility to work from home during a child's illness. Families often do not live in the same community as their extended family, who may have been able to relieve the parents in a crisis. Travelling between work and the program and then to the doctor's office may not be convenient, especially on public transportation in the middle of a Canadian winter! On the other hand, for many of the same reasons, parents may feel pressured to bring their children to the program in the morning, even if the child is not feeling well.

Educators and parents are responsible for establishing a clear understanding of the program's exclusion criteria at the time of enrollment. Unnecessary exclusion of children is unacceptable. With the exception of certain infections, the primary reason for excluding children is that the child does not feel well enough to participate in the program's activities (see Table 4.1, page 164). Staff–child ratios in centres are such that it is seldom possible to give a great deal of individual care to a sick child and still have enough staff to meet the needs of the other children. Also, where would you rather be when you are sick—in a program with a group of energetic children and adults or at home with someone to bring you food and beverages and to care for your needs in quiet surroundings? Obviously, most children would prefer to be at home when they are ill.

Directors evaluate each situation individually. A director will think twice before he or she calls a parent to pick up a child if the parent works in a factory and has been warned about taking time off. However, a director is expected to give equal consideration before calling a parent who has a flexible work schedule. Who are the child care staff concerned about in managing illness?

- The ill child. Educators and the director want to ensure that the child is comfortable while in their care.

- Other children and staff. Educators may be concerned that the child's illness is contagious. Another concern may be the extent of one-to-one care that the ill child needs, and how this affects the quality of supervision available to other children.

- The ill child's parents. Educators and the director consider the effects of the child's illness on the family.

> The program's exclusion policy states that children are excluded when
> 1. an illness prevents the child from participating in routine activities,
> 2. a child requires more individual care than the staff are able to provide without compromising the needs of the other children, or
> 3. a child risks infecting other children or educators as defined in the exclusion guidelines.

Erik and Anastasia in the preschool room have bad colds with runny noses and coughs and are irritable and lethargic. According to the third point in the exclusion policy, excluding children with colds is not recommended (see also Appendix 4.1, page 182). However, both children's behaviour is affected, so the director needs to consider the first two points of the exclusion policy. She must decide if she will

- call both sets of parents to come immediately to pick up their children, or
- call the parents and discuss what is in the best interests of each child. Erik's parents will be able to leave work in an hour and drop him off with his grandfather. Anastasia's mother is a single parent who recently moved to the city to attend university. She is in the middle of exams. She is already stressed and has no one to help care for her daughter. The director and mother discuss the issue and decide that Anastasia will rest in the director's office for the afternoon. If she is still feeling unwell tomorrow, the director will arrange for a volunteer to come to the program and care for her.

Each medical officer of health (MOH) in Canada is responsible for the health of children in centres within his or her geographic area. One of the responsibilities of the MOH is to establish the exclusion criteria for centres. These should be communicated to the physicians as well. There are usually several MOHs working in one province or territory. Because they work independently of one another, centres in different regions may be provided with different exclusion criteria. In some cases, neither centres nor physicians have received written criteria. So it is not surprising that there can be inconsistent expectations among everyone. In *Well Beings*, the Canadian Paediatric Society recommends exclusion criteria that centres, MOHs, and physicians are encouraged to implement (see Appendix 4.1, page 182).

Programs are required to have space available to isolate ill children temporarily. The director's office is often used, or a cot is set up in a quiet, separate part of the play or nap area that allows educators to supervise the resting child. The decision to keep the child in the program until the end of the day is made by the director and educators. The decision is based on issues such as

- what the educators think is wrong with the child,
- the time of day, and
- whether they feel they can care for the child.

Alternative Care Arrangements

There are times when children must be excluded from the program. For some families, this is a minor glitch in their schedule. For others, it creates chaos. Programs require every family to have backup, or alternate, care available (e.g., relative, neighbour, friend) in the event that a child is ill. For parents who have neither job flexibility nor relatives or friends available as backup, alternate care arrangements can be makeshift, unreliable, or inconsistent. This latter situation often puts directors in an awkward position: they know the ill child's home situation but must balance the needs of the other children and staff. In some instances, the director may decide to keep the mildly ill child at the program. In other cases, the director may have to exclude the child and the parents must deal with this decision.

Early Childhood Programs and Health Services for Ill Children

The pressure experienced by parents trying to continue to work or go to school while managing the care of ill children has led to the establishment of centres and health care services specifically for ill children. These services can range from a centre that cares only for ill children to private nursing or trained educators who go into the child's home. The parents pay the cost of these services. In addition, the parents continue to pay the centre for the days that the child is excluded.

These services are relatively few, and they raise questions about the best interests of the ill child. At best, these health services are feasible only for parents who can afford them. No one disagrees that an ill child at home with a loving parent is best. But parents who can't miss work, can't afford private care, and don't have access to alternate adults may be forced to leave a child at home alone—which may raise questions about neglect.

Caring for ill children is a political issue that has not been dealt with in any substantial way. Where does this situation leave children and families?

Name of Child: _____ Date: _____

Arrival Time: _____ Departure Time: _____

Part I: Parents:
Please complete all of the following questions to help us meet the needs of your child today.
Please talk to the staff about any special or confidential information we should be aware of.

Your child slept from _____ to _____ . Did your child sleep well last night? Yes ❑ No ❑

If no, specify the reasons (e.g., teething, illness, over-tiredness, etc.):

_____

_____

When did your child last eat or drink? Time: _____

Type and amount of food or formula: _____

Have there been any changes or disruptions in your child's routine at home?

_____

What kind of mood is your child in today?

_____

Do you have any special comments or instructions for the staff today?

_____

List any medication (prescription or over-the-counter) your child received in the last 24 hours and the reason for giving medication. *(Please remember to complete the Parental Consent and Medication Report Sheet.)*

_____

Part II (to be completed by the caregiver):

Morning snack: _____ Afternoon snack: _____

Lunch: _____ Bottles (times and amounts): _____

Naps: _____

Bowel movements and toileting: _____

(form continues on next page)

Anecdotal (to be completed by the caregiver):

_____

_____

_____

_____

_____

_____

_____

_____

_____

_____

_____

_____

Health Notes (to be completed by the caregiver):

_____

_____

_____

_____

_____

_____

_____

Caregiver's signature: _____

Source: Courtesy of the Canadian Paediatric Society (1996), _Well Beings: A Guide to Promote the Physical Health, Safety and Emotional Well-Being of Children in Child Care Centres and Family Day Care Homes_ (Ottawa: Canadian Paediatric Society), 865–66. Adapted from the Infant Care Centre, University of Winnipeg.

Date: Child's name:

Symptoms: _____

_____

Physician's diagnosis: Exclusion:

Date: Child's name:

Symptoms: _____

_____

Physician's diagnosis: Exclusion:

Date: Child's name:

Symptoms: _____

_____

Physician's diagnosis: Exclusion:

Date: Child's name:

Symptoms: _____

_____

Physician's diagnosis: Exclusion:

Date: Child's name:

Symptoms: _____

_____

Physician's diagnosis: Exclusion:

_____

Name of child: _____ Date: _____

Onset (time): _____ How long has it lasted? _____

Specify symptom(s) (e.g., vomiting, diarrhea, pain, rash, sore throat, cough, runny nose, sore/stiff neck, trouble breathing, etc.):

_____

_____

_____

If taken: Temperature: _____ Circle: Oral / Rectal / Axillary   Time: _____

Any problems eating or drinking?

_____

Any problems with urinating or bowel movements?

_____

OTHER INFORMATION

List any new foods, animals, insects, medication, etc., the child was exposed to:

_____

_____

Specify if this child has been in contact with other ill children:

_____

_____

What has been done for the child?

_____

_____

Comments:

_____

_____

Caregiver's signature: _____

Name of child care facility: _____

Telephone: _____

Source: Courtesy of the Canadian Paediatric Society (1996), *Well Beings: A Guide to Promote the Physical Health, Safety and Emotional Well-Being of Children in Child Care Centres and Family Day Care Homes* (Ottawa: Canadian Paediatric Society), 853.

Name of child: _____ Date: _____

PART I

Diagnosis: _____

Medication(s) (give name, dosage, and how many times a day it is to be taken)
Prescription(s): _____

Over-the-counter: _____

Note: If possible, please prescribe medications to be taken at times when the parents can administer them.

Recommendations for Parents and Caregivers

(Parents are encouraged to discuss any of your recommendations or restrictions of activities with the child care staff to determine if the child's specific needs can be accommodated.)

General: _____
_____
_____

Diet: _____
_____

Level of activity: _____
_____

Date the child can return to child care (see Part II):

_____

Physician's signature: _____ Telephone: _____

PART II: Exclusion Criteria for Child Care Facilities

Physicians please note that reporting requirements to public health may vary between jurisdictions.

Disease	Exclusion	Report
Respiratory Tract Infections		
Colds with Fever/ Common Cold/*Otitis media*	Do not exclude unless too ill to take part in the activities.	No
Conjunctivitis	Exclude only if discharge is pus and then until the antibiotic has been taken for one full day.	No
Pneumonia	Exclude until evaluated by physician.	No

(form continues on next page)

Disease	Exclusion	Report
Gastrointestinal Infections		
Campylobacter/Giardia/ Rotavirus/Salmonella	Exclude until diarrhea is gone.	Yes
Diarrhea	Exclude until diarrhea is gone or physician determines child is not infectious.	Yes: any case of bloody or diagnosed bacterial diarrhea
Escherichia coli/Shigella	Exclude until diarrhea is gone and cultures are negative.	Yes
Food Poisoning	No exclusion required.	Yes
Hepatitis A	Exclude for 1 week after onset of jaundice. Immune globulin may be indicated for children, staff, and family members.	Yes
Norwalk Virus	Exclude until diarrhea and/or vomiting are gone.	Yes
Skin and Scalp Infections		
Head Lice	Exclude until treated. Removal of all nits may be necessary to cure some cases.	No
Herpes Simplex	Exclude for severe illness. Exclusion not indicated for recurrent cold sores.	No
Impetigo	Exclude until antibiotic treatment has started.	No
Scabies	Exclude until treated. Treatment of contacts may be necessary to control outbreak.	No
Other Infections		
Chickenpox	Exclude until 5th day after onset of rash or until all the blisters have crusted, whichever is shorter; may return sooner if illness is mild and able to take part in activities.	Yes
Cytomegalovirus	No exclusion required.	No
Hepatitis B	No exclusion required unless open sores are present. Hepatitis B vaccine and/or Hepatitis B immune lgobulin may be indicated under special circumstances.	Yes. Immediately report any bites that cause bleeding.
Measles	Exclude all cases until at least 4 days after onset of rash. Exclude any child who lacks proof of immunization until vaccinated or until 2 weeks after last case in the child care facility.	Yes. Immediately. Speed is essential in limiting outbreaks of measles.
Meningitis	Exposed children and adults may need antibiotics or vaccine.	Yes. Immediately.
Mumps	Exclude for 9 days; may return sooner if illness is mild and able to take part in the activities. Ensure all children are vaccinated.	Yes
Pertussis	Exclude until 5 days after start of antibiotics or 3 weeks if no treatment given. Contacts may need antibiotics or vaccine.	Yes
Rubella	Exclude for 7 days after onset of rash. All adults should be vaccinated or have blood test to prove immunity. There is risk of severe damage to fetus if a pregnant woman gets rubella during the first trimester.	Yes
Shingles	Do not exclude if lesions can be covered; if uncovered, exclude until all blisters have crusted.	Yes

Source: Courtesy of the Canadian Paediatric Society (1996), *Well Beings: A Guide to Promote the Physical Health, Safety and Emotional Well-Being of Children in Child Care Centres and Family Day Care Homes* (Ottawa: Canadian Paediatric Society), 874–75.

CHILDHOOD INFECTIONS: JUST THE BASICS

Fortunately, most common childhood infections are short-lived and minor. Children become ill regardless of the disease prevention practices implemented in programs, but these practices do reduce the spread of infection. There are far more childhood infections than we have included in this textbook. Our focus is on health promotion in children, not on cures. As educators, your role is not to diagnose but to recognize potential signs of infection and refer children to health professionals. Educators can refer to a number of books and resources describing childhood infections once a physician has made a diagnosis. *Well Beings* is the resource manual of preference for Canadian centres and it includes fact sheets for parents on a variety of infections. Therefore, we have included only the common childhood infections. Understanding the basics and how to manage them addresses the needs of the ill child, parents, other children, and staff. Refer to Appendix 4.1 (page 182) for additional information about managing illness.

The Common Cold

Children in centres can get as many as 8 or 10 colds a year. It may seem that at any one time at least one child has a runny nose or cough. Cold viruses, approximately 200 of them, are spread easily through the air and on contaminated hands and objects. That's why preventing colds is nearly impossible. Another reason is that we spread the cold virus a day or two before we feel a cold coming on. Typically, colds last five to seven days. Symptoms include coughing, sneezing, runny nose, fever, fatigue, and lack of appetite. A child's runny nose may produce a clear discharge at first and then a yellow or green one.

Q. Should children with colds be excluded from the program?
A. No, not from the point of view of infection control. Can you imagine the havoc that would be created both in the program and for the families if every child and educator with a cold were excluded? Instead, educators can

- wash their hands and the child's hands carefully,
- model and encourage children to cover their mouth when they cough and sneeze,
- discard used tissues after use and never use the same tissue to wipe more than one child's nose, tempting as reuse might be when you are out in the playground in the winter,
- ensure that mouthing toys in infant and toddler areas are removed once a child has used them and that all these used toys are cleaned and sanitized daily,
- observe those with colds to ensure that children are feeling well enough to take part in activities, and
- reassure parents that if their child feels well enough to be at the program he or she is well enough to play outside, even in the winter (fresh air is good for the child).

Ear Infections

The eustachian tube, which runs between the middle ear and the back of the nose, is shorter and straighter in young children than in adults. The tube creates a path for fluid behind the middle ear to drain to the back of the throat. The straightness of the tube also permits fluid in the back of the throat and nose to travel into the ear. Ear infections often occur at the same time as colds, which seems logical, because coughing, sneezing, and blowing the nose can force mucus from the nose or throat into the eustachian tube and into the middle ear. The tube may become swollen, which prevents fluid from the middle ear from draining. In such cases, the trapped bacteria may cause infection. The Canadian Paediatric Society (1996, 139) estimates that "almost all children will have had one or more of these infections before 3 years of age." Children with speaking skills can tell you whether they have an earache; for infants you'll observe a change in behaviour—they often become cranky or unhappy. Parents and educators often comment that they see infants pulling or rubbing their ears, but this can be coincidental and shouldn't be relied on as a sign of infection. Physicians can usually confirm ear infection by looking into the child's ear.

> Most ear infections clear up on their own without antibiotics. And sometimes it's difficult for the doctor to tell whether or not a young child has an ear infection. If the doctor is uncertain or if the infection is mild, the doctor will *not* prescribe an antibiotic.
>
> Most children over age 2 years only need 5 days of antibiotic for ear infections. Five days works just as well as 10 days, is easier to give, and exposes the child to less antibiotic.
>
> It is perfectly acceptable to choose not to give antibiotics for an ear infection, and to wait 2 or 3 days to see if it will clear up on its own. (Pennie 2001)

Q. Should children with ear infections be excluded from the program?
A. No. The infection is in the child's middle ear. The bacteria will not spread to other children or educators. A child taking antibiotics should be kept at home for

24 hours. During that period, the antibiotic will have begun to work and the child to feel better, and the parents can watch for any side effects or allergic reaction.

Gastrointestinal Infections: Diarrhea

Diarrhea is the most common symptom of gastrointestinal infection. Basically, diarrhea is a change in the consistency or frequency of an individual's bowel movements. The stool may be very loose or even watery. And—depending on the virus, bacteria, or parasite causing the infection—the stool may contain blood or mucus, and be foul-smelling or mushy in consistency. In addition to the diarrhea, children may have abdominal cramps, fever, nausea, vomiting, or a loss of appetite. Others may just have a couple of loose stools and be otherwise fine.

Educators play an important role in preventing other children or staff from getting the infection. Diarrhea spreads easily among children and if other children do come down with it, the hygienic practices in that program must be called into question. Effective hand washing, strict diapering and toileting routines, and food safety every day, not just when someone is ill, are essential in reducing the spread of intestinal infection.

As educators become familiar with the infants and toddlers, they are able to notice any change in a particular child's bowel movements. Educators should follow these steps when caring for children with diarrhea:

■ Tell the other educators that the child has had one episode of diarrhea. All the educators should be extra vigilant when hand washing and diapering to ensure that stool does not contaminate the environment. The child can remain in the program as long as he or she feels well enough to participate and the stool is contained in the diaper (or the older child is able to get to the toilet in time). Parents appreciate being called so that they are aware of this situation.

■ After the second episode of diarrhea, call the parents to pick up the child. If the child is under six months old or has additional symptoms (such as a fever, loss of appetite, vomiting, blood or mucus in the stool), signs of dehydration (i.e., fewer than four wet diapers in 24 hours; no tears; dry skin, mouth, and tongue; sunken eyes; grayish skin; or a sunken soft spot on top of the head), or changes in behaviour, he or she must be seen by a physician as soon as possible (Canadian Paediatric Society 1996, 147).

■ While waiting for the parents to arrive, prevent the child from becoming dehydrated. Children, especially infants and toddlers, can become dehydrated quickly because they lose more of their body fluids in diarrhea and vomit than they are able to drink. Pediatricians recommend that programs with infants and toddlers have oral rehydration solution (ORS) available for these situations. ORS is available in liquid or powder (e.g., Lytren, Gastrolyte, Pedialyte) and is used to replenish the child's fluid and electrolytes. Offer the child ORS every hour and after every loose bowel movement, either by bottle or in a cup. For infants on expressed breast milk, continue to bottle feed them on demand or at least every two hours. For formula-fed children and toddlers, stop their formula or food and beverages. The physician will advise the parents on the child's diet and fluid replacement (Canadian Paediatric Society 1994, 19–20). Do not offer the child sugary drinks such as fruit juice, pop, sweetened tea, or broth. These fluids do not contain the proper combination of water, salts, and sugar, and may in fact make the child's diarrhea worse (Canadian Pediatric Society 1996, 897).

■ Notify the public health agency if two or more children have diarrhea within 48 hours of each other. These situations are called "outbreaks" and steps must be taken to control the gastrointestinal infection, including determining the cause.

Q. Should children with two or more episodes of diarrhea be excluded from the program?
A. Yes, children must stay home until the diarrhea stops and they have a normal bowel movement. If the diarrhea is caused by bacteria, the child will be prescribed antibiotics. Some children may return earlier if their physician determines that the germ is no longer in the stool (Canadian Paediatric Society 1996, 147–48). Refer to Appendix 4.1 (page 182) for the exclusion criteria that relate to the various types of gastrointestinal infections.

Pinkeye

Pinkeye (or conjunctivitis) is another childhood infection that is easily spread among children. The causes are viruses, commonly, and bacteria, occasionally. These infect the covering of the eyeball. However, children who have allergies or have been exposed to pollutants may develop pinkeye. Watch for the following symptoms in one or both eyes:

■ The whites of the eye are pink or red.

■ The child rubs the eye because it is itchy.

■ The eye may be tearing a lot.

■ There is a clear or pus (thick or yellow) discharge from the eye; the parents may tell you that the eyelid is stuck shut after sleeping.

Pinkeye is a good example of an infection caused by germs spread by indirect contact. A child with pinkeye touches or rubs his or her eyes; the eye discharge contaminates the fingers. In the course of play, the child touches other children's hands or objects, which in turn become contaminated. Now those children who have the eye discharge on their fingers and who touch their own eyes will get pinkeye. Sharing towels among children is another way that pinkeye is spread. The cycle continues until it is broken.

Q. Should children with pinkeye be excluded from the program?
A. Maybe, depending on the cause of the pinkeye. The child's physician needs to see the child to diagnose the infection and determine the cause. When there is pus discharge, the child may be prescribed an antibiotic (eye drops or ointment) to treat the bacteria. If this is the case, children should be excluded until they have taken the medication for 24 hours. Otherwise, the child can return to the program. Regardless of the cause, educators must pay particular attention to hygiene practices to reduce the spread to other children and staff.

- Effective hand washing is critical, for both staff and the child, after wiping or touching the infected eye.
- Never share towels, facial tissues, and so on, among children regardless of whether someone has pinkeye.

Chickenpox

Chickenpox—a word that parents dread, though most of them want all the children in their family to get the illness at the same time and have done with it. For adults who did not have chickenpox as children, it's usually a much more serious infection. The good news is that for children who haven't had chickenpox there is a vaccine available. When children begin in a program, checking whether or not they have been vaccinated is recommended. Children who did not receive the varicella vaccination at about 12 months of age can receive it at an older age. But even with the vaccine available you will most likely care for a few children who have chickenpox.

Chickenpox is common in children because the varicella-zoster virus spreads easily through the air and by touching the liquid in the pox. By the time the red bumps appear, children may have already had a mild fever for a couple of days. Spots appear over two or three days. Gradually the bumps turn into liquid-filled blisters (or pox), which crust over. Some children may be covered in pox; others may have just a few. For many children, the infection is mild and the primary complaint is the itchiness of the pox. It takes 10 to 21 days to tell whether a susceptible person exposed to chickenpox is going to get it. Never give the child acetylsalicylic acid (aspirin) to treat a fever or aches and pains from chickenpox.

Having chickenpox once provides most people with lifelong immunity to it, although some people get chickenpox twice. The virus can remain inactive in our bodies for life, but it can become reactivated and cause shingles. Children or adults with shingles can spread the virus to those susceptible to chickenpox. Shingles is a painful rash of itchy blisters, which often develop around the trunk of the body.

Q. Should someone with chickenpox or shingles be excluded from the program?
A. Yes. It is recommended that children be excluded for five days after the rash (red bumps) appears or until all the pox have crusted over, whichever is shorter (Canadian Paediatric Society 1996, 164). Experts on infectious disease and experts on child care continue to struggle with the question of excluding children with chickenpox. Chickenpox is most infectious a couple of days before the rash appears. This means that while the virus is spreading, no one knows and everyone in the program is exposed. Once the pox appear, what will excluding the child accomplish? Furthermore, the current exclusion recommendation leaves room for interpretation by program staff. Unfortunately, this leads to inconsistencies among programs and even educators within a program. Educators are advised to assess each child individually. What is in the best interests of this child? If the child feels well enough to take part in activities, or if you have enough staff available to provide more individualized care, the child can remain in the program.

Head Lice

Having head lice does not reflect a lack of parenting ability or cleanliness, despite popular belief to the contrary. As a matter of fact, lice like warm scalps and clean hair best! Yet some adults and children still make derogatory comments about people with lice, which can be very hurtful. Children who have head lice may already feel embarrassed, fearful, or ashamed, and educators need to be sensitive to these feelings. Know the facts and effective ways to treat head lice, listen to parents' concerns, dispel stereotypes, and you can manage an outbreak.

Head lice are tiny, greyish insects that live on human hair. Usually they lay their eggs (or nits) on hair behind the ears, on the crown, or at the back of the head. Nits look like dandruff but stick to the hair so that you can't pick or wash them off. You may first suspect head lice when you see a child scratching or complaining that his or her head is itchy. Check for nits on the hair, close to the scalp. The hatched lice shy away from light, so it is unlikely that you will actually see the lice. Although you may be scratching your head just thinking about lice, they actually don't hurt, spread disease, or jump between people. Head lice spread quickly when children have their heads together or share items such as combs, brushes, hats and scarves, headphones, and play clothes. Staff can reduce the opportunities for head lice to spread by

- providing space for each child to store his or her outerwear and a change of clothes without coming into contact with the next child's clothes (e.g., in a cubby/locker, or in bins/baskets, or on hooks);
- stuffing hats and scarves down coat sleeves, especially when coats are hung on hooks;
- having parents provide a comb or brush for their child's personal use, to be kept in the child's space; and
- laundering dress-up clothes weekly. In the event of an outbreak of head lice, the clothes and accessories should be laundered and put away until the outbreak is over. The hats and wigs that can't be washed must be sealed in a plastic bag for 10 days. Dramatic play is an important element of child care programs, and wigs, hats, scarves, and dress-up clothes should be available for children despite the chance of head lice.

Basically, head lice are a nuisance that creates work for the staff and parents at home. If you find one child or educator with head lice, you must check everyone. Then educators must notify all parents, especially those whose children have the lice. Head lice are easily treated with special shampoos and conditioners containing medication, a pediculicide. These products kill lice and nits and prevent re-infestation (if nits are not destroyed, they hatch in seven days). Parents can check with their physician or pharmacist about different brands. There is a range of other treatments used by parents, including putting an oil and vinegar mixture on the head overnight (covered with a shower cap). In the morning, the dead lice and nits are combed out. Parents need to check every person in the household for nits but treat only those who have them. A cautionary note: Some brands of shampoo contain an ingredient called lindane. This chemical is toxic and can be absorbed through the scalp, leading to poisoning (Burroughs Wellcome n.d.).

Q. Should someone with head lice be excluded from the program?

A. Yes. However, children or educators with head lice can return to the program once they have been treated. Whether the program has one child or 10 children with head lice, the program must be cleaned the same way, including vacuuming, washing, sending children's clothes home for laundering, washing stuffed toys and puppets, and so on. Refer to the list provided in *Well Beings* or the public health agency for advice on dealing with head lice. Some public health authorities do not recommend extensive environmental cleaning in family homes. However, because of the number of children and the amount of head-to-head social contact that occurs while children are playing, it is recommended that programs perform these tasks.

In the past, public health nurses were called into programs and schools to do "nit-picking" on every child. Nowadays, directors simply consult with their public health nurse and receive up-to-date information on prevention and treatment, perhaps in a number of languages. However, if a program has recurring outbreaks of head lice or a particular child's parents are not responding to the program's requests to use the treatment, the public health department should become directly involved.

ANTIBIOTIC-RESISTANT BACTERIA

The discovery of penicillin was a medical breakthrough. Since then, more and more antibiotics have been developed for the treatment of bacterial infections. As a result, lives have been saved and the quality of lives improved. Ironically, pharmaceutical firms today are faced with the immediate challenge of discovering new, more potent antibiotics to be used to treat infections caused by bacteria resistant to previously effective antibiotics.

Levy (1998, 49) explains how antibiotics play a role in bacteria resistance:

> When an antibiotic attacks a group of bacteria, cells that are highly susceptible to the medicine will die. But cells that have some resistance from the start, or that acquire it later (through mutation or gene exchange), may survive, especially if too little drug is given to overwhelm the cells that are present. Those cells, facing reduced competition from susceptible bacteria, will then go on to proliferate. When confronted with an antibiotic, the most resistant cells in the group will inevitably out compete all others.

As you read earlier in this unit, bacteria live in our body and work to keep us healthy by fighting invading bacteria. When we take antibiotics, some of the beneficial bacteria are killed, which gives the disease-causing bacteria the opportunity to multiply and cause an infection. And there is the potential for the normal bacteria to become resistant to antibiotics too. Such resistance would, if conditions are right, enable the bacteria to multiply, creating an infection that would be difficult to treat because of the resistance.

Of course, antibiotics continue to be used to treat many bacterial infections. But the soaring overuse of antibiotics must stop. They are often misused for non-bacterial infections (i.e., those caused by viruses) or automatically given for bacterial infections (e.g., ear infections) that may clear up on their own in a couple of days. Treating a cold with antibiotics does not work—period. "Researchers at the Centers for Disease Control and Prevention have estimated that some 50 million of the 150 million outpatient prescriptions for antibiotics every year [in the U.S.] are unneeded" (Levy 1998, 50). Consider that in every developed country one third of all antibiotics are probably prescribed unnecessarily, and that there are fewer controls on such prescriptions in developing countries, and that the use of antibiotics is widespread in livestock breeding and agriculture. Clearly the effect on antibiotic-resistant bacteria is staggering and is ringing alarm bells worldwide.

You may be asking yourself how this information relates to your work in early childhood programs. There is a direct correlation. We know

- that young children in groups are exposed to more illnesses,
- that the additional needs of ill children in attendance make it difficult for educators to provide quality care for all children in the group, and
- that the exclusion of children may prevent others from getting sick.

This last point is where educators should recognize the significant role they can play in decreasing the unnecessary use of antibiotics. These infections are common among young children; also, they are easily spread, and antibiotics are often used as a treatment for some upper-respiratory infections (URIs).

Appendix 4.1 (page 182) contains a table on the management of illness that lays out clearly the exclusion criteria and conditions recommended in *Well Beings* (1996, 194–201) for a child's return to a program As you can see, few respiratory illnesses require that a child be excluded in order to prevent the spread to other children. The most common reason for a child's exclusion is that she or he is too ill to participate in the centre's activities. Yet many practices common in centres are not appropriate, as illustrated in Table 4.1.

How do these exclusion practices affect antibiotic use? If centres require parents to take their child to the doctor because of green nasal discharge (a common symptom of the common cold) and exclude their child from the centre, one may assume that staff will request that the child be on antibiotics before he or she can return.

> Of the 36 CCC [child care centre] directors surveyed, appropriately, antibiotics were most often believed necessary for streptococcal sore throat (n=35 or 97%), ear infection (n=34 or 94%), and sinus infection (n=30 or 83%). However, antibiotics were also believed necessary by some for bronchitis (n=30 or 83%), cough (n=14 or 39%), non-streptococcal sore throat (n=12 or 33%), colds (n=7 or 19%), and "flu" (n=6 or 17%). Of 34 staff members, 13 (38%) believed antibiotics were required in a child with non-specific URI to prevent bacterial infection, 9 (26%) to prevent spread of infection, and 7 (21%) to hasten recovery. Holding these beliefs was significantly more likely to be associated with requesting commencement of antibiotic therapy before return to the CCC on the last occasion a child had been sent home with a URI. In total, 6 (18%) of 34 CCC providers had required that an antibiotic therapy be commenced before return. (Skull et al 2000, 182)

TABLE 4.1 | **Exclusion Practices in Toronto Early Childhood Programs**

CONDITION	USUALLY OR ALWAYS ADVISE MD REFERRAL TO PARENT		USUALLY OR ALWAYS EXCLUDE FROM CHILD CARE FOR...	
	Directors answering yes (%)	Correct	Directors answering yes (%)	Correct
Ear pain	30 (83%)	Yes	23 (64%)	No
Green/yellow runny nose	28 (78%)	No	20 (56%)	No
Cough with phlegm	23 (64%)	No	16 (44%)	No
Unusual behaviour	9 (25%)	Yes	15 (42%)	No
Sore throat	20 (56%)	Yes	11 (31%)	No
Runny nose	7 (19%)	No	7 (19%)	No
Dry cough	15 (42%)	No	5 (14%)	No

Source: S.A. Skull et al. (2000), "Child Care Centre Staff Contribute to Physician Visits and Pressure for Antibiotic Prescription," *Archives of Pediatrics and Adolescent Medicine*, 154: 182.

There are other practices—in addition to having educators understand the principles behind exclusion—that staff can implement in the centre to reduce infections:

- Proper hand washing. One study found that 15% of the centres they surveyed did not meet the recommendations in *Well Beings* (Ying et al. 1998, 310).

- Proper diaper changing routine. The same study found that 2% of centres did not have a specific diapering policy or routine to follow and 8% had inadequate routines (Ying et al. 1998, 310).

- Proper food-handling practices. These include washing off bacterial and possible antibiotic residue from fruits and vegetables.

- The observation of children's behaviour as a key indicator of illness. Another study found that only 25% of the staff referred children to their doctor for this reliable sign of illness (Skull et al. 2000, 182).

- Practising the principles of universal precautions. Researchers have found that 62% of supervisors and directors were either unaware of the term "universal precautions" or lacked an accurate understanding of the term (Ying et al. 1998, 310).

- The purchase and use of cleaning and hand-washing products that are not advertised to be antibacterial.

> ... standard soaps and detergents (without added antibacterials) decrease the numbers of potentially troublesome bacteria perfectly well. Similarly, quickly evaporating chemicals—such as the old standbys of chlorine bleach, alcohol, ammonia, and hydrogen peroxide—can be applied beneficially. They remove potentially disease causing bacteria ... but they do not leave long-lasting residues that will continue to kill benign bacteria and increase the growth of resistant strains long after target pathogens have been removed. (Levy 1998, 48)

We all need to understand when antibiotics are necessary and when they are not. When prescribed an antibiotic, follow the instructions and take the entire prescription. Do not stop taking a prescription once you start feeling better and then save the medication for later use, either by yourself or by someone else.

ADMINISTERING MEDICATION

Fortunately, most healthy children need medication rarely or not at all. And most of the common childhood infections are caused by viruses (e.g., colds, other upper respiratory infections, diarrhea) that are not cured by antibiotics. Strep throat and sometimes ear infections and pinkeye are caused by bacteria that are treated with antibiotics. Occasionally, educators administer medication to children in programs. Educators have a legal and professional responsibility to be familiar with their child care regulations on administering medication. You must know which medications educators are permitted to give, what type of parental consent is required, and how medications are stored, administered, and documented. A program's medication policy should be accompanied by a list of procedures that all educators follow.

As an ECE student, you cannot administer medication to children when you are in program placements; that remains a staff responsibility. After graduation you will eventually be assigned this role, however, so you need to be familiar with the fundamental principles of a medication policy, and the rationale behind it.

Prescription and Over-the-Counter Medications

What is the difference between prescription and over-the-counter (OTC) medications? We are all familiar with physicians prescribing medication when we have a short-term illness (e.g., urinary tract infection, yeast infection, strep throat). Anyone with a particular medical condition, such as asthma, diabetes, cystic fibrosis, or a seizure disorder, is prescribed medication that is taken at specific times each day. Over-the-counter medication, however, is purchased off a shelf in a pharmacy. These medications include cough and cold remedies, painkillers, teething medication (e.g., Orajel), Ovol for flatulence in infants, and medicated creams and ointments.

Child care regulations require that all medication administered in programs be prescribed or, for OTC medication, recommended in writing by physicians. Some provincial/territorial child care regulations may include sunscreens, insect repellents, and diaper creams in their definition of medication and require that the child's physician recommend their use in writing. However, this is the exception rather than the rule across Canada.

Why do OTC drugs require the physician's recommendation in writing before they are administered in early childhood programs? OTC medications are medications despite their easy availability and should not be treated casually. Whenever you take more than one medication at the same time, you put yourself at risk of side effects, because the ingredients from the different medications may interact. As well, drug interactions may influence the effectiveness of the medications.

Vitamins, including chewable ones, are medications. Eating well-balanced, nutritious food provides children with their daily requirement of essential nutrients. Physicians discourage the routine use of vitamins; they are prescribed only when a child has a vitamin or mineral deficiency. Prescribed vitamins can be given at home by parents. Educators do not have to administer the vitamins during the day.

Naturopathic and homeopathic medicine have been practised for centuries in many cultures and are gaining popularity in Canada. Herbal medicines, nutrition, vitamins, ointments, acupuncture, and hydra and physical therapies are used to treat various maladies. Herbal medicines consist of different combinations of herbs and plants that are available over the counter or prescribed by naturopaths. As with any medication, they must be taken with care and knowledge. According to the child care regulations' definition, medications must be prescribed by physicians or dentists—classifications that do not currently include naturopathic doctors. Consequently, parents who use herbal medicines for their children must give them to the children at home. Staff, currently, can't give these medications to the child at the program.

Over-the-Counter Medications: Effective?

Many pediatricians do not recommend using OTC remedies for children (Canadian Paediatric Society 1996). Colds and ear infections have to run their course. Children benefit from extra fluids, rest, and care, but not from many of the OTC medications. One critical review of clinical studies on OTC cold medications found that "over-the-counter cold medications form a common part of every-day medical therapy … The data on their effectiveness are limited and weak, especially for children." Research on the effectiveness of treating children's nighttime coughing with one medication containing codeine, another containing dextromethorphan, and a placebo found that "by 3 days after a visit to a paediatrician because of cough symptoms, the cough will be significantly reduced regardless of specific therapy" (Taylor et al. 1993, 801). Others have reached similar conclusions (Hutton et al. 1991).

When a child is up all night coughing, parents often feel less helpless just giving cough syrup. But besides the ineffectiveness of such medication, other issues should be considered (Schroeder and Fahey 2002). The medications are colourful and tasty, and the liquid preparations do not come with child-resistant caps (which are not childproof anyway). Children can experience mild to serious side effects from OTC cold medications (Gunn et al. 2001).

We also wonder whether children who are given an OTC medication for every sniffle, cough, ache, or pain could potentially develop a lifelong reliance on medication. These medications treat symptoms, not the cause of the illness. We should focus instead on preventive strategies and, when we are ill with a viral infection, let the illness run its course.

Acetaminophen (e.g., Tylenol, Tempra) is an analgesic (or painkiller) and may be recommended by physicians for treating children's aches and pains from a cold and cough. Programs with infants and toddlers still commonly give acetaminophen whenever the child's temperature rises to certain degree, although it is not routinely recommended. In these programs, parents are asked to sign a medication consent form, which is kept in the child's file and referred to each time the child's temperature is elevated. It is unlikely that each child's physician has provided the parents and educators with such a written recommendation. This practice shows how grey the interpretation of a specific child care regulation can be (see Fevers, page 141).

Ensuring the Safe Administration of Medication

Whether the medication is prescribed or recommended by the child's physician, the steps in its administration are identical to eliminate the chance of medication error. The general principles and rationale for the administration of medication in programs are as follows.

- Obtain the parents' written consent to administer any medication. A medication consent form must be completed for each medication, both prescribed and physician recommended. Consent forms should include at least the following information:
  - name of the child and date
  - name of the medication
  - reason why it is needed (e.g., strep throat)
  - amount to be given (dosage)
  - time(s) it is to be given during the day
  - time and date of the last dose in the program, which helps ensure that children don't continue to get medication longer than recommended by the doctor and is particularly relevant to OTC medication (the bottle usually holds more medication than required for two or three days)
  - parent's signature

- Before starting the medication at the program, ask parents whether the child has taken it at home for the past 24 hours. This period allows parents to watch for side effects or signs of allergic reaction to the medication, for the child to get used to the way it tastes or feels (e.g., eye ointment), and for the medication to begin its work. Parents may have a helpful hint or two to share.

- Keep all medication in a locked container out of reach of children. Liquid medications usually require refrigeration, which won't harm capsules, tablets, or creams either. All can be kept in a locked container in the fridge. Sunscreens, insect repellents, and diaper creams do not have to be kept locked, but must be out of reach of children. Diaper creams are kept in the change area.

- Know who is responsible for giving the medication during the day. Programs usually assign this responsibility either to one educator who gives all the medications or to a number of educators who give medication to specific children. Any confusion over this responsibility can lead to a child either getting a double dose or missing the medication altogether.

- Compare the information on the medication label with the information the parent filled in on the consent form. Discrepancies must be verified and corrected.

- All medication, both prescription and OTC, must be kept in the original containers. It is not acceptable, for example, for a parent to pour cough syrup into a glass jar and label it with masking tape. Prescription labels must include
  - child's name (not a sibling's),
  - name of the medication,
  - the dose (amount),
  - the number of times it is given each day, and
  - route (oral, nasal, rectal, eye, ear).

  Sometimes pharmacists place stickers on the container with additional information: "Shake well," "Take with meals," "May cause a photosensitive reaction."

- Follow the steps provided in the program's medication policy for preparing, giving, and recording medication. Know the procedure for reporting and responding to medication errors.

- When children have allergies to medicine, post the children's names and pictures and the names of the drugs at the place where medication is stored and prepared.

- For children who are prescribed adrenalin injections (e.g., Anakit, EpiPen) or inhalers (e.g., Bronkaid Misto-Meter) to treat allergic reactions, always have the medication in the same general area as the child. Adrenalin is an exception to the rule about keeping all medication in a locked container. Although it should be out of reach of children—perhaps in the first-aid kit in the play area—educators must be able to access and administer this medication on a moment's notice. If a child has a severe allergy to insect stings or other allergens found outside, you must take medication to the playground, on walks, and so on. For children with severe food allergies, take it outside only if the child might eat something there (e.g., picnic lunch or snack, on a field trip). All educators must know how to administer adrenalin. It is an emergency when a child needs adrenalin, so educators don't have time to look for the educator responsible for giving medication. Ask the pharmacist for the manufacturer's poster that shows how to give the injection, to display it in the centre. Educators may also be required by the child care regulations to receive training on injections from a health professional or the parents. In any case, auto-injectors are simple to use (see Allergies, page 170).

- Remember the following tips when you give medication to a child:
  - Be honest with the child (e.g., if you don't know how the medication tastes, admit it).
  - Especially for young children, the child who receives the medication should know and be comfortable with the educator administering it.
  - Explain to the child what you are going to do and how he or she can cooperate.

- Never call medicine "candy." Medicines are potentially hazardous products and children must learn how to take medications safely.
- Give the child the medication away from the other children.

Preventing Medication Errors

Medication errors—such as giving medication to a child who wasn't prescribed a drug, mixing up medications among children, giving an incorrect dosage, or putting ear drops in the wrong ear—can occur for a number of reasons. The consequences of such errors range from minor to very serious. However, you can go through your child care career without making any medication errors.

Medication errors result when one or more of the "five rights" has not been verified:

- right child,
- right medication,
- right dose (amount),
- right time, or
- right route (oral, nasal, rectal, eye, ear, injection).

Safeguards:

- Always use a measuring spoon, dropper, or cup that is designed for medication.
- Check the sheet you use to record the administration of medication to ensure that no one has already given the drug to the child.
- Read the prescription label three times:
  1. when you take the medication out of the storage space,
  2. before you pour the medication from the bottle, and
  3. after you pour it and are putting the bottle back in storage.

     During the three checks, compare the prescription label to the parents' medication consent form. Verify that all of the "five rights" are correct.

- If a child tells you that someone else has already given him or her the drug, or that he or she is no longer taking the medication, double-check with the other educators. Another educator could have given the drug and not recorded it, or the drug may have been stopped and the parent forgotten to tell you.
- Immediately record that you gave the medication on the parents' medication consent form.
- Document and report every medication error as soon as you are aware of it.

Assessing the situation:

During school hours, school-agers with asthma or life-threatening allergies are encouraged to be responsible for their own puffer or adrenalin kit and to carry it with them. However, while they are in the school-age program, educators are responsible for these medications. How do we help school-agers understand that expectations differ for them between the school and the child care program? And how do educators in school-age programs advocate for change in child care regulations to bring these programs into line with the school, to create the "seamless day"?

Parents should be encouraged to tell educators when their children are taking medication at home, even when staff don't need to give the drug during the day. Educators may notice that the child is experiencing side effects such as dizziness or fatigue and can notify the parents, who can then talk with their physician.

ALLERGIES AND ASTHMA

Perhaps you have allergies or asthma. Lots of us do. In fact, experts estimate that about 3 million Canadians have asthma (Asthma Society of Canada 2003). It is estimated that one in 10 people have been tested for allergies and are receiving treatment. However, one in four people believe they have allergies but haven't been tested. One in 100 people have severe allergies.

The number of children and adults with allergies and asthma is increasing. Environmental pollutants and sick-building syndrome are playing a significant role in this increase. We can assume that every program has at least one child with allergies or asthma. As such, educators must be aware of these health conditions, and know how to avoid factors that trigger reactions and how to handle reactions when they occur. Depending on their age, children with allergies or asthma may wish to talk with other children about the condition, about how they feel when they get sick, about what they do to make themselves feel better, or about their hospital experiences. These opportunities are wonderful and natural times for children to learn about health.

Allergies

Basically, allergies are the result of our body's hypersensitivity to a substance. These substances are not usually harmful to most people (e.g., pollen, peanuts, feathers, animal fur, perfume, latex); but for those with allergies, they can cause mild to severe allergic reactions.

Fortunately, most allergies are not life threatening. The substances that cause allergies, called allergens, enter our body through breathing, eating, touching, or being stung or bitten. Once the allergen is in the body, our immune system responds by producing antibodies that attack it. These antibodies remain in our body to protect us the next time we are exposed to that allergen, providing immunity. But for people with allergies, repeated exposure to an allergen results in their immune systems' becoming overly sensitive to that particular allergen. An allergic reaction results when the person is exposed to the allergen and the body produces chemicals such as histamines, which cause various physical symptoms (or reactions) such as sneezing, runny nose, vomiting, tightness in the chest, or hives. Table 4.2 lists allergens that are responsible for allergic reactions.

Allergic reactions can cause feelings of fear, discomfort, or anxiety in children and their parents. The goal should be to maintain as normal a lifestyle as possible. It is important to balance supporting a child's awareness of his or her allergens with knowing what to do if the child is exposed and avoiding overwhelming fear and excessive limits on the child's activities.

Most of the symptoms listed in Table 4.2 are from four of the body systems: upper and lower respiratory tract, skin, eyes, and gastrointestinal tract. The more body systems that are affected by an allergen, the more severe the allergic reaction. Severe allergic reactions are most commonly caused by peanuts and nuts, eggs, shellfish, bee and wasp stings, penicillin, and aspirin. In a severe allergy to bee sting, for example, the first sting results in a significant reaction. Any subsequent sting, however, could be fatal. When children are diagnosed with severe allergies, the physician prescribes adrenalin (e.g., Anakit, EpiPen, Bronkaid Misto-Meter) to be administered in the event of severe allergic reaction. In these instances, parents are required to provide the program with an adrenalin kit.

The most severe allergic reaction is called anaphylactic shock, which affects the entire body. *This reaction happens quickly.* Within seconds the child's eyes, lips, and face begin to swell, he or she may get a headache, hives may appear all over the body, the throat may swell and cut off the breathing, and he or she may

TABLE 4.2	Common Allergic Substances and Reactions
COMMON ALLERGIC SUBSTANCES	**TYPICAL REACTIONS**
Environmental dust, mould, pollen, grass, trees*	itchy eyes and nose, nasal discharge, blocked nasal passages, sinus headache, sneezing, wheezing, coughing, shortness of breath
Animals and Birds fur, feathers	itchy eyes and nose, nasal discharge, etc.
Insects stings from bees and wasps	wheezing, hives, swelling of upper airway with difficulty breathing, and in extreme cases swelling of face and anaphylactic shock
Foods eggs, peanuts, nuts, shellfish, milk, and wheat (the latter two are common causes of infant allergies)	vomiting, diarrhea, bloody stools, plus symptoms as for insect venom (such as hives, pallor, weakness, difficulty breathing, and collapse)
Medications and Chemicals medical (e.g., antibiotics) and non-medical (e.g., fabric softener)†	any of the above reactions

* Poison ivy and poison oak cause allergic reactions in the majority of us when we touch these plants.

† Latex in balloons, gloves, condoms, and dental dams can cause reactions in some people.

Source: Courtesy of the Canadian Paediatric Society (1996), *Well Beings: A Guide to Promote the Physical Health, Safety and Emotional Well-Being of Children in Child Care Centres and Family Day Care Homes* (Ottawa: Canadian Paediatric Society), 252.

vomit and have diarrhea. Eventually the child becomes unconscious. All of this can happen in less than 10 minutes. Educators must identify these symptoms immediately, administer the child's adrenalin, and call an ambulance. *To save the child's life, further emergency medical care is needed.* Even if you aren't sure about the child's allergic symptoms, always give adrenalin to the child and call an ambulance. Parents should be encouraged to obtain a medical alert bracelet for any child who has been diagnosed with severe allergies. The bracelet must be worn at all times.

There is no cure for allergies. We try to prevent the reactions by eliminating exposure to allergens whenever possible (e.g., peanuts, shellfish, animals) or at least limiting exposure to allergens (e.g., smoke, dust, pollen). The only treatment for allergies is to alleviate or reduce the effect of the symptoms (e.g., runny noses, itchy red eyes, nasal and sinus congestion) with medications such as antihistamines and decongestants. During hay fever season, children with hay fever may be more comfortable playing outside in the afternoon, because most plants pollinate in the morning.

Preventing Allergic Reactions

First, effective communication is essential between educators and parents to prevent allergic reactions. At the time of enrollment, parents must be asked for the following information about their children's allergies: the name of the allergen(s) and the specific symptoms, steps to prevent exposure to the allergen, what actions the educators should take when a child has symptoms, and what medication the physician has prescribed or recommended. Educators and parents can then develop an allergy care plan that meets the child's needs.

The program's policy and preventive practices on allergies should include all the following:

- a medical form completed by the child's physician outlining the management of the allergies, what educators need to be aware of, and any instructions on handling emergency situations
- the sharing of allergy information with all staff members by
  - posting a list of children with their allergies in the kitchen and eating areas. Adding photos of each child to the list ensures that children are not exposed to known allergens, especially when volunteers, students, and substitute educators enter the program. This is particularly important when the children are younger and when there are children with the same first names. There have been educators who raise concerns around medical confidentiality and the posting of such information. However, the health risk of not sharing this vital information surpasses any such concern and it assists staff and volunteers in providing a safe environment for the children.
  - including the pertinent allergy information with the emergency information cards kept in the first-aid kits.
  - attaching an allergy list to the top of the first-aid kit used outdoors (i.e., on the playground, field trips, walks) that focuses on children who are allergic to substances found outside, such as bees, wasps, animal hair, and feathers.

Educators can quickly refer to this list to prevent or respond to allergic reactions. Educators can also refer to the list before they leave, to make sure they take the adrenalin kits outside for those children who have been prescribed one. The adrenalin kit must always be in the same general area as the child. Educators do not have time to go back to the program and then return to the playground to give the injection. Remember, anaphylactic shock happens very quickly and educators must administer the adrenalin immediately (see Ensuring the Safe Administration of Medication, page 167).

■ an awareness of how food is purchased, prepared, and served. The cooks or educators responsible for snacks and meals must know which children have food allergies, read all the ingredients on labels, and so on. New food labeling regulations came into effect in 2003. Processed food labels now clearly list the ingredients so consumers can avoid foods that provoke allergic reactions. With time, there will be further legislative changes to support the education of consumers in understanding what foods they are eating.

– Use extreme caution for children with allergies to peanuts and peanut products. Educators must take parents' concerns very seriously, because for some children even the smell of peanuts or a trace of grated nuts in a cookie can cause anaphylactic shock. Some early childhood programs have voluntarily banned peanut butter and nut products from their programs. In some jurisdictions, such as in the province of Manitoba, there is a regulation for child care centres and licensed family day care homes that states that "no foods containing known peanut products are served to children under three years of age" (Manitoba Family Services 1998, 58). Obviously, this regulation does not prevent parents from sending nut products in their child's meals, but educators strongly discourage parents from doing so.

■ the posting of menus so parents can make substitutions for foods or food ingredients to which their child is allergic. When the program provides substitute foods, choose foods that look similar to those the other children are having. This can help to normalize eating experiences for children with food allergies.

■ the documenting of all allergic reactions in the child's file. The child's parents must be contacted.

Eighty percent of allergies develop before the age of five. To ensure children's safety, programs need to

■ require all parents to give their children prescribed or OTC medication for 24 hours before educators administer it in the program, so parents can determine whether their child has any side effects or allergic symptoms;

- outline how new foods are introduced to promote early awareness of allergies, which is particularly important for infants (see The Process of Introducing Semisolid Foods, page 225); and

- as a general practice, use unscented laundry and cleaning products and encourage staff not to wear perfumes and colognes, which many people are sensitive to.

Asthma

When someone has asthma, the mucous membrane that lines the airways is chronically inflamed, which narrows the airways (or bronchial tubes). The membranes produce more mucus, which is stickier than normal, resulting in less space in the airways for air to pass through. The cause of the tissue's chronic inflammation is not known.

Asthma varies in severity and is diagnosed when children have recurring episodes of wheezing, coughing, or shortness of breath. Wheezing has been considered the classic asthma symptom. Some people with asthma have a chronic dry cough rather than a wheeze, so their asthma may go undiagnosed because the wheezing can't be heard over the coughing. "Respiratory illness accounted for the greatest proportion of hospital admissions for children aged 1 to 4 years (41%) … Hospital admissions are often recurrent and the result of chronic conditions such as asthma or neurological conditions" (Canadian Institute of Child Health 2000, 72). Approximately 500 people per year die of asthma; many of these deaths could have been prevented through education and management (Asthma Society of Canada 2003).

There are three levels of severity (Kovesi n.d., 9–10):

- Mild intermittent asthma—The child has mild attacks, often occurring shortly after recovering from a cold. The child is prescribed medication for the duration of the symptoms, which is stopped after recovery. The child is then symptom-free until the next cold.

- Severe intermittent asthma—Colds are usually the trigger for an attack, which is often severe, requiring treatment in emergency or a hospital admission. Children with this severity of asthma are often prescribed medication they take every day to reduce the risk of such attacks.

- Chronic asthma—The child experiences the symptoms of asthma almost daily or daily. Even when there is no attack, the child experiences nighttime coughing, symptoms during exercise, and may require a trip to the hospital following a cold. These children not only take medication to prevent attacks, but also take medication to relieve the chronic symptoms.

Fortunately, only a small percentage of children suffer from chronic asthma. But keep in mind that severe asthma attacks can be life threatening and even fatal, because the airway completely closes and no air can get to the lungs (see Table 4.3).

The mucous membranes are more sensitive to allergens (e.g., dust mites, pollen, mould, grass, trees, and weed pollens), substances (e.g., air pollution, perfume, cologne, paint fumes, chemicals, tobacco smoke), cold weather, strenuous

TABLE 4.3	Signs of Managed and Poorly Managed Asthma
MANAGED ASTHMA	**POORLY MANAGED ASTHMA[1]**
Sleep is not disturbed by cough, wheeze, or shortness of breath.	The number of symptoms increases: wheezing, coughing, and shortness of breath, along with a decreased capacity to exercise and/or go about your daily activities.
You don't have symptoms when you wake up.	The use of inhaled bronchodilators increases (i.e., you're not getting relief from the usual amount of medication).
Symptoms during the day are immediately and completely reversed with a bronchodilator inhaler.	The peak expiratory flow rates decrease.[2]
A bronchodilator inhaler is not needed more than twice a day on most days.	Sputum production increases or sputum changes colour (e.g., yellow, green, brown).
Symptoms do not interfere with day-to-day activities, including physical activity.	Nighttime or early-morning awakenings require use of the bronchodilator.

1   If you experience any of the following warning signs, your asthma is out of control and you should adjust your medication and/or contact your doctor.
2   A peak-flow meter is a hand-held device that you blow into to get a reading of how rapidly you can blow out. The meter measures "peak flow rate," or forced exhalation. The meter helps individuals manage their asthma and helps in the detection of worsening airway obstruction and asthma. Not everyone needs to use a peak-flow meter.

Source: Reprinted with permission from The Lung Association, *The Asthma Handbook* (1994), 6, 2.

exercise (episodes in this connection are referred to as exercise-induced asthma, or EIA), upper respiratory infection, colds, emotional upset, sudden changes in the atmosphere or weather, and food additives and preservatives. Any of these may irritate the mucous membranes and trigger an asthma episode. The child has to work hard at breathing because the muscles around the airway tighten, and the lining swells further and produces more sticky mucus. The child may cough frequently, wheeze, breathe at a faster rate, and complain that the chest feels tight, and may have behaviour changes (e.g., tiredness, restlessness, irritability).

Identifying and managing the triggers of the child's asthma episodes is the first line of prevention. Educators can work with the children's parents to identify triggers, to remove or at least reduce exposure to allergens, and to administer prescribed medications. Three of the most common allergens for children are dust mites' feces, pollen, and cat dander. For some children, even being around another child who comes to the program or school with cat or dog hair on his or her clothes can irritate the airways. Dust mites thrive in warm, humid places, live off human skin scales, and can be found on pillows and mattresses, carpets, cloth-covered furniture, and soft toys. Educators can reduce the number of dust mites in programs by regularly dusting, vacuuming, and laundering cloth toys. Many allergens and irritants are found outdoors (e.g., pollens, fumes, tobacco smoke) and in public places and are more difficult to reduce or alleviate.

There are a number of medications that can be prescribed for children to prevent and relieve symptoms of asthma. Reliever medications, called bronchodilators, are used to relax the bronchial tubes during an attack in order for the child to breathe more easily. These medications are often administered in an aerosol inhaler (or puffer), Diskhaler, Diskus, or Turbuhaler, a syrup, or in tablet form (e.g., Ventolin, Airomir, Bricanyl, Berotec). Steroid and non-steroid medications are prescribed for the prevention of asthma attacks (e.g., Beclovent, Pulmicort, Flovent, Singulair). These medications reduce the inflammation of the lung tissue, which in turn reduces the likelihood that the cells in the lungs will release chemicals that cause the asthma attack. They are prescribed in inhaler form to be taken at home (Kovesi n.d., 14, 17). The severity of the child's asthma and the activities determine which medication will be prescribed.

Younger children often use an AeroChamber because they are not yet able to use a puffer, which requires exhaling completely and then pumping the puffer once and inhaling the puff of medication in one breath. Most individuals are prescribed two or three puffs. At one end of the AeroChamber is the hole where the mouthpiece of the puffer is inserted; the face mask is on the other end. The mask is placed over the child's mouth and nose, one puff of the medication is pumped into the chamber, and the child breathes in the medication over at least six breaths. Before the second puff, the child needs to wait one minute to allow the medication to travel through the air passages. This wait between puffs applies to all ages and all types of inhaler.

The program's policy and practices for the care of children with asthma should include

- providing parents with a medical form for the child's physician to complete, which outlines the management of the asthma, what educators must be aware of, and any instructions on medication and emergency situations. Have parents provide you with a copy of the child's asthma action plan;
- sharing this medical information with the child's educators;
- observing the child during strenuous play and in cold weather. If the child starts wheezing or coughing or is short of breath, stop the activity. If the weather is cold or damp, bring the child inside. Have the child sit down to use the bronchodilator. Regular exercise is just as important for children with

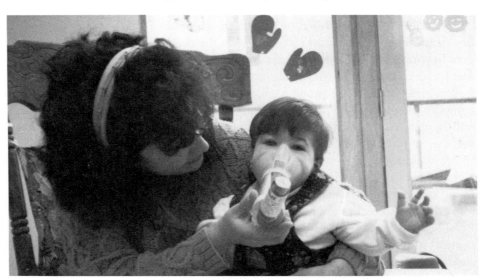

asthma as it is for other children; however, it is important to discuss the child's specific needs for exercise or being outside in the winter or in very hot weather; and

- documenting all asthmatic episodes in the child's file and contacting the child's parents. If an episode doesn't subside after two consecutive treatments of the bronchodilator medicine, the child should be seen by a physician as soon as possible.

REVISITING THE HEALTH PROMOTION ACTION PLAN

Recall the Health Promotion Action Plan introduced in Unit 1. The following example illustrates this plan in practice in terms of preventing and managing childhood illnesses.

Individual Problem Solving and Self-Reliance
Each day, educators have the opportunity to influence individual children's health positively by implementing the program's infection control strategy. Granted, children get sick, and even if they are ill for only a few days the whole family's schedule can be disrupted. Health policies and practices should be supportive, empathetic, and respectful of parents' situations, and they should take into account the program's responsibility for the health of the other children. We often forget that programs are also employers and, as such, the program's board can demonstrate a commitment to employees' families by providing family responsibility leave for staff and permitting staff to bank overtime hours.

Collective Self-Help
Directors can benefit from developing a pool of substitute educators and/or volunteers who can be called on when

- a child is mildly ill but stays at the program and needs extra attention,
- an educator is absent due to illness,
- a program needs extra adults (volunteers or paid), who come in for a few hours each day to cover busier times (e.g., meals, staff break times), or
- a field trip is planned or an activity needs additional supervisors.

Ideally, volunteers and substitutes are in the program often enough that the children and the adults get to know one another. When they are approached by staff, these trusted adults may be interested in providing care for the mildly ill child in the family's home or in their own home when the need arises. For parents who don't have access to alternative (or backup) care, this service could be extremely valuable. In communities where there is a cluster of programs in close proximity, directors could work collaboratively to support families and their staff.

Community Action
Staff have identified the need for a community service that provides care for mildly ill children. Either on an individual basis or with a collective of programs, educators could advocate to a local agency to develop such a service (e.g.,

Victorian Order of Nurses [VON]). In communities with only one or two main employers, most, if not all, of the parents who use the program work for the same company. The program's board could meet with the company's management to discuss establishing family responsibility leave for their employees. Perhaps the local public health agency would work cooperatively with the program and the company.

Societal Change

Provincial/territorial and national child care associations (e.g., Saskatchewan Child Care Association, Canadian Child Care Federation) lobby the government to legislate employers to provide family responsibility leave. These associations are made up of members like you. Individual educators can exercise their democratic right (and responsibility) to vote for political candidates who are committed to child care and the family.

CONCLUSION

Even when an early childhood program implements the infection control strategies covered in Unit 3, children do get sick. Fortunately most of the illnesses are mild and short-lived. Most do not require exclusion or prescriptions. In cooperation with parents, educators address the needs of the ill child yet consider the best interests of the other children and staff.

What's Your Opinion?

TO COLLABORATE OR NOT TO COLLABORATE?

The school-age program is located inside the elementary school. One part-time educator works in the afternoon and after school. Two full-time educators work in the program, preparing activities and planning the curriculum in the morning, and working with children from the half-time kindergarten class in the afternoon. Classroom teachers often expect the educators to care for any mildly ill child who is also enrolled in the school-age program rather than call the parents or keep the child in the classroom until the end of class. At times, the educators manage to accommodate an older ill child in the afternoon. As a result, the teachers expect the educators to be responsible for ill children and to notify parents when the child becomes ill in the classroom. The educators feel resentment toward these teachers.

The teachers and educators need to work cooperatively and collaboratively. Debate both sides of the issue from the perspective of the teachers and the educators. How can this issue be resolved in a way that is in the best interests of the children? Design a policy and procedures for the management of ill school-agers that can be used by teachers and educators. Don't overlook the parents.

ASSESS YOUR LEARNING

Define terms or describe concepts used in this unit.

- health observations
- signs and symptoms
- exclusion
- alternative care
- prescription medication
- over-the-counter medication
- "five rights" for administering medication

- allergies
- allergic substances
- adrenalin kit
- anaphylactic shock
- asthma
- triggers of asthma episodes

Evaluate your options in each situation.

1. One of the two-year-olds is listless and unhappy today. He is unable to participate in the program and needs to be held and comforted. When the director calls his mother, she asks that you take his temperature. You do so, and because the child does not have a fever, the mother refuses to pick him up early.

2. A preschooler has a number of food allergies, so she is often offered other foods at lunch and snack. She cries and says she wants only what the other children eat. Meanwhile, some of the other children only want to eat the same food she eats.

3. One of the families goes to a naturopath as their health practitioner. You also believe that naturopaths have a lot to offer in promoting health. The parents ask you to administer the homeopathic (i.e., not prescribed by a medical doctor) medicine to their child daily. They are willing to sign the medication form. Are you able to administer this medication?

4. One of the preschoolers who has asthma often needs her "rescue" medication (Ventolin inhaler) to prevent severe attacks. Today you are going on a field trip away from the centre, but didn't notice until you are ready to leave that the inhaler is empty. The parent has already left for work. What do you do?

RESOURCE MATERIALS

Organizations

Allergy Asthma Information Association, Box 100, Toronto, Ontario M9W 5K9. Tel. (416) 679-9521 or 1-800-611-7011 (or contact regional office); fax (416) 679-9524. www.calgaryallergy.ca/aaia

Asthma Society of Canada, 130 Bridgeland Avenue, Suite 425, Toronto, ON M6A 1Z4. Tel. (416) 787-4050 or 1-800-787-3880 (or contact regional office); fax (416) 787-5807. www.asthma.ca

Canadian Institute of Child Health, 384 Bank Street, Suite 300, Ottawa, ON K2P 1Y4. Tel. (613) 230-8838; fax (613) 230-6654. www.cich.ca

Canadian Paediatric Society, 100–2204 Walkley Road, Ottawa, ON K1G 4G8. Tel. (613) 526-9397; fax (613) 526-3332. www.cps.ca

Hospital for Sick Children, Centre for Health Information and Promotion, 555 University Avenue, Toronto, ON M5G 1X8. Tel. (416) 813-5819. www.sickkids.on.ca/CHIP

The Lung Association, 3 Raymond Street, Suite 300, Ottawa, ON K1R 1A3. Tel: (613) 569-6411 or 1-888-566-LUNG (connects to regional Lung Associations) or contact regional offices directly; fax (613) 569-8860. (The CLA provides educational sessions on asthma for parents.) www.lung.ca

Printed Matter

A Guide to Asthma for the Parent (1990), by Dr. D. Hughes. Contact The Lung Association or your regional office. (For contact information, see under Organizations.)

A Guild to Asthma for the Teacher (1990), by Dr. D. Hughes. Contact The Lung Association or your regional office. (For contact information, see under Organizations.)

A Guide to Exercise Induced Asthma in Children (1998), by Dr. D. Hughes. Contact The Lung Association or your regional office. (For contact information, see under Organizations.)

"Antibiotic Safety Zone," by Dr. Ross Pennie, McMaster University, Hamilton, ON, www-fhs.mcmaster.ca/path/faculty/pennie.htm (July 2003).

Asthma in Children (n.d.), by Dr. T. Kovesi. Contact The Lung Association or your regional office. (For contact information, see under Organizations.)

Taking Control—Anaphylaxis and You. A booklet and video. Contact Media Works. Tel. (905) 373-9324; fax (905) 373-9027.

The Canadian Allergy and Asthma Handbook (1996), by Dr. B. Zimmerman (Random House of Canada).

The Complete Allergy Book (1997), by June Engel (Key Porter Books).

What to Do When Your Child Is Vomiting and Has Diarrhea (1996), by the Canadian Paediatric Society. (For contact information, see under Organizations.)

BIBLIOGRAPHY

American Academy of Pediatrics and American Public Health Association (1992). *Caring for Our Children: National Health and Safety Performance Standards—Guidelines for Out-of-Home Child Care Programs,* 1st ed. Washington, DC: American Public Health Association and American Academy of Pediatrics.

———— (2002). *Caring for Our Children: National Health and Safety Performance Standards: Guidelines for Out-of-Home Child Care Programs,* 2nd ed. Washington, DC: American Public Health Association and American Academy of Pediatrics.

Asthma Society of Canada (2003). "About Asthma." <www.asthma.ca/adults/about/> (July 2003).

Burroughs Wellcome Inc. (n.d.). *Head Lice Education Program.* Montreal: Burroughs Wellcome.

Canadian Institute of Child Health (2000). *The Health of Canada's Children: A CICH Profile,* 3rd ed. Ottawa: Canadian Institute of Child Health.

Canadian Medical Association (1999). "Canadian Asthma Consensus Report, 1999." *Canadian Medical Association Journal* 161, Suppl: 11.

Canadian Paediatric Society (1997). *Your Child's Best Shot: A Parent's Guide to Vaccination.* Ottawa: Canadian Paediatric Society.

————— (1996). *Well Beings: A Guide to Promote the Physical Health, Safety and Emotional Well-Being of Children in Child Care Centres and Family Day Care Homes.* Ottawa: Canadian Paediatric Society.

————— (1994). *Little Well Beings: A Handbook on Health in Family Day Care.* Toronto: Canadian Paediatric Society.

Division of Infectious Diseases (1997). "Your Child and Antibiotics: Unnecessary Antibiotics Can Be Harmful." Pamphlet. Toronto: Hospital for Sick Children.

Freeman, J.M. (1992). "The Best Medicine for Febrile Seizures." *New England Journal of Medicine* 327: 1161–63.

Giebink, G.S. (1993). "Care of the Ill Child in Day-Care Settings." *Pediatrics* 91: 229–33.

Gunn, V.L., S.H. Taha, E.L. Liebelt, and J.R. Serwint (2001). "Toxicity of Over-the-Counter Cough and Cold Medications." *Pediatrics* 108(3): E52.

Hughes, D. (1998). *A Guide to Asthma for the Teacher.* Merck Frosst Canada Inc. Available from The Lung Association.

Hutton, N., et al. (1991). "Effectiveness of an Antihistamine-Decongestant Combination for Young Children with the Common Cold: A Randomized, Controlled Clinical Trial." *Journal of Pediatrics* 118(1): 125–30.

Kluger, M.J. (1992). "Fever Revisited." *Pediatrics* 90: 846–50.

Kovesi, T. (n.d.). "Asthma in Children." Toronto: The Lung Association.

Levy, S.B. (1998). "The Challenge of Antibiotic Resistance." *Scientific American,* March: 46–53.

Lung Association, The (1994). *The Asthma Handbook.* Toronto.

Manitoba Family Services (1998). *Licensing Manual for Day Care Centres.* Winnipeg: Child Day Care Office, Province of Manitoba.

Pennie, R. (2000). "This Medical Office Is an Antibiotic Safety Zone." Legal-size poster for medical offices. Hamilton: McMaster University. <www-fhs.mcmaster.ca/path/faculty/pennie.htm> (July 2003).

Schroeder, K., and T. Fahey (2002). "Should We Advise Parents to Administer Over-the-Counter Cough Medicines for Acute Cough? Systematic Review of Randomized Controlled Trials." *Archives of Disease in Childhood* 86(3): 170–75.

Skull, S.A., E.L. Ford-Jones, N.A. Kulin, T.R. Einarson, and E.E. Wang (2000). "Child Care Centre Staff Contribute to Physician Visits and Pressure for Antibiotic Prescription." *Archives of Pediatrics and Adolescent Medicine* 154: 180–83.

Smith, M.B.H., and W. Feldman (1993). "Over-the-Counter Cold Medications: A Critical Review of Clinical Trials between 1950 and 1991." *Journal of the American Medical Association* 269(17): 2258–63.

Taylor, J.A., A.H. Novack, J.R. Almquist, and J.E. Rogers (1993). "Efficacy of Cough Suppressants in Children." *Journal of Pediatrics* 122(5, Pt. 1): 799–802.

Tulk, S., and M. Ipp (1992). "Assessment and Management of Childhood Fever and Other Common Pediatric Problems." *Contemporary Pediatrics,* March/April: 26–30.

Warden, C.R., J. Zibulewsky, S. Mace, C. Gold, and M. Gausche-Hill (2003). "Evaluation and Management of Febrile Seizures in the Out-of-Hospital and Emergency Department Settings." *Annals of Emergency Medicine* 41(2): 215–22.

Ying, J., J. Braithwaite, and R. Kogon (1998). "Needs Assessment of Child Care Centres in the Former City of Toronto." *Canadian Journal of Public Health,* September–October: 308–14.

Management of Illness

Please note that requirements for reporting to the public health agencies may vary across Canada. If in doubt, these agencies can provide helpful information.

DISEASE	TRANSMISSION	SYMPTOMS AND SIGNS	INFECTIOUS PERIOD	EXCLUSION	REPORT
Respiratory Infections					
Common Cold	Spread person to person via droplets; indirect spread via contaminated hands, objects, surfaces. Almost always viral.	Runny nose, sore throat, cough, decreased appetite.	1 day before to 7 days after onset.	Do **not** exclude unless too ill to take part in the activities.	No
Cold with Fever	Same as above.	Same as above, plus fever, headache, muscle aches.	1 day before to 7 days after onset.	Do **not** exclude unless too ill to take part in the activities.	No
Ear Infection (*Otitis media*)	Complication of cold.	Earache or irritability, fever and cold symptoms.	Not infectious.	Do **not** exclude unless too ill to take part in the activities.	No
Pinkeye (Conjunctivitis)	Spread person to person by contact with secretions from eye.	Redness, itching, pain, discharge from eye.	For duration of illness or until 24 hours after treatment started.	Exclude only if discharge is pus (yellow, thick) and then until the antibiotic has been taken for 1 full day.	No

DISEASE	TRANSMISSION	SYMPTOMS AND SIGNS	INFECTIOUS PERIOD	EXCLUSION	REPORT
Pneumonia	Spread person to person via droplets; indirect spread via contaminated hands, objects, surfaces. Usually viral.	Fever, cough, rapid or noisy breathing, wheezing, grunting, pale or blue colour.	Varies with cause.	Exclude until evaluated by physician.	No
Strep Throat	Spread person to person.	Fever, sore throat.	Until 24 hours after treatment begun.	Exclude until 24 hours after treatment begun.	Only if an outbreak occurs, i.e., more than 2 cases in a month

Gastrointestinal Infections

DISEASE	TRANSMISSION	SYMPTOMS AND SIGNS	INFECTIOUS PERIOD	EXCLUSION	REPORT
Campylobacter	Germ excreted in stool. Poultry, beef, unpasteurized milk or other food may be source of infection.	Fever, diarrhea, blood in stool, cramps.	For duration of diarrhea.	Exclude until diarrhea is gone.	Yes
Diarrhea	Germ excreted in stool. Spread directly from person to person; indirectly by hands of staff and children, objects, surfaces, food, or water contaminated with germs (young children frequently put fingers and objects in mouth).	Increase in frequency of stools and/or change to unformed, loose, or watery stool. Fever, loss of appetite, nausea, vomiting, abdominal pain; mucus or blood in stool may also occur. Diarrhea may be dangerous in infants and young children because the loss of fluid may cause dehydration.	For duration of diarrhea.	Exclude until diarrhea is gone or physician determines child is not infectious. Notify parents at once if any of the following are present: 2 or more episodes of diarrhea or diarrhea with a fever over 39°C (102°F); repeated vomiting; dehydration; blood or mucus in stool.	Yes. Report outbreaks of 2 or more cases of diarrhea occuring within 48 hours and also any case of bloody or diagnosed bacterial diarrhea.
Escherichia coli (E. coli)	Germ excreted in stool. Poultry, beef, unpasteurized milk or other food may be source of infection.	Fever, diarrhea, blood in stool, cramps.	For duration of diarrhea.	Exclude until diarrhea is gone and the cultures are negative.	Yes

DISEASE	TRANSMISSION	SYMPTOMS AND SIGNS	INFECTIOUS PERIOD	EXCLUSION	REPORT
Food Poisoning	Acquired from contaminated food.	Nausea, vomiting, cramps, diarrhea.	Not infectious.	No exclusion required.	Yes
Giardia	Germ in stool. Spread person to person. Common in child care.	Most children have no symptoms. May have loss of appetite, vomiting, cramps, diarrhea, mushy stool, excessive gas.	Until cured.	Exclude until diarrhea is gone.	Yes, if 2 or more cases occur within a month.
Hepatitis A	Virus in stool. Spread person to person; may also be spread in contaminated food or water.	Most children have no illness. May have fever, loss of appetite, nausea, vomiting, jaundice (yellow colour in skin and eyes).	2 weeks before to 1 week after onset of jaundice.	Exclude for 1 week after onset of jaundice. Immune globulin may be indicated for children, staff, and family members to control epidemic.	Yes
Norwalk Virus	Spread person to person and via air.	Vomiting and prostration for 1 to 2 days.	Duration of illness.	Exclude until diarrhea and/or vomiting are gone.	Yes
Rotavirus	Germ in stool. Spread person to person. Most common cause of diarrhea in child care.	Fever and vomiting precede watery diarrhea. Dehydration may occur rapidly in infants.	For duration of diarrhea.	Exclude until diarrhea is gone.	Yes
Salmonella	Acquired mainly from food, especially eggs and egg products, beef, poultry, unpasteurized milk.	Diarrhea, fever, blood in stool.	While having diarrhea.	Exclude until diarrhea is gone.	Yes
Shigella	Germ in stool. Spread person to person.	Diarrhea, fever, blood and/or mucus in stool, cramps.	For duration of diarrhea. Highly infectious.	Exclude until diarrhea is gone and the cultures are negative.	Yes

DISEASE	TRANSMISSION	SYMPTOMS AND SIGNS	INFECTIOUS PERIOD	EXCLUSION	REPORT
Skin and Scalp Infections					
Head Lice	Spread person to person. Requires close direct contact. Infested hats, clothes may also be involved in spread.	Most children have no symptoms. Some will have itching of scalp. Nits (eggs) are seen attached to hairs near scalp.	Until treated.	Exclude until treated. Removal of all nits may be necessary to cure some cases.	No
Herpes Simplex	Spread person to person. Virus in saliva and infected sores.	Many infections occur without any symptoms. May cause high fever, many painful ulcers in mouth. May recur as cold sores.	For one week during first infection; 5 days during recurrent cold sores.	Exclude for severe illness. Exclusion not indicated for recurrent cold sores.	No
Impetigo	Person to person by direct contact.	Pustules or crusted rash on face or exposed parts of body (arms and/or legs).	From onset of rash until 1 day after start of treatment with antibiotics.	Exclude until antibiotic treatment has been taken for 1 full day.	No
Scabies	Spread person to person. Requires close direct contact.	Very itchy rash. In infants under 2 years, rash may occur anywhere on body. In older children, rash usually appears on fingers, elbows, armpits, abdomen.	Until treated.	Exclude until treated. Treatment of contacts may be necessary to control outbreak.	No. Public health agencies available to help if the problem persists.
Other Infections					
Chickenpox (Varicella-Zoster)	Spread person to person and via air. Very infectious.	Rash with small blisters on top, which become crusted, along with fever, itching.	2 days before to 5 days after onset of rash.	If illness is severe, exclude until 5th day after onset of rash or until all the blisters have crusted, whichever is shorter. If mild and child is able to take part in activities, no exclusion is required.	Yes

DISEASE	TRANSMISSION	SYMPTOMS AND SIGNS	INFECTIOUS PERIOD	EXCLUSION	REPORT
Cytomegalovirus (CMV)	Spread person to person. Virus in urine and saliva.	Usually causes no illness. Can infect fetus during pregnancy.	Whenever virus present in urine or saliva.	No exclusion required.	No
Hepatitis B	Virus present only in blood and certain body fluids (semen, cervical secretions). Virus is not in stool. Spread by contact with blood or by sexual intercourse.	Illness uncommon in children. Illness in adults is more severe and more prolonged than hepatitis A. May cause severe liver disease or liver cancer.	From weeks before onset to months or years after recovery from illness. May be infectious for life.	No exclusion required unless open sores are present. Hepatitis B vaccine and/or hepatitis B immune globulin may be indicated under special circumstances.	Yes. Immediately report any bites that cause bleeding.
Measles	Virus in respiratory secretions. Spread person to person. Very infectious.	Fever, cough, runny nose, inflamed eyes for 1 to 3 days before onset of rash. Rash is large red spots that often join together; starts on face and spreads rapidly over body. Illness lasts 5 to 10 days.	2 days before onset of fever and cough (3 to 5 days before onset of rash) until 4 days after onset of rash.	Exclude all cases until at least 4 days after onset of rash. Exclude all children who lack proof of immunization until vaccinated or until 2 weeks after last case in the child care facility.	Yes. Speed is essential in limiting outbreaks of measles: notify health department at once.
Meningitis	Spread person to person, requiring close direct contact.	Fever, marked fussiness and/or sleepiness, vomiting, stiff neck, coma, seizures. Very severe infection. Seek emergency care immediately.	Until treated with antibiotics (if caused by bacteria).	Exposed children and staff may need antibiotics or vaccine.	Yes. Immediately.
Mumps	Virus in respiratory secretions. Spread person to person.	Enlargement of salivary glands causing swelling of cheeks and face. May have fever, headache, abdominal pain. Many children have no illness.	7 days before to 9 days after swelling. Most infectious 2 days before onset of swelling.	Control difficult because many children have no symptoms. Exclude for 9 days, less if the illness is mild and child is able to take part in the activities. Ensure all children are vaccinated.	Yes

DISEASE	TRANSMISSION	SYMPTOMS AND SIGNS	INFECTIOUS PERIOD	EXCLUSION	REPORT
Rubella (German Measles)	Virus in respiratory secretions. Spread person to person.	Many children infected but have no illness. May have mild fever, sore throat, swollen glands in neck but no rash. Rash consists of small red spots that start on scalp and face and spread rapidly over entire body.	Few days before until 7 days after onset of rash.	Exclude for 7 days after onset of rash. All staff should be vaccinated or have blood test to prove immunity. There is risk of severe damage to fetus if a pregnant woman gets rubella during the first trimester.	Yes
Whooping Cough (Pertussis)	Bacteria in respiratory secretions. Spread person to person. Very infectious.	Begins as cold with profuse runny nose and cough. Cough gets progressively worse and occurs in paroxysms, or spasms. Face red or purple during coughing spells and child may vomit. Fever uncommon.	From onset of runny nose until 3 weeks after onset of paroxysms or whooping.	Exclude until 5 days after start of antibiotics or 3 weeks if no treatment given. Contacts may need antibiotics or vaccine.	Yes

Source: Courtesy of the Canadian Paediatric Society (1996), *Well Beings: A Guide to Promote the Physical Health, Safety and Emotional Well-Being of Children in Child Care Centres and Family Day Care Homes* (Ottawa: Canadian Paediatric Society), 973–76.

UNIT 5

Nutrition

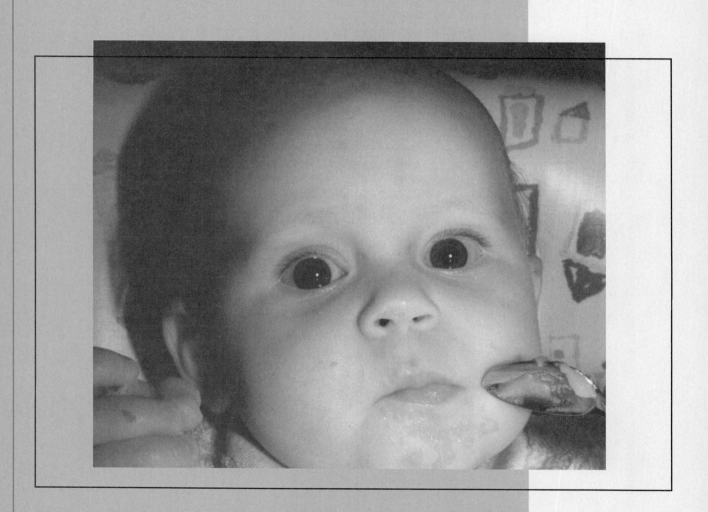

CONTENTS

Factors That Shape Eating Habits   191
   SEVERAL FACTORS THAT AFFECT EATING HABITS   191

Nuts and Bolts of Nutrition   200
   ROLE OF NUTRIENTS   200
   THE FOUNDATION FOR HEALTHY EATING: *CANADA'S FOOD GUIDE*   201

Nutrition Labels and Food Processing   209
   NUTRITION LABELS   209
   FOOD ADDITIVES   211
   BEING INFORMED CONSUMERS   215

Healthy Eating Habits   216
   CREATING A POSITIVE EATING ENVIRONMENT   216
   INFANT NUTRITION   220
   TODDLER NUTRITION   227
   PRESCHOOL NUTRITION   229
   SCHOOL-AGE NUTRITION   230
   CONCERN ABOUT AMOUNTS OF FOOD EATEN   231

Providing Foods and Menu Planning   235
   PROVIDING FOOD IN THE EARLY CHILDHOOD PROGRAM   235
   MENU PLANNING   239

Food Safety   242
   REDUCING THE RISK OF CHOKING   243
   FOOD SAFETY PRACTICES   243
   MICROWAVE OVEN SAFETY   248

Revisiting the Health Promotion Action Plan   250

Conclusion   250

What's Your Opinion? TO RISE TO THE CHALLENGE OR NOT?   251

Assess Your Learning   251

Resource Materials   252

Bibliography   253

TABLES

TABLE 5.1   WHAT FOOD CAN MEAN   194
TABLE 5.2   FUNCTIONS OF NUTRIENTS   200
TABLE 5.3   RECOMMENDED DAILY SERVINGS   202
TABLE 5.4   KEY NUTRIENTS IN *CANADA'S FOOD GUIDE*   202
TABLE 5.5   EXAMPLES OF SERVING SIZES FOR PRESCHOOLERS   206
TABLE 5.6   VARIETY OF FOODS   207
TABLE 5.7   DEVELOPMENTAL CHARACTERISTICS RELATED TO EATING   217
TABLE 5.8   POSITIVE EATING ENVIRONMENT: CHECKLIST   219
TABLE 5.9   APPROXIMATE SERVING SIZES: 4 TO 12 MONTHS OF AGE   227
TABLE 5.10   MENU PLANNING CHECKLIST   242

FIGURE

FIGURE 5.1   NUTRITION FACTS TABLE: A SAMPLE   210

APPENDIXES

APPENDIX 5.1   NUTRIENTS: THEIR FUNCTIONS AND FOOD SOURCES   256
APPENDIX 5.2   EATING WELL WITH *CANADA'S FOOD GUIDE*   259
APPENDIX 5.3   LUNCH PROGRAM MENU   261
APPENDIX 5.4   MENU FOR PRESCHOOLERS AND SCHOOL-AGERS   262

Nutrition is the science of food and how it is used by the body. Discussion on nutrition includes these facts:

■ Food has different meanings for each individual.
■ Eating patterns are shaped by interrelated factors in our lives.

Nutritious food is essential for all dimensions of our health. This key factor is the cornerstone in developing and evolving nutrition programs for young children. Educators' motivation plays an essential role in promoting children's well-being. It is important to balance children's rights to have control over what and how much food they consume with adults' responsibility to provide

■ enough food,
■ a variety of wholesome foods, and
■ an eating environment that promotes healthy eating.

FACTORS THAT SHAPE EATING HABITS

For most people, food usually means more than just relieving hunger and providing nourishment. The meaning that food carries can be positive and healthy and be associated with celebrations, including special foods, holidays, social time with family and friends, and religious or ethno-cultural events. Other meanings may be negative and not conducive to health or well-being; these may result in eating for the wrong reasons (see Emotional, page 193).

Think about how you view food generally, the food choices you make, and how you feel before, during, and after eating. Awareness of our emotions, attitudes, and behaviour toward food and eating is necessary before we can foster healthy eating habits in children. If we perpetuate myths or model poor eating habits—such as a focus on dieting—we influence children negatively and may unwittingly foster in them lifelong eating problems.

To list and discuss six factors that shape our eating habits.

To be aware of food insecurity in Canada.

Several Factors That Affect Eating Habits

Several factors must be considered when we look at nutrition: physical, emotional, social, cultural, body image, and economics. The interaction of these factors and others results in complex dynamics that educators need to be aware of to promote healthy attitudes toward nutrition and eating.

Physical

The first factor that comes to mind is our physical need for food. Nutrients in food provide the building blocks for cell and tissue growth, provide the regulators for many of the body's functions, and provide fuel for energy. Each nutrient can play a specific role or multiple roles. The way nutrients interact with the other factors is very complex. Nutrition affects a child's thinking and learning capacities, for example. A child who is weak from poor nutrition will have little energy to learn or socialize (Guy 1997, 51). Canadian nutritional guidelines have been established for the intake of nutrients (vitamins, minerals, proteins, fat, carbohydrates) for children and adults. The guidelines take into account that variations exist in the requirements for nutrients among individuals. Growth rates and body types vary, because we all differ in our genetic makeup, even from our siblings. The human body's need for energy varies with age, body size, growth patterns, gender, level of physical activity, and basal metabolic rate (the rate at which your body uses energy for essential bodily functions).

Physical Activity

We know that physical activity goes hand in hand with nutrition as part of a healthy lifestyle. Individuals who maintain a moderate level of daily activity help their bodies work more efficiently, often by increasing their basal metabolic rate and bone density. Children enjoy physical activity just for the fun of it, but it supports their physical fitness and positive self-image.

Approximately one hour a day of physical activity is healthy for most young children. Early childhood legislation requires a minimum amount of time each day for outdoor play. However, this requirement doesn't ensure that children are physically active during that time and the specified time is just a minimum. Educators should make sure that children are outside for longer periods or more than once during the day. Are the children running, jumping, hopping, climbing, swinging, riding tricycles, moving to music, or playing ball and active games? Or are they standing around or spending most of their time at more sedentary activities—playing in the sandbox or at the water table, playing marbles, or taking part in dramatic play? Although children don't have to be moving all the time, educators should be aware of how much each type of activity is occurring. A dramatic increase in the percentage of children in Canada who are obese has been reported in the *Canadian Medical Association Journal* (Tremblay and Willms 2000, 1429). Today, almost 25% of Canadian children are obese. This is a serious public health threat, especially when we consider that children who are obese are likely to continue to be so in adulthood. Obese adults have higher risks for diabetes, heart disease, orthopedic problems, many other chronic problems, and premature death. Although there are a number of contributing factors to this complex problem, the alarming trend has been attributed primarily to physical inactivity and over-consumption of high-calorie foods (Andersen 2000, 1461).

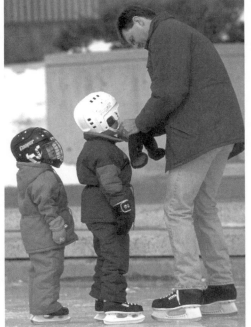

Since activity patterns are established early in life, educators must encourage each child to be physically active. What kind of behaviour are we modelling as educators? Are we standing around, passively supervising, or talking with staff? This behaviour may discourage children's enjoyment of physical activity. On the other hand, our active involvement encourages children and increases our own fitness levels.

Sensory Experiences

Eating is a truly sensory experience. When you watch young children eat, they see, smell, taste, and touch the food. They hear the crispy, crunchy, and squishy sounds that food makes. From infancy, we begin to develop taste preferences. Several studies have shown that newborn babies innately prefer sweet tastes. This preference, however, may be altered early on by introducing other tastes. Older infants and young children often prefer a saltier taste (Clark Lowry 1999, 1). Children's love of dill pickles and salty broth sometimes surprises adults. There is interest in, but no conclusions yet on, some of the genetic links between taste preferences. Young children also react to texture, generally preferring soft, fluffy foods (e.g., pudding) and crisp vegetables. Meats are not favoured generally, because they are difficult to chew with primary teeth.

Families' ethno-cultural food habits are powerful, especially for children's developing tastes. A study was conducted in a Mexican community to see how the people developed a taste for chili peppers. This food is a daily staple in their community and the gradual respectful introduction of chili peppers from infancy resulted in a preference for this taste by preschool age. Lambert-Lagacé (1993) suggests that, using this approach, broccoli should be easy!

Emotional

The emotional component of nutrition is related to individual likes and dislikes. It may simply be a matter of taste differentiation, or a desire for or aversion to food associated with a positive or negative experience. For example, a child who is forced, rather than gently encouraged, to eat yams may develop an aversion to yams. Table 5.1 shows ways that children can develop positive or negative associations with food. As you read the list, consider which food meanings may have a positive or negative effect on children's emotions.

TABLE 5.1	What Food Can Mean
POSITIVE AND NEGATIVE ASSOCIATIONS WITH FOOD	
Security	When an infant cries, someone feeds and cuddles him or her, which contributes to a sense of security.
Insecurity	When a family is unable to provide enough food regularly, the child's ability to predict events may be jeopardized.
Pacifier	A child who is always given food whenever he or she cries, regardless of whether the child is hungry, views food as a pacifier rather than a means of nourishment.
Learning	A young child learns about the world by experiencing food through the five senses.
Punishment	Parents withdraw food, often dessert, because of inappropriate behaviour, or may send the child to bed hungry.
Reward	Children are offered food, usually sweets, as a reward for success or "good" behaviour.
Individuality	A child uses food as a way to express individuality (i.e., food likes and dislikes).
Love	The child learns to give and eat food to show love (e.g., chocolates on Valentine's Day, or a mother saying, "Don't you like mommy's dinner?," which equates rejection of the food with rejection of her).
Comforter	Food is used to relieve boredom or loneliness, to handle anxiety or disappointment (e.g., following rejection by a friend, a child is comforted with cookies or candy). The child learns to use food as a coping mechanism.
Fear	An unpleasant experience with food (e.g., choking) causes a child to fear eating that food in the future.
Approval	A child tries to win approval and acceptance through food, by eating and refusing what his or her peers eat and refuse (e.g., a school-age child rejects foods from home that had been readily accepted until the child's friends commented negatively on it) or by "cleaning off the plate" for daddy.
Weapon	A child with little control over his or her environment uses food for revenge or to get attention (e.g., by refusing to eat, demanding food, throwing food).

Children enter early childhood programs with their repertoire of familiar foods based mostly on what their families served and the emotional and social status that these foods hold. Children quickly pick up messages that may make them more or less responsive to a new food.

 If a two-year-old's parent has told her to eat all her vegetables before she can have dessert, it is no mystery that she will give the dessert a higher status than the vegetables, reinforcing her preference for dessert.

Social and Cultural

The social and cultural aspects of eating have significant influence in our lives and are linked with physical and emotional forces; food often has deep personal meaning. It would be rare not to see food playing a significant role in any social gathering. Some foods are more likely to be served in certain social situations— such as hot dogs at ball games and popcorn at movies. Many food traditions in social gatherings are related to particular ethno-cultural or religious holidays, such as cabbage rolls as one of the 12 meatless dishes prepared at Ukrainians' Christmas Eve, Chinese cake at Chinese New Year, special baked goods at Passover or Easter, and turkey at Thanksgiving. Eating with other people tends to be viewed as a more enjoyable experience than eating alone. Do you, or someone you know who lives alone, eat in front of the television for company? Eating together can promote positive values, such as awareness of your needs and desires as well as those of others, sharing, learning respectful rhythms of talking and listening, and celebrating as a community (see Creating a Positive Eating Environment, page 216).

Young children who eat with positive adult companionship eat better than those who have no or negative adult intervention (Escobar 1999, 54). The way foods are viewed by others in our midst affects the status of the food. If parents and educators treat all nutritious foods with equal respect, children are more likely to try a variety of them. If certain foods are given lower status, children are liable to share that view.

Traditional ethno-cultural preferences for food are often strongest in families that have recently come to Canada. When ethnicity is an important aspect of family life, parents often continue to prepare traditional foods and perhaps combine them with contemporary foods of North America. We often associate North

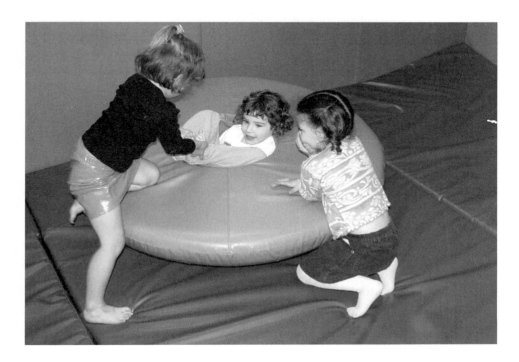

American foods with the highly processed, high-fat, and refined-sugar foods that are not as rich in nutrients as many of the more traditional, ethno-cultural foods. *Canada's Food Guide* encourages Canadians to reduce their intake of highly processed, refined foods (Health Canada 2007). The World Health Organization (2003, 16) has expressed alarm about the major change in peoples' diet around the world, first in industrial countries and more recently in developing countries. Chronic lifestyle diseases are the result of a myriad of factors, but they are undeniably linked to the energy-dense diets high in animal fat that are replacing traditional plant-based diets in much of the world. Educators should try to be aware of and reinforce traditional, ethno-cultural food preferences, particularly those higher in nutrients (e.g., vegetables and fruits) and less refined (i.e., whole grains).

We are bombarded daily with information and pressure from media—newspapers, magazines, radio, television, movies, videos/DVDs, Internet, and video games. Television has the most dramatic influence on young children, as revealed by the amount of television that children watch. Statistics Canada (cited in Canadian Paediatric Society 1996, 540) estimates that children aged 2 to 11 watch an average of 20 hours per week. Young children are unable developmentally to discriminate between the commercials and the television show, which makes them vulnerable to advertisements for non-nutritious foods. Also, children notice that many shows depict "cool" children and adolescents regularly eating low-nutrient snack foods such as chips and cookies or complaining when they eat vegetables. Furthermore, the significant amount of sedentary TV time that children could be spending in physically challenging activities does not contribute to optimal health. Watching television is also associated with snacking on high-fat and high-sugar foods.

Parents, educators, and other adults in children's lives can have a significant influence on their acceptance of a variety of foods. The more someone experiences different foods, the more likely that child is to develop a taste for them. Children who have had less exposure to new foods are more likely to be picky eaters and unwilling to try new foods, which creates a vicious circle (Pelchat and Pliner 1986).

Body Image

Maintaining weight within a normal range is conducive to health. However, the range that has been considered normal, particularly for women (though it is becoming more of an issue for men), has been narrowly defined by the fashion industry, the media, and some factions of the dance and sport domains. Society continues to focus too much on body weight. This preoccupation has, in fact, contributed to the dramatic overall rise in obesity (obesity in Canadian children has doubled in the past 20 years) and eating disorders in our society over the past few decades. How? Dieting is one of the most powerful triggers for the development of disordered eating (the behaviour) and eating disorders (a diagnosed illness) (National Eating Disorder Information Centre [NEDIC] 2003, question 16).

Dieting by restricting calories or food groups will almost certainly cause problems that are counterproductive:

- The metabolism will slow down as the body tries to fight the starvation process.
- The weight will return in a short time.
- Lowered self-esteem or depression is common due to feelings of failure.

The process and philosophy of dieting ignore the fact that healthy people come in all shapes and sizes and, instead, tie personal worth to physical thinness. Natural body weights, based on genetic predisposition and managed when we treat our bodies with respect through healthy eating and regular physical activity, do not come close to those of the runway models for the vast majority of women and men. The ideal body image is often portrayed as the unattainable "perfect" body (usually associated with thinness). Children, especially girls, from a very young age can become obsessed with their weight if they are surrounded by these dangerous messages. "By age 6 or 7, many girls are fearful of being fat and think they need to lose weight" (NEDIC 2003). A survey of seven-year-old girls and boys found that they consistently ranked depictions of obese children the lowest in attractiveness (Feldman et al., cited in Sheinin 1990). Women receive ubiquitous messages from the fashion, media, and diet industries that they are never good enough, and that they must deprive themselves to continually fight the natural size of their body. Young men are also expected to have muscular "six-pack" bodies. In addition, the "fear of fat" that pervades our society results in social prejudice and discrimination against individuals who weigh more than what is deemed acceptable. This can damage their self-esteem and result in extreme dieting, creating a vicious circle.

According to a large school-based study in Ontario (Jones et al. 2001):

- More than 27% of girls aged 12–18 years had disordered eating attitudes and behaviour.
- Dieting, binge eating, purging, and use of diet pills were cited at all ages, including 12% of 12- to 14-year-old girls who reported binge eating in the previous month and 7% self-induced vomiting.

Children gain some fat prior to puberty as part of the normal growth process. This gain often coincides with an increased concern with body image, and the cycle of dieting may begin. The study recommends interactive education that doesn't simply teach principles of healthy eating, but also focuses on the positive aspects of the self to validate girls' experiences and feelings, while providing them with tools to understand the societal pressures that they face.

Many young children are eating less than the recommended amount of food and calories and are showing low muscle mass. This evidence suggests that lack of physical activity plays a role in their weight gain. The tendency in our society to diet adds to the problem rather than helps, because lowering food intake tends to slow our metabolism rather than make it run more efficiently. *Canada's Food Guide,* on the other hand, focuses the message of eating well and being active today and everyday (Health Canada 2007).

This issue is important in early childhood education and care because educators, like everyone else, are profoundly influenced by media messages. Remember the great impact you have on children and how they look up to you.

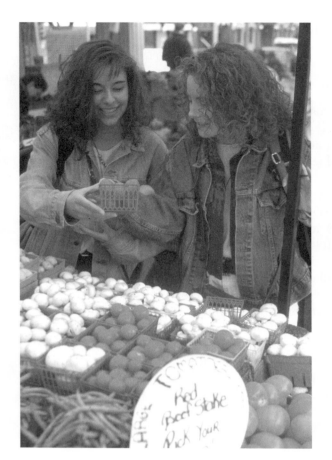

It is important to be sensitive to the subtle messages (e.g., you are constantly on a diet) and the overt ones (e.g., you comment to a child that he or she is chubby or skinny) that you send to children.

Economics

In Canada, an exciting range of foods is available in many urban communities. However, this is not the case in all Canadian communities. Even when a vast range of foods is available, they may not be used due to cost or perhaps because many people are unsure of how to prepare them.

Family incomes and parents' awareness of nutrition directly influence the quality of the family's dietary intake. That is, higher levels of family incomes and parents who are knowledgeable about cooking contribute to better dietary intake. Better-off parents can afford and prepare a wider variety of wholesome foods. Families with lower incomes not only have less money in their food budget but also may lack adequate transportation, which limits their access to bulk purchases, sales, or lower-priced but more nutritious foods. Small neighbourhood convenience stores, for example, may not carry a variety of fresh fruits and vegetables or may charge higher prices.

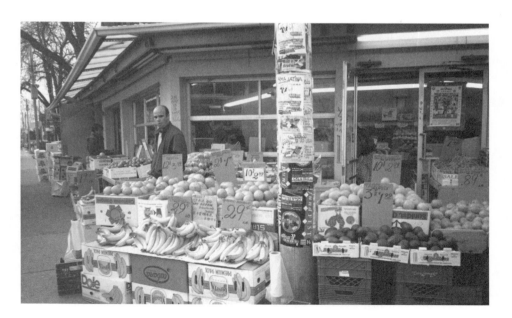

Parents may choose to spend part of their food budget eating in restaurants. Eating out shapes eating habits because restaurant menus limit food choices and affect how foods are prepared. Even so, many families with young children eat in fast-food places that serve mainly high-fat and fried food. Children's choices are influenced by marketing of children's "meal deals," comprising a hamburger, fries, pop, and toy. Some of these fast-food restaurants offer to increase the portion sizes for a small increase in price, thus encouraging individuals to eat larger portions because they see the deal as a bargain.

Food Distribution

Food is one of the most basic needs of every human being. However, in Canada and around the world, people do not have equal access to food. The world's food system is complex in some ways and simple in others. Many of us assume that inadequate food production causes many people, especially in developing countries, to go hungry. This is not the case. In some developing countries, much food is exported to meet commitments to pay the national debt. Consequently, the people of these countries go hungry not only because of their inability to pay for food but also because inadequate quantities of food stay in the country. Hunger is a matter of food distribution, economics, and politics (White 1990).

"Since the word *hunger* evokes images which make it difficult for some people to seriously consider hunger as a problem in Canada, it has been proposed that the term *food insecurity* be substituted" (McIntyre 1994, 34). Let's look at Canada's food system to illustrate this point of view. Many areas in Canada have access to an array of foods throughout the year due to national and regional food production, high-tech food processing and storage, international trade, and transportation. The over-production of food in North America and Europe has actually led to major storage problems and incredible waste. Plentiful harvests, however, don't make the food producers (farmers) rich. Instead, farmers are at the mercy of the retailers—the huge food corporations that buy their produce. The rise of transnational food corporations and the high cost of farming are two of the main reasons why so many farms have gone bankrupt. For those of us who do not go hungry, convenient and cheap food may seem to be in our best interest. But when we look at the overall picture, we see that these are not the priorities that will improve the human condition. Looking at the sheer quantity of food in grocery stores, it is hard to comprehend that so many Canadians go hungry because of food insecurity due to poverty.

Food banks are "Band-Aid" solutions to the poverty and food insecurity experienced by families in Canada. Food banks have become an institution in Canada for many families whose breadwinners work at low-paying jobs or depend on social assistance and who can't manage the cost of food on top of rent, utilities, clothing, and transportation. Many children are hungry day in and day out, which affects their short- and long-term physical, emotional, and social well-being. In a country as rich as Canada, it is atrocious that so many children and families go hungry. Poverty is a complex social issue that must be addressed by all levels of government and communities across Canada.

To list the seven categories of
nutrients and describe main
functions.

To understand the principles
behind *Canada's Food Guide.*

To explain the important aspects
of *Canada's Food Guide* as it
relates to children.

NUTS AND BOLTS OF NUTRITION

Understanding the basics of nutrition enables us to understand the important role that eating healthy food plays in promoting health.

Role of Nutrients

Nutrients are substances that are found in food. They are divided into seven categories: carbohydrates, proteins, fats, vitamins, minerals, fibre, and water.

Appendix 5.1 (page 256) expands on the description of nutrients, what foods they are found in, and their functions. Remember the following points about nutrients:

■ All nutrients needed by the body are found in food. In addition to the seven categories listed above, there are hundreds of other chemicals found in foods (e.g., phytochemicals found in fruits and vegetables). There is no such thing as the perfect food. Eating a varied diet usually provides our body with all the vitamins and minerals we need. Supplements such as folic acid for pregnant women or vitamin D for breast-fed babies are routinely recommended by health care practitioners. However, parents who give their children daily vitamin or mineral supplements "for their health" should evaluate the short- and long-term safety of this practice. Keep in mind that these supplements are not a substitute for food. "Real food is complex and offers many substances including antioxidants and phytochemicals in desirable proportions" (Deverell 1998, E5).

■ Many nutrients work best when combined with one or more other nutrients.

Our body absorbs iron better in the presence of vitamin C, and calcium needs both phosphorus and vitamin D to build bones and teeth.

■ Many foods are not simply a carbohydrate, protein, or fat, but are a combination of two or three nutrients.

TABLE 5.2	Functions of Nutrients
CATEGORIES	**FUNCTIONS**
• carbohydrates • proteins • fats	• provide calories (or energy) needed for work and physical activity • support bodily functions; e.g., proteins are needed for cell growth and repair
• vitamins • minerals • fibre • water	• are essential for helping the body regulate its functions; e.g., water-soluble vitamin C helps the body absorb iron (a mineral) as it is transported through the body by water

The yolk of an egg is high in fat, but the white is high in protein. Most cheeses and meats are a combination of protein and fat. The energy from whole-grain bread comes mostly from carbohydrates with a little from protein and fat.

- We all need the same nutrients, but how much we need of each nutrient varies with age, size, activity level, and other factors.

Children need more calcium because of bone and tooth formation. A very physically active teenager needs more food energy than a less active one.

- The quality of nutrients is affected by how food is grown, harvested, stored, and prepared.

Broccoli provides more of the B vitamins, especially folate, and vitamin C when it is raw than when it is boiled until soft, because most of the B and C vitamins are lost in the water—they are water soluble.

- Rinsing fresh fruit and vegetables under running water with a mild soap removes soil and pesticide residue. Although peeling produce (e.g., apples, cucumbers) results in a loss of fibre, vitamins, and minerals, peeling may be advisable if there is concern about pesticide use. Other ways to avoid vitamin and mineral loss are to

  - cut, tear, or chop produce just before use to reduce the loss of vitamin C;

  - microwave, pressure cook, steam, or stir-fry vegetables just until tender;

  - avoid boiling vegetables; and

  - save cooking water for soups or stews.

- Eating too much or too little of any nutrient can contribute to or cause disease. Reduce the amount of fat, sugar, and salt you eat by using less or none at all in cooking and at the table. The taste for salt is learned. Herbs and spices provide interesting alternatives.

A high-fat diet can contribute to heart disease and some forms of cancer. A low-iron diet can cause iron deficiency (anemia).

The Foundation for Healthy Eating: *Canada's Food Guide to Healthy Eating*

Health Canada's *Food Guide* is based on two principles of healthy living—eating well and being active everyday for everyone two years of age and older (Health Canada 2007). *Canada's Food Guide's* recommendations for the amounts and types of food supports meeting the daily requirements of vitamins, minerals, and other nutrients. Healthy eating contributes to your overall health and vitality and helps reduce your risk of medical conditions such as obesity, certain types of cancer, heart disease, type 2 diabetes, and osteoporosis (Health Canada 2007). The four food groups have a range of recommended daily servings based on the different ages and stages of individuals (see Table 5.3).

TABLE 5.3

Recommended Daily Servings

| AGES IN YEARS | 2 - 3 | 4 - 8 | 9 - 13 | 14 - 18 | | 19 - 50 | | 51+ | |
SEX	GIRLS AND BOYS			FEMALES	MALES	FEMALES	MALES	FEMALES	MALES
Vegetables and Fruit	4	5	6	7	8	7–8	8–10	7	7
Grain Products	3	4	6	6	7	6–7	8	6	7
Milk and Alternatives	2	2	3–4	3–4	3–4	2	2	3	3
Meat and Alternativesfibre	1	1	1–2	2	3	2	3	2	3

Source: *Eating Healthy with Canada's Food Guide.* Health Canada. Adapted and reproduced with permission of the Minister of Public Works and Government Services Canada Health Canada, 2007.

e.g. A young woman who is moderately active can eat five or six servings of grain products (e.g., 30 g [1/2 cup] of cereal, two slices of whole-grain bread, 120 g [2 cups] of noodles in a particular day), which is adequate for her needs. If she increases her daily physical activity or becomes pregnant, her daily need for grain products will increase to seven or eight servings.

Table 5.4 lists the key nutrients in each food group and highlights the importance of eating a variety of foods to obtain the daily recommended nutrients.

TABLE 5.4

Key Nutrients in *Canada's Food Guide*

VEGETABLES & FRUIT +	GRAIN PRODUCTS +	MILK PRODUCTS +	MEAT & ALTERNATIVES =	FOOD GUIDE
	protein	protein	protein	protein
	fat		fat	fat
carbohydrate	carbohydrate			carbohydrate
fibre	fibre			fibre
thiamin	thiamin		thiamin	thiamin
	riboflavin	riboflavin	riboflavin	riboflavin
	niacin		niacin	niacin
folacin	folacin		folacin	folacin
		vitamin B^{12}	vitamin B^{12}	vitamin B^{12}
vitamin C				vitamin C
vitamin A		vitamin A		vitamin A
		vitamin D		vitamin D
		calcium		calcium
iron	iron		iron	iron
	zinc	zinc	zinc	zinc
magnesium	magnesium	magnesium	magnesium	magnesium

Note: Each food group is essential. That's because it provides its own set of nutrients.

Source: *Using the Food Guide*, Health Canada. Adapted and reproduced with permission of the Minister of Public Works and Government Services Canada, 2003.

Canada's Food Guide recommends making food choices that are healthier, limiting foods and beverages that have few nutrients and are usually high in fat, salt or sugar or both. Examples include: cakes and pastries, chocolate and candies, cookies and granola bars, ice cream and frozen desserts, doughnuts and muffins, french fries, potato chips, nachos and other salty snacks, fruit flavoured drinks, soft drinks, sweetened hot or cold drinks. In early childhood programs, nutrition policies and practices that minimize the use of "less healthy foods" can contribute to children's interest in more nutritious foods.

Research on diet and disease has shown that most Canadians have a diet that is lower in fibre and higher in fat than is optimal for health and for lowering risk factors for chronic illnesses such as heart disease, some cancers, and obesity. Canadians are urged to continue to increase their intake of foods composed of complex carbohydrates (i.e., breads, cereals, vegetables, fruit) to replace the energy derived from the fat in meat and milk products, and particularly in high-fat, low-nutrient or junk foods such as potato chips, chocolate bars, and doughnuts. In response to this research, *Canada's Food Guide* emphasizes eating grain products, vegetables, and fruit (Health Canada 2007). For anyone ready to improve his or her eating habits, these two strategies are good places to start. However, Health Canada (2007), reminds us that too much fibre can be a problem for growing children, whose small stomachs must be able to contain enough calories for growth. Serving raw vegetables with a dip made with a dairy product, for example, is a good way both to promote fibre and to provide enough food energy.

Currently, most Canadians get more than they need of their daily calories (or energy) from saturated and trans fats. Fat is important for body functions such as providing essential fatty acids and carrying fat-soluble vitamins through the body. However, research into links between fat intake and disease has resulted in recommendations that, although more complex than a decade ago, are clearer and more encouraging. The type and amount of fat we consume is equally important. The following summary outlines the general suggestions. Keep in mind that ongoing research may result in future adjusted recommendations (Schardt 2002, 1):

■ Limit your intake of both saturated and trans fats combined to less than 10% of daily calories or about 20 g a day. Saturated fats are found in meats, animal products (e.g., cheese, eggs) and tropical oils (e.g., palm kernel oil, coconut oil). Trans fats are created when liquid oils are manufactured to produce more solid fats such as shortening and margarine. Health Canada's recent updated food label requirements includes listing both saturated and trans fat percentages when applicable to help the consumer identify them (see Nutrition Labels, page 209).

■ Mono- and polyunsaturated fats (e.g., olive, canola, soy, and sunflower oils, non-hydrogenated margarine, and fats found in nuts, seeds) are thought to maintain or increase our HDL ("good" cholesterol). They are a healthier choice, eaten in moderation, than saturated and trans fats.

■ The best polyunsaturated fats contain high amounts of fatty acids called omega-3 and omega-6 fats that appear to help protect the heart by raising the HDL ("good" cholesterol level). Eating two to five servings of seafood a week, particularly fattier fish such as salmon or sardines, or fish such as trout, sole, halibut, and tuna, will provide enough of these fats. If you don't eat fish, find another way to ensure your intake of omega-3 and 6 fatty acids, such as fish-oil pills or a small amount of flaxseed oil daily.

Although not all fats are equal when it comes to our health, the total amount of all fats is important to consider, because all are equally high in calories. Keep in mind that young children's needs for fat differ from that of older children and adults.

Relating *Canada's Food Guide* to Children

During the first two years of life, children undergo a period of rapid growth and development. At no other time in your life does your body need a diet as high in fat—approximately 50% of the total daily calories—to provide you with adequate energy and fatty acids. This is the primary reason why children under two are not included in Canada's food guidelines. A second reason is that the gradual intro-duction of solid foods over the first two years does not relate to *Canada's Food Guide*. What about children over two years old? Health Canada (2007) recent changes to the Canada's Food Guide includes preschoolers.

Milk Products

In the second year of life, most infants make a transition from breast milk or formula to cow's milk. Between 12 and 24 months, children should drink homogenized milk. Children at that age need whole-milk fat for brain development. Toddlers are not yet eating the variety and quantity of food to provide them with the daily dietary requirement for fat, so milk products remain the primary source of fat.

Some parents and even some doctors start the one-year-old on lower-fat milk (skim, 1%, 2%) if they believe the baby is too chubby—though there is little or no correlation between body fat in infancy and later childhood. This example illustrates society's fear of fat. In fact, if the one- to two-year-old drinks lower-fat milk, he or she may be hungry and tend to eat more food. Whole milk not only provides babies with essential fats but also contributes to their sense of fullness.

Partly skimmed milk (1% and 2%) is not recommended and skim milk is inappropriate in the first two years (Canadian Paediatric Society 2002). By this age, most children are eating a number of foods that are higher in fat, which reduces the need for milk to supply essential fatty acids. By the time children are school age, they can be offered 1% or skim milk. Although they still need the cal-cium and other nutrients that milk provides, they don't need the same percentage of dietary fat and are usually eating adult-sized servings.

What Is a Child-Sized Serving?

To determine developmentally appropriate serving sizes, look at the recommenda-tions in *Canada's Food Guide* and cut the quantity by approximately

- 2/3 to 3/4 for toddlers,
- 1/4 to 1/2 for preschoolers, and
- 1/4 or nil for school-agers.

Because of the important role that dietary fat plays in children's growth and development, we'll look now at the recommendations on fat intake for children:

- Children are individuals and between the age of 2 and adolescence their developmental needs differ greatly in terms of growth patterns and energy needs.
- In the preschool years, growth rate slows, activity levels are generally high, and appetite varies greatly, resulting in erratic food intake. Energy-dense foods enable preschoolers to meet energy and nutrient needs. Despite an erratic food intake, there is evidence that young children can self-regulate food intake over a 24-hour period. Small, frequent feedings, with a variety of food choices, are important for meeting nutritional requirements during this phase.
- In young school-agers, growth is more constant. Their growth patterns and energy needs continue to vary among individuals. Fluctuations in appetite are common, and fatigue, excitement, and vigorous activity can all interfere with daily food intake.

Conclusions

- Providing enough energy and nutrients to ensure adequate growth and development remains the most important consideration in children's nutrition. Small, frequent feedings play a significant role in providing energy in children's diets.
- During childhood years, nutritious food choices should not be eliminated or restricted because of fat content. During early adolescence an energy intake adequate to sustain growth should be emphasized with a gradual lowering of fat intake. Once linear growth has stopped, fat intake as currently recommended for adults is appropriate.
- Food patterns that emphasize variety and complex carbohydrates and include lower-fat choices are appropriate and desirable for children.
- Physical activity and healthy eating are important lifestyle habits for children.

Recommendations

- From the age of 2 until the end of linear growth, there should be a transition from the high-fat diet of infancy to a diet that includes no more than 30% of energy as fat and no more than 10% of energy as saturated fat.
- During this transition, energy intake should be sufficient to achieve normal growth and development. Food patterns should emphasize variety and complex carbohydrates, and include lower-fat foods. Physical activity should be stressed. There is no evidence to show that restricting fat intake in children reduces illness in later life or provides benefits during childhood.

Source: *Nutrition Recommendations Update ... Dietary Fat and Children*, Health Canada, 1996. Adapted and reproduced with permission of the Minister of Public Works and Government Services Canada, 2003. Reference: "Dietary Reference Intakes for Energy, Carbohydrate, Fiber, Fat, Fatty Acids, Cholesterol, Protein, and Amino Acids" (prepublication copy, 2002), Panel on Macronutrients, Subcommittee on Interpretation and Uses of Dietary Reference Intakes, and the Standing Committee on the Scientific Evaluation of Dietary Reference Intakes, National Academies Press, Washington, DC.

See also Table 5.5. But remember that every child is an individual. His or her appetite can vary greatly with age, gender, activity level, and other factors.

TABLE 5.5   **Examples of Serving Sizes for Preschoolers**

FOOD GROUP	ONE CHILD-SIZED SERVING
Vegetables and Fruit	
fresh vegetable or fruit	1/2 to 1 piece (medium size)
frozen or canned vegetables or fruit	50 to 125 mL (1/4 to 1/2 cup)
salad	125 to 250 mL (1/2 to 1 cup)
juice	50 to 125 mL (1/4 to 1/2 cup)
Grain Products	
bread	1/2 to 1 slice
cold cereal	15 to 30 g
hot cereal	75 to 175 mL (1/3 to 3/4 cup)
bagel, pita, or bun	1/4 to 1/2
muffin	1/2 to 1
pasta or rice	50 to 125 mL (1/4 to 1/2 cup)
soda crackers	4 to 8
Milk Products	
milk	500 mL (2 cups) per day
cheese	25 to 50 grams
yogurt	75 to 175 grams (1/3 to 3/4 cup)
Meat and Alternatives	
meat, fish, or poultry	25 to 50 grams
egg	1
beans	50 to 125 mL (1/4 to 1/2 cup)
tofu	50 to 100 grams (1/4 to 1/3 cup)
peanut butter	15 to 30 mL (1 to 2 tbsp)

Source: *Canada's Food Guide to Healthy Eating*, Health Canada. Adapted and reproduced from "Focus on Preschoolers: Background for Educators and Communicators," with the permission of the Minister of Public Works and Government Services Canada, 2003.

Multicultural Foods and *Canada's Food Guide*

Often educators caring for children from various ethno-cultural backgrounds are unfamiliar with the foods that they commonly eat at home. They may wonder whether the foods fit into the four food groups. *Canada's Food Guide* is designed to be flexible enough to include most foods. Obviously, many foods are eaten by almost all cultures, where available. Often the style of cooking and the spices used differ between cultures. Chicken, for example, may be fried, baked, boiled, roasted, or cooked with different spices, batters, and sauces, depending on preferences and availability of ingredients. A Mexican chicken dish that is prepared with chocolate tastes quite different from chicken Kiev, chicken parmesan, or stir-fried chicken with vegetables. Table 5.6 shows an assortment of foods that are commonly used in a variety of cultures, to help you identify the foods commonly associated with particular ethno-cultural backgrounds.

TABLE 5.6	Variety of Foods
FOOD GROUPS	**FOOD IDEAS**
grain products	pita, bagel, bannock, roti, tortilla, chapati, naan, baguette, pretzel, challah, pasta, cous-cous, bulgur (e.g., in tabouli salad), buckwheat, millet, quinoa, basmati rice, rice cake, dumpling wrapper, cassava bread
vegetables and fruit	okra, guava, mango, papaya, star fruit, breadfruit, soursop, plantain, coconut, wild berries such as huckleberries and thimbleberries, Asian pear, cassava (a root veg-etable), akee, lychee, bok choy, mushroom, dandelion and beet greens, water chestnut, fern root, vegetable marrow, mustard greens, bamboo shoots, soybean sprouts, summer squash, longan, cactus fruit, chayote, taro root
milk products or calcium-rich foods	goat milk, evaporated milk, feta cheese, tofu made with calcium, yogurt, fish or animal bones used in soups and stews, almonds
meat and alternatives*	moose, venison, beaver, wild game, chickpeas or garbanzo beans (e.g., in falafel, hummus), soybean (e.g., in soymilk, tofu), peas and rice, black-eyed peas, legumes (e.g., kidney beans, peas, navy beans, lentils, peanuts), organ meats such as kidney, heart, and liver, chorizo (a hot sausage), squid, shellfish, cockles, mussels

*Some cultural beliefs and religions restrict eating some meats or advocate vegetarianism. For example, Hindus and Sikhs can eat goat, fish, and pork but not beef. Muslims can eat goat, beef, and chicken but not pork, and all meat must be prepared according to Muslim dietary law. Similarly, many Jews can eat fish, beef, chicken, and lamb but not shellfish or pork, and meat must be prepared according to Jewish dietary law. Many cultures use meat sparingly, as a complement to the meal rather than the main focus. This may at times be due to the higher cost of meat, but it is becoming apparent that less rather than more meat is an effective way to reduce fat in the diet.

. . . .

Kidney and pinto beans are common in Latin American dishes; tofu is often used in Chinese dishes; roti, chapati, and naan are breads used in many Southeast Asian dishes; and wild berries are commonly used by non-urban Native Canadians.

e.g.

. . . .

Vegetarianism

Vegetarianism means different things to different people. Generally, it means choosing a plant-based way of eating. It is hard to determine how many people in Canada are currently vegetarian, but at least reducing the percentage of animal foods we eat seems to be a practice growing in popularity. Some people become vegetarians because they don't like the taste of meat. Others may have a difficult time digesting meat. Many, however, have based their decision on reasons of per-sonal health, ethics and animal rights, the environment, concerns about world hunger, the cost of meat, and religion (Melina et al. 1994, 5–8). Some people are not vegetarian but have decided to eliminate some meat, such as red meat, from their diet. Their reason may be to lower cholesterol or fat intake, or to help themselves in the transition to vegetarianism. Soybean, a staple for vegetarians and available in many forms (e.g., tofu, flour, milk), is now recognized as a nutritional powerhouse and is recommended for everyone (Driedger 1997, 55).

Vegetarians are classified according to the foods that they include in their diet:

- Lacto-ovo vegetarians, who comprise the vast majority of vegetarians in Canada, do not eat animal flesh but do eat animal products such as milk and eggs.
- Pesco vegetarians eat fish in addition to foods of plant origin.
- Lacto vegetarians eat milk and milk products but not eggs.
- Ovo vegetarians eat eggs but not milk.
- Vegans eat only foods of plant origin.
- Macrobiotic vegetarians base their diet on a system of 10 regimes that become more restrictive as they move from one regime to the next. At one end they can eat small amounts of fish and dairy products with plant-based foods and at the other end they eat *only* brown rice and water.

People who are vegetarian have to be conscious of what their choice means nutritionally. They need to ensure that they are getting adequate amounts of complete protein and minerals (e.g., iron, zinc) and vitamins (e.g., B_{12}) found in meat. The building blocks of protein are amino acids; we get eight essential amino acids from foods. Animal flesh and its products include all of these simultaneously, whereas most plant foods have fewer. Simply eating a lot of vegetables, grains, and fruits without complete protein is not healthy eating. Learning how to complement protein is easy. Ideally, the complementary proteins are eaten together or within a few hours of each other to ensure that they form a complete protein. Some critics of vegetarianism believe that growing children cannot get the nutrients they need, such as calcium, without eating meat. This concern is unfounded, particularly for lacto-ovo vegetarians, who consume milk products. It is important to remember that any family, vegetarian or not, can have adequate or poor nutrition. Here are some examples, from Melina et al. (1994, 56), of complementary proteins, along with the country or region known for them.

- Combining grains and legumes:
  - bread and split pea soup (Canada)
  - crackers and lentil soup (Middle East)
  - rice and tofu (Orient)
  - cornmeal tortillas and vegetarian chili (Mexico)
  - chapatis and dahl (India)
  - pita bread and falafel (Middle East)
  - pita bread and hummus (Greece)
  - sticky bun with black bean sauce (China)

- Combining grains and nuts:
  - granola or muesli with nuts (Switzerland)
  - pasta with pine nuts (Italy)
  - rice with cashew-vegetable stir-fry (China)

It is more challenging for vegans to get all the nutrients they need, but if they understand and practise good nutrition principles they will ensure that their nutrient needs are met. In vegan families, it is important that pregnant women's and children's increased need for protein, fat, calcium, iron, B_{12}, and other nutrients be considered. For vegan infants who are not breast-fed, commercially prepared soy-based infant formula is recommended during the first two years to provide adequate nutrients and energy for growth and development (Canadian Paediatric Society 2002).

Macrobiotic diets, which are very restrictive, are of particular concern for children. Milks made from grains, beans, and seeds, for example, are inadequate for infants and children. "Severe nutritional deficiencies and growth retardation have been reported on numerous occasions in macrobiotic children" (Melina et al. 1994, 3).

Educators who have concerns about a child's nutritional intake, regardless of the type of diet, should talk with the parents. If you still have questions or need clarification, you may wish to consult with a dietitian-nutritionist.

NUTRITION LABELS AND FOOD PROCESSING

With few exceptions, the more processed the food, the more additives are used. A number of processes are included in the general definition of food processing, including curing meat (e.g., bacon, ham), increasing the length of time for storage/shelf life (e.g., canned fruit, vegetables), or combining a number of ingredients to make a food (e.g., hot dogs, bread).

Everything we eat seems to be potentially hazardous, so how do we reduce risk? Over the years, many early childhood education students, educators, and program cooks have voiced frustration over the information printed on food labels. However, food labels can increase our understanding of healthy eating, enabling us to make more informed decisions about choosing foods that are nutritious. As a matter of fact, 71% of Canadians surveyed by the National Institute of Nutrition in 1997 reported using product labels as a source of nutrition information (Mongeau 1998, 2). This percentage may be rising as Health Canada has recently moved from optional to mandatory nutrition labelling on most prepackaged foods, a process that was phased in over a few years.

Nutrition Labels

We can learn a lot about foods and make informed choices by reading labels. This is particularly true as of January 2003 when Health Canada passed the New Nutrition Labeling Policy, making a standardized Nutrition Facts table mandatory. The Nutrition Facts table is easy to read, consistent in design, and includes information across almost all prepackaged products (see Figure 5.1). Exemptions include fresh fruits and vegetables; raw meat, poultry, and seafood; food products made and packaged on site; and products with little or no nutrient value (e.g., coffee beans, spices).

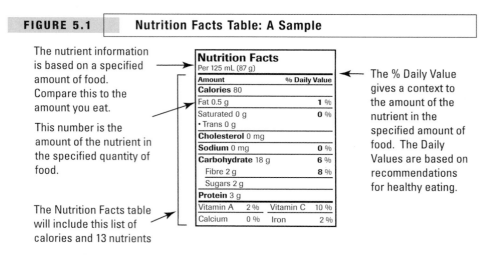

FIGURE 5.1   **Nutrition Facts Table: A Sample**

The nutrient information is based on a specified amount of food. Compare this to the amount you eat.

This number is the amount of the nutrient in the specified quantity of food.

The Nutrition Facts table will include this list of calories and 13 nutrients

The % Daily Value gives a context to the amount of the nutrient in the specified amount of food. The Daily Values are based on recommendations for healthy eating.

Nutrition Facts
Per 125 mL (87 g)

Amount	% Daily Value
Calories 80	
Fat 0.5 g	1 %
Saturated 0 g	0 %
• Trans 0 g	
Cholesterol 0 mg	
Sodium 0 mg	0 %
Carbohydrate 18 g	6 %
Fibre 2 g	8 %
Sugars 2 g	
Protein 3 g	
Vitamin A 2 %	Vitamin C 10 %
Calcium 0 %	Iron 2 %

Source: "Nutrion Facts Table," Health Canada (2003). <www.hc-sc.gc.ca/english/media/releases/2003/2003_01bk1.htm> (July 2003). Reproduced with the permission of the Minister of Public Works and Government Services Canada, 2003.

What information is included in a Nutrition Facts table? The table lists calories and 13 core nutrients for a specific amount of food (a serving). The nutrients are mostly given in weights such as grams or milligrams, and then translated into a percentage of recommended daily value. Vitamins and minerals are given as percentages of daily value. Both saturated and trans fats are listed separately, and carbohydrates are divided into fibre and sugars. This consistent format helps the consumer to learn to use it quickly, and evaluate whether this food has enough of the nutrients he or she needs or wants.

In addition to the Nutrition Facts table, other nutrition information can be found as nutrition claims, and the ingredient list from most to least weight. For individuals with food allergies (e.g., to peanuts, milk solids, soy, wheat, dehydrated eggs) this list is essential, since it names ingredients to be avoided. It is also useful for people on special diets (e.g., gluten-free, diabetic).

Nutrition claims are now regulated by Health Canada criteria, specifying the wording to be used in order to prevent misleading claims, which has been a problem in the past. Nutrition claims include both nutrient content claims (e.g., "reduced in fat," "very high source of fibre") and diet-related health claims (e.g., "a healthy diet rich in a variety of vegetables and fruit may help reduce the risk of some types of cancer"). Note that the nutrition information doesn't refer to some other information you may find on labels, such as statements related to allergens (e.g., "may contain traces of peanut"), food biotechnology information (e.g., regarding genetically modified organisms, or GMOs), certified as organic, irradiation processes, or the "best before" date.

An expiry date or "best before" date or a code is stamped on the label or somewhere on the package (e.g., the bottom or top of the cereal box) to indicate when the contents may spoil or lose nutrients or taste. A date must appear on all foods that spoil within 90 days, except for meats, which show the date the food was packaged. Actual calendar dates are useful to both the consumer and the store manager.

Food Additives

Since 1964, Health Canada's Health Protection Branch has required rigorous testing on food additives before they are approved. There are more than 2800 food additives approved for use in Canada (Driedger 1997, 59). Some food additives work as preservatives. Others are used simply to make the food look appealing (e.g., colouring).

The good news is that research shows that most additives do not pose a threat to your short- or long-term health. However, some additives may be of concern when used regularly for long periods. In these cases, we must consider the concept of synergy. Synergism is defined in the *Nelson Canadian Dictionary* as "the interaction of two or more agents or forces so that their combined effect is greater than the sum of their individual effects." We are exposed to hundreds of chemicals daily, most of them necessary and harmless. However, when we have a choice of ingesting some that may not be in our best interests, why not choose the healthier alternative?

Food quality suffers when additives and processes are used to ensure cosmetic attractiveness and a long shelf life. The less real (natural) food there is in a product, the less corporations need to rely on natural growing (farmers' livelihoods) and weather conditions (White 1990, 6). Conflicting claims frustrate consumers.

Pollution Probe (1994) defines food additives as any chemical, whether natural or synthetic, that is deliberately used in the growth, processing, storage, or distribution of food. Food additives are grouped into two categories, as follows.

- Food-processing additives include
  - colours, which make food look more appealing,
  - preservatives, which keep food from going bad,
  - flavours and flavour enhancers, which make food taste better,
  - sweeteners, which make food taste sweeter (e.g., aspartame),
  - texture agents, which give food a pleasing texture, and
  - processing agents, which make processing easier (Pollution Probe 1994, 24).
  - Unintentional additives are those that are intentionally used in the cycle of food production but inadvertently remain in or on food when we eat it (e.g., chemicals from food packaging, pesticide residue, and hormones or antibiotics from animal products) (Pollution Probe 1994, 97).

Many children favour meats that are highly processed, such as hot dogs, ham, bacon, bologna, salami, and other luncheon meats. Children often like processed meats because they are easy to chew and taste salty. If children eat these meats regularly, they often learn to choose processed meats over other meat and alternatives. Children's consumption of these meats raises concerns because they are highly processed, usually high in saturated fat and salt, and contain nitrates and nitrites.

Nitrates and Nitrites

Nitrates and nitrites are additives used to preserve meat. They prevent the growth of bacteria that cause a type of serious food poisoning called botulism (see Food Safety Practices, page 243), and they preserve the red colour in meats and enhance flavour.

When we eat nitrates, our body first converts them to nitrites. The body then converts nitrites to nitrosomines, which are thought to cause cancer. "Nitrosomines have been described as 'the most potent cancer-causing agent known to science'" (Trum Hunter, cited in Pollution Probe, 1994, 50). You may wonder why nitrates and nitrites are added to foods in Canada if they are known carcinogens. The primary reason is that they have preservative qualities. Because botulism is a serious health risk, there is legitimate public concern about the potential for outbreaks in the absence of adequate food preservation. Nitrates can be found in vegetables that have been exposed to nitrogen fertilizer; due to leaching, nitrates can get into the ground water. There is less concern about the vegetable sources because of the presence in the foods of vitamin C, which prevents the formation of nitrosomines in our bodies.

Nitrate and nitrite-free brands of processed meats are available, so their wide use is not necessary. Soy-based alternatives such as tofu hot dogs do not contain these additives. Eating a meat-based hot dog or salami sandwich now and then is not as great a concern as the regular consumption of highly processed meats. Many people eat processed meats daily because they are convenient, inexpensive, and tasty. When children are offered them both at home and in the early childhood program, they develop a way of eating that is likely to perpetuate the regular consumption of these meats for a lifetime. Even if the processed meat is nitrate- or nitrite-free, the large amounts of saturated fat and salt makes it inadvisable as a regular food choice.

You can introduce other types of protein—without nitrates and nitrites—that children enjoy. Perhaps in addition to the obvious other meat and fish options, you could try more vegetarian dishes that combine foods to provide complete protein. There are also soy products, such as TVP (textured vegetable protein), which resemble meat and provide complete protein. TVP is easy to use in pasta or rice sauces, chili, lasagna, and so on, and is an inexpensive way to get protein without saturated fat (see Vegetarianism, page 207).

Aspartame

Aspartame is being added to many foods, beverages, and snack products. This sweetener is manufactured from an amino acid and so is easily digested by your body. Many adults regularly consume products with aspartame—gelatin desserts, yogurt, puddings, beverages, gum. Some parents encourage their children to eat these products because they are concerned about children eating too much sugar.

Although the long-term health effects on children who consume high quantities of aspartame are not yet known, the amount of aspartame that children consume should be limited. Research has shown that sugar is not the evil we once thought it was. It does not cause hyperactivity. And concern about high-sugar foods replacing more nutritious foods can apply also to foods containing aspartame. If children are filling up on high-sugar, low-nutrient foods, they should be encouraged to eat fewer sweet foods rather than substitute with sweet foods containing aspartame. Although aspartame doesn't contribute to tooth decay, the regular brushing and flossing of teeth should be fostered in children.

In early childhood programs, staff should provide foods that are as natural as possible and have been processed as little as possible. Aspartame, which is a highly processed substance, does not comply with this recommendation.

Pesticides

Pesticides are commonly used in farming, except in organic farming, to kill organisms (or pests) on vegetables, fruits, and grains during the growing season. Pesticides are an example of unintentional additives, because some chemicals remain in or on the food after harvest. As a general rule, all of us should try to minimize our exposure to pesticides, due to short- and long-term concerns about health. Agriculture Canada approves all pesticides before use and has banned some that are still used in other countries (e.g., DDT). Relative to most countries, Canada uses fewer pesticides in agriculture. However, imported produce may have higher concentrations of pesticides, including those that are banned in Canada.

There are particular concerns about the potential effects of pesticides on children, because their developing bodies may be more readily affected by toxins. Children also tend to eat a lot of fruit and drink a lot of fruit juice. What can we do to reduce the amount of pesticides we eat? Wash produce in a mild solution of dish soap with water or a diluted mixture of water and vinegar or lemon juice. Although you will lose some fibre and vitamins by peeling fruits and vegetables, you will reduce your exposure to pesticides. Buying organic produce and lobbying policymakers to reduce both the commercial and residential use of pesticides are two ways to promote everyone's health. Some municipalities have successfully done so and others are in the process of reducing the use of pesticides.

Food Biotechnology: Genetically Modified Organisms and Food Irradiation

For hundreds of years, farmers have performed genetic engineering on their plants and animals by breeding them selectively to possess superior qualities, such as corn that is much larger and sweeter than its original wild ancestor. This process took centuries, but today's biotechnology is able to speed up and make the process of genetic selection much more precise. Modern genetic engineering holds the power to change even the most basic patterns of life by manipulating DNA material. Genetic engineering is much more far-reaching than simple food technology, as attested by the controversies in animal (e.g., Dolly, the cloned sheep) and human cloning. The potential for both positive and negative outcomes is awesome. This powerful science has and will have a definite impact on our food supply. Two food technologies that are receiving a lot of attention and consumer concern are genetically modified organisms (GMOs) and food irradiation (Sizer and Whitney 2000, 539–43).

Genetically Modified Organisms

Genetically modified foods include organisms that have undergone genetic engineering. For example, one bacterium was given the ability to make the enzyme rennin, needed to produce cheese. The gene for making rennin was snipped from a calf's DNA cell, transferred to a bacterial cell, which reproduced itself into mass production to be used in making cheese (Sizer and Whitney 2000, 540).

Canada's Food and Drug Act defines a GMO broadly as an organism exhibiting characteristics not previously observed in that organism, regardless of how the new characteristics were developed. This definition has contributed to much debate in Canada over the development of labelling for GMOs, mostly because it is the transfer of genetic material from one species to another that concerns many consumers and environmental groups. Mandatory labelling based on a more specific definition is in place in the European Union and Japan.

Many commonly used foods such as soybeans are genetically modified to be used for a variety of purposes in food production. The potential benefits of GMOs include the ability to feed many more people with increasing demands for foods and shrinking farmland, and for affordable, easy-to-prepare foods that are nutritious, safe, and good-tasting. However, the full extent of human health risks is not known, with the possibility of allergic reactions, nutritional changes, and the creation of toxins. This issue will continue to be debated over the next few years.

Food Irradiation

Food irradiation involves exposing food to gamma rays to reduce insect infestation or microbial contamination or to slow the ripening or sprouting process (Sizer and Whitney 2000, 539). Supporters of the process claim it is safer than spraying food with chemical pest-control products to protect them from spoilage caused by bugs and moulds. Although most of the radiation passes through the food, a small amount is absorbed and remains in the food. Irradiation does not make food radioactive. Health Canada approved irradiation for potatoes, onions, wheat, and wheat flour in the mid 1960s, and for spices in 1984. Spices are the most commonly irradiated food worldwide. Health Canada has proposed amendments to the Food and Drug Act to expand the types of foods allowed to undergo irradiation (e.g., meat, poultry, fish).

Proponents of this proposal believe that this will help protect the public through more thorough food safety procedures. Critics of food irradiation point out that although the process eliminates the use of some chemicals, most pesticides are applied before harvest, while plants are still growing. Irradiation does not cut down on the use of chemical pesticides by farmers. There are concerns that irradiation kills bacteria but not necessarily the toxins that the bacteria produced in the food before they were killed. Foods that look and smell fine may be contaminated with dangerous toxins that lead to food poisoning. Irradiation destroys some vitamins and thus reduces the nutritional quality of the food. Like labelling of GMOs, the issue of food irradiation will continue to be debated in Canada over the coming years.

Being Informed Consumers

Nutrition labels help us select foods for healthy eating. If you're not in the habit of reading product labels, you will probably be overwhelmed by a list of unpronounceable and obscure ingredients. You may also find that it is a time-consuming process at first, especially if you are comparing your favourite brand with its competitors. No one expects you to remember the names of all the ingredients, what they are and do, and which should be avoided or at least limited in consumption. But by reading labels of the products used in the home or early childhood program, you will soon compile a list of acceptable and unacceptable products for the shopping list. This will drastically reduce the time that is needed to shop.

Whether you are at home or at work, when you are trying to reduce the amount of fat, sugar, salt, and additives, here are a few tips for reading labels to evaluate products for healthy eating.

Fat:

- Use equal serving sizes when comparing two products for fat content.
- Choose milk, yogurt, or cottage cheese with 2% fat rather than whole milk for children over two years of age. For school-age children and adults the fat content can be reduced to 1% or skim.
- Choose cheeses with 15% milk fat (m.f.) or less.
- Select meats that are lower in fat (e.g., poultry, fish), and when selecting red meats choose leaner cuts (e.g., lean ground beef).
- Look for canned fish packed in water or vegetable broth.
- Read the product's label for the content of saturated and trans fats. Remember that daily values of these combined should not exceed 20 grams.

Sugar:

Note that ingredients ending in "ose" are types of sugar—glucose, maltose, lactose, dextrose, fructose. You may be familiar with the obvious types of sugar, such as granulated and icing sugar, brown sugar, honey, corn syrup, and molasses. Compare the amount of sugar and fibre in the carbohydrate section of the Nutrition Facts table on the label. Remember to choose foods higher in fibre and lower in sugar.

Salt:

The word "sodium" in the Nutrition Facts table alerts you to the presence of salt. If the word "salt" does not appear on the list of ingredients, there may still be salt in the product. There may be a number of sodium additives, such as monosodium glutamate, sodium bicarbonate, sodium metabisulphite, and disodium guanylate.

To state the practices that create a positive eating environment and encourage children to try new foods.

To describe appropriate principles and practices in infant feeding.

To consider the unique aspects of the growth and development of toddlers that affect their nutrition and eating habits.

To identify developmental issues for preschoolers and school-agers that affect their eating behaviour.

To consider reasons why there may be concerns about children under- or overeating.

HEALTHY EATING HABITS

The responsibility in feeding can be divided as follows: "Parents are responsible for what is presented to eat and the manner in which it is presented. Children are responsible for how much and even whether they eat" (Satter 1990, 14). This philosophy is based on respect for children and a desire to give them control over what they eat, so that they can respond to their own bodily needs and learn to eat for the right reasons. When this independence is taken away, they can soon learn to eat for the wrong reasons. An obvious example is when we insist that children finish a plate of food after they have already told us they are full. It is no wonder that children then become anxious about mealtime, and may even become over-weight because they are eating more food than they need or not gain enough weight because they assert themselves and refuse to eat. These mealtime situations can affect children's relationships with parents and educators when tensions and frustrations run high.

Children's growth and development play a key role in determining their readiness for food as well as their interests in food and socializing. By accommodating children's development, educators ensure that individual nutritional needs are met and that eating environments are designed to promote positive eating habits.

Table 5.7 lists the developmental characteristics related to eating. Learning to recognize these characteristics will help you make sure that children are receiving the food and nutrition they need.

Creating a Positive Eating Environment

The environment in which children eat is as important as the foods offered to them. It can either promote or hinder healthy eating and it can meet or inhibit children's social and emotional needs. Nutritious foods are of no value to children if they don't eat them. On the other hand, we know that any form of force-feeding or pressuring children does not work, especially for the long term. A positive environment is a much better option, regardless of the age group. When meals or snack times become negative experiences, with unhappy children or educators, review the checklist in Table 5.8 and identify which criteria have not been met.

Encourage children to try new foods. Here are a few suggestions:

- Present one new food at a time.
- Introduce the food when children are most hungry (e.g., at the beginning of a meal as an appetizer). You may be surprised at how excited preschoolers get when they hear you mention the word "appetizer," and how much they enjoy eating raw vegetables and dip, or celery in a glass of tomato juice.
- Serve the new foods with familiar ones.
- Offer small amounts.
- Talk about the colour, texture, taste, shape, and smell of the food.
- Encourage the children to help you prepare the new food.

TABLE 5.7   **Developmental Characteristics Related to Eating**   w w w

AGE	PHYSICAL	SOCIAL/PERSONAL
Birth to 4 months	• turns mouth toward nipple that brushes cheek • sucks and swallows	• recognizes the breast or bottle as the source of food by about 10 weeks • excited by sight of food (e.g., breast, bottle)
4 to 6 months	• sucking strength increases • chewing motion begins • uses tongue to move food in mouth • begins to finger-feed	• excited by sight of food
6 to 9 months	• holds a bottle • drinks from a cup held by adult • rotary chewing begins • tongue movement has increased and allows for more manipulation of food	• begins to show likes and dislikes for foods
9 to 12 months	• tries to use spoon • chews up and down • finger-feeds with a refined grasp	• conscious of what others do and imitates their examples
12 to 18 months	• grasps and releases food with fingers • uses spoon awkwardly • turns spoon in mouth • uses cup, but release poor	• wants food others are eating • loves performing
18 to 24 months	• appetite decreases • likes eating with hands • likes experimenting with textures	• ritual becomes important (e.g., has to have milk in red cup) • displays food preferences • distracts easily
2 to 3 years	• holds glass in hand • places spoon straight into mouth • spills a lot • chews more foods, but choking still a hazard	• has definite likes and dislikes • insists on doing it "myself" • ritualistic • dawdles • has food jags (e.g., refuses to eat anything but peanut butter sandwiches) • demands foods in certain shapes or whole foods • likes to help in kitchen
3 to 4 years	• holds handle on cup • pours from small pitcher • uses fork • chews most food	• improved appetite and interest in food • favourite foods requested • likes shapes, colours, ABCs • able to choose between two alternate foods

(table continues on next page)

AGE	PHYSICAL	SOCIAL/PERSONAL
		• influenced by TV commercials • likes to copy food preparer
4 to 5 years	• uses knife and fork • good use of cup • good self-feeder	• rather talk than eat • food jags continue • motivated to eat by incentives • likes to help • interested in nature of food and where it comes from • peer influence increasing
5 to 6 years	• feeds self	• conforming • less suspicious of mixtures but still prefers plain foods • social influence outside home increasing • food important part of special occasions
6 to 8 years	• refined small motor skills and eye–hand coordination (e.g., able to use some simple kitchen equipment such as can opener, toaster) • slow growth • high energy level	• shares and takes turns • table manners improving • eager to please • significant peer pressure (e.g., less willing to try new foods) • can follow steps for simple recipes almost independently • good sense of humour (e.g., creating funny names for recipes) • can delay gratification for a short time
8 to 11 years	• more coordinated (can usually use most kitchen equipment, e.g., knives, microwaves; may need supervision with stove) • physical competence important for self-concept status with peers • responsible for most self-care	• can set standards for own behaviour • often conforms to rules set by peers (e.g., high-status foods, trading lunch foods) • enjoys choosing and preparing foods, connecting nutrition with everyday life
11 to 13 years	• dramatic physical changes associated with onset of puberty, approximately a year earlier for girls than boys • increased nutritional needs (e.g., calcium, iron	• may be moody with hormone changes • looking for self-identity, may resist adults' nutritional advice • may restrict food intake due to body image pressures, especially but not only girls

Source: Adapted with permission from D. Gillis (1989), "Promoting Nutritional Health during the Preschool Years: Canadian Guidelines," Ottawa: Network of the Federal/Provincial/Territorial Group on Nutrition and National Institute of Nutrition, 23.

TABLE 5.8	Positive Eating Environment: Checklist			
			YES	NO

The atmosphere is relaxed. For example, if children are expected to come in from outdoor play and immediately wash hands to eat, their difficulty in relaxing at the meal is not surprising. Educators need to think about sequence and transition needs for children.

Distractions are at a minimum, and children are encouraged to focus on what they eat. Balance this with a warm social environment where children can talk calmly while sitting.

Children's rights are respected (i.e., not forced to eat foods they don't like or teased for not being skilled with spoons or forks).

Individual food likes and dislikes are acknowledged, promoting the child's self-esteem.

Children are guided (by adult modelling) to observe certain behaviour while eating, developing a sense of self-respect and respect for others. Educators eat meals with children and model positive eating attitudes and behaviour.

Children are encouraged to develop their five senses in enjoying a variety of foods.

Children are not forced to conform to rigid rules or expected to have perfect table manners. For example: Positively reinforcing children's use of "please" and "thank you" is far more effective than demanding that every time a child wants or receives something at the table she must use these words (e.g., repeatedly asking children, "What's the magic word?"—which is not only patronizing but misleading, since we don't always get what we want).

Food, beverages, and desserts are not used as bribes or punishments. Depriving children of food is never acceptable. When unacceptable behaviour does not relate to eating (e.g., arguments over toys at playtime), there is never any association made with food as a punishment or as a reward if he or she stops (e.g., "If you keep fighting, you won't have snack," or "If you stop doing that, you can have dessert").

Children are provided with developmentally appropriate opportunities to be involved in serving themselves. Children can start with giving themselves small servings and can have more if they would like, giving them control over the amount of food on their plate. Toddlers, preschoolers, and school-agers serve themselves as often as possible.

- Snacks are set out where two or three children can serve themselves at a table.
- Milk is served in small pitchers so children can pour their own.
- Family-style serving dishes are used at the table.

There are well-maintained chairs, tables, plates, and utensils suited to the children's size and development.

The table is made as attractive as possible (e.g., by laminating place mats that children make). Children are involved whenever possible in setting the table.

Foods served for celebrations and holidays are nutritious and fun.

Children are encouraged to share food experiences from their own ethno-cultural or regional backgrounds and are introduced to foods from around the world as a part of the regular menu.

Parents are encouraged to

- comment on and ask nutritional questions about the program's and their child's nutrition,
- contribute nutritional foods and snacks for special occasions and are invited to participate, and
- provide favourite ethno-cultural recipes.

- Encourage but don't insist that children taste the new food. If they reject it or say "I don't like it," accept their comments and offer it again in a week or two. The more often they see the new food, the more familiar it becomes, and the more willing they will be to accept it.

- Ask children what they didn't like about the new food. Maybe you need only change the way the food is prepared. If this food is familiar to families in the program, ask the parents for ideas about preparing it for or with the children.

- Remember that if children see educators enjoying or at least trying the new food, they may be encouraged to try it too. However, you aren't expected to force yourself to eat something you dislike. Besides, if you have it in your mouth but your body language says "It's disgusting" and your comments are negative, the children will understand your true feelings.

Infant Nutrition

At no other time in our lives is there as dramatic a rate in our growth and development as during the prenatal period and infancy. Infants double their birth weight by five months of age and triple it within the year. In the same year, they will be $1\frac{1}{2}$ times as long as they were at birth (e.g., 51 cm, or 20 inches, at birth and 76 cm or 30 inches, at 12 months). Infants' brains continue to grow and they quickly develop motor skills. As well, infants move from being able only to suck and swallow to finger-feeding in 12 months (see Table 5.7, page 217). During the first year of life, one of infants' fundamental needs is to have their nutritional requirements met by their parents and educators. Without all the essential nutrients, infants' growth, development, learning, and play will be negatively affected.

Parents and educators must communicate effectively—meaning daily written and verbal communication—so that consistency of care between home and program can be provided.

Breast Milk and Infant Formula

The best nutritional choice for infants is breast milk, for a multitude of reasons. Here are some of them.

- Human milk is perfectly suited to infants. It is species-specific.
- It contains the ideal quantities and quality of the three energy-producing nutrients (carbohydrate, fat, protein). The concentration of these nutrients adjusts to the needs of the baby, both daily and over time. For example, breast milk produced in the evening has a higher fat content so that the infant will stay full longer (Canadian Child Care Federation 2001, 2).
- The essential fatty acids promote the best possible nerve and brain development.
- The large amount of lactose (sugar), compared with the milk of other species, helps in the development of the central nervous system.
- It contains the right balance of most essential vitamins and minerals. Breast milk does not contain vitamin D, and the physician may prescribe a vitamin D supplement while infants are exclusively breast-fed.
- The protein in breast milk is easily digested in comparison to proteins from other foods. Protein is the most difficult nutrient for us to digest. Cow's milk, peanuts, and eggs are some of the most highly allergenic foods because they are high in protein.
- Breast milk contains antibodies that provide infants with immunity against some infections during breast-feeding. Exclusively breast-fed infants are also less likely to be the victims of Sudden Infant Death Syndrome (SIDS) (Canadian Child Care Federation 2001, 2).
- Breast-fed infants are less likely to develop allergies. Infants may react to certain foods that their mother has recently eaten (e.g., after she eats broccoli, the infant experiences flatulence).

"Breastfeeding promotes mother-baby attachment, which increases baby's cognitive, social and emotional development" (Canadian Child Care Federation 2001, 2). Many mothers who breast-feed need support in making the transition from home to work. Early childhood settings should strive to be breast-feeding-friendly environments. A mother may want to continue nursing after her infant is enrolled in the early childhood program. Those few women whose workplace is located close to the program may be able to come during the day to nurse their infant. Other mothers may bring in bottles of expressed breast milk and may breast-feed the infant at drop-off and pick-up. Find ways to be flexible so that the infant's needs are met. Many mothers nurse at home and provide formula for the child during the day. There are also mothers who wean their infants before returning to work, so the child has infant formula exclusively. There should be a comfortable chair or rocker for the mother and child and a relatively private place if she chooses.

Infants who are offered expressed breast milk or formula at the early childhood program will usually have been introduced to a bottle at home first. Infants who are used to receiving their nourishment from the breast may have a difficult time with this transition or they may accept the bottle readily.

We know that HIV can be spread from a pregnant woman who is HIV positive to her child through her breast milk after the baby is born. When her HIV status is known, her physician will advise her not to breast-feed. We also know that individuals can be HIV positive and not know they are, so there may be HIV-positive mothers who are breast-feeding their babies.

Early childhood programs are already required to have all baby bottles labelled with the children's full name. Educators must ensure that the baby receives only his or her bottle. If a baby is fed a bottle of breast milk that is not his or her own, educators must call the local public health agency. Public health staff will then determine whether the baby has been exposed to HIV and how to proceed. The director should also be instructed about notifying the baby's parents. Expressed breast milk does not present risks when it comes in contact with someone's skin (e.g., it has been spit up, or during a test of the milk's temperature on the top of your hand). Discouraging mothers from providing expressed breast milk for their infants in programs is not an acceptable response to the issue of HIV. High-quality early childhood education and care programs already implement the practices that prevent the spread of HIV in children.

For babies who are not breast-fed, commercial formula is essential for the first 9 to 12 months of life. Most formulas are made of either modified cow's milk or soy protein and include the infant's needs for water, fatty acids, carbohydrate (lactose), protein, and vitamins and minerals. Iron-fortified formulas are recommended for the first 9 to 12 months. It is important to prevent iron-deficiency anemia, rather than treat it, because anemia is a risk factor for possible irreversible developmental delays (Canadian Paediatric Society 2002, 39). Commercial formulas are designed to be as similar to breast milk as possible. For more information on infant nutrition, refer to *Nutrition for Healthy Term Infants* (Canadian Paediatric Society 2002) (see Resource Materials, page 252).

Bottle-Feeding

Bottle-feeding time is an ideal time for educators to hold and cuddle infants. It is not a time to be rushed. The practice of bottle propping is absolutely unacceptable because of the risk of choking and dental caries (tooth decay). Feeding is one of the important daily care routines; it helps infants to develop safe, secure, and trusting relationships with their educators. Infants who can sit without support and, especially, toddlers may prefer to sit and drink their bottle independently. Educators should discourage toddlers from walking around with a bottle in their mouth. Obviously, the child must never be left unsupervised.

In many infant programs, parents bring in one bottle for each feeding during the day. Each bottle is filled with approximately the amount of formula or expressed breast milk that the infant drinks in one feeding. There could be four bottles, each with 90 mL (3 oz) of formula. After the child has drunk from the bottle, do not give him or her leftovers at the next feeding. Formula and breast milk are perfect media for the growth of germs, and during sucking germs enter the bottle. Therefore, leftovers must be discarded (see Food Safety Practices, page 243).

Some early childhood programs are in the practice of having educators prepare the formula for each infant every day. The parents provide cans of their infant's specific brand. However, considering the amount of care and interaction that infants and toddlers need from their educators and that the educator–child ratio is already 1:3 or 1:4, educators' time should be spent more productively. Since parents already make formula for their infants to drink at home, it is not unrealistic to expect them to bring bottled formula needed at the program. As well, the logistics of clearly identifying all the individual bottles and nipples, sterilizing water, containers, measuring equipment, (unlined) bottles, and nipples, and ensuring sterility of the formula are an unnecessary burden on the educators.

First Foods

Early introduction of semisolid foods is not good practice in promoting optimal nutrition. Before six months of age, children's bodies are not fully ready for food. Breast milk or formula provides all the essential nutrients. At around six months of age, most infants are ready to try chewing and swallowing some semisolid foods (Canadian Paediatric Society 2002).

If a young infant is fed semisolid food, most of it will be found undigested in the stool. Infants' digestive and renal systems are too immature to cope with anything other than breast milk or formula. Infants don't produce enough saliva or digestive enzymes, and their kidneys cannot yet filter much protein. These infants are also more vulnerable to developing food allergies. Semisolid foods are less of an allergy risk to infants once they've reached the age of six months and their immune system has begun to mature.

Parents may believe that their infants need to eat solid foods as early as two or three months of age because the child seems more hungry or is waking up more often during the night. Many parents interpret this to mean that the breast milk or formula isn't filling up the child. In fact, infants simply go through growth spurts and need extra nutrients; all they need is extra breast milk or formula for a week or two to get through the spurt. It is a myth that very young babies sleep better at night when they are fed infant cereal. In reality, "prolonged sleep reflects the baby's total neurological development and has very little to do with the food she eats, colic being one exception" (Lambert-Lagacé 2000, 126). Understandably, parents want the best for their baby and are concerned about why she or he seems hungry. Relatives and friends may also have assumed that adding solid foods early was good practice and may be encouraging (or pressuring) parents to do the same. They may suggest, for example, adding infant cereal to the formula in the bottle.

Ideally, parents consult their infant's physician to determine on an individual basis when to introduce semisolid foods. This decision will be based somewhat on increased nutrient needs and on whether the infant has at least doubled his or her birth weight, although motor abilities and interest in other family members' foods also influence the decision. In turn, the parents and educators work together in the feeding process.

The introduction of semisolid foods should be a slow process. This respects the infants' nutritional and emotional needs, so that eating food is a positive experience for self-esteem rather than a process that infants can fail at or experience negative feelings about because it happened too early. Infants should have as much control as possible in the feeding process. Watch for the following signs of infants' readiness to start with semisolids:

- better able to sit up
- can move their head back to indicate fullness or uninterest
- can move their head forward to indicate hunger or interest
- can hold a spoon, although it will be months before they use it effectively
- have shown interest in putting food on their hands and some food has eventually reached their mouth

Developmentally, infants need sensory experiences, including food experiences, to begin to understand their world. Some babies need and enjoy this type of sensory exploration more than others. Don't be surprised if some parents are concerned about seeing their infants with their hands in the food—perhaps feeling that educators are encouraging their infants to play with their food. Once again, effective communication between parents and educators is important in negotiating compromise.

One obvious difference in feeding practices has to do with fundamental values in cultures.

. . . .

Your program's goal is to encourage infant and toddler independence. You encourage the infant to use a spoon while you have a second spoon for feeding. However, the parents' philosophy may emphasize the importance of interdependence—connection with the family is a priority; the feeling of being connected is much more important than self-sufficiency. Feeding with interdependence in mind means that the adult feeds the infant, perhaps into the preschool years, as part of this value. This is not an issue of right or wrong but of two different views. With discussion, a compromise will be reached.

. . . .

The Process of Introducing Semisolid Foods

Even though infants are now ready for semisolid foods, they are not ready to have the food replace the nutrients in the breast milk or formula. Until the age of around nine months, the infant should be offered the formula or breast milk first and then semisolid food. After nine months, the child can eat the semisolids first and then finish the meal with a bottle. By this time they are eating a variety of foods and in enough quantity to ensure they are getting the essential nutrients.

Parents should introduce each food at home several times before it is offered in the early childhood program. Parents know their child best and will recognize any allergic reaction to the new food. Parents should wait three to five days before trying the next new food to observe any reaction the child may have, such as undigested food in the stool, gas, rashes, breathing difficulties, or any other sign that the child may be sensitive or allergic to the food. Parents often introduce cereals first, followed by vegetables, fruit, and meat and alternatives.

Cereals

Infant cereals are usually introduced first. Rice cereals are least likely to cause allergies; they can be followed by other single-grain cereals and then by mixed-grain cereals. The commercially prepared infant cereals (e.g., Pablum) are best suited to infants because they are a good source of iron in a form that is easily absorbed. Their other nutrients, including protein, carbohydrates, and fats, are easily digested. Infants have an increased need for iron around six months. The introduction of cereals takes three weeks to a month if these foods are introduced gradually.

Vegetables and Fruit

There are two schools of thought on the introduction of vegetables and fruit. Some experts believe that there is no difference between the two and that they can be alternated. Other experts suggest starting with vegetables because many are easily digested and because if fruit is introduced first, some infants may be less likely to accept the less sweet taste of most vegetables. Fruit would follow three or four weeks after the vegetables. Regardless of which perspective parents choose, here are some points to keep in mind:

- Carrots, squash, sweet potatoes, asparagus, green peas, cauliflower, and broccoli need to be cooked and puréed.
- Ripe fresh fruits such as bananas, mangoes, and papayas can be mashed. Apples, pears, peaches, and plums need to be peeled, cooked, and puréed.
- Limited intake of fruit juice is acceptable, but the consumption of a lot can contribute to inadequate intake of other nutrients and energy, poor weight gain, and possibly diarrhea (Canadian Paediatric Society 2002).
- Real fruit juice should be diluted with equal parts water and given from a spoon or cup only. Programs can support this practice by having a policy that states that juice will be served in cups only, and that bottles of juice brought from home will be transferred to a cup. By the time a child is ready for juice, he or she is developmentally ready to drink from a cup. Juice in bottles encourages children to drink far more juice than the daily requirement of fruit and contributes to dental caries (see Dental Health Education, page 449).

Meat and Alternatives

Meats and alternatives are high in protein, a number of minerals, and some fat. Meats are usually introduced about three months after cereals. This additional time gives the infant's digestive system even more time to mature, which makes it better able to digest proteins.

When feeding infants, here are a few points to remember:

- All foods need to have a puréed texture when they are introduced, and become less puréed and more lumpy as the infant is better able to chew and may have some teeth. Some infants go from semiliquid cereals and puréed baby foods to finger foods and table foods in just a few months (Canadian Paediatric Society 2002).

- It is never acceptable to pressure a child into eating.

- Foods that are helpful for teething infants include dry toast and soft pieces of fruit or vegetables (e.g., a ring of green pepper). Most store-bought teething biscuits contain sugar and are not recommended.

Lambert-Lagacé has suggested a pattern to follow in introducing these foods:

- Start with white meat such as chicken, turkey, or fish.
- Continue with beef, veal, liver, or lamb.
- Introduce mashed silken tofu.
- Avoid processed meats such as ham and bacon because of high sodium and nitrite content.
- Choose fish that have less PCB residue, such as small farmed fish or ocean fish— sole, flounder, grouper, haddock, halibut, monkfish, salmon, or tuna.
- Introduce one new meat (or alternative) every three to four days.
- Offer homemade or commercial baby food.
- At first, serve only 5 mL (1 tsp) alone, not mixed with vegetables.
- Offer this food group at the midday meal.
- Never add salt or seasonings.
- Gradually increase to a maximum of 90 mL (6 tbsp) daily by the end of the first year.

Source: *Feeding Your Baby the Healthiest Foods: From Breast Milk to Table Foods.* Copyright © 2000 by Louise Lambert-Lagacé. Reprinted by permission of Stoddart Publishing Co. Limited.

Table 5.9 provides a guide for approximate serving sizes for infant foods. As infants develop a repertoire of foods and can chew more effectively, fewer table foods need to be restricted from them, except foods that are a concern for choking.

TABLE 5.9	Approximate Serving Sizes: 4 to 12 Months of Age			
AGE	DRY CEREAL	VEGETABLE	FRUIT	MEAT
4 to 6 months	up to 120 mL (8 tbsp) daily*			
7 months	120 mL (8 tbsp)	60 mL (4 tbsp)		
8 months	120 mL (8 tbsp)	75 mL (5 tbsp)	90 mL (6 tbsp)	
9 months	120 mL (8 tbsp)	90 mL (6 tbsp)	105 mL (7 tbsp)	45 mL (3 tbsp)
10 months	135 mL (9 tbsp)	120 mL (8 tbsp)	120 mL (8 tbsp)	45 mL (3 tbsp)
11 months	135 mL (9 tbsp)	135 mL (9 tbsp)	135 mL (9 tbsp)	60 mL (4 tbsp)
12 months	150 mL (10 tbsp)	150 mL (10 tbsp)	150 mL (10 tbsp)	60 mL (4 tbsp) or 1 egg

*Many five- to six-month-old infants are able to eat vegetables and fruit too.

Assessing the situation:

The parents of an eight-month-old girl haven't yet introduced semisolid foods, not even infant cereal. Marie's source of nutrition is her mother's breast milk. Marie is interested in what the other children are eating. She is hungry half an hour after you feed her a bottle of expressed breast milk. However, when you mention this to her mother, she assures you that she will be starting Marie on infant cereal soon. That was three weeks ago and Marie's mother hasn't followed through. What are the issues of concern for educators? How should you proceed?

Toddler Nutrition

Toddlers are at a stage where they are developing a sense of autonomy (a sense of independence) and balancing that need with the need to feel connected with their parents, families, and peers. As a result, parents and educators have the challenging role of respecting the toddlers' need for autonomy but setting limits to promote trust and security (see Table 5.7, page 217).

Toddlers' growth slows to a rate of only half to one-third of what it was in the first 12 months, but exploration speeds up. Except during growth spurts, toddlers won't be as hungry as when they were younger and they may eat less overall. Their appetite can be inconsistent. Many toddlers can override any desire to eat when they are overexcited, overtired, or angry with their parents or educators. Some parents and educators become concerned about this natural change in eating habits and pressure toddlers to eat. This is not appropriate practice at any age, but is a big mistake with toddlers, who will assert their independence. When an adult and a toddler get into a power struggle, nobody wins!

Poor eating habits now can pave the way for eating problems that last a lifetime. Toddlers can become anxious about mealtimes, or refuse to eat, or have temper tantrums because of frustration. Parents and educators need to remember that most young children will eat when they are hungry and when they are offered a variety of nourishing foods. It is a toddler's job to assert his or her independence and it is the trusted adult's job to confirm his or her security by providing firm but reasonable limits.

Some things to keep in mind when toddlers are eating:

- Remember the division of responsibility: educators have indirect control of feeding (i.e., selecting and presenting nutritious foods, setting routine times for snacks and meals, creating a pleasant atmosphere, maintaining developmentally appropriate standards of behaviour at the table, helping the children attend to their eating) and children have direct control of eating (i.e., deciding what and how much they eat). Some enjoy or need adult assistance with feeding.

- Many have a hard time sitting long enough to eat a whole meal if it is holding them back from doing other things.

- Toddlers typically dawdle over food. Rather than focus on the dawdling and the inconvenience this brings to the flow of the program, it is more effective to give reasonable but firm limits, such as "You have 10 more minutes for lunch" and, after the allotted time, calmly remove the child's plate without commenting on how much the child ate.

- Practical hints:
  - Use child-sized unbreakable plates, bowls, and utensils.
  - Toddlers often eat very small serving sizes (sometimes one-quarter of an adult's serving size). Avoid dishing out large amounts of food; they may seem overwhelming to a toddler. This may turn the child off his or her food.
  - Provide finger foods, so that toddlers are not always expected to use utensils, which is an emerging skill and not always an easy one to master.
  - Serve soup thin enough to drink or thick enough to eat with a spoon.
  - Cut foods into bite-sized pieces.
  - Avoid serving very chewy foods.
  - Children need to sit down to eat.
  - Take special care to avoid foods that may cause choking (see Reducing the Risk of Choking, page 243).

- Toddlers are often afraid to try new things (neophobic) and so tend to be afraid of new foods. The more familiar toddlers are with foods, the more they like them. Coaxing toddlers to try new foods tends to make them resist the idea more. But if they see a new food offered with no outside pressure several times, they will eventually try it and the food becomes less and less an aversion. Expect toddlers to refuse a new food and avoid thinking, "Oh, they didn't like it so we won't make it again!"

- Toddlers learn to like most foods that they originally rejected. However, in the process, they may do things like spit out the food if its texture, flavour, temperature, or other aspect is unusual to them. This is a learning process that should not be discouraged, because it usually leads to more openness toward food. If their behaviour (e.g., spitting out) is not tolerated, toddlers are less likely to risk trying new foods again. You may argue that permitting this behaviour wastes food or encourages poor table manners. Throwing away a piece of vegetable a few times is worth the long-term benefit when the children decide that they like that vegetable after all. In terms of manners, if you expect toddlers to demonstrate proper etiquette, you will be disappointed! Table manners are learned over time, and they should not be a priority for toddlers at mealtime.

- Toddlers have food jags, which means that they refuse all but one or two favourite foods for a period. This too is part of normal development and should be handled casually. Continue to offer a variety of foods at meals and snack times, and most children eventually start accepting other foods again.

- The Canadian Paediatric Society (2002) recommends small, frequent, nutritious, and energy-dense feedings of a variety of foods from the different food groups to meet the nutrient and energy needs during the second year.

Preschool Nutrition

During the preschool years, children gain only about 2.5 to 2.75 kg (5 to 6 lbs) per year. However, between the ages of two and five, children's head and body shapes change dramatically—a five-year-old no longer looks like a baby. Most preschoolers come through the toddler stage feeling that they have some power and autonomy, and most have an awareness that others have rights too. Preschoolers take increasing initiative as they become better at everything they do. With more language, they learn to express themselves in social ways and to work things out with other people. Food jags, dawdling, fear of new foods, and other toddler nutrition issues tend to diminish and are fairly uncommon by four years of age, especially if the adults had not given these issues undue attention when they were toddlers. Children in this age group tend to be interested in their body and keen to learn about how foods affect their body, where foods come from, cooking, and advertising (see Table 5.7, page 217; Nutrition Education, page 442).

Some things to keep in mind when preschoolers are eating:

- Children are individuals, and their appetites and interest in food fluctuate.
- Establish clear expectations for mealtime behaviour. Preschoolers are capable of understanding what is and isn't appropriate behaviour, as well as logical consequences (e.g., Carlos spills milk on the floor and understands that he will help you clean it up, or Emily throws the second piece of her sandwich on the floor and understands from your earlier comments that now she is finished eating and needs to leave the table).
- They have a genuine interest in learning about others, so this is an opportune time to begin to learn about other cultures, foods, and ways of cooking.
- When introducing a new food, do not pressure a child to try it.

School-Age Nutrition

This stage in a child's life brings many developmental changes, but in terms of actual physical change most children do not go through dramatic growth until early adolescence. School-agers vary in height and body shape and are aware of these differences. Concerns about dieting and the fear of fat may heighten in later school-age years, particularly in girls but also with boys. Children make the transition from a primary focus on their families to increasing influence from peers and other outside influences (e.g., media). Concerns about sedentary lifestyles can be an issue at any age, but there seem to be obvious differences in energy level during the school-age years.

. . . .

e.g. Most school-aged children who are involved in sports and games with friends have a high energy level. Others who spend large periods of time at activities such as watching television or playing video games will likely be lethargic and lack motivation to be active.

. . . .

The power of peers is evident in how children react to food among themselves, but these reactions are influenced also by their preschool experiences with foods. Children who are already open to trying new foods may continue in this positive way by increasing their repertoire. Children who have not been introduced to a variety of foods may be more judgmental about peers' food choices that are different from their own.

. . . .

e.g. A vegetarian child who brings a tofu burger for lunch may be asked to share it by one child who is open to new foods, but teased by another child for eating something different.

. . . .

School-agers need to understand the reasons for what they are doing. They are concerned with mastery and accomplishment as part of their self-esteem. For this reason, preparing food is popular with this age group. If a program can provide opportunities for learning to make breakfast, the children may also be able to do so at home. Through learning processes such as this, we promote their need to experience success that is recognized by self and others. School-age nutrition education can include the relationships between food production and consumption, recycling and composting, food wastage and packaging, and the environment (see Table 5.7, page 217; Cooking with Children, page 444).

Older school-agers may find it stigmatizing to be separated from other children (some of their friends) while eating lunch at the school just because they participate in the program's lunch program. Children who bring lunches may do a lot of trading of foods among themselves, which may not be a problem unless some children bring in high-status, low-nutrient foods for snacks or desserts and encourage other children to bring candy or chips to trade.

Concern about Amounts of Food Eaten

Every child and adult fluctuates in the amount of food he or she eats, for any number of reasons—growth spurts, illness, fatigue, hot weather, time of day, or food preferences. Educators first determine whether the child's eating pattern is one that their program can easily accommodate or whether it is a legitimate reason for concern. To determine this, educators examine two issues:

- their own personal perceptions and preconceived definitions of how much a child of that age should eat and at what times of day, and
- the child's body build—in other words, whether she or he is growing within the normal range of growth and development.

Let's look at three reasons why children may be temporarily eating a lot of food. If the child is growing within the normal range, there isn't cause for alarm, for the following reasons:

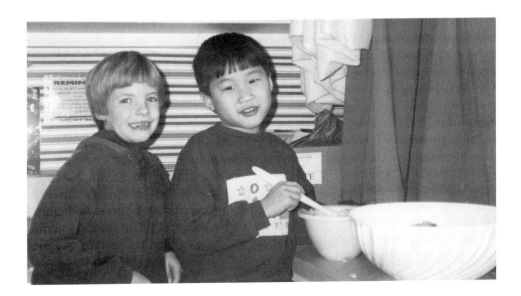

1. Perhaps the child is going through a growth spurt.

....

e.g. During a growth spurt the child's body requires extra nutrients and calories (or energy) for a limited time (a few weeks or a month or two). Interestingly, growth spurts often occur in the spring and may also follow a period of illness (e.g., in a child with asthma who had a difficult time during the winter). Understanding growth and development and getting to know children assists educators in expecting growth spurts.

....

2. Perhaps the child enjoys eating more at a particular time of day.

....

e.g. One child, like a lot of adults, is a slow starter in the morning and isn't ready to eat much of a breakfast before leaving home. By mid-morning she is ready to eat more than one serving of the snack. Another child is too busy playing to leave the activity to eat morning snack, but by lunch time he is ravenous. Remember, *Canada's Food Guide* suggests that we avoid looking at food intake on a meal-by-meal basis and instead look at overall intake in a 24-hour period (Health Canada 2007). Early childhood programs that have incorporated some flexibility into the nutrition program can accommodate children's body rhythms. At the same time, we recognize that eating regularly during the day helps children maintain their energy level.

....

3. Perhaps the child does not have access to a lot of food at home.

....

e.g. The family's budget does not stretch far enough to buy a consistent amount of food throughout the month. As a result, the child comes to the program hungry many days, or even every day. Programs need to have enough food available to provide extras and second helpings for hungry children. Educators' concern for the child and family does not end on Friday afternoon but extends to weekends and their access to enough nutritious food. Some programs work with food banks to supplement the food supply for families that live with food insecurity.

....

Therefore, daily observation of children and communication with parents are important in meeting children's nutritional needs and in determining their eating habits at home. Perhaps the child's parent tells you that he eats a large breakfast at home, which explains why he usually does not eat a mid-morning snack or a full lunch. Although because of their energy levels most children are more interested in food in the morning or at lunch, every child's body rhythm and metabolism are unique.

Early childhood programs with children who have recently arrived in Canada should ensure that the menus reflect the types of food eaten at home. The nutrition program should include some foods that are familiar to every child in the program. You can achieve this by asking parents for their favourite recipes. This is also one way that children learn about one another's ethno-culture. When you offer children familiar foods, they feel secure and relaxed and enjoy eating. New children are often shy and reserved around snack and mealtimes and need educators' extra support.

A three-year-old boy, who was new not only to the program but also to Canada, would eat nothing all day. The parents and educators were concerned about his well-being. The mother explained to the educator that her son did not like to eat around people he did not know. So she brought food from home and an adult with whom the child was comfortable sat with him at lunch time separated from the rest of the group by a partition. He was more relaxed under these circumstances and enjoyed the one-to-one interaction and the familiar food. After a week of this arrangement, they moved into the room with the rest of the group but sat at a table on the other side of the room with the trusted adult. The child could observe the other children, who by now were more familiar to him. When he was offered the food prepared at the program, he decided to try some. After this week of transition, the child felt much more relaxed, and by the third week he had joined his peers. He was soon eating well and his family no longer had to provide food from home.

Concern about Body Weight

We all have to be conscious of our society's notion of "ideal" body image and the role that we may play in perpetuating these stereotypes. Nevertheless, some children and adults are either below or above the average range of body mass by age, gender, and height. And physical or emotional concerns may be associated with being over- or underweight.

For children who eat large amounts of food, the best time to determine whether an imbalance exists between food energy and the body's demand for energy is when the child is gaining so much weight as to become overweight. If, however, the child is losing weight and is not growing in height, there may be concern about being underweight.

Educators' daily observations of children's eating patterns assist in identifying the contributing factors. A child who is overeating

- eats more than the recommended daily servings of any of the four food groups but in particular the milk products and meat and alternatives;
- chooses foods that are high in fat or sugar or both (i.e., foods outside of the four groups) over nutritious foods;
- does not participate in physical activity; or
- eats because of emotions—for example, boredom.

A child who is undereating

- eats less than the recommended daily servings of any of the four food groups, especially from milk products and meat and alternatives, resulting in an insufficient fat intake;
- chooses not to eat enough food for fear of being overweight;
- has a level of physical activity high enough that more food energy is used than is obtained by eating;
- is not active, but being more active would increase the child's appetite; or
- does not eat because of emotions—for example, stress or sadness.

If the educators determine that there is reason to be concerned, the next step is to meet with the child's parents. Obviously, consistency between home and program is beneficial. Some parents may not share the educators' concern for the child; others may need nutritional education and information to enable them to support their child. Parents should be encouraged to consult with the child's physician, and perhaps the child and the parents would benefit from consulting with a dietitian-nutritionist. To ensure that the physician's or dietitian-nutritionist's recommendations are carried out consistently between home and the program, daily communication between parents and educators is essential.

Educators and parents can address the following reasons why children might be overeating:

- poor eating habits (e.g., consistently choosing high-fat foods)
- insufficient physical activity for the amount of food eaten
- eating for the wrong reasons, such as emotional reasons (see Emotional, page 193)
- adults in their lives who model overeating
- stress at home, early childhood program, or school that may contribute to poor eating habits
- a physiological or psychological reason for weight gain (a physician would need to diagnose such a medical or emotional condition)

Educators and parents can address the following reasons why children might be undereating:

- poor eating habits (e.g., drinking too much milk or juice, leaving no room for food)
- fatigue
- limited variety of foods they will eat
- stress at home, early childhood program, or school that may contribute to poor eating patterns
- adults in their lives who model excessive dieting or negative stereotypes about larger body types
- security felt only with family and the foods served at home
- a physiological or psychological reason for the weight loss (a physician would need to diagnose such a medical or emotional condition—for example, anorexia)

The most important point to remember in approaching overeating and children is that dieting is never an option. Dieting (restricting food) produces a vicious circle of unhealthy eating patterns. It is dangerous enough when adults begin this dieting cycle, but much worse when children begin to diet. Considering children's great needs for growth, dieting robs them of their potential by

- not providing their body with the daily nutrient requirements,
- contributing to a lowered basal metabolic rate (when the body is not getting the energy it needs, it slows to function on fewer calories than it needs), and

- making them feel deprived and singled out if the other children are not subject to dietary restrictions.

Self-esteem is of great importance to children and adults, and dieting does not contribute to self-esteem, especially when more than 95% of individuals who diet and lose weight eventually regain the weight. In a word, dieting is inappropriate! Rather than consider weight loss, it is more effective to focus on decreasing the child's rate of weight gain. We help children to develop a positive and balanced outlook toward healthy eating and physical activity through increased awareness of foods and nutrition, by focusing on enjoyable daily physical activity, and by modelling healthy behaviour such as being active in the playground.

PROVIDING FOODS AND MENU PLANNING

Food is provided in early childhood programs in a number of ways. The most common arrangements are

- having the food prepared somewhere else and brought to the program (e.g., by a caterer, restaurant, or community kitchen). Often programs choose this option when they do not have complete kitchens;
- preparing food in the program, with an on-site kitchen and cook;
- requiring the families to bring food for their children;
- combining two of the above (e.g., an infant and toddler program provides the snacks and the parents supply their child's lunch and formula or breast milk, or a preschool program prepares the snacks and meals are catered); and
- having agency nutrition programs, often sponsored by government, or foundations conduct breakfast or lunch programs.

Understanding the basics of menu planning helps you not only as a student but also after you graduate. The menu is basically the culmination of the program's nutrition program put into practice.

Providing Food in the Early Childhood Program

Early childhood programs that prepare food on the premises or bring in catered food usually offer one or two snacks and lunch or supper, or both, depending on the hours of operation and their early childhood regulations. As part of the conditions for a program's licence, public health inspectors usually review the food preparation, equipment, and storage and serving facilities annually.

Financial constraints or limited kitchen facilities are often the reason why parents bring in some or all of the food. Programs need a refrigerator to store food and a stove, hot plate, or microwave oven to warm food. In some cases, the program provides milk and juice.

Regardless of how the food is provided, educators are responsible for ensuring that children have access to adequate nutrition each day. This job is simpler when food is prepared in-house or is catered, because staff develop the menus and establish the list of acceptable foods and beverages to be served to the

To outline ways in which foods can be provided in an early childhood program.

To explain rotation menus and list the steps in writing menus.

children based on the program's nutrition policy. And, of course, enough food is available to provide children with second helpings.

You may think that when parents bring food for children, educators can relax and focus on other aspects of the program. However, since the educators are responsible for ensuring adequate nutrition for the children during the day, programs must have nutrition policies in place that cover

- the food and/or beverages that the program provides,
- the times for snacks and meals,
- the parents' responsibilities,
- a list of acceptable or unacceptable foods and beverages for parents to use as a guideline in providing the food, taking care to respect families' food preferences, and
- recommendations for environmentally friendly food containers and packaging.

Even in these programs, supplementary food will be on hand. There may be times when someone forgets a lunch at home or in the car, a child is still hungry after finishing her or his snack or lunch, a parent does not send or cannot afford to send enough food, or a parent consistently sends foods that are high in fat, sugar, or salt but low in other nutrients. So it can be more of a challenge for staff when the parents provide food and/or beverages for the children.

· ·

Putting a basket of fruit or other nutritious finger foods out at lunch makes sense. Hungry children can help themselves. This reduces the stigma associated with the children having to ask educators for food.

· ·

Educators want children to have adequate nutrition and to become knowledgeable about food choices. Depending on the child's age, nutrition education is part of the program. As with any issue that educators have about children, they need to be sensitive in their approach, handle the issue discreetly, and maintain confidentiality. Food and eating habits are personal aspects of someone's identity, upbringing, and ethnicity, and can be closely connected to self-esteem. Making disparaging comments about a child's lunch or, even worse, throwing part or all of the lunch away, are both unacceptable and disrespectful practices. These practices will not make the parents receptive to talking with educators.

Before approaching parents, educators must ask themselves a number of questions:

- How frequent is the problem and how long has it been happening?
- Has the parent experienced a recent emotional or financial setback that may temporarily affect the family's everyday life?
- Are the food products familiar to the educators? If not, find out more about the food and its preparation. It may be nutritious after all, and it can be an opportunity for new foods to be integrated into the program.

Sonali is a vegetarian and her lunches don't have milk or meat. Because you are unfamiliar with the principles of vegetarianism you assume that she isn't getting the protein or calcium she needs. Some plant sources of calcium (e.g., almonds, figs) may be part of Sonali's daily mainstay. You want to educate yourself about vegetarianism; asking her parents to explain their family's diet helps you do this. As for the parents, you have demonstrated an interest in their child and they are pleased that they have knowledge and skills to share with you.

Ways to Provide Enough Nutritious Food

Children and adults need to eat breakfast to obtain the food energy to work, learn, and play. Many young children go to bed between 7:30 and 9:30 p.m. With the exception of infants, who wake up for a bottle or nursing, children wake up in the morning having fasted for 10 to 12 hours. The demands that rapid growth, development, and everyday activities place on children make it important that they eat enough nutrients to fuel growth and activity for several hours.

Morning Snacks

Many programs offer a flexible time for morning snack. They recognize that offering the snack at a designated time for all children cannot meet the individual nutritional needs of children.

Christopher gets out of bed as early as 6:00 a.m., eats breakfast, and leaves for the program. He is usually ready for his snack before 9:30 a.m.

Regular snacks provide a necessary and positive contribution to a child's food intake. Morning snacks that include foods from three of the four food groups provide the essential nutrients. They should be acceptable for dental health, too. The snack could be available for a set period—for example, from 7:30 to 9:30 a.m.—rather than offered as a group snack. Children then have control over when to eat, and can respond to their body rather than to a time imposed by the program. Because they have a smaller stomach, growing children need the opportunity to refuel (if they choose to) every two to three hours. It is also helpful for relatively stable blood sugar levels, rather than dropping low ("I'm starved") and then soaring high ("I'm stuffed") due to ravenous eating.

Dietitian-nutritionists are sometimes concerned that if there aren't set times for eating, children will develop grazing habits—eating constantly with no awareness of body signals for hunger. Having flexible morning snack enables children to eat when they are hungry (and not ravenous) and adequately addresses dietitian-nutritionists' concerns. Obviously, the snack would not be available between 9:30 and 11:30 a.m. or noon, when lunch is served.

Keeping in mind that children have individual body rhythms, just as adults do, there are those who do not eat breakfast, for a variety of reasons:

- Some children may not enjoy eating or drinking as soon as they get up in the morning.

NEL

UNIT 5 NUTRITION   237

- There may be no time to eat during the morning rush to get out of the house and drop everyone off. Time pressure on families is a significant reason for children's being hungry in the morning.

- Children who have not had a good night's sleep may not have an appetite for several hours after they wake up.

- Some children will have eaten only part of their breakfast at home or on their way to the program. And they will need to finish it or have the morning snack to supplement it when they arrive at the program. Other children may have eaten a doughnut or Danish on the way to the program, which provides some quick energy but none of the nutrients needed for a morning's activity.

- Some families just don't have the food available for breakfast every day. The problem may be more acute at the end of the month, when there is little or no money left in the budget.

- Some parents who don't eat breakfast themselves may not see the importance of providing breakfast for their children. Or because of the parents' modelling, the child refuses to eat breakfast.

Morning snacks can be simple yet nourishing. Children who eat a nourishing breakfast at home will probably want less of each food, or fewer of the items.

Here are a few simple snack ideas that include three of the four food groups. These snacks are easy to prepare even in programs with limited kitchen facilities.

- cold or hot low-sugar cereal, milk, and fruit (fresh or canned in its own juice)
- pita bread with hummus and fruit or vegetable juice
- cottage cheese with fruit and whole-grain crackers
- melted cheese, tomato, and alfalfa sprouts on unbuttered whole-grain toast
- banana egg pancakes (blend one ripe banana with two eggs and grill the small pancakes on a nonstick griddle) and milk
- blender drinks (e.g., milk or yogurt and fruit or juice; eggs must not be used in blender drinks because of the risk of salmonella food poisoning)
- scrambled tofu (soybean curd) on whole-grain toast with fruit
- almond butter on crackers with fruit
- yogurt with fruit and wheat germ

Child Nutrition Programs

Many elementary schools have developed breakfast programs because children were arriving at school hungry and unable to concentrate on their work. Some programs located within such schools have been able to use these programs as well. Communities are recognizing the contribution of nourishing food to children's everyday well-being and are responding with child nutrition programs across the country. Some are sponsored by government, non-governmental agencies, nonprofit organizations (e.g., Breakfast for Learning, Canadian Living Foundation), and business. Then there are food banks. These are not solutions to large-scale problems, but they at least reduce children's day-to-day hunger and ultimately have a positive effect on well-being, including the ability to learn.

Child nutrition programs are responsive to the communities served, since they may be delivered in a variety of ways, and may be part of an overall plan involving community kitchens or gardens.

FoodShare's Coalition for Student Nutrition, an Ontario-wide network of individuals and agencies committed to better nutrition for children, has developed eight guiding principles for a child nutrition program:

- The program supplies nutritious and safe food, regardless of family income.
- The program is accessible and non-stigmatizing so it is universal and flexible, and does not replace welfare reform.
- The program is community-based and administered in a way that respects the individuality of the community and addresses its unique needs.
- The program is culturally appropriate so it is sensitive to and respects individual and community diversity.
- The program empowers children and families so parents are not made to feel that their role in the raising of their child is being taken away from them.
- The program creates a nurturing, warm, caring environment in which children can participate freely.
- The program has enough financial stability to ensure continual funding.
- The program provides public education about creative ways to nourish children adequately and properly, both in school and at home.

Source: Adapted from Coalition for Student Nutrition, FoodShare, Toronto.

Menu Planning

Menus may be prepared in early childhood programs by

- the director,
- the educators,
- the cook, or
- the dietitian-nutritionist, who may be available for programs affiliated with a hospital, a community college, or a workplace with a cafeteria.

Each of these options brings strengths and weaknesses.

- The expertise of a dietitian-nutritionist is a definite asset. However, if the same menu is used in a number of programs, there is no opportunity to respond to individual aspects of the community in which each program is located.
- A knowledgeable cook can get immediate feedback from the children on how they feel about the food. A cook can be creative with the menu and see what works and what doesn't.
- When meals are catered, the menu plan is probably written by the caterers, but the program should make sure that the caterer accepts and responds to ongoing feedback.

Effective menus reflect a variety of foods that are developmentally appropriate, take into account ethno-cultural dishes, have little repetition of recipes during the four- to eight-week rotation, and introduce new foods and recipes regularly, including foods that children are learning to prepare and eat. Educators' ability in reading and developing menus is beneficial for a number of reasons:

- They identify the menus that are adequate in terms of nutrition, appeal, and variety.
- They know how menus can be corrected, improved, or made more creative, especially when younger children turn away from their food and older ones comment "Not that again!"
- They suggest the appropriate substitutions for foods when a child is allergic. Serving foods as similar as possible to those that the other children eat is ideal to normalize children with allergies.
- They work within the nutrition budget and identify food wastage or unnecessary spending.

Advantages of Rotation Menus

Menus are planned on a rotational basis for periods of four, six, or eight weeks. Four weeks is a short period of time, which means that every fifth Monday the cycle starts again. Children are likely to become bored with the lack of variety in this case. Longer rotation cycles offer greater variety in foods, and no one has to eat the same recipe more than a few times every six or eight weeks. Not many of us could say that about our cooking at home!

Developing four six-week rotation menus, one for each season, has several advantages:

- You can take advantage of the fresh produce that is available in season at its lowest prices and, in the summer, food that is grown locally or regionally. Perhaps some vegetables can be grown by the children (depending on your geography and growing season).
- The six-week menu would be rotated only once, since each season lasts three months.
- You can serve foods that are more popular in certain seasons, such as soups in winter and cold plates in summer. Of course, favourite dishes (e.g., spaghetti) can be part of every rotating menu—once or twice in six weeks for the favourite foods is not too often!
- The six-week menu provides a vehicle for introducing new foods to children. It is in the children's best interests to plan a balance of familiar foods and new foods.

Getting Down to Writing Menus

The prospect of facing a page of blank squares and knowing that you must fill those and five more pages with exciting recipes can be somewhat daunting. Like other skills, planning menus takes experience to develop. A good place to start is by critiquing menus that you find in books or early childhood programs during your placements (see Appendixes 5.3 and 5.4, pages 261–262). Consider the following suggestions:

1. *Begin with a number of resources at your fingertips.* The most important one is *Canada's Food Guide*, followed by any guidelines for healthy snacks, simple recipes, lists of different vegetables, fruits, juices, breads, and so on that the program has access to.

2. *Know the number of snacks and meals that are served each day.* Programs that are six hours per day or longer should offer foods that constitute at least 50% of the *Canada's Food Guide* daily requirements. As a rule, the two snacks and one meal combined consist of a total of three servings from grain products, three servings from the vegetables and fruit group, one to two servings from milk products, and one serving from meat and alternatives.

3. *A menu-planning format applies to children over 12 months of age.* As a student, you will gain a fundamental understanding of menu planning, which provides you with the basis for adapting menus to the age group that you will be working with.

· ·

There may be concerns about foods that can cause choking in younger children. Educators working with children under 12 months of age work directly with the parents to ensure that the nutritional needs of the infants are met, including the introduction of semisolid foods.

e.g.

· ·

Steps to Follow for Each Week's Menu

■ Begin by choosing foods for the five lunches:

  1. Select the meat and alternatives.

  2. Select the grain products that would complement the meat and alternatives.

  3. Select the vegetables and fruit.

  4. Add the milk or a milk product.

■ Next, choose foods for the morning snacks:

  5. Select foods from three of the four food groups (see Morning Snacks, page 237).

■ Then choose foods for the afternoon snacks:

  6. Select foods from two of the four food groups. (Children's nutritional requirements are usually lower in the afternoon than in the morning.)

■ Evaluate your week's menu with the menu-planning checklist (see Table 5.10).

■ Finally, because you are developing a rotational menu, the four, six, or eight weeks of menu plans should be checked for repetition of recipes, for the introduction of at least one new food or recipe a week, and against the food budget.

TABLE 5.10   **Menu Planning Checklist**

	YES	NO
Nutritional requirements: • vegetables and fruit—at least three servings • grain products—three servings • milk products—at least one serving • meat and alternatives—at least one serving • drinking water—availability at all times is encouraged		
Menus are varied, interesting, and creative (e.g., variety of colours, shapes, textures, tastes). Natural colours of fruit and vegetables, especially when raw, are appealing; a single colour on a plate is not appetizing. Meals should have a variety of shapes and textures to appeal to children's sense of sight, taste, and hearing. Experimenting with new foods, ethno-cultural recipes, and different herbs and spices encourages children to explore a variety of flavours. Be careful not to serve two strong-tasting foods together.		
Menus are planned and served with children in mind (e.g., some finger foods, child-sized servings, age-appropriate dishes and utensils). Preschoolers and school-agers have opportunities to serve themselves.		
Snacks are low in sugar and are nutritionally acceptable.		
Desserts, if provided, are a nutritional part of the meal (e.g., fruit, yogurt, homemade puddings).		
Real, unsweetened fruit juices are provided—not fruit drinks with added sugar or sweetener.		
Foods that have been through a number of food processes or have several additives are not served (e.g., instant potatoes, pudding mixes, processed meats).		
Foods served for celebrations and holidays are nutritious and fun.		
All allergies have been considered while planning menus and at the time of serving meals and snacks.		
Menus are posted in an obvious place for parents to read.		
The posted menu corresponds with what is actually served.		

To outline ways to reduce the risk of choking, to prevent food-borne illnesses, and to use a microwave oven safely.

FOOD SAFETY

This section includes three safety issues relevant to food and children: choking, food-borne illnesses, and microwave ovens. Children are at risk of choking on food because pieces of food are too large or they are not concentrating on what they are doing (e.g., talking while they have food in their mouth, eating while running around). Providing nutritious food for children goes beyond purchasing it and menu planning. It is of utmost importance that food is safely stored, handled, prepared, and served. Because the immune system of young children is not yet mature, they are even more vulnerable to food-borne illnesses than are adults. Microwave ovens are great timesavers in early childhood programs. Although using a microwave at work is basically the same as using one at home, be especially careful when warming bottles of milk or baby food.

Reducing the Risk of Choking

As children grow and develop, they improve their ability to eat a variety of foods. They start with liquids and move to foods that are puréed, to minced or chopped foods, and finally they are able to bite off and chew solid pieces of food. The risk of choking is high whenever children are given foods that are not developmentally appropriate. All children must be supervised when they are eating. Children can choke on food when they have food in the mouth while laughing or crying, or when they put pieces in their mouth that are too big. Other behaviour that should be monitored while eating includes proper posture while seated, proper chewing, eating too quickly, or eating and drinking at the same time. Educators should be formally trained in handling emergencies, including choking.

Educators can follow simple guidelines in food preparation to reduce the risk to children significantly. Hard, small, and round foods, whether smooth or sticky, can block a young child's airway (Canadian Paediatric Society 2002). Educators should never serve the following foods to children under four years of age:

- popcorn (lower-risk grain products include pretzels or whole-grain dry cereals)
- hard candy or gum
- raisins
- whole peanuts and other nuts
- foods on toothpicks or wooden sticks
- fish with bones

Some foods need special preparation:

- Spread nut butter thinly on crackers or bread. Never permit children to eat it straight from a spoon or finger. For many children under four, thin nut butter with juice or milk. (Note: Many programs are now "peanut-free" environments, due to life-threatening allergies, but possibly allow other nut butters—e.g., cashew, almond. In fact, at least one province or territory's early childhood regulations now prohibit food products containing peanut products to be served to children under the age of three.)
- If meat or vegetarian wieners are served, dice them for children under four and cut them down the middle for older children.
- For children under four, grate or finely chop raw carrots and hard pieces of fruit, cut grapes into at least four pieces, remove pits from fruit, and remove all bones from fish (Canadian Paediatric Society 1996, 352–53).

Food Safety Practices

Food-borne illnesses are usually caused by bacteria or by toxins produced by bacteria. Some types of food-borne illnesses are very serious—e.g., *Clostridium botulinum* (or botulism), which is rare but can be deadly—while others (e.g., *Clostridium perfringens*) produce symptoms such as mild abdominal pain, diarrhea, and nausea, and usually last a day or less. What we may assume is a 24-hour flu may actually be food poisoning. Infants and young children are vulnerable to food-borne illness for many reasons, including body size and immature systems. Honey is a risk factor for infant botulism and should not be fed to infants under 12 months old. Staff have been directed to avoid raw eggs and foods containing them because of the risk of salmonellosis (caused by bacteria transmitted from hen to eggshell) (Canadian Paediatric Society 2002).

Because the food we eat isn't sterile, some bacteria are always present. Food provides an ideal environment for bacteria to multiply or produce toxins. Bacteria thrive in warm and moist environments and need something to eat. Given time enough to multiply or produce toxins, bacteria occur in food in numbers large enough to cause food poisoning. Certain foods present a higher risk for food-borne illnesses:

- most of the high-protein foods such as meats, fish, and eggs
- custards and cream fillings
- salads with mayonnaise
- gravies and sauces

It is not surprising that summer picnics with sandwiches that have meat or egg fillings or devilled eggs, combined with poor refrigeration or cooling and the warm sun, can cause food poisoning. The bacteria are in their glory: absolutely perfect conditions for them to thrive!

Food becomes unsafe to eat when we do one or more of the following things:

- practise inadequate personal hygiene
- use dirty equipment or cooking surfaces (e.g., counters, playroom tables)
- handle and prepare food improperly
- serve food that has spoiled
- store food improperly
- do not control infestations of insects or rodents

The following is only a preliminary discussion of food safety, though it includes the essentials of what students and new graduates need to know when working in programs. However, educators who are responsible for cooking or persons who are hired as cooks should take a formal food-safety course. Information about these courses is available through any public health agency. In accordance with the public health inspectors' food protection guidelines, programs must develop and implement safe kitchen and food-handling practices.

Personal Hygiene

Effective hand washing is essential both before and after handling food in any way, as well as during food preparation when handling different types of food (e.g., after handling raw meat, wash your hands before you touch any other food). In addition, follow these hygiene practices:

- Keep your hair clean and, if it is long, tie it back.
- Avoid chewing gum, because saliva easily falls on the food or cooking surfaces.
- Wear an apron to prevent bacteria from your clothes getting into food.
- Do not prepare or serve food to children when you know you have an infectious illness.
- If possible, avoid kitchen duties and feeding children if you are also responsible for changing diapers that day.

Cooking Equipment and Surfaces

Used bowls, utensils, cutting boards, and counters have bacteria on them. If they are not cleaned and sanitized properly, the bacteria remain on the surfaces and get into food. How can we prevent this cross-contamination?

- Post cleaning and sanitizing procedures. Daily and weekly schedules include all food contact surfaces, utensils, dishes, pots, and equipment (e.g., mixer, fridge, microwave oven).

· ·

e.g.

Clean and sanitize cutting boards and knives that have been used for raw meat or poultry immediately after use. Assume that all raw meat and poultry have bacteria present (e.g., salmonella in chicken and raw eggs), which will be killed with thorough cooking. Cleaning and sanitizing prevent the cross-contamination of food that comes in contact with the contaminated board or knife. What might happen is that the bacteria land in a food that doesn't need to be cooked, and the food is left at the danger zone temperature range that allows the bacteria to multiply and cause food poisoning. Separate cutting boards should be used—one for raw meat, another for everything else.

· ·

- Clean and sanitize counters and food preparation areas before and after preparing food.
- Clean and sanitize tables that are used for playing and eating before and after eating.
- Follow the dishwashing routine to ensure clean dishes and utensils.
- Discard cracked dishes, cups, and glasses, because cracks trap bacteria. If a utensil, plate, or cup drops to the floor, place it with the dirty dishes.

Safe Food Handling

The way we handle food affects its safety. One of the most important factors in handling food is its temperature. The general rule is "keep hot foods hot and cold foods cold." In other words, foods that are either piping hot (above 60°C, or 140°F) or refrigerator cold (below 4°C, or 39.2°F) are out of the danger zone. This zone is the temperature range in which bacteria thrive, and it includes our normal room temperature (20° to 22°C, or 68° to 71.6°F). High-risk foods should never be kept at room temperature for more than two hours (Health and Welfare Canada 1993, 9).

It may seem like a waste to throw out food when you are unsure that it is still safe to eat, but the risk you take in serving it is too great. If children or adults eat contaminated food, they may experience discomfort, mild or serious illness, or even death. Clearly, summer outings and picnics must be well planned with food safety in mind.

. . . .

e.g. Using an insulated container to transport food and freezing the sandwiches so that they are thawed but not lukewarm by lunch time are safe strategies. Select foods that are low risk.

. . . .

Thawing meat or poultry must be done carefully, by ensuring that the food does not reach room temperature if possible. All frozen food should defrost in the refrigerator unless the microwave oven is used. Keep the thawed meat in the fridge until you are ready to cook it. This cold temperature prevents the bacteria from multiplying quickly.

Organize preparation times so that all the foods are ready at approximately the same time. This way, you avoid situations where some foods are starting to cool while others haven't finished heating. Because children don't like their foods really hot, programs often have all the food ready 10 to 15 minutes before serving the children. This period is long enough to let the food cool a bit but short enough to prevent bacteria from multiplying. For infants and toddlers, cool the food quickly by stirring. Other important suggestions follow:

- Use a meat thermometer when roasting poultry and meat to ensure that the internal temperature reaches the specified cooking temperature. When the outside of meat is cooked, the inside may be still harbouring live bacteria.
- Keep your fingers on the outside of clean cups and bowls and hold clean utensils by the handles.
- Rinse fruit and vegetables thoroughly before using them. If you suspect the use of pesticides or waxes, scrub under warm water (you may want to use a little dish soap) or peel off the skin.
- Never transfer food from one child's plate to another's.
- Taste food with a spoon that you have not used for stirring and use a clean one if you taste again.
- Use serving utensils whenever possible, but don't go overboard by using tongs to pass out crackers and slices of bread.
- Discard food left on children's plates and liquid left in their cups.
- Wipe the tops of cans before you open them.

Food Spoilage

We've all turned our nose away from a container that smells of sour milk. We can feel the green slime in the bottom of the bag of lettuce or see mould growing on food left at the back of a fridge. Yet we can't always tell when food has spoiled.

And often food that causes food poisoning looks, tastes, and smells fresh. Beyond cooking and serving food safely, other preventive practices can be considered to ensure that no one eats spoiled food:

- Buy food from a reputable store or supplier.
- Don't buy or accept foods that are rotting or have passed the expiry date on the label. Avoid cans with large dents that could have broken the seal and cans that leak or have bulging ends.
- Never use home-canned foods in programs, even if you eat them at home. The biggest risk of botulism poisoning in this country involves home-canned (in Mason jars) vegetables or meat (Health and Welfare Canada 1993, 13).
- Never use unpasteurized milk, even for cooking.
- Never give raw eggs in any form (e.g., eggnog, raw cookie dough, Caesar salad dressing) to children to eat because of the risk of salmonella. Avoid cracked eggs.
- When in doubt throw it out—whenever you are unsure about whether to use or serve a food.

Safe Food Storage

Safely storing uncooked foods and leftovers is one more way to prevent bacteria from multiplying quickly. Here are the basic guidelines for food storage:

- Regularly check the thermometer (which programs are required to have) in the fridge to ensure that it is set at the right temperature.
- Store meat and poultry in containers to prevent blood or juice from leaking onto other foods.
- Write the date on leftovers and use within three days or discard.
- Store non-perishable foods in airtight plastic containers with a label and the date they were filled. Keep containers off the floor and in a well-ventilated space that is cool and dry.
- In the cupboards and the fridge, place newer containers of food behind the older ones, ensuring that you use older foods first.

Assessing the situation:

You notice a pot of spaghetti meat sauce sitting on the kitchen counter early one afternoon (spaghetti is on the menu for tomorrow). You ask the cook whether it should be in the fridge. She answers, "I'm letting the sauce cool down first because it has to be at room temperature before it goes into the fridge. Otherwise it will go bad." Is it safe? Why?

Controlling Insect and Rodent Infestation

Insects (e.g., flies, cockroaches, ants) and rodents (e.g., mice, rats) carry germs and spread them wherever they go. An infestation of insects in food (e.g., ants in a container of flour) means the food is spoiled and must be discarded. Few early childhood programs have rodent problems, but those that do must consult with their local public health inspector and an exterminator to eliminate the problem immediately. Insects, however, are a constant concern. Flies and ants are widespread. In some areas, cockroaches commonly inhabit buildings. Controlling insects inside buildings presents a challenge because insecticides, though they get rid of insects, also have the potential to contaminate food, surfaces, toys, and so on. However, there are alternatives available that are not as dangerous to humans. Public health inspectors advise staff on types of products and may suggest a "people-friendly" insecticide first.

Rather than having to deal with insect or rodent infestations once they are under way, staff can take the following preventive steps to make the building less attractive for pests in the first place.

- Store food properly (i.e., in airtight containers, dry places).
- Don't leave food on counters or tables.
- Clean and sanitize cooking and eating surfaces so that crumbs and spills are removed.
- Sweep the floor after children eat (cockroaches eat dust and food particles).
- Avoid storing food under a sink.
- Check boxes and other containers that are brought into the building—cockroaches like to travel!
- Maintain screens and other barriers that insects might try to get through.
- Close off spaces around pipes under sinks, and close cracks and holes in doors and walls to the outside.
- Act quickly when you notice the first few insects.
- Rinse out recyclables before they are placed in the blue box.
- Compost appropriate kitchen scraps outdoors, if possible.
- Properly store and empty garbage both inside and outside the building. Keep the area around garbage cans free of litter and spills.
- Line all garbage cans with plastic bags and use snug-fitting lids. Preferably, indoor containers should open with a foot pedal. Open wastebaskets should be kept out of children's reach. Containers should be emptied at least once a day—more often if there are problems with odours (e.g., in diapering area).

Microwave Oven Safety

Microwave ovens are commonplace in homes, staff rooms in workplaces, cafeterias, and early childhood settings. Although they are convenient and easy to use, they can be hazardous if used improperly. To ensure the safe preparation of foods, the following guidelines are recommended:

- Use only microwave-safe containers, preferably non-plastic containers. Plastic food wraps, which are made with nonylphenols, are of concern when heated.

- Stir and test all food coming out of the microwave oven to prevent scalds and burns. Food heats unevenly, resulting in hot spots in the food. As well, the food can be very hot while the container remains cool.
- Keep the microwave clean of spills and splatters to prevent germs from contacting the food that is left inside.
- Ensure that school-agers who use the microwave oven to warm lunches and snacks do so safely.

Warming Bottles

Placing the infant's bottle in a container of hot tap water or an electric bottle warmer is more than sufficient to do the job, but it does take a few minutes. So the microwave oven often becomes the preferred warming method. Yet the risk of scalding infants from formula heated in the microwave oven is a real concern. Health professionals do not recommend using microwave ovens for this purpose. But if you do, consider the following suggestions:

- As with all microwaving, the container must be microwave safe, and there are issues for both glass and plastic bottles. If plastic bottles are used, those that have become cracked need replacing because the hairline cracks trap milk and germs. Because glass absorbs microwave energy, the glass bottle can crack or explode. In the case of bottles with disposable plastic liners (bags), check the instructions on the manufacturer's label to see if they're safe in microwave ovens. It is safer to microwave in a glass container (e.g., measuring cup) and then transfer warmed milk to the bottle.
- Remove the cover and nipple from the bottle before putting it into the microwave. This allows heat to escape and prevents steam from collecting under the nipple.
- Do not heat a 120-mL (4-oz) bottle for more than 30 seconds or a 240-mL (8-oz) bottle for more than 45 seconds at full power.
- Put the nipple back on the bottle and then invert the bottle 10 times. Microwaves vibrate the molecules, especially water, fat, and sugar, and the friction creates temperatures within the bottle that vary at the top, bottom, sides, and centre of the formula. Mixing is necessary to ensure that there are no hot spots to scald the child during feeding. Handle the nipple along the edge that fits onto the bottle, and avoid touching the part of the nipple that the child sucks.
- Always test several drops of the formula on the top of your hand (not on the inside of your wrist). The formula should feel cool. You are trying to take the chill off the formula, not trying to heat it up. When the formula feels warm, it is higher than your body temperature and may be too hot to feed to the child (Clark Lowry 1993, 3).

REVISITING THE HEALTH PROMOTION ACTION PLAN

With reference to the Action Plan for Health Promotion introduced in Unit 1, the following are examples of possible actions relating to our food system.

Individual Problem Solving and Self-Reliance

- Learn how to read food labels. Use Health Canada's regulated Nutrition Facts table to make healthy choices when you're food shopping.
- Become aware of fat (especially saturated and trans fats), sugar, and salt content of foods and try to keep *Canada's Food Guide* in mind when making food choices.
- Choose foods that are less processed.
- Select organic meat and produce, if possible.
- Buy foods with a minimum of packaging.
- Buy produce and other foods grown in Canada.
- Involve children in nutrition experiences.
- Incorporate active living to complement the benefits of good nutrition.

Collective Self-Help

- Get involved in food cooperatives.
- Participate in food share programs.

Community Action

- Join a community kitchen.
- Advocate for improvements at local supermarkets.
- Support student nutrition programs.

Societal Change

- Lobby for government support for stricter laws in reducing the use of chemical fertilizers and pesticides, GMOs, and food irradiation.
- Get involved in nongovernmental agencies advocating for updating the Food Guide according to recent nutrition research, and for continued work on food labeling and packaging laws and new standards for grading produce based on its nutrition rather than its attractiveness.
- Support better deals for farmers.
- Support organic farming.

CONCLUSION

Although parents and educators cannot ensure that individual children develop good eating habits for a lifetime, they can provide children with

- an adequate variety of nutritious foods that are safe to eat,
- an environment that fosters or encourages healthy attitudes toward food and eating, and
- a model for healthy eating habits.

From infancy on, the right of children to decide how much to eat and what foods to eat in an emotionally respectful environment takes priority in early childhood programs. The five principles to healthy eating guide us to eat well and lead physically active lives.

What's Your Opinion?

TO RISE TO THE CHALLENGE OR NOT?

At a program, the parents provide lunches for their children and the staff warm foods in the microwave oven, as required. Educators have observed that one toddler's lunch routinely consists of highly processed foods. A typical lunch for Peter is a cut-up wiener or piece of salami, french fries, and a store-bought dessert (e.g., cupcake with icing). Vegetables or fresh fruit are rarely provided. The most natural and nutritious part of the meal is the milk provided by the program. When an educator speaks to the parents about the lunches and about providing more variety, Peter's mother says that those are the only foods that he will eat. The educator explains that Peter eats the variety of foods that the program provides for snacks each day. At a staff meeting, one of the other educators suggests that no further action be taken about Peter's lunches.

If you were working in the program, how would you feel about this situation? Has this situation been resolved to your satisfaction and in the best interests of the child? Support your position.

ASSESS YOUR LEARNING

Define terms or describe concepts used in this unit.

- nutrition
- factors that shape eating habits
- body image
- disordered eating
- eating disorder
- food insecurity
- nutrients and functions
- key nutrients
- *Canada's Food Guide*
- food groups
- vegetarianism
- complementary protein
- food processing
- nutrition labels
- Nutrition Facts table

- genetically modified organisms
- food irradiation
- food additives
- food jags
- positive eating environments
- advantages of breast milk
- formula
- semisolid foods
- overeating
- undereating
- menu planning
- food safety
- risks of choking
- food-borne illness

Evaluate your options in each situation.

1. The practice at your program placement is for the educators to serve food and to insist that the preschoolers eat everything. There have been a number of power struggles lately, and lunch time has become an unpleasant experience for everyone. The staff have asked you for suggestions.

2. The parents of an active, healthy eight-year-old tell you that they are concerned about their daughter's weight and insist that she be given only one serving of each food at mealtimes. Also, for snacks she is to have only fruit and vegetables.

3. Although the preschoolers eat in small groups at tables, there are a number of groups in the room. The noise level can get high, creating a less-than-calm eating environment, especially for children who are easily distracted.

4. An 18-month-old who has been in the program for three months will eat only jarred or puréed baby food that his parents provide. He refuses the more textured food that the program serves. Related to this, educators are concerned that his language development is being affected. The parents are worried that if they don't provide puréed food, their son will go hungry.

5. You're planning a day-long summer trip to a park with all the infants, toddlers, and preschoolers. Your responsibility is to make arrangements for the food and beverages.

RESOURCE MATERIALS

Organizations

Allergy Asthma Information Association, National Office, 32 Mare Crescent, Box 100, Toronto, ON M9W 5K9. Tel. (416) 679-9521, national toll-free 1-800-611-7011; fax (416) 679-9524 (or contact provincial/territorial office). www.calgaryallergy.ca/aaia

Canadian Restaurant and Food Services Association, Allergy Aware Program, 316 Bloor Street W., Toronto, ON M5S 1W5. Tel. (416) 923-8416, national toll-free 1-800-387-5649; fax (416) 923-1450 (or contact regional office). www.crfa.ca

FoodShare, Education and Research Office, 238 Queen Street W., Toronto, ON M5V 1Z7. Tel. (416) 392-6653; fax (416) 392-6650. (Available as a resource for any group in Canada interested in school nutrition programs, whether for breakfast, snack, or lunch.) www.foodshare.net

La Leche League of Canada, National Office, 18C Industrial Drive, Box 29, Chesterville, ON K0C 1H0. Tel. (613) 448-1842; fax (613) 448-1845. (Support groups in various cities across Canada.) www.lalecheleaguecanada.ca

National Anti-Poverty Association, 440–325 Dalhousie Street, Ottawa, ON K1N 7G2. Tel: (613) 789-0096; fax (613) 789-0141. www.napo-onap.ca

Other Websites of Interest

Canadian Association of Food Banks: www.cafb-acba.ca

Food Safety and You, Canadian Food Inspection Agency: www.inspection.gc.ca/english/corpaffr/publications/fsydas/tabdese.shtml

Canadian Paediatric Society: www.cps.ca

Health Canada: www.hc-sc.gc.ca

National Eating Disorder Information Centre: www.nedic.ca

National Institute of Nutrition: www.nin.ca

Pollution Probe: www.pollutionprobe.org

Printed Matter

Additive Alert! What Have They Done to Our Food? A Consumer's Action Guide (1994), by Pollution Probe (McClelland & Stewart).

All Shapes and Sizes: Promoting Fitness and Self-Esteem in Your Overweight Child (1994), by T. Pitman and M. Kaufman (HarperCollins).

Child of Mine: Feeding with Love and Good Sense (1991), by E. Satter (Bull Publishing).

Cook and Learn: A Child's Cook Book: *Pictorial Single Portion Recipes* (1981), by B. Veitch and T. Harms (Addison-Wesley Publishing).

Cooking Vegetarian (1996), by V. Melina and J. Forest (Macmillan Canada).

Having Fun with Healthy Foods: A Daycare Menu Planning Manual (1993), by Department of Health, Nova Scotia.

Better Baby Food: Your Essential Guide to Nutrition, Feeding and Cooking for All Babies and Toddlers (2001), by J. Saab and D. Kalnins (Robert Rose Inc.).

How to Get Your Kids to Eat … But Not Too Much (1990), by E. Satter (Bull Publishing).

Nutrition for Healthy Term Infants (2002), by the Canadian Paediatric Society <www. hc-sc.gc.ca/english/media/releases/1998/9825ebk2.htm> (July 2003).

Real Food for a Change (1999), by W. Roberts, R. MacRae, and L. Stahlbrand (Random House Canada).

"Sharing Ideas about Breast Milk Expression, Storage and Feeding," in *Well Beings: A Guide to Promote the Physical Health, Safety and Emotional Well-Being of Children in Child Care Centres and Family Day Care Homes* (1996), by the Canadian Paediatric Society.

Starting Right: A Nutritional Guide for Your Child's First Three Years from the Canadian Paediatric Society (available from H.J. Heinz Company of Canada, 5650 Yonge Street, 16th floor, North York, ON M2M 4G3; national toll-free 1-800-268-6641).

BIBLIOGRAPHY

Andersen, R.E. (2000). "Commentary: The Spread of the Childhood Obesity Epidemic." *Canadian Medical Association Journal* 163(11): 1461.

Canadian Child Care Federation (2001). "Supporting Breastfeeding in Child Care." *Nourish and Nurture Neurodevelopment* Resource Sheet #57 (Spring):1–2.

Canadian Paediatric Society (2003). "Nutrition Recommendations Update: Dietary Fat and Children." Report of the Joint Working Committee of the Canadian Paediatric Society and Health Canada. Reference No. N94-01. Reaffirmed February 2003. <www.cps.ca/english/statements/N/n94-01.htm> (July 2003).

——— (2002). "Nutrition for Healthy Term Infants." <www.hc-sc.gc.ca/ english/media/releases/1998/9825ebk2.htm> (July 2003).

————— (1996). *Well Beings: A Guide to Promote the Physical Health, Safety and Emotional Well-Being of Children in Child Care Centres and Family Day Care Homes.* Ottawa: Canadian Paediatric Society.

Clark Lowry, L.L. (1999). "The Development of Taste During Infancy." *In-Touch* 17(4)(Fall): 1–2.

————— (1993). "The Use of the Microwave Oven for Heating Bottles of Milk." *In-Touch* 11(2)(Summer): 3–4.

Deverell, J. (1998). "Are We Buying Better Health with Vitamins, Herbals?" *The Toronto Star,* 14 August, E1, E5.

Driedger, S.D. (1997). "Eating Right—New Research Points the Way to Proper Diet for Health-Conscious Canadians." *Maclean's,* 27 October, 50–61.

Escobar, A. (1999). "Factors Influencing Children's Dietary Practices: A Review." USDA Government Documents 12(3&4): 44–55.

Evers, S. (1995). "Nutritional Issues for Low-Income Children." *RAPPORT* 10(4)(Fall): 5–7.

Gillis, D. (1989). "Promoting Nutritional Health During the Preschool Years: Canadian Guidelines." Ottawa: Network of the Federal/Provincial/Territorial Group on Nutrition and National Institute of Nutrition.

Guy, K., ed. (1997). *Our Promise to Children.* Ottawa: Health Canada.

Health and Welfare Canada (1993). *Food Safety: It's All in Your Hands.* Ottawa: Minister of Supply and Services.

Health Canada (2007). *Eating Well with Canada's Food Guide.*

————— (2003). "Nutrition Facts Table." <www.hc-sc.gc.ca/english/media/releases/2003/2003.01bk/1.htm> (July 2003).

Health Canada (2003). "Nutrition Facts Table." <www.hc-sc.gc.ca/english/media/releases/2003/2003.01bk/1.htm> (July 2003).

————— (2002a). "Canada's Food Guide to Healthy Eating: Focus on Preschoolers." <www.hc-sc.gc.ca/hpfb-dgpsa/onpp-bppn/food_guide_preschoolers_e.html> (July 2003).

————— (2002b). "Food Guide Facts: Background for Educators and Communicators." <www.hc-sc.gc.ca/hpfb-dgpsa/onpp-bppn/food_guide_background_intro_e.html> (July 2003)

————— (2002c). "Using the Food Guide." <www.hc-sc.gc.ca/hpfb-dgpsa/onpp-bppn/using_food_guide_e.html> (July 2003).

Jones, J.M., M.P. Olmsted, M.L. Lawson, and G. Rodin (2001). "Disordered Eating Attitudes and Behaviours in Teenaged Girls: A School-Based Study." *Canadian Medical Association Journal* 165(5): 547–59.

Lambert-Lagacé, L. (2000). *Feeding Your Baby the Healthiest Foods: From Breast Milk to Table Foods.* Toronto: Stoddart.

————— (1993). *Feeding Your Preschooler: Tasty Nutrition for Kids Two to Six.* Toronto: Stoddart.

McIntyre, L. (1994). "Lessons from Child Nutrition Programs across Canada." *NutriAction '94: Conference Proceedings.* Toronto: FoodShare.

Melina, V., B. Davis, and V. Harrison (1994). *Becoming Vegetarian: The Complete Guide to Adopting a Healthy Vegetarian Diet.* Toronto: Macmillan Canada.

Mongeau, E. (1998). *The Role of Dairy Products in the Canadian Diet.* Ottawa: Canadian

Agri-Food Research Council.

National Eating Disorder Information Centre (2003). "Questions and Answers." <www.nedic.ca/qa.html> (July 2003).

Pelchat, M.L., and P. Pliner (1986). "Antecedents and Correlates of Feeding Problems in Young Children." *Journal of Nutrition Education* 18: 23–29.

Pollution Probe (1994). *Additive Alert! What Have They Done to Our Food? A Consumer's Action Guide.* Toronto: McClelland & Stewart.

Satter, E. (1990). *How to Get Your Kid to Eat ... But Not Too Much.* Palo Alto, CA: Bull Publishing.

Schardt, D. (2002). "Face the Fats." *Nutrition Action Newsletter,* July/August: 1–6.

Sheinin, R. (1990). "Body Shame: Body Image in a Cultural Context." *Bulletin,* National Eating Disorder Information Centre 5(5) (Nov.): 1–3.

Sizer, F., and E. Whitney (2000). *Nutrition Concepts and Controversies,* 8th ed. Toronto: Wadsworth Thomson Learning.

Tremblay, M.S., and J.D. Willms (2000). "Secular Trends in the Body Mass Index of Canadian Children." *Canadian Medical Association Journal* 163(11): 1429–33.

White, P. (1990). *The Supermarket Tour: A Handbook for Education and Action.* Toronto: Toronto Public Interest Research Group.

World Health Organization (2003). "Diet, Nutrition, and the Prevention of Chronic Diseases: WHO Technical Report Series 916." *Report of a Joint WHO/FAO Expert Consultation.* Geneva: World Health Organization.

Nutrients: Their Functions and Food Sources

THE ENERGY PROVIDERS	ROLE	FOUND IN
Carbohydrates	supply the body's main source of energy; assist in utilization of fats, spare protein so it can be used for tissue formation	breads, cereals, pasta, potatoes, rice, legumes and lentils, fruits and vegetables and their juices, milk and milk products, sugar
Proteins	build and repair body tissues, including muscles, bones, blood; manufacture anti-bodies necessary to fight infection	meat, fish, poultry, milk and milk products, eggs, legumes, and lentils, tofu, nuts and seeds and their spreads (e.g., peanut butter), breads and cereals in combination with other protein sources
Fats	provide the most concentrated source of energy, carry fat-soluble vitamins, provide essential fatty acids necessary for normal growth and healthy skin	butter, margarine, cooking fats and oils, salad dressings, meats, poultry and fish, egg yolk, nuts and seeds and their spreads, milk and milk products, avocado, foods prepared with fats and oils such as cookies, pastries, cakes, fried foods

THE FAT-SOLUBLE VITAMINS	ROLE	FOUND IN
Vitamin A	forms healthy skin and membranes, assists in bone growth and tooth development, promotes good night vision, repairs tissues	yellow or orange fruits and vegetables, dark-green leafy vegetables such as spinach, egg yolk, cheese, milk, butter, and margarine
Vitamin D	regulates calcium and phosphorus absorption and utilization in formation and maintenance of bones and teeth	fortified fluid, evaporated or powdered milk and margarine, tuna, salmon, sardines. Vitamin D is the "sunshine vitamin" available through exposure to ultraviolet rays.
Vitamin E	prevents oxidation of fat in tissues, especially important in red blood cell membranes and lungs	vegetable oils, margarine, whole-grain cereals, wheat germ, bean sprouts, nuts and seeds and their spreads

(appendix continues on next page)

WATER-SOLUBLE VITAMINS	ROLE	FOUND IN
Thiamin (Vitamin B$_1$)	helps release energy from carbohydrates; enables growth and repair of tissues, especially nerve and muscle; aids in maintaining normal appetite	whole-grain or enriched breads, cereals, and pasta, milk and milk products, pork, nuts and seeds and their spreads
Riboflavin (Vitamin B$_2$)	assists in release of energy, aids cell division and promotes growth and repair of tissues, maintains healthy skin and eyes	milk, yogurt, cottage cheese, whole-grain or enriched breads, meat and poultry
Niacin (Vitamin B$_3$)	helps release energy from carbohydrates, protein, and fats; assists in the synthesis of fat; maintains healthy skin, gut, and nervous system	whole-grain and enriched bread, cereals, and pasta, peanut butter, meat, fish, poultry, legumes, milk, cheese
Vitamin B$_6$	assists in protein, carbohydrate, and fat metabolism, promotes normal functioning of central nervous system	chicken, fish, whole-grain breads and cereals, egg yolk, bananas, avocados
Folate	aids red blood cell formation and protein metabolism	dark-green leafy vegetables, broccoli, Brussels sprouts, oranges and orange juice, bananas, milk and milk products, wheat germ, cereals enriched with folate
Vitamin B$_{12}$	promotes normal blood formation, maintains healthy nervous tissue, aids in protein synthesis	meat, fish, poultry, milk and milk products, eggs
Vitamin C	strengthens connective tissue, bones, skin, muscles, teeth, blood vessels; promotes normal nerve function; enhances absorption of iron	citrus fruits, vitaminized apple juice, dark-green leafy vegetables, green and red pepper, tomatoes, broccoli, potatoes, strawberries

THE MACROMINERALS	ROLE	FOUND IN
Calcium	builds and maintains strong bones and teeth, promotes normal blood clotting and healthy nerve function	milk and milk products, salmon and sardines with bones, dark-green leafy vegetables, broccoli, soy milk, tofu
Phosphorus	aids in formation and maintenance of strong bones and teeth, transportation of nutrients and regulation of energy balance; helps maintain body's acid balance	meat, fish, poultry, eggs, milk and milk products, soy milk, tofu, whole-grain breads and cereals
Magnesium	helps in formation and maintenance of strong bones and teeth, transmission of nerve impulses and release of energy	dark-green leafy vegetables, legumes, seafood, milk and milk products, cereals

(appendix continues on next page)

THE MICROMINERALS	ROLE	FOUND IN
Iron	combines with protein to form hemoglobin, the part of red blood cells that transports oxygen and carbon dioxide, and also myoglobin, which provides oxygen to cells	meats, fish and poultry, whole-grain or enriched breads, cereals and pasta, iron-fortified infant cereals, dark-green leafy vegetables, dried fruits such as raisins
Fluoride	facilitates formation and maintenance of decay-resistant teeth	fluoride-containing water and foods prepared in it, toothpaste
Zinc	functions as part of several enzymes involved in many diverse metabolic roles necessary for growth, development, and energy release	meat, poultry, fish, whole-wheat breads and cereals, legumes, lentils, nuts and their spreads
Iodine	aids in production of thyroid hormones, which regulate energy metabolism and growth rate	iodized table salt, seafood, vegetables depending on regional iodine content of soil and water

DIETARY FIBRE	ROLE	FOUND IN
	indigestible material, which promotes normal elimination of waste from the colon and may have other physiological effects	whole-grain breads and cereals, legumes, fruits, and vegetables

WATER	ROLE	FOUND IN
	the main constituent of the body; necessary for transporting nutrients, promoting metabolic processes, regulating body temperature, eliminating body waste	tap water, beverages such as milk and juices, soups and a wide variety of foods, especially fruits and vegetables

Source: Adapted from D. Gillis (1989), "Promoting Nutritional Health during the Preschool Years: Canadian Guidelines," Ottawa: Network of the Federal/Provincial/Territorial Group on Nutrition and National Institute of Nutrition, 29–32.

Eating Well with Canada's Food Guide

5.2

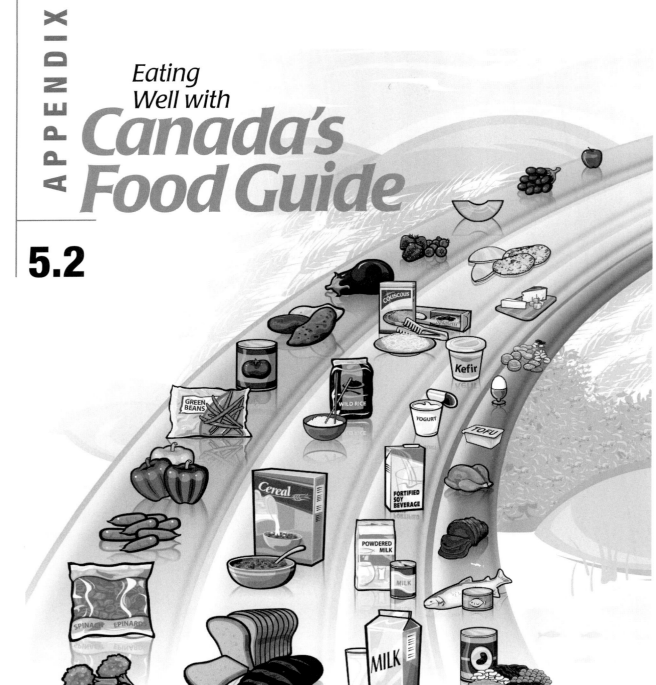

Canada

Recommended Number of Food Guide Servings per Day

Age in Years	2-3	4-8	9-13	Teens 14-18		Adults 19-50		51+	
Sex	Children Girls and Boys			Females	Males	Females	Males	Females	Males
Vegetables and Fruit	4	5	6	7	8	7-8	8-10	7	7
Grain Products	3	4	6	6	7	6-7	8	6	7
Milk and Alternatives	2	2	3-4	3-4	3-4	2	2	3	3
Meat and Alternatives	1	1	1-2	2	3	2	3	2	3

The chart above shows how many Food Guide Servings you need from each of the four food groups every day.

Having the amount and type of food recommended and following the tips in *Canada's Food Guide* will help:

• Meet your needs for vitamins, minerals and other nutrients.
• Reduce your risk of obesity, type 2 diabetes, heart disease, certain types of cancer and osteoporosis.
• Contribute to your overall health and vitality.

What is One Food Guide Serving?
Look at the examples below.

Vegetables and Fruit

Fresh, frozen or canned vegetables 125 mL (½ cup)

Leafy vegetables Cooked: 125 mL (½ cup) Raw: 250 mL (1 cup)

Fresh, frozen or canned fruits 1 fruit or 125 mL (½ cup)

100% Juice 125 mL (½ cup)

Grain Products

Bread 1 slice (35 g)

Bagel ½ bagel (45 g)

Flat breads ½ pita or ½ tortilla (35 g)

Cooked rice, bulgur or quinoa 125 mL (½ cup)

Cooked pasta or couscous 125 mL (½ cup)

Cereal Cold: 30 g Hot: 175 mL (¾ cup)

Milk and Alternatives

Milk or powdered milk (reconstituted) 250 mL (1 cup)

Canned milk (evaporated) 125 mL (½ cup)

Fortified soy beverage 250 mL (1 cup)

Yogurt 175 g (¾ cup)

Kefir 175 mL (¾ cup)

Cheese 50 g (1 ½ oz.)

Meat and Alternatives

Cooked fish, shellfish, poultry, lean meat 75 g (2 ½ oz.)/125 mL (½ cup)

Cooked legumes 175 mL (¾ cup)

Tofu 150 g or 175 mL (¾ cup)

Eggs 2 eggs

Peanut or nut butters 30 mL (2 Tbsp)

Shelled nuts and seeds 60 mL (¼ cup)

Oils and Fats

• Include a small amount – 30 to 45 mL (2 to 3 Tbsp) – of unsaturated fat each day. This includes oil used for cooking, salad dressings, margarine and mayonnaise.
• Use vegetable oils such as canola, olive and soybean.
• Choose soft margarines that are low in saturated and trans fats.
• Limit butter, hard margarine, lard and shortening.

Source: Eating Well with Canada's Food Guide, Health Canada, (2007). Reproduced with the permission of the Minister of Public Works and Government Services Canada, 2007.

NEL

Lunch Program Menu

MONDAY	TUESDAY	WEDNESDAY	THURSDAY	FRIDAY
		• cheese & potato perogies • garlicky green beans • tomato wedges • apples	• pineapple meatballs • brown rice • peapod & carrot stir-fry • bananas	• lentil burger in pita pockets • salad • baked potato wedges • ice cream
• tomato & rice soup • tuna sandwiches • cucumber rounds • oranges	• Jamaican beans & rice with roti • celery & carrot sticks • apples	• spaghetti • caesar salad • pears	• chicken with teriyaki vegetables • brown rice • honeydew melon	• P.D. Day
• macaroni & cheese • spinach salad • watermelon	• beefy Spanish rice casserole • broccoli (raw & cooked) • cantaloupe	• oven-fried lemon chicken • corn • carrot & raisin salad • oranges	• three-cheese pasta • garden salad • strawberries	• chicken, rice & bean soup • cheese sandwiches • apples
• scrambled eggs in pita pockets • oven-baked potato wedges • green pepper sticks • oranges	• lasagna • garlic bread • garden salad • apples	• cheesy-bean burritos • caesar salad • cantaloupe	• chicken curry • brown rice • cauliflower & broccoli (raw with yogurt dip) • pears	• pizza • vegetable sticks • bananas
• Santa Fe beans • garden salad • apples	• tofu sausages • mashed potatoes with parsley • broccoli (raw & cooked) • strawberries	• chicken cacciatore • garlic bread • salad • oranges	• fish sticks (homemade) • fries • zucchini carrot bake • watermelon	

Note: Milk and water are provided at lunch.

Source: Adapted with permission from Ferncliff Day Care and Fern Avenue Public School, Toronto, ON.

Menu for Preschoolers and School-Agers

	MONDAY	TUESDAY	WEDNESDAY	THURSDAY	FRIDAY
A.M. snack	• banana-egg pancakes topped with crushed pineapple	• fresh fruit salad with yogurt and granola	• hot cereal and milk • orange and grapefruit sections	• egg salad on corn bread • grape juice	• banana split in middle with almond butter filling • fruit juice
Lunch	• soybean burgers • oven-baked potato wedges • spinach and carrot salad with feta cheese dressing • apple slices • milk	• pad Thai (sweet & sour rice noodles with chicken, tofu, and bean sprouts) • crunchy coleslaw • milk	• Jamaican roti (chickpeas, potato, spinach rolled in flatbread) • coconut rice & peas • fried plantain • milk	• minestrone soup (beans, vegetables, and ABC noodles) • rice crackers with Colby cheese • kiwi circles • milk	• tacos (hard tortillas or pita with refried beans, cheese, lettuce, tomato, guacamole) • seedless red & green grapes • milk
P.M. snack	• raisin-bran muffins • celery sticks • milk	• tea biscuits • pear slices	• raw broccoli & cauli-flower spears • individual yogurt dilly dip bowls	• bannock with apple butter • tomato-vegetable juice with celery sticks	• hummus (chickpea & sesame pâté) • mini pitas • fruit juice

Notes:

Water is available with all snacks and meals.

Preschool and school-age children are involved in preparing food and serving themselves as often as possible. Some adjustments to the food selections and preparation are necessary if this menu is to be used with toddlers. Infants will have individual menus to best meet their stage of development and specific dietary needs.

Source: Adapted with permission from Rory Magill, Wakefield, PQ.

Safety Promotion

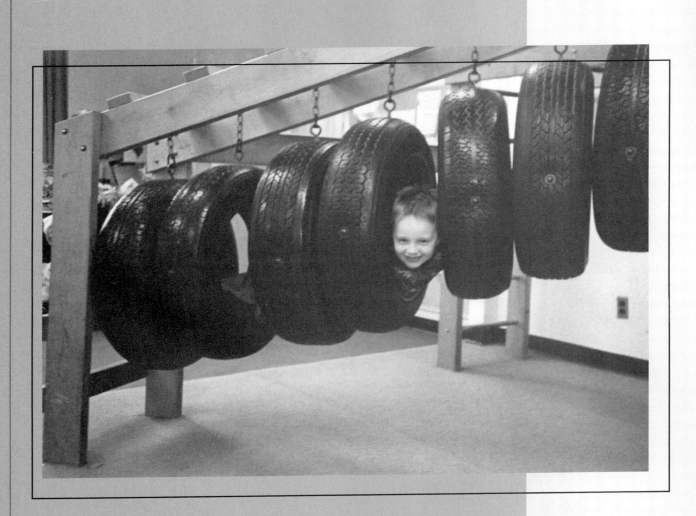

CONTENTS

The Five W's of Safety   *266*
    WHO   266
    WHY   267
    WHERE   269
    WHEN   270
    WHAT   271

How Can We Promote Children's Safety?   *279*
    TRAINING   281
    PHYSICAL ENVIRONMENT   282
    SUPERVISION OF CHILDREN   298
    SAFETY RULES: A LEARNING PROCESS   302

What's the Rest of the Story?   *308*
    BEING OUTDOORS SAFELY: SUMMER AND WINTER   308
    WALKS AND FIELD TRIPS   318
    ENVIRONMENTAL CONTAMINANTS   321
    BEING PREPARED FOR EMERGENCIES   326

Revisiting the Health Promotion Action Plan   *331*

Conclusion   *333*

What's Your Opinion? TO CLIMB OR NOT TO CLIMB?   *333*

Assess Your Learning   *333*

Resource Materials   *334*

Bibliography   *335*

TABLES

TABLE 6.1   PLAYGROUND EQUIPMENT AND INJURY RATES   270
TABLE 6.2   IMPLEMENTING PREVENTION STRATEGIES   273
TABLE 6.3   USING INFANT AND TODDLER EQUIPMENT SAFELY   285
TABLE 6.4   SUGGESTED FACILITIES AND EQUIPMENT FOR
                  PLAY ACTIVITIES   288
TABLE 6.5   RECOMMENDED PROTECTIVE SURFACING   290
TABLE 6.6   SOME ELEMENTS THAT MAY APPEAR IN A SUPERVISED
                  PLAY AREA   296
TABLE 6.7   WHAT DOES THE UV INDEX MEAN TO ME?   313
TABLE 6.8   THE UV INDEX: TYPICAL SUMMER MIDDAY VALUES   313

APPENDIXES

APPENDIX 6.1 WEEKLY SAFETY CHECKLIST   338
APPENDIX 6.2 INJURY REPORT   344

An integral part of growing up is trying new things in order to become competent. Whether it is learning to walk, ride a bike, cut with a knife, or draw with a crayon, acquiring a new skill is a learning process. As such, it may take a child a number of attempts before he or she masters the skill. Do you remember learning to ride a bike? You probably fell off more than once! Minor scrapes, bumps, and bruises are a normal part of childhood.

It is a tremendous responsibility to ensure children's safety in early childhood education and care programs, but it is not an insurmountable one. We don't want to design a risk-free environment. The goal of safety promotion in programs is to find a workable balance between a safe and a challenging program. Children who are not physically challenged are understimulated. This understimulation can have the following consequences:

- The children stop seeking challenges, which affects their development and self-esteem.
- They turn to their peers for stimulation, or they turn against them, which either way often results in antisocial and hurtful behaviour.
- They direct their natural desire for trial-and-error learning to times and places in which the risks may be much greater (e.g., toddlers climbing up on bookshelves or from chairs onto counters rather than using developmentally appropriate climbing equipment under adult supervision).

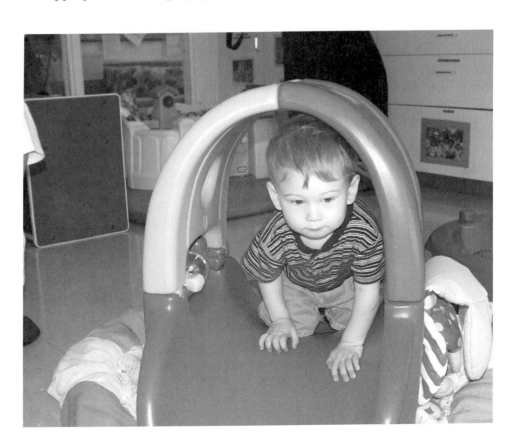

Quality early childhood programs offer children the physical and human resources to experience challenges safely and learn from them. Educators pay attention to the four components of safety promotion: training, physical environment, supervision of children, and safety rules. Before discussing how to promote safety, we'll look at childhood injuries from the perspective of the five W's: who, why, where, when, and what.

THE FIVE W'S OF SAFETY

OBJECTIVE

To describe the nature of childhood injuries and factors that increase risk.

An important role for educators is to design and implement injury prevention strategies in early childhood programs. To develop policies and strategies that are relevant, practical, and effective, educators first understand the nature of childhood injuries and factors that increase risk. Educators also draw on their knowledge of children's development and how that affects the types of injuries experienced at different ages.

Who

Safety is an important consideration in everyone's life. An average day for an adult includes several activities with an element of risk: showering, shaving, eating peanut butter on toast for breakfast, navigating the ice-covered front steps of the house, crossing the street, and driving to work. Children face potential risks in their daily lives too. "Injury and poisoning were the greatest single cause of death for preschool children in 1997, accounting for 32% of deaths. In other words, many deaths during the preschool years may have resulted from predictable, preventable events" (Canadian Institute of Child Health 2000, 74). Some children's injuries are the same as adults'. Others are directly related to children's growth and development and becoming competent at small and large motor skills. Learning to crawl, walk, climb, ride a bike, or use scissors involves risks, and children sometimes fall or cut themselves while developing these skills. Nonetheless, we can't prevent injuries by stopping children's growth or development any more than our parents could prevent ours.

We will not use the term "accident" in this unit, as it implies that an event was due to bad luck or fate and that nothing could have been done to prevent it. The word "injury" is used here, as in current safety publications, since injuries are very often preventable. Some statistics on children's injuries in Canada:

- Injuries account for 32% of deaths for one- to four-year-olds, 41% of deaths for five- to nine-year-olds, and 52% of deaths for 10- to 14-year-olds (Statistics Canada, cited in Canadian Institute of Child Health 2000, 74, 106, 107).

- Injuries due to falls are the leading cause of hospitalization for children aged 1 to 14 years (Statistics Canada, cited in Canadian Institute of Child Health 2000, 73, 104, 105).

- From birth to 19 years of age, the injury death rate is about twice as high for boys as girls (Statistics Canada, cited in Canadian Institute of Child Health, 2000, 193).

Why

Individual differences in temperament may explain why one child is more of a risk taker, less fearful, more adventurous, or more inquisitive than another. Risk takers are more likely to be in situations that put them at risk of injury. Gender differences play a role in injuries because boys are often involved in more physically challenging activities. Gender differences in this respect are not yet fully understood. Possible factors include risk perception, peer influence on risk taking, and parental responses to children engaging in risky behaviour. Regardless of individual, gender, or family response differences, educators must evaluate the safety of the equipment being use and maintain levels of supervision appropriate for the activity and the age of children. However, educators' supervision cannot focus only on the adventurous children, or boys in general, since all children are susceptible to injuries.

Children learn through exploration. Together with maturation, children reach developmental milestones. Understanding children's growth and development is essential in anticipating injuries and thus preventing or reducing their severity. The physical and cognitive developmental immaturity of young children increases their risk of injury compared to that of older children and adults. Here are some of the reasons why:

- Children go through such rapid growth spurts that sometimes their sensory perception doesn't keep up (e.g., a child gets taller, but she senses that she is shorter, misjudges her height with the monkey bar, and bangs her head).

- Children have yet to learn how to control impulses. They are unaware of the potential harm to themselves when they do whatever comes to mind (e.g., running into the street to retrieve a ball, leaning over into a pail of water, following peers to the highest level of the climber where they aren't physically able to handle the challenge).

- Children learn through trial and error. When children's environments are not developmentally appropriate and challenging, their experiments involve activities that can be dangerous (e.g., a toddler trying to walk up the chute of a slide because no climber is available).

- Children under three years of age are usually not aware of others' safety and may contribute to the harm of others.

Starting with infants and toddlers, we'll examine aspects of children's growth and development as they relate to safety.

Infants

- are learning to roll over from front to back, which puts them at risk of falling from heights (e.g., change tables, counters, furniture) or suffocating if placed on a soft or buoyant surface. They may roll onto their tummy, but then, unable to roll back, smother themselves when their face is buried in a pillow or adult water bed.

Infants and toddlers

- are developing stronger grasps and those who can stand, crawl, or walk put themselves at risk of
  - falling down stairs,
  - pulling on an appliance cord hanging down the front of a counter,
  - grabbing a cup of hot coffee or tea from a table,
  - becoming tangled in drapery cords and strangling, or
  - pulling off small parts from a toy and choking.
- have not yet developed an awareness of potential harm. Toddlers will run in front of a moving swing. At this age, most children love playing in water and are not able to discern the difference between supervised water play and playing in the toilet water alone.
- have a tendency to put everything in their mouth (sensorimotor learning), which puts them at risk of poisoning and choking.
- are active explorers and thus are prone to bumps, bruises, and scrapes from losing their balance and attempting new tasks.
- are often like little whirlwinds, because their quest for learning about their world leaves little time for caution.

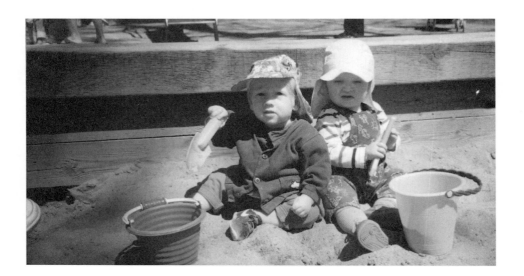

Preschoolers

- are adept at running, climbing, and pedalling a tricycle by the time they are four. They are becoming more competent and confident on playground equipment and are looking for new and advanced challenges (e.g., climbing even higher up the climber, jumping off the swing while it is still moving).
- are in the preoperational stage of cognitive development. As a result, they are unable to judge the speed of a car, the height of the climber's fire pole, or the danger of deep water or matches. They also are unable to distinguish clearly between reality and fantasy. Many children watch television, especially car-

toons, which focus on invincible superheroes. These shows may lead some preschoolers to believe that they too can leap from high places or fly.

■ want and need to have increasing levels of independence, but with this comes risk (e.g., a child can't learn to cut with a knife without using one, so she may cut herself even when using a dull one).

School-agers

■ are developing competencies in many areas and need to be given more independence and responsibility. Issues concerning children's personal safety arise both at home and in the school-age program. In school-age programs, there are fewer educators per child (a higher staff–child ratio), resulting in less direct supervision. Children are required to use their own decision-making skills and judgments in various situations—leaving the playground to go into the school to use the bathroom, riding a bike to school, using a neighbourhood playground in the evening without a parent. Before delegating new responsibilities to a child, adults must consider the child's age, level of maturity, track record, and reliability, as well as the inherent safety risks within the school, program, or neighbourhood.

. . . .

Jessica took off her bike helmet after rounding the corner and didn't stop at stop signs. She is not permitted to bicycle to school until she demonstrates that she can follow safe cycling practices consistently.

e.g.

. . . .

■ are paying more attention to interacting with their peers than to what they are actually doing (e.g., a child who is so busy talking to friends on the ground may not notice that he or she has moved to the edge of the climber), so physical injuries often result. On the other hand, children can get so involved in an activity that they are oblivious of everything around them (e.g., during a game of tag, a child so determined not to be tagged runs into someone else while running away).

Aside from injuries attributable to these growth and development factors, children are injured from both the use of developmentally inappropriate or poorly maintained equipment and the lack of adequate supervision or rules.

Where

Houses and apartments are designed for adults. Most children spend more time at home than they do in early childhood programs, so it is not surprising that children are more often injured at home:

■ 81% of children under one year old

■ 73% of children aged one to four years old

■ 54% of children aged five to nine years old

However, for children aged 10 to 14 years, the rate shifts from 23% of their injuries occurring at home to 29% in educational settings (Canadian Institute of Child Health 2000, 46, 68, 98, 99).

Compared to other environments, early childhood programs are less dangerous places for children.

Yet these facts do not mean that we can be complacent about safety in early childhood programs, because injuries happen there too. Children can slip in spills from a water table, pinch their fingers in a door, and run into each other. "In a review of 400 consecutive reported [child] care injuries, a Manitoba study found that the playground is the site of the highest number of injuries [at centres]. Most of these mishaps were falls. The problem did not arise from a lack of supervision, but rather from the physical environment itself. Many playgrounds do not have adequate [impact-]absorbing surfaces under play equipment" (Stanwick 1993, 23), although this has changed over recent years due to strict adherence in some provinces and territories to Canadian Standards Association (CSA) requirements. School-aged children in particular are at risk of falling on stairs because of frequent use in many school buildings and the likelihood of going up and down unsafely (e.g., taking two stairs at a time, jumping down, not using the handrail).

Of the emergency room visits for injuries, 54% of the injuries occurred on the playground for five- to nine-year-olds and 31% for children between birth and four years old (CHIRPP, cited in Canadian Institute of Child Health 2000, 69). Almost 42% of playground equipment injuries occurred in public playgrounds and parks, while 33.9% were in school and centre playgrounds. Table 6.1 shows the particular playground equipment associated with injuries for specific age groups.

On climbers, children lost their balance or grip on a bar. Many falls from slides occurred when children stood on the top and lost their balance, were pushed off the ladder, or landed badly at the end of the slide (and suffered a twisted foot or ankle, for example). Children sustained injuries as a result of falls while swinging or jumping off while the swing was still in motion. Passersby have been struck by moving swing seats (Health Canada 1997, 202–3).

When

Injuries can happen at any time. But there are particular situations or conditions in which the likelihood of injury increases. Childhood injuries in programs often happen

TABLE 6.1	Playground Equipment and Injury Rates	w w w	
	SLIDES	SWINGS	CLIMBERS
1–4-year-olds	34%	30.5%	24.1%
5–9-year-olds	20%	20%	46.9%
10–14-year-olds	19%	29.5%	37.6%

Source: Reproduced with the permission of the Minister of Public Works and Government Services Canada, 1999.

- when children are tired or hungry;
- when children new to the program are not fully aware of the environment or don't know how to use play equipment safely;
- when educators relax their level of supervision (e.g., while talking among themselves in the playground), or overestimate a child's abilities, or do not anticipate potential consequences of an activity or a child's behaviour;
- when educator–child ratios are not adequate for the activity, whether it is cooking with children or going for a walk;
- when the daily routine is disrupted (e.g., a familiar educator is absent and the care routine and level of supervision are affected);
- when a new piece of play equipment arrives and the children become too excited and preoccupied to follow safety rules; or
- when field trips introduce children to unfamiliar situations and unexpected hazards.

What

Every year children in Canada are killed or permanently disabled by six types of injuries: motor vehicle collisions and traffic mishaps, drowning, burns, choking, suffocating and strangling, falls, and poisoning. From the educators' perspective, some of these injuries are more relevant to their day-to-day work than others.

In programs, choking and falls are, of course, much more likely than motor vehicle collisions. Educators must be aware of choking during snacks and meals. They must be prepared for falls all the time. And even though educators will not be thinking of car mishaps during the day, they can help children learn traffic rules when they are riding tricycles (e.g., by staying on the right side of the path and putting up a stop sign at path intersections) or when they are out for walks.

Increasing our awareness of the major causes of childhood injuries and death can have a significant and positive impact on safety promotion at home and at work. The next section provides an overview of the six types of childhood injuries.

Motor Vehicle Collisions

Traffic-related injury, including injuries to passengers in vehicles, pedestrians, and cyclists, is a significant safety issue for all children. Many pedestrian and cyclist injuries have resulted from individuals not obeying traffic rules (e.g., jaywalking or crossing against a traffic light).

> The largest number of pedestrian injuries and deaths due to traffic collisions are reported for school age children (5–14). In 1995, 1,396 school age children in Canada were killed or injured while crossing an intersection. Another 464 school-aged children were killed or injured running out into the road. Research has shown that children under 9 are not developmentally ready to make safe traffic judgments. (Canadian Institute of Child Health 2000, 109)

Cyclists' injuries tended to be more serious when safety equipment (e.g., helmet) was not worn (see Table 6.2). A head injury can traumatically change a child's life forever. The skull can be fractured or broken by an impact of a speed as low as 7–10 kilometres an hour. Helmets reduce the risk of brain injury by up to 88%, yet when Safe Kids Canada (2002, 1) surveyed 284 Canadian children between the ages of 11 and 14, they learned that

- 55% didn't always wear a helmet on bicycles,
- 70% didn't use a helmet when on in-line skates, and
- 84% didn't use a helmet when on skateboards and scooters.

In Canada 45 children have died from incidents related to school buses between 1987 and 1996 (Transport Canada 2001). This happens when the child disappears from sight in front of the bus and the bus pulls away. Some children are hit by another vehicle passing the bus as they cross the road. Programs that transport children on buses must supervise the children directly.

Drowning

Of the children under 14 who drown in swimming pools, 75% are between one and four years old. In other bodies of water, 51% of all drownings are children under 14, with 39% of them being between one and four years old (Canadian Red Cross Society, cited in Canadian Institute of Child Health 2000, 76). Few drownings or near-drownings occur in programs. Still, young children can drown in as little as 4 cm ($1\frac{1}{2}$ in.) of water, which means that educators must supervise young children around all water and help them develop a respect for it. In order to promote children's independence in toileting, many preschool programs are designed with an open door that leads from the playroom to the washroom. Educators should remember that children under three years (and some older children) need adult supervision in the washroom to assist with hygiene and ensure safety around the toilets, in particular to prevent drowning (see Table 6.2, page 273).

TABLE 6.2 | Implementing Prevention Strategies

FALLS

Infants and Toddlers				Preschoolers			School-Agers						
Birth	12 mths	18 mths	24 mths	3 yrs	4	5	6	7	8	9	10	11	12

- off furniture, change tables, counters (1)
- out of highchairs, cribs, strollers (2)
- out of windows (3)
- down stairs (4)
- riding toys, tricycles, bicycles, and in-line skates (5)
- playground equipment (6)
- slip or trip on water, ice, sand, toys, carpeting, extension cords (7)

CHOKING, SUFFOCATING, AND STRANGLING

Infants and Toddlers				Preschoolers			School-Agers						
Birth	12 mths	18 mths	24 mths	3 yrs	4	5	6	7	8	9	10	11	12

- suffocate on pillows, mattresses, and adult waterbeds (1)
- strangle in dangling blind and drapery cords, pull toys, soother strings (2)
- choke on small toys (<4 cm or 1.5 in. in diameter), toy parts that can be pulled off (e.g., buttons, clothing) (3)
- choke on latex balloons, suffocate from plastic bags (e.g., dry-cleaning bags) (4)
- choke on foods (5)
- suffocate when loose scarves and hoods get caught on playground equipment (e.g., slides) (6)
- choke when eating too quickly or talking, laughing, or running while eating or eating large pieces of food (7)

DROWNING

Infants and Toddlers				Preschoolers			School-Agers						
Birth	12 mths	18 mths	24 mths	3 yrs	4	5	6	7	8	9	10	11	12

- wading pools and swimming pools (1)
- puddles, pails, or large containers of water (2)
- creeks, rivers, lakes, oceans (3)

continued

TABLE 6.2

TABLE 6.2 Implementing Prevention Strategies (continued)

MOTOR VEHICLES

Infants and Toddlers				Preschoolers			School-Agers						
Birth	12 mths	18 mths	24 mths	3 yrs	4	5	6	7	8	9	10	11	12

- not in proper child restraint seats (1)
- lack of or improper use of seat belts (2)
- running or playing on the street (3)
- riding bicycles on the street (4)

POISONING

Infants and Toddlers				Preschoolers			School-Agers						
Birth	12 mths	18 mths	24 mths	3 yrs	4	5	6	7	8	9	10	11	12

- consumes potentially hazardous substances such as cleaning products; alcohol; medications (e.g., vitamins); certain flowers, plants, and berries; perfume, nail polish, and remover (1)
- eats cigarettes and butts (2)
- takes dare to seek approval from peers, drinks or eats unknown fluid or substance that is hazardous (3)
- drugs or alcohol overdose (4)

BURNS

Infants and Toddlers				Preschoolers			School-Agers						
Birth	12 mths	18 mths	24 mths	3 yrs	4	5	6	7	8	9	10	11	12

- scalds from hot tap water, beverages, soups (1)
- burns from stoves and ovens, heat radiators, fireplaces, wood stoves (2)
- sticking objects in electrical outlets, chewing on electrical cords (3)
- metal buckles and vinyl-covered car seats exposed to the sun (4)
- metal slides exposed to the sun (5)
- playing with matches or lighters (6)
- using the stove or electrical appliances while cooking (7)

continued

TABLE 6.2 | **Implementing Prevention Strategies (continued)**

The following suggestions appear in the order in which the risk factors are listed in each category.

FALLS

1. Always keep one hand on the child during diaper changes. Never put children on counters or tables even when they are in a baby chair or seat. Until children are able to climb on and off chairs, sofas, etc., never leave them there unattended.

2. Keep furniture away from the windows. Windows should be secured with screens or stops or grills to prevent opening more than 10 cm (4 in.).

3. Secure safety gates on all stairwells (top and bottom) so that infants and toddlers cannot access stairs without an adult. Safety gates must be screwed securely into the wall (do not use pressure-type gates). Install handrails at children's height. Make sure there is good lighting. Keep stairs clear of toys, shoes, clothing, etc. Model safe behaviour on the stairs. Supervise young children using stairs.

4. Actively supervise children. Establish developmentally appropriate rules for riding toys. Create safe riding paths. Begin using bike helmets for children on riding toys and tricycles. Encourage parents to enroll school-age children in bicycle safety courses. Establish a program policy covering school-age children riding bicycles and using in-line skates while in the early childhood program, including parental permission and the use of recommended safety equipment.

5. Actively supervise children. Help children learn the appropriate use of and safety rules for play equipment. Check and maintain play equipment and protective surfaces regularly. Ensure natural surfaces are topped up seasonally and as needed. Document the regular maintenance checks.

6. Immediately wipe up spills of water (e.g., water table). Keep sidewalks and stairs clear of ice and snow. Sweep up sand on floor under sand table. Keep toys off walkways in the rooms. Do not use scatter rugs. Do not run extension cords across floors where people walk or under carpeting (fire hazard).

CHOKING, SUFFOCATING, AND STRANGLING

1. Do not provide pillows in cribs for infants under 1 year old. Remove plastic wrapping from crib mattresses. Never use garbage bags as mattress covers. Do not hang mobiles over the cribs. Keep plastic bags out of children's reach.

2. Strings on soothers and pull toys must not be longer than 15 cm (6 in.).

3. Avoid giving children under 3 years objects smaller than 4 cm (1.5 in.). Check their toys for small parts that can be easily removed.

4. Ban the use of latex balloons in programs. Safely discard deflated foil balloons, because they can suffocate young children.

5. Know which foods can cause choking in children (see Reducing the Risk of Choking, page 243).

6. Tie and tuck scarves into coats. Ensure hoods are fastened snugly. Clothing manufacturers are redesigning hoods that fasten with Velcro rather than drawstrings. Have a policy prohibiting drawstrings on clothes. Do not permit children to wear dramatic play clothes on play equipment.

7. Prohibit the attachment of ropes, strings, cords, skipping ropes, etc., to play structures. Use only climbing ropes that are designed and manufactured for play structures.

8. Encourage children to eat slowly and chew properly. Model safe eating habits.

DROWNING

1. Never leave children unsupervised in the pool, regardless of their age. Empty portable wading pools immediately after use and store upside down. Teach children water safety.

continued

TABLE 6.2   Implementing Prevention Strategies (continued)

2. Actively supervise infants, toddlers, and preschoolers in the washroom. Check playground for stagnant puddles of water. Keep diaper pails out of children's reach. Never keep pails or basins filled with water or cleaning solutions near children.

3. Teach children to respect water, not to play near creeks and rivers, not to go on the ice in the spring. Canals, rivers, and lakes used for ice skating must be safe to use. Boats used to transport children must have an appropriately sized approved flotation device for each child and adult.

MOTOR VEHICLES

1 & 2. When programs provide transportation for children, appropriate child restraints or seat belts must be used. If educators are aware of parents not using proper restraints for their children, be advocates for children (e.g., encourage or assist parents in obtaining and using the restraints). Make sure safety education with preschool and school-age children includes the buckle-up message.

3. Actively supervise children. Ensure that gates and fences around the playground are maintained. Reinforce the message that very young children are never to run onto the street or cross it without holding an adult's hand. Help preschoolers and school-agers learn traffic safety and laws.

4. Help children learn bicycle safety rules and ensure that children wear CSA-approved and properly fitted bicycle helmets. Model safe bike riding.

POISONING

1. Regularly identify and remove potentially hazardous products in the interior space and playground. Keep all medication locked and out of reach of children. Keep first-aid kits out of reach. Staff and parents must keep purses, knapsacks, and diaper bags off the floor and out of children's reach. Post the poison control centre's phone number by every phone. Teach children not to eat plants or berries without checking with an adult first.

2. Enforce the no-smoking policy in programs. Educators who smoke outside must not leave cigarette butts on the ground where young children can pick them up. Ashtrays must be carefully emptied and kept out of reach.

3 & 4. Provide education opportunities on drug and alcohol abuse for school-age children and parents (e.g., invite a guest speaker).

BURNS

1. Younger children must be supervised around water at all times. Ensure that the temperature of the hot water from faucets does not exceed 43°C (110°F). Hot beverages or fluids are not permitted in the play area, nor may staff drink them while holding children.

2. Kitchens must be inaccessible to unsupervised children. Children must be supervised during all cooking activities. All sources of heat (e.g., radiators, hot-water pipes, registers) accessible to children must not exceed 43°C (110°F). Install physical barriers around fireplaces, wood stoves, furnaces, hot-water heaters if children have access to them.

3. Cover all unused electrical outlets with plastic outlet covers. Electrical cords should be out of children's reach.

4. Cover car seats, child restraints, and strollers with a blanket or towel to shade them from the sun. Older children and educators should be in the habit of checking vinyl seats and belt buckles before getting in the vehicle.

5. Place metal slides in shaded areas or plant trees or erect a structure that provides shade. Use metal slides in the morning before it gets too hot. If possible, pour cold water to cool the metal; there may be days when the slide is closed.

6. Matches and lighters must never be within children's reach. Keep purses, diaper bags, knapsacks, etc., off the floor and out of reach. Children can learn the fire message, "Stop, drop, and roll."

7. See Cooking with Children, page 444.

Burns

There are four types of burns: contact burns, scalds, electrical burns, and chemical burns. In early childhood programs, children's burns usually result from scalding by hot tap water, soups, or beverages (including burn injuries to the mouth from microwaved bottles), and contact burns from hot metal such as slides (see Table 6.2, page 274). A survey by Safe Kids Canada (2001, 1) indicated that 70% of Canadian parents did not know that scalds from hot liquids, not fire-related burns, were the most common cause of burn injuries to children.

Choking, Suffocating, and Strangling

Choking results from inhaling or ingesting food or objects that obstruct the person's airway. Suffocation or strangulation occurs when external forces (such as a pillow over the face or a dangling scarf wound tightly around the neck) prevent air from entering the lungs. If a person is deprived of oxygen for four minutes, brain damage can occur. Educators must focus on food, unsafe eating behaviour, and toys that can cause choking. Latex balloons (often used in celebrations) should be banned from programs, as they are a major choking risk. They have been banned from all children's hospitals in Canada. The use of Mylar balloons is safer; however, once deflated, Mylar balloons must be discarded safely just like plastic bags. Strangulation can result when clothing becomes caught on slides and climbers, and the child's head or clothing gets trapped in play equipment (see Table 6.2, page 275).

Falls

Falls are by far the most common cause of injury in early childhood environments—not surprisingly, because they can happen anywhere at any time!

Falls in early childhood programs can happen both indoors and outdoors. While most falls result in minor injuries such as cuts, scrapes, or sprains, others can be serious or even life threatening, causing broken bones, head injuries, or internal or external bleeding. Playground falls are common and can be serious, especially if the child falls onto an inadequate protective surface. And, like adults, children trip on stairs, mats, loose carpets, toys, and other objects and slip in spills of water or sand (see Table 6.2, page 275).

The main reason for both tricycle and bicycle injuries was that children hit something while they were riding. Children most frequently received injuries to the head and neck (e.g., cuts, scrapes, dental damage, concussions, fractures) as well as cuts, bruises, abrasions, dislocations, sprains, and fractures of legs and arms. How can educators reduce the number of cycling injuries in programs and help children learn lifelong safety habits? Educators are encouraged to consider including the following practices in their policy.

- Have children wear bike helmets on riding toys and tricycles so they see them as a natural part of riding.
- Ensure that riding paths are designed so that children can't crash into objects.
- Ensure that children are actively supervised.

- In school-age programs, staff should develop a policy for bikes, in-line skates, and skateboards that stipulates that children travelling to their programs wear helmets and other safety equipment recommended for each activity. Parents may not support your position, but while the children are under your supervision you can either have them wear the safety equipment or prohibit the activity. When helmets become required by law in your province or territory, you can enforce the law. In the case of in-line skating, statistics show that of the in-line injuries reported in 1998,
  - 52.4% occurred on roads, sidewalks, parking lots, or bike paths;
  - 50.5% were due to skates simply losing their balance;
  - 56.8% were children between 10 and 14 years old;
  - 47.6% of the injuries were fractures, with forearms and wrists being the most likely sites; and
  - 49.5% were wearing a helmet and 34.8% protective padding (Canadian Hospitals Injury Reporting and Prevention Program 2000).

Currently, it is unlikely that you will find many programs with toddlers and preschoolers wearing helmets on the riding toys and tricycles. Some families find the cost of new or used safety equipment prohibitive. Perhaps programs could canvass families or the neighbourhood for equipment no longer in use. This equipment could be swapped or given to individual families. In the area of bike safety, national organizations provide support and education (see Organizations, page 334).

Educators who travel to work on bikes are encouraged to wear a properly fitted helmet, not only for their own safety but also to model safe behaviour to children. Legislation requiring bike helmets is mandatory for children under 16 years old in several provinces and under consideration in other provinces and territories.

Poisoning

Poisoning is rarely fatal but can result in serious illness. It is a common pediatric emergency that can be a traumatic experience. In fact, poisoning is the fourth cause of injury hospitalization for preschoolers (Canadian Institute of Child Health 2000, 73). Poison proofing is the term commonly used to describe the process of identifying and keeping potentially hazardous products out of children's reach. However, it's important to recognize that poison proofing is an ongoing process, not a one-time thing (e.g., in an early childhood setting you have products locked away, but parents put purses and diaper bags on the floor that may contain products that children can get into). It's logical that poisonings happen much more often in children's homes. Early childhood settings usually don't have many hazardous products (pesticides, paints, gasoline, medications, nail polish and remover, ashtrays and cigarettes, alcohol, etc.), and the ones they have are locked out of the children's reach (as part of the poison proofing at the program). Almost any substance taken in sufficient quantities can be a poison (see Table 6.2, page 274). Poisoning can occur when someone

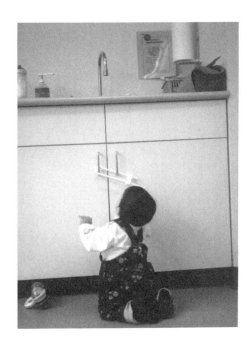

- eats or drinks a hazardous product,
- touches or spills a product on the skin and the chemical is absorbed through the skin, or
- breathes in fumes of liquids.

HOW CAN WE PROMOTE CHILDREN'S SAFETY?

The challenge for educators is to provide an environment that is not only developmentally challenging but is also as safe as possible so that children can be physically active and gain new skills. Educators and parents recognize that bumps, scrapes, and bruises are a normal part of growing up. Children are inevitably injured when using play equipment. However, the likelihood of broken bones and head or internal injuries is minimized if the equipment is developmentally appropriate, the protective surfaces are adequately maintained, the children use the equipment properly, and the educators actively supervise their activities. By modelling safe but not overly anxious behaviour, adults help children develop an awareness of safety. The adage "Do as I say, not as I do" does not apply to safety, nor to anything else, for that matter. Children will adopt adults' behaviour, whether it is appropriate or not.

. . . .

It is much more likely that children will learn safe pedestrian behaviour when they see the adults using the crosswalks (flashing the lights and pointing), waiting for walk signs, stopping to look both ways before crossing the street, and not walking between parked cars. The opposite can also be true. If children see adults breaking safety rules that they have been told to follow, they will not see how these rules apply to their own safety.

. . . .

Educators' observation skills are continually tested in terms of identifying the following elements to ensure children's safety:

To understand the importance of training, including emergency training, in safety promotion.

To identify strategies in an ongoing evaluation of the indoor and outdoor environment.

To view active supervision as an essential component of injury prevention and to identify the various factors that affect the level of supervision.

To understand the limited role that safety rules play in injury prevention and describe the essential considerations in developing and adapting rules for each age group.

- changes in children's physical and cognitive abilities
- the need for changes in the play area's design or layout
- hazardous equipment and playing surfaces
- inappropriate use of equipment
- tired or hungry children
- questionable use of safety rules or levels of supervision for specific activities

We use scenarios throughout this section to illustrate how educators can anticipate and prevent serious childhood injuries. Educators' understanding of children's development is an integral component in injury prevention.

e.g. You would not permit a toddler to use the school-ager's slide any more than you would permit a 10-year-old to drive. Although the toddler might manage to climb the steps and sit down before sliding, he or she could fall at any time. Moreover, the slide itself is designed for children much larger than a toddler and has spaces between the steps and at the top that toddlers could fall through. Similarly, although the 10-year-old could reach the gas pedal and drive a car in a straight line, that child is incapable of handling potential road hazards. In both of these examples, the children are neither physically nor cognitively ready to accomplish these tasks.

The following four components are interconnected and one or more can either cause or prevent injuries:

- training
- physical environment
- supervision of children
- safety rules

- The climber is developmentally appropriate but the protective surface is not maintained. The children understand the safety rules for using the climber, and an educator is assigned to supervise the children. Kamal loses his balance on the ladder and falls to the ground. He suffers a mild concussion because the protective surface was not up to standard.

- Children are playing too close to the swings. However, the educator anticipates that a child might be hit by a moving swing, moves the children to an appropriate area, and reviews the safety rules with them.

Training

Once you complete your ECE training, you will be equipped with entry-level skills and knowledge. No one should expect you to be ready or willing to accept a supervisor's role. However, you will be able to take an active role in safety promotion because you will know the fundamental principles of child development and how to integrate them with your observation skills. Your knowledge and abilities in injury prevention will be enhanced as you improve your observation skills through work experience. Promoting safety in the early childhood program involves positive attitudes, knowledge, and behaviour. Your commitment to seeking up-to-date information about safety, putting this information into practice, and modelling safe behaviour yourself are all part of your responsibility. Training opportunities may be on the job, or through courses, conferences, and possibly ongoing committee work or networking.

One possible consequence of injuries is the need for educators to administer first aid to children. Although regulations vary across Canada, all early childhood regulations stipulate that a specified number of the educators in a program must have current first-aid certificates. First-aid techniques cannot be learned solely from a book. Try putting on a sling properly from looking at a picture! It's not as simple as it may appear. Educators must know how to manage choking in children and adults, and how to apply first aid. Ideally, ECE training programs ensure that their students take a standard first-aid course applicable to children and receive a certificate from a first-aid training program recognized by their early childhood office. Every student is strongly encouraged or required to obtain certification in cardiopulmonary resuscitation (CPR), including infant/child CPR. Certification in first aid and CPR not only demonstrates your professional commitment to safety but is an important and relevant skill on a résumé. A second consequence of injuries is that educators must document all injuries that occur while children are under your care, even when first aid was not administered (see Injury Reports, page 327).

Serious Occurrences

Training can also arise from analyzing serious occurrence reports. Every province and territory defines what is reportable as a serious occurrence by the department or agency and outlines the procedure and forms to be completed. The category of serious occurrences covers more than the obvious injuries that happen to children and adults, or even death, but also includes other incidents such as:

- a child being missing, even for a short period of time;
- a disaster on the premises, such as a fire;
- a threat of disaster, such as a bomb scare;
- any allegations of abuse or mistreatment of a child against staff, ECE students, volunteers, or other adults; and
- any serious complaint made by or about a child, parent, or staff. Serious occurrence reporting is an ongoing process with annual summary and analysis reports. These reports provide the opportunity for individual agencies and the ministry to review and reflect on possible patterns of occurrences. Patterns "suggest a need for training, support or internal policy modifications, and the identified steps to address any of these needs. Upon reviewing the report, ministry may also identify possible issues or action that could require follow-up by the service provider, and/or more general information that could inform ministry policy work" (Ministry of Community and Social Services, June 2000, 7). For optimal safety promotion, it is essential that educators recognize the importance of reporting serious occurrences consistently and view the annual review process as a training opportunity to continue learning about high-quality early childhood environments. Reflecting and acting on program changes means that everyone benefits. Provincial/territorial and municipal agencies related to child care go beyond requiring accountability. They also play critical roles in advising and training to improve the quality of early childhood programs.

Physical Environment

Children's safety is one of the main priorities when designing and furnishing the physical setting. When prioritizing steps in promoting children's safety, the physical environment tops the list (ahead of supervision and safety rules). Regardless of the level of adult supervision or children's own awareness, children are at undue risk when the environment itself is inherently dangerous. Safety features should include the safe placement of electrical outlets and heating radiators and vents or electric baseboard heaters, safety glass in doors and the windows that separate rooms, doors that won't crush fingers, handrails on stairs for children, and hot water temperatures that won't scald. These and other safety features such as smoke alarms and carbon monoxide detectors are the concern of the early childhood office, director, and board of directors. We focus here on the safety issues that have the most relevance to educators in their day-to-day work.

Infants and toddlers are rapidly changing and learning new skills. Educators draw on their knowledge of growth and development and their observation skills to identify changes in each child and in the social relations among the children as a group. In response, educators may have to adjust the overall layout of the play area and frequently remove or add new and more challenging play material and equipment to meet individual children's next stage of development. Toddler programs that are sterile environments devoid of large motor challenges can result in children withdrawing, becoming aggressive (e.g., biting), or physically challenging themselves in inappropriate ways.

Assessing the situation:

Ten-month-old Jared is learning to climb. He is particularly fond of climbing on the box that covers the heat radiator in the playroom. On one attempt, he falls backward onto his bottom and bangs his head on the floor. How could you have prevented this injury?

Organizing the indoor space provides opportunities for educators to prevent injuries for all age groups:

- In planning the room arrangement, consider the traffic areas so that paths lead children between activity centres rather than through them, without creating congestion.
- Provide areas with enough space for children to explore material and so that other children don't have to walk through that area.
- Establish boundaries by using shelves or dividers and carpeting to your advantage, to break up open spaces that children would run in.
- When considering where to place the table and chairs in the playroom, allow enough space for the chairs to be pulled out while the children stand and sit during an activity and for a clear walkway behind the chair. (The walkway will reduce the likelihood of children tripping on chair legs.) This rule applies also to easels.
- Provide storage units and organize the space so that children can return materials and supplies. Add pictorial labels to shelves, boxes, and so on, to guide children in putting toys and material away during cleanup.
- Secure all shelving so that it cannot be tipped over. Limit the height so that educators can view the room.
- Ensure that the block area is away from the traffic area.
- Choose round or curved tables rather than straight-edged tables.
- For the water and sand tables:
  - Place them on tile floor for easy cleanup (because children and staff can slip in spilled water and sand).
  - Keep cleanup tools handy at children's level (e.g., dustpan, broom, mop).
  - Sand on the floor should either be discarded or put into the outdoor sandbox.

Furniture

Furniture should meet the needs of both the children and the adults. Tables, chairs, cots, activity centres, bookshelves, and so on must be durable and of a size that suits the children who use them. However, early childhood facilities are also workplaces, so they must also meet the physical needs of the adults who work in them. Adult chairs should be available in the eating area and comfortable chairs or sofas in the play area for educators to read books, cuddle children, and feed infants. But don't forget that the adult-sized furniture must also be child-safe.

- A 15-month-old boy is crawling around a rocking chair at the same time that an educator is giving an infant her bottle. The boy's fingers become caught under a runner.

- A preschooler uses the levered handle for a recliner's footrest and her hand gets caught in the metal mechanism when she closes it.

From the standpoint of safety, much of the furniture manufactured for infants must meet the safety criteria established by Health Canada's Consumer Product Safety. Their publication *Is Your Child Safe?* assists educators and parents in purchasing used furniture that meets the safety standards. Did you know that it is against the law to sell a crib made before September 1986 because it will not conform to these standards?

With the cribs, highchairs, strollers, and possibly playpens in place in programs, what are the practices needed to ensure children's safety on a daily basis? (See Table 6.3.)

Walkers give infants a vehicle that can propel them at speeds that they are unable to handle. An infant walker has a rigid frame with a fabric seat and leg openings attached to a wheeled base. Adults are surprised at just how fast a baby can pick up speed in a walker, which often makes it impossible for an adult to stop the child before she or he tips over or crashes down the stairs. Since the infant is off the floor, he or she can reach cords and objects off low tables, which can lead to burns, poisonings, and other injuries. Since 1989 manufacturers have voluntarily ceased the production and sale of walkers in Canada. Yet parents continue to buy them from street vendors and garage sales, borrow and lend them, or buy them outside of Canada.

In addition to the safety hazards, walkers put infants in an upright position, though many of them may not be able to sit unsupported. Infants' physical development evolves through a series of stages in which each stage prepares them for the next. Walkers not only confine children but also prevent them from moving naturally using their developing skills and abilities. There is absolutely no reason for caregivers to provide infants with walkers. Quality child care provides good modelling for parents. Walkers in centres should be banned; otherwise, parents get the impression that they are appropriate equipment for babies. There are safe alternatives to mobile baby walkers such as stationary activity centres (Safe Kids Canada 2003 ii, 1). New ideas and designs in furniture and play equipment must be evaluated for safety on an ongoing basis.

Indoor Play Equipment

Programs provide children with play materials, equipment, and toys manufactured for children. Play materials can also be inexpensive objects found around the house—empty plastic containers, wooden spoons, measuring cups, blankets, scarves and hats, used clothes, pillows, cardboard boxes, pieces of wood, sand,

TABLE 6.3   **Using Infant and Toddler Equipment Safely**

EQUIPMENT	SAFETY PRACTICES
Cribs	• The railing must be up and secure after putting the child in to sleep. • Bumper pads and large stuffed toys should not be in the crib once the child can stand up inside so that neither can be used by the child to climb over the side. • Never provide an infant with a pillow because of the risk that an infant who has rolled face down will be unable to roll over and avoid suffocation. • To prevent strangling, blind and drapery cords must be secured away from cribs. Strings attached to mobiles and crib gyms must not be within children's reach (lying or standing).
Highchairs	• Never leave children unsupervised. • Always use the safety belts, but don't assume that children can't wiggle out of or unfasten them. • Ensure that the child's fingers, hands, and head can't be trapped when putting on or taking off the tray. • Help children learn that they must always sit down in the chair and that standing is not permitted. • Don't place chairs near doorways, stoves, fridges, or walls where children could tip the chair over by pushing against it with their feet. • When chairs are not in use, keep them out of reach of children to prevent toddlers from trying to climb on them.
Strollers	• Never leave children unsupervised. • Check that all locking mechanisms are secure, ensuring that the stroller doesn't collapse. • Check all the brakes. • Use brakes when children are getting in and out or when parked with children inside. • Watch that hands and fingers are clear before reversing the handle. • Always use the safety belts, but don't assume that children can't wiggle out of or unfasten the belt. • Don't overload the handles with knapsacks, bags, etc., that can cause the stroller to tip. • Help children learn that they must always sit down.
Playpens*	• Ensure that the sides are up and secure. • Avoid large stuffed toys and boxes, etc., that children can use as steps to climb over the side. • To prevent strangling, blind and drapery cords must be secured away from playpens; mobiles and crib gyms with strings must not be within children's reach (lying or standing). • Keep playpens out of direct sunlight, as hot vinyl might burn the child's skin. • Check the vinyl mattress or railings for tears that children could bite off and choke on. • Do not use for children who either are tall enough or weigh enough to crawl over or tip over the playpen.

* When not sleeping, infants and toddlers must have the freedom to explore, play, and socialize in environments that are safe and secure. The routine use of playpens is discouraged for children of any age. Some programs use them for young infants outside or as a temporary safe place before returning children to the play area after diapering.

Source: Adapted from the Canadian Paediatric Society, *Well Beings: A Guide to Promote the Physical Health, Safety and Emotional Well-Being of Children in Child Care Centres and Family Day Care Homes* (Ottawa: Canadian Paediatric Society, 1996), 408–17.

and water. Toys and materials must be developmentally appropriate to ensure the safety of the particular age group using them. Toys for school-aged children, for example, often have small pieces and removable parts, such as doll clothes and accessories or limbs, which can be pulled off and might choke younger children. Paints, glues, and coloured paper must be non-toxic to protect children who put them in their mouth.

Each day, educators inspect toys for the following:

- broken parts or pieces; when found, they are repaired or put safely in the garbage
- torn seams on stuffed toys and dolls that could permit stuffing to come out
- chipped paint, rusting metal, etc.
- sharp or splintered edges
- exposed hinges or pinch points between moving parts
- frayed rope

Outdoor Play Equipment

The outdoor environment in the early childhood program is filled with joy and learning, especially when it is designed to meet the needs and interests of the chil-

dren and when educators give the outdoor curriculum the ongoing attention it deserves. The play-based nature of the outdoor environment provides an opportunity to enhance all areas of the child's development, such as physical, problem solving, language, social development, creative expression, and, of course, self-esteem. Outdoor play can enhance physical agility and fitness, reduce stress through games, provide contact with nature, fuel the imagination, and bestow freedom of movement—the list is almost endless. Many resources are available to support educators' awareness and planning of the outdoor curriculum, which is essential to a quality early childhood education and care program (see Resource Materials, page 334).

Most serious injuries in early childhood programs occur on the playground. The CSA standards are intended to promote and encourage the provision and use of outdoor play spaces that are well designed, well maintained and innovative (CSA 2003, 1). If operators do so, the contribution to children's health is substantial. At present, the challenge with stringent standards is achieving optimal safety, but not to the extreme, which can eliminate the integrity of developmentally appropriate risk. Wherever possible, the standards indicate modifications to the development of play spaces and equipment in order to make them accessible to children with a range of special needs.

The CSA suggests a range of environments and equipment for play activities, dividing the age groups into preschool (18 months to 5 years old) and school-age (5 to 12 years old), recognizing 5 as a transition age for physical growth and development and acknowledging the fact that as children get older, their abilities, interests, and needs change. Educators are responsible for ensuring that children safely use equipment designed for appropriate age and ability levels (see Table 6.3, page 285, and Table 6.4).

In the vast majority of playground injuries, two characteristics of the environment have a major influence on the severity: the quality of the cushioning material and the height the child falls from. The ground space under and around each piece of equipment, called the encroachment area, must have a surface that cushions a child's fall as much as possible. The encroachment areas help protect not only the children using the equipment but also those walking by. Whenever possible, the areas should be clearly marked off to create pathways that can be followed by children and staff. This should prevent anyone from getting hit by a swing, by a child jumping off the climber, or by someone coming off the end of a slide.

Pressure-treated wood is sometimes used in the construction of play structures or used as a border to contain the cushioning material that covers the encroachment areas. Pressure-treated wood has been treated with a chemical wood preservative called chromated copper arsenate, which protects the wood from damage by insects, mould, sun, and water. Over time, chromium, copper, and arsenic can leach out of the wood onto its surface and into the ground surrounding the structure, which raises safety concerns. Although small amounts of arsenic are not thought to be harmful, it is always best to avoid unnecessary exposure, because arsenic is a known human carcinogen (i.e., it causes cancer). Children may be particularly vulnerable to long-term effects (see Environmental Contaminants, page 321). Children playing on such a structure can have substantial exposure because they often play for long periods of time and frequently put their hands into their mouth. The most obvious solution is to avoid using pressure-treated wood when building structures or marking off encroachment areas, selecting instead cedar, redwood, metal, and plastic as safer alternatives. For facilities with existing pressure-treated wood, the safety of these structures should be evaluated by licensing bodies that will make requirements or suggestions on minimizing exposure.

The layout of the equipment is another factor in the design of a safe playground. The CSA (2003, 25–29) requires an obstacle-free protective surfacing zone, dependent on the type of play equipment.

In 2003, CSA amended their 1998 publication, *Children's Playspaces and Equipment Standards*, to acknowledge some variations for small children's fenced play spaces. These play spaces are defined as areas that contain public use playground equipment designed for children from 18 months to 5 years of age while being supervised by adults. In addition, this entire space is completely surrounded by at least a 1.2-m (4-ft.) high fence with a lockable entrance gate. Such variations are around encroachment zones in this type of play space. An encroachment zone is not required in the following cases:

TABLE 6.4   Suggested Facilities and Equipment for Play Activities

ACTIVITY	SUGGESTED FACILITIES AND EQUIPMENT
Preschool and Kindergarten Children (Toddlers) **Physical play**	• a hard-surface route, preferably a large or circular one for wheeled toys • facilities and space for large-muscle activities such as climbing equipment or swings • soft open space for running or ball games (the space for physical play may approximate 40% of the space in a playground)
Social play (play together in small groups)	• playhouse and other structures to encourage imaginative play • landscaped enclosure • table and benches/chairs
Manipulative cognitive play (to create, manipulate)	• sandbox • water play such as spray pad • natural areas • pots and pans • outdoor blocks, boards • outdoor drawing board
Quiet retreat play (to rest, imagine, or watch)	• enclosure, landscaped or fenced • table with seating • perch or hideaway
School-age Children **Physical play** a) games with balls or aerial objects (such as Frisbee, ball hockey, or kite flying)	• open and level space of grass or hard surface, uninterrupted by trees or electric wires; enclosure, fence, or berm • seating at periphery
b) ground-related games using the whole body (such as tag, roller-skating)	• open, level hard-surface area, or grassy area, not necessarily flat; enclosure, fence, or berm • seating at periphery
c) strategy games requiring smaller spaces (such as marbles, hopscotch, or tetherball)	• protected small areas 1–3 m² (25 sq. ft.) • smaller hard-surface or grass areas
d) activities that challenge dexterity and muscular control	• climbing structures, balance bars, swings
Manipulative cognitive play	• loose materials such as blocks, boards, sand, water sprays, natural areas (some of these activities require supervision; see relevant sections of CSA standards for details)
Social play	• table and seating, table games, sheltered space, natural area

(continued on next page)

Sand Play Areas for All Ages

- Size. The sand area should be large enough to encompass activities by several groups of children without interference. The total sand play area should be in proportion to the size of the overall play area. Where there are likely to be large numbers of children of varying ages, the total area for sand play may be divided into several smaller sand play areas. A 2 x 2 m (4 m^2) (40 sq. ft.) sand area can be a comfortable cognitive sand play area for a group of up to 10 children. A minimum total sand play area of 6 x 7 m^2 (42m^2) (450 sq. ft.) is desirable in public parks and other public play areas. (This total should not include impact sand in the equipment area.) Sand play is a very popular play experience for children of all ages, and the play area design should maximize the total amount of space for sand play.

- Types of Sand. The sand for creative play should pack together for moulding. Thoroughly washed brick sand, or an equivalent, such as seaside sand, should be used. Blow sand should not be used. The sand should be free of organic material, dirt, clay, silt, iron, asbestos, and other contaminants.

- Depth of Sand for Play. The sand depth should allow for major excavations by the child, without disturbing the foundations and drainage. A minimum sand depth of 200 mm (8 in.) is recommended. The preferred depth of sand is 450 mm (18 in.).

Source: The CSA Standard CAN/CSA-Z614-03, *Children's Playspaces and Equipment.* With the permission of Canadian Standards Association, material is reproduced from CSA Standard, **CAN/CSA-Z614-03,** which is copyrighted by Canadian Standards Association, 178 Rexdale Blvd., Toronto, Ontario M9W 1R3, **www.csa.ca.** While use of this material has been authorized, CSA shall not be responsible for the manner in which the information is presented, nor for any interpretations thereof.

- the platform height or the highest point of a slide is 1.2 m (4 ft.) or less
- an enclosed to-fro swing seat has a pivot height of 1.8 m (6 ft.) or less above the protective surface
- a playhouse has a designated play surface, but due to the enclosure (fence) a child cannot fall to the surface below in a given direction (CSA 2003, 29–30)

A child can receive a fatal head injury from falling just 30 cm (12 in.) onto protective surfacing or concrete. CSA standards specify the types of materials that can be used for each piece of equipment and how deep these materials must be. Sand, pea gravel, or wood bark chips are used. Some programs use synthetic (manufactured) materials as the cushion material in playgrounds. This material, made from recycled tires, comes in sheets of various thicknesses and allows for water drainage. The best-suited material depends on the specific piece of equipment, the age of the children using it, weather conditions, availability, and cost (e.g., sand that is constantly soaked by rain loses some of its impact-absorbing quality, so pea gravel that allows water drainage may be a better choice). Tables 6.5 and 6.6 elaborate on the various materials used as protective surfaces. The material most suitable may also depend on the focus of the play space. For example, if a program has a vision to develop an outdoor space that is as natural an environment as possible, sand or wood chips are obviously more compatible with this vision.

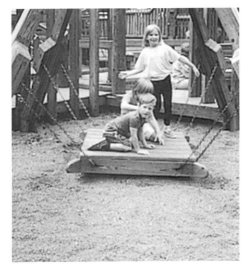

TABLE 6.5	Recommended Protective Surfacing

D.1 General

All playground protective surfacing systems must be considered according to their merits. At each stage of selection, specification, acquisition, installation, maintenance, and repair, there are costs that must be balanced with the advantages and disadvantages of the surface system or combination of systems. When loosefill material is used, a minimum depth of 300 mm is recommended.

D.2 Wood Chips/Bark Mulch

D.2.1

Bark mulch generally results from pruning and disposing of trees as part of urban tree management and landscape maintenance programs or the debarking of trees in the forest or mill. It can contain twigs and leaves from the trees and shrubbery that have been processed. Wood chips are generally uniformly crushed shreds or chips that contain no bark or leaves. The wood must be separated prior to chipping or processing to ensure that no woods containing toxic substances or allergens are included in the final product.

D.2.2

The advantages of this material include the following:

a) the initial cost is low;

b) it is easy to install;

c) it allows for good drainage;

d) it is less abrasive than sand;

e) it is readily available;

f) it is less attractive than sand to cats and dogs;

g) the mildly acidic composition of some woods retards insect infestation and fungal growth; and

h) users of the playground will generally not use the wood chips for other purposes or play with it.

D.2.3

The disadvantages of this material include the following:

a) rainy weather, high humidity, or freezing temperatures can cause it to compact;

b) with normal use over time, it combines with dirt and other foreign materials;

c) over time, it decomposes, is pulverized, and compacts. The greater the quantity of leaves or moisture, the faster the rate of decomposition;

d) its depth can be reduced by displacement due to children's activity or by material's being blown by the wind;

e) it can be blown or thrown into children's eyes;

f) it is subject to microbial growth when wet;

g) it can conceal animal excrement and trash (e.g., broken glass, nails, pencils, and other sharp objects that can cause cuts or puncture wounds);

h) it spreads easily outside the containment area; and

i) it can be flammable.

(continued on next page)

TABLE 6.5	Recommended Protective Surfacing (continued)

D.3 Engineered Wood Fibre

D.3.1

Engineered wood fibre generally results from grinding virgin or new wood, which has been debarked and contains no leaves, to specific dimensions and performance criteria. The wood must be separated prior to chipping or processing to ensure that no woods containing toxic substances or allergens are included in the final product.

D.3.2

The advantages of this material include the following:

a) it is easy to install;

b) it allows for good drainage;

c) it is less abrasive than sand;

d) it is readily available;

e) it is less attractive than sand to cats and dogs;

f) the mildly acidic composition of some woods retards insect infestation and fungal growth;

g) users of the playground will generally not use the material for other purposes or play with it;

h)   it is free of bark and leaves; and

i) it is less likely than other loosefill material to conceal animal excrement and trash (e.g., broken glass, nails, pencils, and other sharp objects that can cause cuts or puncture wounds).

D.3.3

The disadvantages of this material include the following:

a) rainy weather, high humidity, and freezing temperatures reduce its effectiveness;

b) with normal use over time, it combines with dirt and other foreign materials;

c) over time, it decomposes, is pulverized, and compacts. The greater the level of moisture, the faster the rate of decomposition;

d) its depth can be reduced by displacement due to children's activity or by material's being blown by the wind;

e) it can be blown or thrown into children's eyes;

f) it is subject to microbial growth when wet;

g) it can conceal animal excrement and trash (e.g., broken glass, nails, pencils, and other sharp objects that can cause cuts or puncture wounds);

h) it spreads easily outside the containment area; and

i) it can be flammable.

D.4 Sand

D.4.1

Sand is naturally occurring material that will vary in texture and composition depending on the source and geographic location from which it is mined. Once mined, the raw sand is processed or manufactured through washing, screening, and other actions, to provide specific grades and classifications. *(continued on next page)*

D.4.2

The advantages of this material include the following:

a) the initial cost is low;

b) it is easy to install;

c) it does not easily support microbial growth;

d) it is readily available;

e) it is non-flammable; and

f) it is not susceptible to vandalism except by contamination.

D.4.3

The disadvantages of this material include the following:

a) rainy weather, high humidity, and freezing temperatures reduce its effectiveness;

b) with normal use over time, it combines with dirt and other foreign materials;

c) its depth can be reduced by displacement due to children's activity or by material's being blown in the wind;

d) it can be blown or thrown into children's eyes;

e) it can be swallowed;

f) it can conceal animal excrement and trash (e.g., broken glass, nails, pencils, and other sharp objects that can cause cuts or puncture wounds);

g) it spreads easily outside the containment area;

h) small particles bind together and become less cushioning when wet; when thoroughly wet, sand reacts as a rigid material;

i) it can be tracked onto other surfaces; when installed in conjunction with a unitary surface, the fine particles can reduce the shock-absorbing properties of porous unitary material. The abrasive characteristic of sand can damage most other surfaces, including non-porous unitary materials and surfaces outside the playground; and

j) it adheres to clothing.

D.5 Gravel

D.5.1

Gravel is a naturally occurring material that will vary in texture and composition depending on the source and geographic location from which it is mined. Once mined, the raw gravel is processed or manufactured through washing, screening, and other actions, to provide specific grades and classifications. Crushed or broken gravel is unacceptable, as this material does not allow for the displacement of the particles.

D.5.2

The advantages of this material include the following:

a) the initial cost is low;

b) it is easy to install;

c) it does not easily support microbial growth;

d) it is readily available;

e) it is non-flammable;

f) it is not susceptible to vandalism except by contamination; and

g) it is less attractive than sand to animals.

(continued on next page)

D.5.3

The disadvantages of this material include the following:

a) rainy weather, high humidity, and freezing temperatures reduce its effectiveness;

b) with normal use over time, it combines with dirt and other foreign materials;

c) its depth can be reduced by displacement due to children's activity;

d) it can be thrown into children's eyes;

e) it can be swallowed;

f) it can become lodged in bodily openings such as the nose and ears;

g) it conceals animal excrement and trash (e.g., broken glass, nails, pencils, and other sharp objects that can cause cuts or puncture wounds);

h) it spreads very easily outside the containment area;

i) small particles bind together, become less cushioning, and form hard pan;

j) it can be tracked onto other surfaces. When on other hard surfaces, the rolling nature of the gravel can contribute to slip-fall injuries; and

k) it is difficult to walk on.

D.6 Shredded Tires

D.6.1

Shredded tire materials are the result of grinding, buffing, or crushing a whole tire or any part of the tire. The tire particle must not contain any metals or foreign contaminants. Some processing techniques provide for the pigmenting of the outside of the black rubber; this must be non-toxic and contain no allergens such as latex.

D.6.2

The advantages of this material include the following:

a) it is easy to install;

b) it is not abrasive;

c) it does not easily support microbial growth;

d) it is not susceptible to vandalism except by contamination; and

e) it is less attractive than sand to animals.

D.6.3

The disadvantages of this material include the following:

a) it can contain wires or other metal components;

b) its depth can be reduced by displacement due to children's activity or by material's being blown by the wind;

c) it can be blown or thrown into children's eyes;

d) it can be swallowed;

e) it can contain lead and other toxins;

f) small or dust-sized particles can enter and remain in the lungs;

g) when wet, small particles will stick to clothing and skin;

(continued on next page)

| **TABLE 6.5** | **Recommended Protective Surfacing (continued)** |

h) it can become lodged in bodily openings such as the nose and ears;

i) it can conceal animal excrement and trash (e.g., broken glass, nails, pencils, and other sharp objects that can cause cuts and puncture wounds);

j) it spreads easily outside the containment area; and

k) it is difficult to walk on.

D.7 Mats or Tiles

D.7.1

Mats or tiles are generally the result of a combination of a chemical binder and rubber filler product. The mats or tiles can be manufactured according to a combination of heat, pressure, or an ambient application of a mixture within a form or mould. The mats or tiles can appear to be monolithic in a single- or multiple-layer system or can have a support or leg structure combined with a firm top. Mats or tiles can be porous or non-porous to water. Pigmentation of the surface can be provided through the pigmentation of the binder holding the rubber particles or through utilizing coloured rubber particles or chips. Mats or tiles are manufactured in various thicknesses, lengths, and widths, depending on the properties desired by the manufacturer.

D.7.2

The advantages of this material include the following:

a) it requires low maintenance;

b) it is easy to clean;

c) it provides consistent shock absorbency;

d) it is not displaced by children during play activities;

e) life-cycle costs are generally low;

f) good footing can be provided (depending on the surface texture);

g) it can harbour few foreign objects;

h) generally, no retaining edges are required; and

i) it makes the playspace accessible to people with disabilities.

D.7.3

The disadvantages of this material include the following:

a) the initial cost is relatively high;

b) the base materials can be critical for thinner materials;

c) it often must be used on almost smooth uniform surfaces without deviation in slope;

d) it can be flammable;

e) it is subject to vandalism (e.g., ignited, defaced, cut);

f) it can curl up and cause tripping;

g) it can shrink and cause an accumulation of dirt and debris that does not absorb impact;

h) it can become hard over time as a result of environmental degradation. This would necessitate a total removal and replacement and would incur added costs unless the damage were to be covered by warranty or insurance;

i) some designs are susceptible to frost damage;

(continued on next page)

TABLE 6.5 **Recommended Protective Surfacing (continued)**

j) the locations of seams, anchors, and other fasteners cannot attenuate impact to the same degree as the balance of the mat or tile; and

k) mechanical fasteners or anchors can become dislodged and present a hazard to the user.

D.8 Poured-in-Place

D.8.1

A poured-in-place surface is generally the result of the combination of a chemical binder and rubber filler product. It can be manufactured using single or multiple layers of materials and binders, and generally is monolithic. Poured-in-place surfaces are generally porous; however, they can be non-porous to water through the application of a non-porous material. Pigmentation of the surface can be provided through the pigmentation of the binder holding the rubber particles or through utilizing coloured rubber particles or chips. Poured-in-place surfaces are manufactured in various thicknesses, depending on the properties desired by the manufacturer.

D.8.2

The advantages of this material include the following:

a) it requires low maintenance;

b) it is easy to clean;

c) it provides consistent shock absorbency;

d) it is not displaced by children during play activities;

e) life-cycle costs are generally low;

f) it does not require smooth uniform surfaces without deviation in slope;

g) good footing can be provided (depending on the surface texture);

h) it can harbour few foreign objects;

i) generally, no retaining edges are required; and

j) it makes the playspace accessible to people with disabilities.

D.8.3

The disadvantages of this material include the following:

a) the initial cost is relatively high;

b) the base materials can be critical for thinner materials;

c) it can be flammable;

d) it is subject to vandalism (e.g., ignited, defaced, cut);

e) it can shrink and cause an accumulation of dirt and debris that does not absorb impact at the edges;

f) it can become hard over time as a result of environmental degradation. This would necessitate a total removal and replacement and would incur added costs unless the damage were to be covered by warranty or insurance; and

g) some designs are susceptible to frost damage.

TABLE 6.6   **Some Elements That May Appear in a Supervised Play Area**

Shelter

Consideration should be given to providing some protection from sun and inclement weather. Creative play activities and fine motor activities can also be provided in such shelters. The design should be such that children can be easily supervised.

Storage

Some storage space is required in most supervised playgrounds. This should be a secure space for maintenance, materials, and equipment storage. If the design of the storage area allows for play use by children, there should be no possibility of children being trapped inside. The supervisor should be able to lock the door in an open position as well as lock it shut.

Water: Water Play Areas

When possible, play areas should provide access to water to promote creative, social, and intellectual (cognitive) development. Play facilities that encourage playing with water are recommended. These could take the form of play streams, water channels, faucets, or manual pumps.

Loose Materials

Loose materials are an essential ingredient for creative play and should be provided wherever possible. They should be provided in a supervised area with defined limits, such as an enclosure. A flat area, separated and protected from physical play activities that may interfere, should be provided. Recommended loose materials include the following:

a) hollow wooden blocks or large unit blocks and boards (20 mm x 200 mm, or 1 inch x 8 inches) in various lengths. The suggested dimensions for the hollow wooden blocks are 200 mm x 200 mm x 200 mm (8 inches x 8 inches x 8 inches) and 200 mm x 200 mm x 400 mm (8 inches x 8 inches x 16 inches). These should be stable enough to allow children to build small-scale spaces. All edges should be rounded, and the blocks or boards should possess the characteristics of a safe toy for young children. They should be finished for outdoor use and suitable in size, weight, and bulk for handling by small children;

b) containers of all kinds;

c) blankets, rugs, pieces of cloth, old clothes for dress-up;

d) wagons and other wheeled toys, including wheelbarrows;

e) paper and craft materials;

f) balls and other objects;

g) bolsters, cushions, and other soft and foam objects;

h) play parachutes and other elements for cooperative games.

Handles and grips on items should enable young children to achieve secure gripping and manipulation. Other loose materials to be used outside the specified creative play area may also be offered. These can include props to encourage role play and dramatic play by young children and tools and hardware for the activities of older children.

Garden Plots

Where possible, garden plots should be made available to school-age children. Supervision is necessary for the distribution of gardening tools and for watering. A knowledgeable adult can provide useful training for the children in good gardening techniques.

Cushioning materials are critical safety features, but there is a height above which a child in a fall is likely to sustain serious injury. A fall from a height greater than 1.5 m (5 ft.) could be fatal even if there were 22 cm (9 in.) of pea gravel covering the encroachment area (Safe Kids Canada 1997, 5). Challenging, enjoyable playgrounds offer a wide range of experiences; they do not place the emphasis on the limited challenges that the height of the equipment offers to children.

Over time, equipment shows the effects of daily use and weathering. Walking and running pack down some protective surfaces, such as sand. Whatever material is used must be maintained to ensure that it is fulfilling its purpose. For these reasons, educators are responsible for regularly checking the surfaces and maintaining the equipment. Programs that use public or school playgrounds cannot assume that the equipment is inspected regularly. Educators should check the equipment and promptly report problems and concerns. The next time you walk by a school or public playground, stop and examine the condition of the protective surfacing under the climbing equipment. You may have legitimate cause for concern for children's safety!

Depending on the problems with equipment, educators decide whether children can use a particular piece of equipment. Ultimately staff are responsible for the children's safety. Staff are accountable if they knowingly permit children to use defective equipment or if it is shown that an apparent defect was not identified. In addition, educators take children off-site to other playgrounds and need to be able to assess the safety of that environment. Placing children at risk in an inherently unsafe environment, regardless of the level of supervision, is not ethically acceptable and can affect liability.

Assessing the situation:

One winter day, eight-year-old Joanna is playing on the climber in the school playground. The protective surface under the climber is covered with ice. Her hands slip from the rungs and she falls to the ground. She is admitted to the hospital's emergency department with a broken arm. Her friend, Michael, had to run to tell an educator that Joanna was lying on the ground. What risks should have been identified? How could Joanna's injury, and other injuries, have been prevented?

Conducting Safety Checks

Educators' observations obviously play a significant role in preventing injuries throughout the day. Children, activities, issues, concerns, and other distractions will prevent any educator from identifying every potential safety risk in the environment. For this reason, regular safety checks are an essential component of injury prevention. Each day, the first educator who arrives in the morning, preferably before the children arrive, will walk through the interior of the space and playground looking for items that must be attended to immediately. This could include replacing a burned-out light bulb in the stairwell, putting the plastic outlet covers in unused electrical outlets, or removing cat feces from the outdoor sandbox. As well, cupboards may have been left unlocked or hazardous products left out on a counter or floor when the space was cleaned the night before.

Before children go out to the playground each morning, educators need to conduct a quick check, looking for garbage, sharp objects (e.g., broken glass, discarded needles), discarded condoms, animal feces, protruding nails, puddles of water, ice on the protective surfaces, or wood chips that have been scattered by the wind or through use. Many early childhood facilities, depending on municipal regulations, must complete written checklists daily.

Like our homes, early childhood facilities experience considerable wear and tear. Ideally, directors design standard checklists that are relevant to their particular building and playground. Weekly, monthly, and yearly safety checklists can be used to identify hazardous items, faulty equipment, and general maintenance requirements. These are available from a variety of sources, including the Canadian Paediatric Society's *Well Beings* (1996) and your municipal and provincial/territorial licensing agencies.

Documenting these checks and subsequent actions is part of an overall risk management program that also reduces the risk of legal liability. Safe Kids Canada (1997, 6) suggests three classes of potential hazards:

- Class A: a condition that could cause major injury or fatality, and needs to be corrected immediately (e.g., an entanglement point on a slide)
- Class B: a condition likely to cause serious injury with temporary disability, and needs to be corrected as soon as possible, before next scheduled inspection (e.g., sand needs topping up under a climber)
- Class C: a condition likely to cause minor injury, or that doesn't meet CSA standards, and may need long-term planning or budgeting

Reference must be made to the CSA's publication whenever a playground evaluation, a new playground, or changes or additions (i.e., retrofitting) are under consideration to make the most informed decisions and reduce the risk of legal liability in the event of an injury.

Supervision of Children

Child care regulations have established minimum educator–child ratios and maximum group sizes for the different age groups. Do you know your province or territory standards? Refer to your early childhood regulations to complete the following information:

Educator–Child Ratio	Group Size
infants:	___ : ___
toddlers:	___ : ___
preschoolers:	___ : ___
school-agers:	___ : ___

Adequate staffing is essential in the supervision of children. Children are naturally curious and often do not understand the potential dangers or consequences of their actions. Combine this fact with the excitement felt by children who are having fun or trying something new, and the potential for children to forget safety rules or use equipment unconventionally is much higher. While supervising children, educators should always assume that children can do more today than they could do yesterday. The comment "I didn't think Tony could roll over yet, so I thought it was safe to leave him on the diaper change table for a few seconds!" indicates the educator's inability to apply developmental theory to early childhood practice. This comment points out that the educator did not follow a very basic safety practice with infants and toddlers. In some ECE training programs, this student's behaviour would be grounds for expulsion. Making assumptions about children's abilities can lead to injuries. Therefore, educators must actively supervise children.

Afternoon naps usually begin after lunch, when children are naturally tired and have full tummies. This is the time when educators take their own lunch breaks. With some staff off for lunch, there are fewer educators working unless additional adults come in to cover during these times. Here is the challenge: How do the remaining educators adequately supervise all the children? Both those children who are napping and those who are playing require supervision. For preschoolers, the nap and play areas are usually in the same room, which facilitates supervision. However, for infants and toddlers the nap room is usually separate from the play area. As well, infants and toddlers typically sleep at different times during the day and for extended periods. Educators regularly go into the nap room to check on, re-settle, or bring out the children who have awakened. Baby monitors are an inexpensive but valuable piece of equipment for educators to use in addition to regular supervision. What program could support having an educator in the nap room most of the day? (As an aside, position young infants on their backs or sides to sleep. Research has indicated a link between sleeping on the tummy and sudden infant death syndrome, or SIDS. Once children can reposition themselves while sleeping, this practice is not applicable.)

During Indoor Play

Equipment, toys, supplies, furniture, storage, and physical space should be developmentally appropriate for the children using them, so that much of the educators' supervision is focused on facilitating play and guiding children's social behaviour. From the standpoint of injury prevention, the level of supervision depends on the inherent risks of the activity, the ages of the children, and the applicable rules.

- Infants and toddlers must never be left alone during water play. Older preschool children do not necessarily need an educator to be directly at the water table at all times.
- Preschoolers and school-agers involved in woodworking must be supervised directly.
- A small group of school-agers are playing a board game in the hall. Though they are out of view, you know where they are; they are still within earshot.

e.g.

During Outdoor Play

Outdoor play presents educators with unique supervisory challenges because of the greater risk of injury from increased physical activity and a less structured environment. Outdoor play needs to be scheduled when all educators are working, rather than when some are away at lunch or on a break. Outdoor play time is not a time when staff can be distracted by talking together. The outdoors provides children with a much less confined place in which to play. The equip-

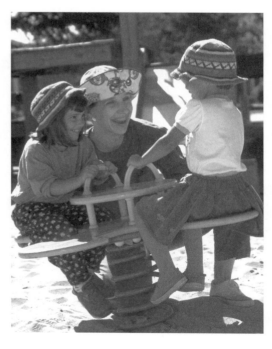

ment is physically challenging and some pieces, such as the climber, have inherent dangers because they enable children to climb high off the ground. And children must be protected from people who pose a potential threat, including parents without custody and strangers.

Ideally, the layout of the area provides and encourages smaller groups of children to gather throughout the playground (e.g., sandbox, garden plot, water table, painting easels, places in the shade, swings, slides, climber), rather than congregate in one or two areas. Educators should spread out throughout the playground and move among the play spaces for which they are primarily responsible. Equipment, especially the climber, should have one educator who is directly responsible for supervision. Another person could supervise children on the swings and slide. Tubular slides present special safety concerns because the tube blocks educators' view of children sliding down. Furthermore, a child's clothing, hood, or scarf could become caught and cause strangulation. This is why programs should have a policy that bans drawstrings on hoods and that requires scarves, if worn, to be tucked into the coat. As well, educators must be vigilant in ensuring that skipping ropes, cords, ropes, and so on, have not been tied to play structures and, when found, are taken down immediately. A program policy should spell out that only ropes designed for climbing should be attached to such structures.

Outdoor play is a time for preschool and school-age children to choose the activities they will take part in. While these older children do not always need educators to take as active a role in their activities, educators should not be any less involved in supervising what the children are doing. Joining in children's activities on their level often means the adult is jumping in a leaf pile, playing tag, or being a partner in ball play. Following the child's lead doesn't mean that the adult cannot suggest new ideas to extend play and then the children decide whether or not to accept your suggestion (Theemes 1999, 70).

For infants and toddlers, educators cannot let their guard down for a second. Infants who haven't yet learned to creep or crawl can sit on a blanket with toys and books. But once they can travel, there is no end to what they can do. Take a close look at what young children can find in the grass and soil. A puddle of water could drown a young child. A stone could cause choking. However, these potential risks should not exclude these children from outdoor play. Even very young children can begin to learn what they can and cannot safely put in their mouth, with educators' guidance.

Beyond the regular level of supervision, more vigilant supervision is required at certain times, such as when a new piece of equipment is added to the playground. At first, this piece of equipment will be more popular and children will need extra supervision until the novelty wears off. Children need time to become familiar with any necessary safety rules; children aged four and older can be involved in developing them. Field trips are also times when additional supervision is required. Directors generally arrange for volunteers, often parents, to provide extra adults to improve the adult–child ratio (see Walks and Field Trips, page 318).

Assessing the situation:

On a field trip to the zoo, a group of 24 preschoolers and three educators take time out to use the small playground. While there, two children crash into each other and another child is hit by someone on the swing. What can you learn from this scenario? What would you do differently next time to prevent injuries?

Prevention of Missing Children

Educators must know the whereabouts of all children at all times. Preventing children from wandering away from the group on a field trip or out of the playground is far easier than trying to locate a child after he or she has gone missing—and easier than suffering the emotional consequences experienced by the child, other children, educators, and, of course, the parents.

Implement the following measures to ensure children's personal safety:

■ Maintain a daily attendance record that provides educators with a head count and tells them quickly who is absent or who has already gone home with his or her parent.

- Secure all exits from the building and ensure that young children cannot open them.

- Control entry into the building with a security system, which in some regions may involve simply locking the outside doors.

- Lock the playground gate when children are outside and have one educator responsible for conducting regular head counts.

- Establish the steps to follow if a child goes missing from the program, the playground, or a field trip. Design a search plan for the building, playground, and surrounding neighbourhood. Staff may find it useful to contact an agency that deals with missing children, or the local police department, to assist them in developing a plan that meets their needs (see Planning Successful Field Trips, page 319).

Safety Rules: A Learning Process

Most of us don't consciously think about the fact that our daily lives are governed by rules. Yet we don't plug in the electric radio near the bathtub. We follow traffic laws while driving and understand the consequences if we are stopped by the police. And we read the instructions before connecting a propane tank to the barbecue—or at least we should!

Society must have rules so that people can coexist. We cannot get a driver's licence until we are 16 years old or older. Society has determined that by that age, we are physically and cognitively ready to operate a vehicle, understand and follow the traffic laws, and accept the serious responsibility of driving.

Adults guide children with rules necessary for their own safety and the safety of others and for respecting shared property. The ultimate goal is to learn to behave responsibly and to develop self-control during childhood. To promote this development we try to provide children with an early childhood environment that respects their need for autonomy and independence, their need to have some control over their world. The process of learning takes time. Children gradually gain more independence and responsibility based on their level of cognitive, physical, emotional, and social development. Children start to learn to follow rules with a simple rule for an activity, and gradually they work toward an understanding of rules that are more complex. This process enables older children to learn problem-solving and decision-making skills based on their own safety and their respect for others and property. At this point they rely on the attitudes, knowledge, and skills that they have developed and less on adult guidance and supervision. Rules learned in childhood pave the way for lifelong patterns of behaviour.

· ·

An educator guides a toddler to pedal her riding toy along the path. As a preschooler, Allison learns to not ride double on tricycles, to slow down on the curves of the path, and to wear a bike helmet. As a school-aged child, she attends a bicycle safety course and rides to and from school. By the time she is a teenager and young adult, Allison is capable of making her own decisions about riding bikes and can transfer this knowledge and these skills to driving a vehicle.

· ·

Whose Need for Control?

Most of us, children included, want to enjoy the feeling of independence and a sense of control over our lives. Consequently, young children often say, "You're not the boss of me!" in response to an adult's power over them. Children react this way for one of two reasons. They naturally want to be in complete control, so the rules imposed by adults are considered to be an infringement on their freedom and desire for independence. Nurturing educators recognize this but also know that a secure environment for children includes consistent expectations. Second, the children may be legitimately reacting to adults who are inappropriately using their own need for power to control children. When educators are in a power struggle with children, they must always ask themselves whether a particular rule is really in the children's best interest or is simply a way to control them. Educators who have overwhelmed children with rules for absolutely everything have set themselves up for countless power struggles with children. In the long term, this practice increases the potential for making children feel incompetent and lacking in the confidence to make independent decisions.

There are always situations that require educators to act immediately, regardless of the child's response, because the child or others are in danger. Following the incident, the educator can then talk with the child about what has happened and help him or her understand the reasons behind the safety rule.

....

- A toddler stands up to run down the slide.
- Two children are fist-fighting.
- A school-aged child jumps from the top landing of the stairwell.

....

e.g.

Often, educators observe a child breaking a safety rule but putting no one in danger. To prevent a power struggle with the child, the educator takes a moment to reflect on the intent of the rule rather than react immediately:

- Should the rule be adapted or eliminated because the child's skills and abilities have increased?
- Has the rule any foundation? If not, it should be eliminated.

Educators should meet regularly to evaluate the safety rules. This enables them to validate their assumptions about the rule by considering the children's changing skills and abilities, the activities and inherent risks, the condition and maintenance of equipment, and the children's responses to the rules. This can also be an opportunity to evaluate other rules and to revise or eliminate unnecessary ones. Whenever possible, children should be included in developing and evaluating rules for specific activities. These are opportunities for children to begin learning to look at the bigger picture of safety, developing observation skills, identifying risks and anticipating possible outcomes, understanding the rationale behind the rule, and so on. A potential danger to children can be our own attempt to protect them. If they can't understand the rationale for rules, or if the rules are unbending, we could be setting up children for injuries. They will be denied opportunities to build their decision-making skills, develop their confidence in their ability to think for themselves, and consider the reasons for their being asked or pressured to do something by others.

Guidelines for Safety Rules

Whenever you are in the process of developing safety rules, remind yourself that rules play a role in injury prevention, but they should not be the primary preventive. Rules alone cannot ensure children's safety. Educators will consider the following elements in developing rules:

- the age of children
- whether the activity is developmentally appropriate
- the potential risks in the activity or play equipment and possible outcomes
- the design of the physical environment
- the level of supervision and modelling
- previous injuries related to this activity

Obviously, if an activity is not developmentally appropriate, it should either be adapted or cancelled. A long list of rules does not ensure injury prevention. In many instances, rules are unnecessary or can be reduced in number when the prevention strategies have been implemented.

- Before permitting children to use the climber in a neighbourhood playground for the first time, educators check that the climber is developmentally appropriate and well maintained. They will be sure that there are enough staff available to supervise the climber and the remainder of the playground before developing rules for the preschool children.

- A three-year-old can say, "Stop, look, and listen before you cross the street." However, even though the child does that when you're there, you cannot assume that he or she is able to cross the street safely alone.

No one list of safety rules fits every early childhood program's requirements. Rules depend on the philosophy of the program and the age of the children, as well as the particular group of children, types of equipment, design of the physical indoor and outdoor space, and so on. Rules are ever changing, requiring an ongoing awareness for appropriateness and utility. It is better not to have a rule than to have one that has lost its value. Similarly, it is better to have fewer rather than more rules.

You are invited to participate in an activity, but before you begin you are presented with this list of rules:
- Don't run.
- Don't eat during the activity.
- Stay away from the red area.
- Keep your hands to yourself.

- Keep your voice down.
- Keep your shoes on.
- Don't climb on the furniture.
- Put everything away when you're done.

Now close your eyes and recite all the rules you have just read. Then repeat them tomorrow morning without reading the list. Unless you have a photographic memory, you probably will not remember more than one or two rules either now or tomorrow. How then can we expect children to remember and follow a list of rules for each piece of play equipment and activity? How many of these rules are stated in positive terms?

. . . .

It is often easy to come up with many rules for using equipment or other activities. When a piece of equipment or activity has more rules attached than are essential, they may reduce everyone's enjoyment, may cause children to become frustrated, and may in fact be either unsafe or developmentally inappropriate. Educators who continually restate the same rule many times a day probably should re-evaluate either the rule or the activity. Limit the number of rules by prioritizing what is most important for the children's safety. To ensure that safety rules are appropriate and effective, think about the following criteria:

- Consider children's development. (A rule that expects toddlers to share is frustrating for everyone, yet older preschoolers can be expected to share. Instead, positively reinforcing toddlers when they do share helps to promote sharing.)
- State rules in positive terms. They focus on what children can do rather than what they can't do.
- State rules in clear and simple language, especially those for younger children.
- Make sure rules are realistic, with enough freedom to encourage creative play but enough restrictiveness to prevent unsafe behaviour.
- Enforce rules consistently using gentle reminders and positive acknowledgment when children follow them. Threats, yelling, sarcasm, or any other tactics that can scare, intimidate, or embarrass children should never be used—this is emotional abuse. Children who have difficulty following important safety rules, even after being reminded, should be removed from that particular activity with an explanation of why removal is a logical consequence.

. . . .

The educator says, "Sand can get in children's eyes when you throw it. You need to find something else to do right now." However, give the child the opportunity to return to the activity later, which demonstrates your confidence in the child's ability to follow the rule.

e.g.

. . . .

- Rules are modelled by educators. Modelling helps children understand the importance and necessity of rules.
- Rules are developed, whenever possible, with the involvement of preschoolers and school-agers. (When a new toy is available, you can ask children what could happen if…? and what would then be important guidelines or rules for using it?)
- Rules provide teachable moments to point out sensible safety guidelines.

When a child or adult trips over a toy, it is an ideal time to mention why the rule about putting toys away before moving to the next activity is important. Yet care must be taken not to lecture or nag children constantly or else they are likely to tune us out!

- Rules are reviewed with children before they begin an activity that they haven't done for several months (e.g., woodworking, using the riding toys outside now that the snow has melted).

➤ I. RULES AND BALL PLAY

Let's use ball play to demonstrate some possible rules for children in different age groups and how the type and number of rules would evolve.

Infants and Toddlers

Ball play involves exploring, throwing, or rolling balls with little accuracy across a room, in a playground, or to an educator. Infants' and toddlers' eye-hand coordination is still developing, they are just becoming aware of cause and effect, and they are not yet ready to share. Therefore, a rule for ball play is usually unnecessary for this age group. Instead, educators should provide children with plenty of soft, light, midsize balls to prevent problems. Constant active supervision and guidance are required.

Preschoolers

Between the ages of two and five, children improve their accuracy in throwing balls. They may play simple games with peers, such as pitch and catch, hot potato, or soccer. It is a good idea to continue using softer rubber or inflated balls and light ones. Appropriate rules for this age group would be:

- Throw the ball to someone, not at someone.
- Put away the balls when you are finished so no one trips over them.
- Keep balls in the large area when playing inside.
- When outside, you can bounce the ball on this wall because it doesn't have windows and people won't be walking between you and the wall.
- When a ball goes over the fence, an adult will get it.

Obviously, only one or two of these rules would be needed at any one time!

continued

School-Agers

These children develop more complex ball skills, play cooperative and competitive games and sports, and often break up into teams. They may be quite accurate and powerful in throwing balls and using bats. Except for the general guidelines about not harming self, others, or property, rules depend on the particular ball game. While they are learning a ball game like soccer, dodge ball, street hockey, baseball, or volleyball, educators can help them develop and understand the safety rules of the game. In baseball, for example:

- Play in an area away from other children.
- Wear a helmet when at bat.
- Put the bat down after swinging. Don't throw it.

In dodge ball (if permitted in the program), for example:

- Use a light, soft rubber ball.
- Aim below the waist.

II. RULES AND SWINGS

We'll use swings to demonstrate some possible play equipment rules for children in different age groups and how the rules might evolve.

Infants and Toddlers

Educators usually have to lift children into a swing. Because an educator has to be right there with an infant, rules aren't needed. Older infants and toddlers may need rules such as these:

- Hold on with both hands.
- Stay sitting until the swing stops.

Preschoolers

These children are learning to use swings with less direct adult involvement. There is quite a difference between the ability of a two-year-old and that of a five-year-old on swings. The following examples are more appropriate for children who have become competent on swings and can use them independently:

- Stop the swing completely before getting on or off.
- Look carefully when walking in front of or behind moving swings.
- Only one child may be on the swing at any time.

continued

e.g.

OBJECTIVES

To describe safety issues related to seasonal changes.

To discuss the principles and practices in planning and conducting field trips.

To be aware of situations in which child protection is a concern.

WHAT'S THE REST OF THE STORY?

The remainder of this unit is devoted to other safety-related issues that educators should consider. Some of these pertain to safety on a daily basis, such as protecting children from the seasonal elements and going for walks; others are of a more general nature, such as injury reports and responding to emergencies.

Being Outdoors Safely: Summer and Winter

Can you imagine living in a place where the weather is always the same? Maybe you can if you're reading this unit in the middle of winter with a wind chill of −34°C (−29°F)! Canada's changing seasons provide us with wonderful opportunities to participate in a variety of activities and sports, but the hot and cold weather pose certain safety considerations.

Summer

The suntan remains popular—a symbol associated with health, active living, and attractiveness. After a long winter, the allure of the sun can be overwhelming, especially when one feels the warmth on the face and skin. In the past few years, however, there has been a concerted effort to educate the public about the dangers of sun exposure. Pamphlets, magazine articles, and television commercials outline the relationship between ultraviolet (UV) radiation and skin cancer (e.g., melanoma), eye damage, and premature aging of the skin.

How do educators protect themselves and children while outside during the summer? They can begin by limiting or avoiding outdoor play and walks between 11 a.m. and 2 p.m. (Peak hours may vary by an hour one way or the other.) However, if children are to get outside even twice a day, a compromise needs to be reached: shade must be available, fluids offered, and sunscreen, hats, sunglasses, and clothing must be used. Children are more sensitive to UV exposure than adults because they have thinner skin and on average spend more time outdoors than adults. One in seven children will get skin cancer in his or her lifetime. One severe sunburn during childhood doubles the risk of developing skin cancer (Canadian Dermatology Association 2003, 4).

About 30 minutes before going outside, educators should liberally apply sunscreen lotions with a sun protection factor (SPF) of at least 15. Liberal application means at least 5 ml (1 tsp) on the face and on each arm, for example. Remember to apply lotion above where shorts and sleeves stop, since they ride up the legs and arms while the children are playing, and also to the top of the children's feet when they are wearing sandals. When children are very active and sweating, lotion should be applied more often to give 100% UV protection. Children using wading pools or sprinklers either need to wear a waterproof sunscreen or have regular sunscreen re-applied when they get out of the water. As added sun protection, children can wear T-shirts over their bathing suits to protect their shoulders, back, and chest. Remember to have the children change into dry T-shirts once they are finished playing in the water as the wetness reduces the fabric's sun protection.

Programs may prefer to use communal bottles of lotion, since it is much faster to do one child after another than to use 20 different bottles of lotions and try to keep them all straight. As well, all the bottles must be kept out of reach of children. In these programs, staff check with parents to ensure that they approve of the type that is used. Some children may have a skin reaction to a particular brand of sunscreen, most often ones that contain PABA. Educators do not have to wash their hands after each application. Not only is that time consuming, but also the risk of spreading infection through sunscreen is negligible even when someone has a cut or scrape, because these should be covered with either clothing or a Band-Aid. The only time that hand washing may be warranted is when a child has an allergy to the sunscreen brand used by the program; then the educator needs to wash off the program's lotion before applying this child's own. Older preschoolers should be learning to apply their own lotion. These children need supervision to ensure that they don't get lotion in their mouth or eyes and that they adequately cover all exposed skin. By the time they are school-aged, most children should be responsible for this task. Remember, it takes about 10 minutes for unprotected skin to sunburn in the summer sun. Therefore, a lotion with an SPF of 15 provides children with 150 minutes of protection. Don't forget that sunscreen should be applied in the early spring and also late into the fall. Choose lotions that

- are broad-spectrum, acting against UVA and UVB rays;
- don't contain alcohol (which may sting skin and eyes);

- are unscented (will not attract insects); and
- don't contain PABA.

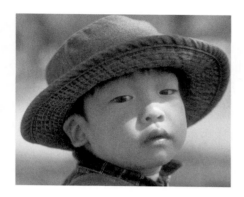

Everyone should wear hats, preferably with a wide (3-inch or 7.5-cm) brim that shades face, ears, and neck. Some children don't like wearing hats but may be more likely to wear baseball caps, which are very popular. Don't forget to put sunscreen on their ears and the back of their neck. Child-sized shatterproof sunglasses with 100% UV protection are now available at low prices; parents should be encouraged to provide their child with a pair. Although many toddlers and young preschool children may not keep them on, this at least introduces them to the idea. Ideally, children wear long-sleeved shirts and long pants, although this seems impractical when it is very hot or humid. Whatever clothing is worn, it should be loose fitting and cool to help reduce sweating.

Ensure that shade provided by trees, table umbrellas, awnings, or other structures is accessible to children to play in. Children should be encouraged to come into shade every half-hour while outside. Wading pools should be placed in the shade. Sunscreen is not a replacement for shade.

Physical activity in hot weather puts children at risk of becoming dehydrated because the body loses water through sweating. Offer water to children before they go outside and encourage them to drink water several times while outside and again after they are back inside. Pay particular attention to children who are using the play equipment and running around, as they will be losing more water through sweat. Children can be dehydrated and not complain of thirst.

> ## ➤ INTERESTING FACTS ABOUT THE SUN

- Fiction: A tan is healthy. Fact: A tan indicates that your skin is already damaged.
- Fiction: A tan protects me from the sun. Fact: A dark tan on a white person offers an SPF (sun protection factor) of about four. An SPF of 15 is recommended when skin exposure is unavoidable.
- Fiction: Black skin protects me from the sun. Fact: People with black skin can get sunburns and skin cancer. Black skin gives an SPF of eight at most.
- Fiction: You can't get burned on a cloudy day. Fact: Up to 80% of the sun's rays can penetrate light clouds, mist, and fog.
- Fiction: You can't get burned if you're in the water. Fact: Water offers minimal protection. Water surface reflection can intensify the sun's rays on your skin.
- Fiction: Baby oil is a good sun lotion. Fact: Baby oil may intensify the effects of the sun and may cause skin to burn faster.

Source: "A Parent's Guide to Sun Protection," Health Canada (1999). www.hc-sc.gc.ca/hecs-sesc/ccrpb/fiction_fact.htm (July 2003). Reproduced with the permission of the Minister of Public Works and Government Services Canada, 2003.

Remember how germs are spread and do not use a communal drink bottle or shared cups. If you don't have access to running water outside, bring out a jug and enough cups for everyone.

Keep in mind that infants

- should be shaded from the sun at all times. Their skin protection system not fully developed, and for most of their first year they cannot move out of the sun on their own. And they can't tell you when they are getting too hot or thirsty.
- should get plenty of fluids even if they are just lying on a blanket in the shade. Young children can become dehydrated very quickly because they have more surface area (skin) in relation to their body mass than adults do. Signs of dehydration and treatment are discussed in the section on diarrhea (see page 158).
- should wear T-shirts over their bathing suits when they are in the wading pool.
- should not, when under the age of six months, have sunscreen applied, because they may put lotion-covered hands or feet in their mouth. Also, the lotion may irritate their skin.
- should, whenever possible, be dressed in loose-fitting clothes that have long sleeves and pants (or long-sleeved cotton jumpers) and should wear hats.

Certain medications can cause skin reactions such as rashes, swelling, blisters, or redness that looks like an exaggerated sunburn. Photosensitivity reactions are relatively common. Symptoms can appear immediately once the skin is exposed to sun or several hours after exposure has ceased. Interestingly, symptoms may develop only on skin that wasn't covered by clothing or may appear anywhere on the body. Symptoms can last for several days, even after the prescription is completed. Some of the commonly prescribed medications that can cause photosensitivity are some antibiotics, antihistamine creams, oral contraceptives (the pill), and sunscreen containing PABA. Some of the medications prescribed for the management of diabetes, cystic fibrosis, and mental health disorders can cause photosensitivity reactions (see Administering Medication, page 165).

Do you ever hear adults say to children, "Just do what I say because I'm the parent" or "I don't have to do that because I'm the adult"? Take a moment to think about the behaviour that educators model if they sunbathe, compliment one another on their tans, or refuse to wear hats and sunglasses or to apply sunscreen at work. The adult who tells children that they must do things because he or she told them so is, in fact, controlling children.

UV Index and the Humidex

Ozone is a layer of gas 20 kilometres (12 miles) thick surrounding the earth 15 to 35 kilometres (9 to 21 miles) above the surface. Ozone filters out most of the sun's ultraviolet (UV) rays so that they don't reach the earth (Environment Canada 2002c). Basically, the more UV rays we are exposed to, the faster our skin is damaged. Cloudy days don't necessarily protect us from UV rays. The darker and thicker the clouds, the more UV rays that are blocked. Fluffy and thin clouds don't block UV rays, and UV rays that are reflected off bright surfaces (e.g., sand, concrete, water, snow) increase our exposure. In Canada, people living at higher elevations (e.g., in the mountains) get more UV rays because the air is cleaner and thinner. And UV exposure increases the closer you are to the equator, so there will be more in southern Ontario than in the Arctic (Environment Canada 2002b).

UV rays are strongest in the summer, but during other seasons too educators need to be aware of UV rays (e.g., a sunny winter day in the Rockies). In the summer, the weather reports usually provide the UV index for the day. UV is measured on a scale of 10, with 10 indicating the shortest sunburn time, typically on a sunny summer day. Tables 6.7 and 6.8 put the UV index into practical and relevant terms so that educators can prevent skin damage to children and themselves.

Depending on where you live, you may be used to hearing weather reports on the radio or television include not only the day's temperature but also the UV index and the humidex (e.g., "It's 32°C today, but the relative humidity makes it feel like 42°C"). The more moisture there is in the air, the less sweat evaporates off skin, which is why people feel hot and sticky when it's very humid outside. Basically, the humidex value is calculated using the temperature and the relative humidity. How does the humidex tell us what it's like outside?

- 20° to 29°C (68° to 84°F): It's comfortable for most.
- 30° to 39°C (86° to 102°F): Most will feel discomfort, some more than others.
- Over 40° (104°): Almost everyone will be uncomfortable. Most activities and work must be restricted.

Educators use their discretion when the humidex reading is high to ensure that children playing outside do not become dehydrated or sick. Perhaps outdoor

TABLE 6.7	What Does the UV Index Mean to Me?	
UV INDEX	**CATEGORY**	**SUNBURN TIME**
over 9	extreme	less than 15 minutes
7–9	high	about 20 minutes
4–7	moderate	about 30 minutes
0–4	low	more than 1 hour

When the UV index is over 9, UVB is extremely strong and you will burn in less than 15 minutes. (Sunburn times are for light untanned skin; the times are somewhat longer for those with darker skin.) Even if you do not get a burn, you may still be damaging your skin.

Source: Environment Canada, "Living with Ultraviolet" (2002b).
www.ns.ec.gc.ca/udo/uv/uvandyou.html (July 2003).

TABLE 6.8	The UV Index: Typical Summer Midday Values
CANADIAN COMMUNITIES COMPARED TO THE TROPICS AND THE NORTH POLE	**UV INDEX**
Tropics	10.0 (extreme)
Toronto	8.0 (high)
Halifax	7.5 (high)
Edmonton	7.0 (high)
Yellowknife	6.0 (moderate)
Iqaluit	4.8 (moderate)
North Pole	2.3 (low)

Source: Adapted from Environment Canada, "Living with Ultraviolet" (2002b).
www.ns.ec.gc.ca/udo/uv/uvandyou.html.

activities could be limited in duration and restricted to quieter play in the shade, or perhaps water play could be made available.

Insects and Repellent

To avoid attracting insects, wasps, and bees, avoid serving sweet food and beverages outside and keep garbage containers far from the play area. Exercise caution when a child has an allergy to bees or wasps and be sure that his or her adrenalin kit is outside with the educators and the child. Remember that if the insects are prevalent and are biting, the best option may be to keep the children inside or to arrange to use a community centre or school gym to get physical exercise, even if it's only for a few days.

Repellents are used to repel mosquitoes, ticks, fleas, and biting flies. Repellents are poisonous and must be kept out of reach of children. The West Nile virus is becoming more of a concern across Canada. But we also need to put this virus into perspective as the risk of infection is low for most Canadians and the risk of serious health effects from the virus are even lower (Health Canada 2003). Eliminating places for mosquitoes to breed is a first step. In early childhood programs, the staff are already doing that for the safety of children; for example, wading pools are always emptied, ponds are not permitted, etc. Programs ensure that the window screens fit properly. Mosquitoes are most active at dawn and dusk, which are times that are outside the hours of operation for most programs. Even so, at those times of day it is very unlikely staff and children would be outside. Wearing light-coloured clothing and a hat is recommended. Wearing long sleeves and pants, although recommended, may not be practical in the heat of the summer.

Do not apply DEET on children under six months old. Use clothing or mosquito netting over strollers and carriages, or avoid going outside if the insects are particularly bad. A drop of white vinegar or oil of citronella behind ears, knees, and wrists may help keep insects away.

For children between six months and two years old, repellent with DEET should not be applied more than once a day and only at a concentration of 10% or less. For children between 2 and 12 years old, a product with 10% or less is recommended, and it shouldn't be applied more than three times in a day. For anyone older than 12, a concentration of no more than 30% DEET should be used (Pest Management Regulatory Agency 2003).

Remember the following points if you use repellents:

- Choose lotions rather than sprays.
- Look for a product that is not combined with a sunscreen.
- Apply sparingly and only on exposed skin, not under clothes or diapers.
- To prevent children getting the repellent in their mouth, do not apply on their face, hands, and fingers.
- Never permit young children to put repellent on themselves or others. Older preschoolers may apply it with supervision and most school-agers should have learned how to apply it safely.
- Once children are back inside, wash off the repellent.
- Obtain the parents' written permission before using repellent.

Winter

Winter conjures up pictures of chattering teeth, knee-high snowdrifts, and icy roads. Yet winter also has beautiful blue skies, clean crisp air, and snow that sparkles like diamonds. Snow is a wonderful play medium for winter activities and sports. Children can have great fun in playgrounds, even though in most regions of Canada it will be very cold. Getting outside in the winter provides all of us with much needed physical activity, fresh air, and sunlight, which is the best source of vitamin D.

Dressing appropriately for the weather goes a long way toward making winter activities enjoyable and safe. Scarves and hoods can become caught on play equipment, resulting in strangulation. Ensure that scarves are tied, with the ends tucked into the coat or parka, and that hoods are tied snugly around faces. Some clothing manufacturers are now making cordless hoods that fasten with Velcro rather than cords.

Most of our body's heat is lost through our head. Wearing appropriate winter hats, toques, hoods, and so on is equally important for adults and children in protecting us from chill and our ears from frostbite. Exposed skin freezes in just a few minutes when it is cold enough outside. Noses, cheeks, ears, fingers, and toes are most prone to frostbite. Watch the children to ensure that their hats, hoods, and scarves do not slide out of place and that someone hasn't got a boot full of snow.

Watch for children who take off their mitts when using play equipment. Toddler snowsuits often come with mitts (without thumbs) that snap onto the cuffs. Toddlers quickly become frustrated with mitts and pull them off because they can't do anything with their hands. Parents should be encouraged to provide toddlers with non-slippery mittens with thumbs. Unless the mitts or gloves are leather, they get wet quickly during play. Wet mitts not only chill children's hands but also increase the likelihood of frostbite. Programs may have mitt-drying racks or ask parents to send two or three pairs of mitts each day so that children have a dry pair to wear during the afternoon.

As discussed in the section on summer safety, educators have a professional responsibility to dress appropriately for the weather conditions when supervising outdoor play. If it is cold enough for children to be wearing hats, mitts, winter boots, and zipped-up coats, educators should wear the same. This is not only to model the behaviour for the children but also to protect themselves from chill and frostbite.

Children may complain that they are cold or wet. Obviously, if they are wet they must go indoors and change into something dry before going back outdoors. However, some children will tell you that they are cold from the moment they step out the door. Often they need to be encouraged to start moving around so that they warm up. Educators can help them by moving around themselves and inviting children to join them. Yet after being outside for some time, some children will be cold and should go inside to warm up.

We often begin our winter mornings by listening to the day's temperature and wind-chill factor. Wind chill causes objects to cool to air temperature more rapidly than they would in calm wind conditions. The wind chill is expressed in temperature-like units, but because it is not the actual air temperature, it is given without the degree sign (Environment Canada 2002a, 1). The Canadian Paediatric Society (1996, 449) suggests that children remain indoors under the following conditions:

■ when the temperature is below −25°C (−13°F), regardless of the wind-chill factor
■ when the wind-chill factor is reported as −28°C (−15°F) or below, regardless of the temperature

Here are important wind-chill benchmarks published by Environment Canada (2002a, 2):

■ −27°C: risk of frostbite in prolonged exposure.
■ −35°C: frostbite possible in 10–15 minutes.
■ −40°C: wind-chill warning will be issued. Frostbite possible in less than 10 minutes.
■ −45°C: be ready to cut short or cancel outdoor activities. Frostbite possible in minutes.
■ −60°C: *Danger!* Frostbite possible in under two minutes.

Some early childhood regulations stipulate an outdoor temperature below which it is deemed too cold for children to play outdoors. Obviously in some regions of

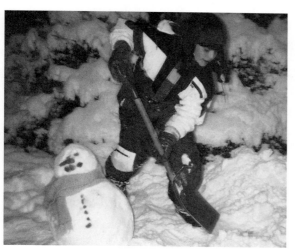

Canada, people are accustomed to long, cold winters and have appropriate winter clothing to minimize the amount of exposed skin. In other regions, where cold weather occurs less frequently, children may have to remain indoors for several consecutive days. Centre staff may want to explore options within the community that would provide space for children to be physically active every day.

Catching falling snowflakes on our tongue is a lot of fun. Blankets of fresh white snow are inviting to eat. Yet children should be discouraged from eating fallen snow (on the ground, fences, benches, etc.) or licking icicles, which can be contaminated with dirt or pollution or animal or bird feces or urine. On mild days it's hard for any of us to resist picking up snow and making snowballs. Children naturally want to throw balls and snowballs are no exception. However, people can easily be injured by snowballs that are thrown too hard or that contain stones. Perhaps you can reach a compromise on snowballs. Designate a wall (without windows) or a tree that snowballs can be thrown at, although you will still have to supervise to ensure that children do not throw balls at one another. Children can also be encouraged to build walls, animals, people, and so on, with snow.

It would be hard to find an adult who grew up in Canada who didn't try to stick his or her wet tongue on cold metal, contrary to parental warnings. So you won't be surprised if some children freeze their tongue to metal objects and perhaps suffer a painful injury.

Frostbite occurs when the skin and underlying tissue gets frozen. Frostbite may not always be painful, but the skin or patch of skin (e.g., nose, cheeks) looks white, and in advanced cases may be blistered.

You need to know what to do when a child's tongue becomes stuck to metal:

First Aid
1. Try to prevent the child from pulling away from the metal.
2. Blow hot breath onto the stuck area or pour warm water onto the object.[1] Gently release the child.
3. If bleeding occurs, such as on the tongue, grasp the tongue with folded sterile gauze and apply direct pressure[2] (Canadian Paediatric Society 1996, 237).

[1]An experienced educator suggests putting a small container filled with hot tap water in a coat pocket before going outside. The water will cool off and it is immediately available.
[2]This is just one more reason that a first-aid kit must always be brought out to the playground.

You will need to know what to do if frostbite occurs:

First Aid
1. Carefully handle and re-warm the area only if there is no chance of a re-freezing before returning to a warm place.
2. If you are outside, warm extremities by holding them in someone's hands or armpits. Warming ears and noses with a warm palm is enough for mild freezing.
3. Treat deeper freezing by holding the extremity in warm water (40.5°C to 43.3°C [105°F to 110°F]) for 20 minutes.[1]

[1]Children should be seen by their doctor or an emergency room physician to ensure that there is no permanent skin damage (Canadian Paediatric Society 1996, 236).]

Activities in the Winter

Winter sports such as skating, tobogganing, and skiing all have the potential to cause injuries. To reduce the risk of injury, educators must ask themselves five safety questions when they are planning winter sports:

1. Is this activity developmentally appropriate for the children?
2. Is the location designed for children to use (e.g., the height of the tobogganing hill) and are there potential hazards—trees, walking paths, ditches, or a road—at the bottom of the hill?
3. What are the potential dangers? How can they be reduced or eliminated?
4. What safety equipment must children wear? Is there enough equipment for each child?
5. Can we recruit enough staff or volunteers for supervision?

For example, toboggans and sleds are dangerous if improperly used, and can cause head, pelvic, and back injuries. If planning such an activity, please keep the following safety considerations in mind:

- avoid sliding near roads, driveways, trees, poles, rocks, and water
- make sure children wear protective helmets
- stay seated and don't overload toboggans or sleds
- remove all scarves and drawstrings
- climb the hill to the side, away from others sliding down
- be extra careful on icy hills—children will go faster than they expect

We can get sunburned in the winter, too, because snow and ice reflect the sun's rays. Sunscreen and lip balm with SPF should be used when children are outdoors for several hours. The lotion also helps protect the skin from windburn.

Walks and Field Trips

Children need to expand their world in many ways and directions, and walks and field trips provide opportunities for learning and enjoyment. Yet unfamiliar surroundings increase the opportunity for injuries, especially for children. Whether educators are taking a small group for a walk to the public park or a group of six- and seven-year-olds to the planetarium by public transit, advanced planning ensures that the outing is safe as well as developmentally and educationally relevant.

Programs have developed written policies and procedures regarding walks and field trips. Walks are often a regular part of an early childhood program, as when infants and toddlers go out in strollers or wagons every day. Educators at programs without a playground need to walk children to neighbourhood playgrounds daily. In both cases, staff obtain written parental permission for walks at the time of enrollment. Parents then know that their children are frequently being taken off the premises and can discuss any concerns that they may have with the staff.

Planning Successful Field Trips

The key to safe field trips is careful planning. It is important to reiterate the educators' responsibility for children's safety at all times. Remember that you need to consider all aspects of the field trip, including

- preparing the children and adults,
- transporting the group to and from the destination,
- assessing the actual activity and physical environment, and
- evaluating the trip on returning.

An itemized list is useful in planning, but educators also have to brainstorm to anticipate other issues that may come up and determine how they can prevent confusion or injuries. Organizing the routine walk to the local playground is quite different from bussing a group to a conservation area. Posting a checklist for walks saves time and ensures that educators take everything they need. But even a routine walk may present a surprise that requires educators to make a decision and ensure the group's safety. You have probably planned an event down to the last detail and then something unexpected happens. That invariably happens on field trips too. Educators need to think on their feet and apply their safety knowledge and skills to make responsible decisions.

e.g.

- Finding that half a block of sidewalk has been ripped up, educators and toddlers have to walk along the road past the construction to get to the playground. This is not ideal, but the staff carry it out as safely as possible. Responsible educators will talk about what happened with the children on returning to the program, and next time choose a new route, if possible, until the construction is completed.
- Two of the parents who had volunteered to accompany your group to the children's theatre presentation announce at the last minute that they are unable to attend. What do you do—cancel the trip, phone around for other volunteers, or…?

Educators have some basic but important questions to ask themselves when they plan field trips:

- Is the trip developmentally appropriate for the age group? Who benefits by taking infants to a planetarium? For infants and toddlers, it often makes sense to plan simple trips that are close to the program—a trip to a neighbourhood library, for example.
- Is the trip educationally appropriate? Taking a preschool group to the mall because the adults want to shop is irresponsible. Trips that do not relate to the interests and learning needs of the children are also more likely to be

unsafe, because bored children of any age tend to look for other stimulation, such as pushing one another or wandering away from the group.

- Do the educators believe that the children are able to understand and follow the trip's guidelines?

Taking a newly formed group of preschoolers on a field trip that requires several rules may be asking for problems. Instead, start with short walks and excursions, helping children to develop an awareness of safety rules, and progress from there.

- Have educators select a way to quickly identify the members of their group while out in a public place where there may be other groups of children (e.g., T-shirts, smocks, or ball caps all in the same colour, or a visible tag with the program logo and phone number). School-aged children don't want to be embarrassed; involve them in the decision of identifiable clothing. Why is it important not to have the child's name on a tag on his or her clothing?

Ensure that one educator does regular head counts before leaving the program, several times during the trip, before leaving again, and on arrival back at the program. Staff are encouraged to have a recent colour photograph of each child as well as his or her age, height, weight, and eye colour. If a child is missing, a photo and description will be useful. Instamatic photographs work well and the description of the child can be written in the white space under the picture (see Prevention of Missing Children, page 301).

- Are there enough adults to ensure safety? Make sure to have more than the legislated minimum number of adults—that is, improve on the adult–child ratio and even more so on trips with younger children or children with specific needs. Some programs find it difficult, if not impossible, to recruit volunteers or parents to join them on trips. Staff may take smaller groups of children at a time, over a few days (on visits to the fire station on Tuesday, Wednesday, and Thursday, for example). These programs may have included this model in their field trip policy.

- Is there quick access to a phone? Bringing a cell phone is the best solution; if this is not possible, ensure that a phone is nearby in case it is needed.

Many programs use a walking rope for children to hold when walking as a group outside the program's property. Staff believe that by holding onto a knot or handle attached to a rope, the young children are safer. Educators assume that they are able to keep track of the children because they are in an orderly line, and that children will not dash off. The use of ropes is a debatable issue among educators. We do not, however, support the use of ropes, for a number of reasons:

- The use of ropes implies that the educators don't believe that the children are competent enough to follow the rules for walks. Toddlers who aren't ready to follow the rules should be in strollers or wagons that they can get out of in order to walk around in a park or playground.

- When one child trips, all the children holding on may also fall, which is potentially more hazardous than not having a rope.
- Educators who rely on the rope as a security measure may not notice when one child lets go.
- Holding onto a rope is not a natural way to walk and thus doesn't provide young children with a realistic experience. It also may encourage them to depend on educators rather than to develop a natural awareness of their surroundings and safety.
- Some people in the community already view early childhood as an institutional setting. Seeing children walking along the street holding onto a rope may reinforce that negative view of early childhood.

Environmental Contaminants

We have discussed concerns about UV rays, humidity, and wind chill, but there are many other environmental factors that environmentalists and researchers are bringing to our attention. Since the 1940s, hundreds of thousands of new chemicals have been introduced into our world in the name of progress and a better standard of living.

The impact of this chemical onslaught on the environment, wildlife, and humans is alarming and still unfolding. Many toxic substances are classified as neurotoxins, hormone disruptors, carcinogens, and respiratory irritants. Some chemicals fit into more than one of these categories. Cell and reproductive changes are becoming more evident as affected generations develop and reproduce. Largely unknown, however, is the impact of synergy: the effect of chemical combinations to which we are exposed. We all breathe the same air and drink the same water, so these chemicals know no boundaries, and that makes pinpointing their effects even more complex.

Our health is also affected by contaminants that aren't necessarily chemical additives. For example, the tragedy in Walkerton, Ontario, was caused by *E. coli* bacteria in the cattle manure that had been spread onto the fields near the wells that supplied the town's drinking water. This contamination resulted in a number of people dying and many more becoming ill. The aftermath of this incident highlights the crucial role of accountability and strict government policies and procedures on a societal health promotion level.

Awareness and action by individuals, groups, and governments are the keys to moving away from a destructive path. The discussion here will focus on why children are more vulnerable to environmental contaminants, environmental concerns known to affect children's health, and possible actions using the health promotion action plan (see Revisiting the Health Promotion Action Plan, page 331). It is beyond the scope of this discussion to describe the many types of toxic substances and their effects. For further information, consult the resources listed at the end of this unit.

Children's Vulnerability to Environmental Toxins

Although a wide range of opinion exists among professionals regarding the impact of environmental factors on health and safety, there is no doubt that children are more vulnerable than adults to environmental contaminants, both immediately (acute reactions) and in the long term (chronic effects). Some of the reasons for children's increased risk are as follows.

- Children's tissues and body systems (e.g., nervous, respiratory, reproductive, digestive, and immune) are not fully developed and are thus more susceptible to damage. Their growth is regulated by hormones, and many environmental toxins are possible "hormone disruptors" (Chance and Harmsen 1998, S11).

- Children inhale toxins faster than adults, because they breathe more rapidly, have smaller airways, and take in more air relative to their body weight than adults do (South Riverdale Community Health Centre 2003, 5).

- Children eat more fruits and vegetables and drink more liquids in proportion to their body weight than do adults. Therefore, their potential exposure to toxins such as lead, pesticides, and nitrates is greater (Children's Environmental Health Network 2003, 5).

- Young children spend more time close to the ground and often put their hands in their mouth. These actions expose them to toxins in dust, soil, and carpets, as well as to pesticide vapours floating close to the ground (Chance and Harmsen 1998, S9).

- Children absorb nutrients in the gastrointestinal tract more quickly than do adults, and this may increase their susceptibility. For example, because children have a greater need for calcium, they absorb more of this mineral when it is present in the gastrointestinal tract, but the body will absorb lead instead of calcium if it is present. An adult absorbs approximately 10% of ingested lead, while a toddler absorbs 50% (Children's Environmental Health Network 2003).

- Children's ability to detoxify and excrete toxins differs from adults' (Children's Environmental Health Network 2003).

Children who live in poverty are disproportionately at risk of exposure to environmental toxins. These children are more likely to live in industrial areas, closer to smokestacks, garbage dumps, and highways with exhaust fumes. Their home environments are more likely to be improperly designed and poorly maintained buildings, with poor indoor air quality, old paint (which may result in lead exposure), old plumbing, and parking lots backed onto apartment buildings (Chaudhuri 1998, S26).

Environmental Concerns and Children's Well-Being

The following section covers four environmental issues of great concern to children's health and safety: air pollution, lead, pesticides, and PVCs (polyvinyl chlorides).

Air Pollution

Climate changes are contributing to increased air pollution. How? Greenhouse gases in our atmosphere hold in the heat. These trapped gases are increasing with the use of fossil fuels (i.e., oil, coal, natural gas) to create power and heat. This blanket-type effect is gradually increasing the average temperatures in Canada, which can have serious consequences to our health. As billions of tons of greenhouse gases, including harmful pollutants such as ground level ozone, sulphur dioxides, and nitrogen oxides, are added to the atmosphere every year, smog is produced. Health Canada estimates that air pollution is the cause of 5,000 premature deaths a year (Canadian Institute of Child Health 2002). For reasons listed earlier, children are severely affected by air pollution. Air pollution, both indoors and out, can affect respiratory health and influence children's behaviour (e.g., irritability may result from mild reactions to air contaminants). Although there is controversy about the over-diagnosis and the causes of asthma, "there is substantial evidence that asthmatic and non-asthmatic children have significant adverse health responses to many air contaminants" (Raizenne et al. 1998, S46) (see Asthma, page 174). The leading concerns in outdoor air pollutants have been ozone, suspended particles, and sulphur compounds. "Exposure to ozone has been associated with increased asthma rates in children as well as a reduction in lung function, and also causes exercise-related wheezing" (Children's Environmental Health Network 2003).

Indoor air pollutants include substances such as tobacco smoke, carbon monoxide, radon, formaldehyde, mercury, and asbestos. Ironically, use of these substances was intended to improve quality of life. The presence of some of these substances has resulted in better insulation, decreased ventilation (which has contributed to problems with airtight buildings), increased indoor humidity and higher temperatures, and more furniture and conveniences.

There are a number of ways to improve indoor air quality and reduce children's exposure to environmental contaminants. One obvious way, which has been successful in public places in Canada, is to ban smoking indoors. Parents and educators who have not yet been able to quit smoking need to recognize the importance of smoke-free environments for children.

Other suggestions for improving indoor air quality concern children's exposure to dust and other potentially harmful substances. Ensure that the facilities' surfaces, furniture, counters, and shelves are easy to clean and that they are cleaned on a regular basis. Use unscented cleaning and laundry products, and encourage staff not to wear perfumes or colognes, which some people are allergic to. Limit the amount of carpet used within a program. Avoid its use in high-traffic areas where people are wearing shoes or boots and where food or play materials such as paint and play dough are used. Purchase carpeting that is hypoallergenic and cleans well. Ensure that it is vacuumed daily and steam-cleaned regularly. In programs without infants and toddlers, consider eliminating carpeting altogether. Even in those programs with infants and toddlers, other things could be used on the floor instead of carpets (e.g., mats). Window coverings, especially horizontal blinds, tend to trap dust. When selecting window coverings, consider roller blinds. Select fabrics and designs that can be removed and washed easily.

To help protect children outdoors, enforce a no-idling zone during pickup and drop-off times and prohibit smoking close to the building.

Lead

Lead exposure has been associated with serious illness and even death. Scientists now know that even low-level lead exposure can affect a child's brain development and nervous system, leading to possible behavioural and learning difficulties and reduced intelligence (Harvey 2003, 1–5). It is impossible to avoid lead exposure completely, but safety awareness and precautions limit exposure, which is important because no level of lead is considered safe. A great public health success in the 1970s was the elimination of lead from gasolines. Lead-based paint, found in and on the exterior of older buildings (lead was used as a pigment in paints until shortly after World War II), remains a hazard for many children. Information about how to determine if this is a problem and how to safely remove lead-based paint is readily available.

Exposure to lead in dust and soil is a main concern, because preschoolers are likely to ingest dust and soil every day. Houses and apartments and early childhood settings situated near industries that have used lead, or are situated on busy streets, may contain high levels of lead because lead can remain in the soil for decades and contaminate vegetables grown in that soil. Another source of lead contamination is old lead piping and soldered pipes. Municipally treated drinking water is almost lead-free when it leaves the water plant, but it may pick up lead from the plumbing systems of older houses or apartments or from a lead-containing solder common in newer copper systems. In some areas, plumbing codes now limit the content of lead in solder. Lead accumulates when water stands in the pipes, so the first water out of the tap generally contains the most lead. Running the water for a few minutes can reduce the lead content, and hot water picks up more lead than cold, so use cold water from the tap for drinking, cooking, and making baby formula.

Did you know that jewelry containing lead is readily available? In the summer of 2000, Health Canada surveyed 95 imported jewelry items intended for children and found that 69% contained lead in amounts from 50% to 100% (Harvey 2003, 3). Toys, such as small toy cars, often contain lead. The federal government aims to have regulations in place for children's products and jewelry by April 2004 (Harvey 2003, 5). To help parents and educators determine whether an item or soil contains lead, there are a number of lead test kits sold at major hardware stores (see Resource Materials, page 334).

Pesticides

Pesticide products registered by the federal government to control pests such as insects, rodents, and weeds have been an ongoing concern because of their obvious toxicity. Recently there have generally been more stringent standards and regulations to prevent acute (immediate) episodes of toxicity, though children may be more liable than adults to experience latent (delayed) effects over the course of their lifetime (Children's Environmental Health Network 2003). Using chemicals to treat our lawns and gardens and to de-flea our pets exposes us to long-term hazards. Insect repellents are likely more hazardous than the bug bite itself (South Riverdale Community Health Centre 2003, 32). A number of health concerns—allergies, hormone disruption, and developmental neurotoxicity, to name a few—have possible associations with pesticides.

In 2000, the Supreme Court of Canada upheld a bylaw passed by the town of Hudson, Quebec, that banned the cosmetic use of pesticides within the town's borders. This ban includes both public land, such as parks, and private property. This landmark decision has paved the way for a number of communities in Canada to pursue similar bylaws. Of course, the attempts are challenged by lawn chemical companies, but it seems that the movement to ban pesticide use is gaining momentum. The general public is becoming more aware of natural alternatives to pest control. Loblaws, the largest grocery chain in Canada, has put a policy into effect only allowing the sale of natural lawn and garden products.

PVCs

PVCs (polyvinyl chlorides) produce plastics that tend to last for many years and are difficult to destroy. When they are burned, the fumes are even more toxic. PVCs and the phthalates added to them as a plastic softener captured a lot of national and international media attention in the late 1990s due to efforts to ban their use in mouthing and teething toys and rattles. The most immediate concern with phthalates in PVCs is that they leach out of the plastic fairly easily and are thought to be hormone disruptors, interfere with the hormone systems in children. In 1998, Canada's federal government followed the lead of the European Union and banned the use of phthalates in teething rings and other infant toys. Another concern with plastics is the use of lead, cadmium, and other heavy metals, along with various chemicals, in their manufacturing. The consumer may incorrectly assume that any product intended for children would have undergone stringent testing before being put on the market. To ensure children's safety, Cooper et al. (2000, 224) recommend that Health Canada develop a precautionary materials-use policy, requiring that consumer products be manufactured with materials that are inherently safe, rather than react to the consequences of hazardous materials.

Plastics have become a significant part of our environment in the last 30 years. One look around (indoors and outdoors) in an early childhood setting and it is obvious that we have come to depend on plastic toys, equipment, and utensils. It is likely that hazardous substances can be replaced with safer alternatives in the production of plastic products. We may also find that rethinking the use of some plastic products is worthwhile. Suggested ways to reduce children's exposure to hormone disruptors found in PVCs include:

- Never microwave food in plastic containers, as the chemicals leach out. Use glass, Pyrex, china, or ceramic dishes. Baby bottles should be warmed in hot water (see Warming Bottles, page 249.). Silicone nipples and pacifiers or soothers do not contain phthalates.

- Use fabric teethers when possible.

- PVC mini-blinds contain lead that breaks down and becomes a dust on the surface. Wash this away carefully and often.

- Hard plastics are a better choice than soft, squishy plastics for children who chew on toys (Canadian Child Care Federation and Association of Canadian Community Colleges 1998).

Possible Actions to Promote Environmental Health and Safety

When we consider the vast and still relatively unknown aspects of environmental contamination, we can become overwhelmed and feel powerless to make a difference. However,

> as increasing attention is paid to reducing the production, use and discharge of some of the most toxic substances, it becomes clear that options are available. Motivation to clean up has come from regulations, from economic signals, from consumer demands, and from all in combination. (World Wildlife Foundation 1998, 2)

Being Prepared for Emergencies

Educators should have an up-to-date first-aid certificate that equips them with the knowledge and skills

- to help them remain calm,
- to administer basic first aid or at least to ensure that their actions do not make an injury worse while waiting for emergency medical services (make sure you know the number for dialing emergency medical services),
- to use the supplies in a first-aid kit, and
- to know when to call emergency medical services.

Throughout your ECE training you will work in programs, and one of your first tasks when starting in a new program will be to familiarize yourself with its emergency policy and procedures and take part in fire drills. Be sure you know where the following are located in the building:

- emergency exits and posted evacuation routes (floor plan with exits indicated)
- first-aid kits
- fire extinguishers and fire alarms (read the operating instructions)
- smoke detectors and carbon monoxide detector
- emergency phone numbers within the community, as well as the children's parents' numbers
- blankets and flashlights

Injury Reports

An injury report should be completed whenever a child or educator is injured—even when the injury appears to be minor. Minor cuts can become infected. A head injury may show no immediate observable symptoms, but changes in behaviour can develop hours later. When in doubt, always complete an injury report. Educators should also document the injury in the child's file and make reference to the completed injury report. The injury report provided at the end of this unit covers the pertinent information, including the time and date, educator's signature, and who was notified. A line drawing is provided so that educators can mark where the injury is on the body (see Appendix 6.2, page 344).

The primary purpose of the injury report is to serve as a legal document. Clear and succinct documentation is required to report the injury as objectively as possible. Depending on the child's injury and the outcome, these reports may be reviewed by the early childhood office, police, or lawyers if the question of professional liability or suspected child abuse is raised. A copy of the injury report is usually placed in the child's file.

The report also serves as a tool for staff in developing injury prevention strategies. Educators use the report to evaluate a specific injury or a series of similar injuries in their program. From this information, educators first consider the five W's of safety promotion:

- who
- why, such as the level of supervision, what the child was doing at the time, and his or her developmental stage
- where, such as on a particular piece of play equipment, its general condition, the protective surface, or on a walk or field trip
- when, such as the time of day and weather conditions
- what happened in chronological order, the type and extent of the injury, and what the injury looks like (size, colour, location on the body).

Educators then consider everything they learned about this incident to determine and implement the necessary changes to prevent similar injuries in the future, or at least to reduce the severity. More serious injuries will be reported as serious occurrences (see Serious Occurrences, page 281). The following are a few possible alterations either in practice or to equipment:

- Increase the level of supervision.
- Modify, repair, or remove a piece of play equipment.
- Review the safe use of play equipment with the children.
- Reorganize a particular planned curriculum with children (e.g., reduce the number of steps in a preschool cooking activity and the number of children to supervise them better with cutting and cooking).
- Eliminate a particular planned event with children (e.g., a field trip to horse-back ride with preschoolers).

Children's Safety at Pickup Times

Educators are responsible for the safety of children until the children leave the premises with their parents or persons authorized by the parents. Program staff may be faced with a situation in which an unauthorized person arrives to pick up a child, or conditions are deemed unsafe for releasing a child to the parent, or no one comes to pick up the child at the end of the day, or school-agers are permitted to leave unattended.

School-Aged Children

School-agers range in age from 6 to 12 and their abilities, skills, and need for independence vary.

Some parents feel that their children are competent and can handle the responsibility of being at home alone and the children may want it that way. Other families feel they have no option but to leave their children at home on their own after school. In response, many communities have a telephone number that children can call if they are lonely, need someone to talk to, or are worried about something. And the community in which they live may play a role in parents' sense of safety and their level of comfort in having children home alone. According to the Canadian Institute of Child Health, school-age children who are at home alone are clearly at increased risk for injury, missing meals, and other health and well-being problems (Canadian Institute of Child Health 2000, 93).

The law requires that parents provide reasonable provision for the safety of children under age 16. However, this law is vague in terms of what is considered reasonable. School-age programs are then faced with the dilemma of creating a policy on the release of school-agers at the end of the day. Programs' policies depend on their philosophy, their setting (urban versus rural), their location within a city, and the parents using the program. Ultimately, educators and parents all want children to gain increasing levels of independence and responsibility. Most adults realize that developing autonomy through opportunities to manage some risk is beneficial for children.

The program can foster autonomy in school-aged children by integrating the concept of "intermittent supervision" (Young 1994, 43–44). "While children benefit from a gradual expansion of boundaries, attention must be paid to the abilities of the child and the potential risks present in the environment" (43). When developing an intermittent supervision policy, the program considers issues such as program philosophy, physical layout, and length of time for transitions. In addition, depending on perception of community safety, this policy may include the requirement of peer buddies (i.e., children are with a peer during these non-adult supervised times).

- Children in pairs move independently of an adult from their classroom to the school-age program within the building or outside to a portable.
- Children go inside the school to use the washroom (e.g., in buddy pairs) and then return to the playground.

At the time of a child's enrollment, parents are made aware of this approach to supervision and are given an opportunity to discuss any concerns they may have. School-age programs may require that parents sign a permission form regarding intermittent supervision within the program. There are a number of reasons why children may leave the site without adult supervision: they may walk home from the school-age program, go to an off-site after-school activity, or walk to the corner store on an errand as a way to gain autonomy. But no educator would permit unsupervised activities such as these without prior consultation.

Programs work out the specific arrangements for each child with the parents. This agreement is put in writing in the child's file. Before parents permit their children to walk home alone, for instance, school-agers' educators and parents determine the child's readiness and safety factors. As stated above, a program policy or guideline may include a peer buddy system. The following questions should be asked.

- Has the child asked his or her parents to allow walking home alone and does the child understand what it will be like to be home alone? If this request has not been made by the child, he or she is unlikely to be ready for this responsibility.
- Does the child's teacher feel that the child is developmentally ready? Teachers can provide parents and educators with valuable insights into children's behaviour (e.g., "Every time I step out of the classroom, Sandra is doing something that endangers her safety," or "Danny follows guidelines well and demonstrates initiative").
- What are the potential risks for the child on the way home from the early childhood facility?
- What kind of adult support is available to the child at home (e.g., neighbour, clerk in the corner store, children's telephone help line, telephone access to parents)?

Unauthorized Persons

Parents must feel confident that educators will not permit an unauthorized person to take their child from the program. To protect children from abduction, programs require an authorization policy and procedures that ensure that only authorized individuals pick up children. Parents and the program must have a written agreement that lists the people that parents authorize to take their children from the program. (Some parents will authorize one person only.)

If the list is part of a contract with the parent and an employee releases a child to a person not named in the list, the program will not only be in breach of contract but also of their provincial/territorial regulations. If the child is injured, a negligence action (lawsuit) may follow. Staff cannot release a child to anyone who has not been authorized in writing. A parent cannot add a name to the list over the phone. However, due to unexpected work responsibilities or travel problems, parents may find themselves in situations in which they can't get to the program in time to pick up the child. A parent might then call and tell the educator that a friend will come to the program even though this person isn't on the authorized list. These situations are grey areas. Educators have to be practical and exercise common sense.

The parent has called the program first, and authorized the person for this specific day, and the child knows that person. It would be unlikely that the staff would refuse to release the child to this individual. There may be times when someone arrives who is not on the list and the parent has not called the program. Even if the child is happy to see that person and would be comfortable leaving with him or her, educators are legally responsible not to release the child to this unauthorized person. In this situation, the educators must call the parents. The parent may simply have forgotten to tell the staff that morning. To avoid a similar situation in the future, the parents can add this person's name to the written agreement. The least likely occurrence, but the one of most concern, is that this person is in fact attempting to take the child without the parent's permission.

Non-Custodial Parents

Many children live in families in which parents are either separated or divorced. Many of these families have workable agreements for child custody and visitation. In cases of joint custody, there usually aren't concerns for the child's safety. However, there are situations in which agreements are not straightforward. From educators' perspectives, parents must provide a copy of the custody order and a photograph of the non-custodial parent. If situations arise when the custodial parent releases the child to the other parent, the custodial parent must provide the staff with written permission. All educators must be apprised of these custody agreements to ensure that a child is not released to a non-custodial parent without authorization. Educators should be cautious if the non-custodial parent arrives on a day other than the one that had been agreed on. Staff can't assume that releasing the child is acceptable to the other parent simply because it's a different day. Parents, not strangers, are responsible for most child abductions.

What do staff do when an unauthorized non-custodial parent insists that the program release the child to him or her? Educators may face a verbal or physical confrontation with this parent. In this situation, staff need to

- calmly ask the parent to move to an area with more privacy (more than one educator should be with the parent), or at least have staff move all children away or outside;
- have someone call the custodial parent so he or she knows what is happening. Depending on their rapport, the custodial parent may be able to talk to the other parent or quickly come to the program; and
- call the police if the parent loses control or tries to leave with the child.

Children in Need of Protection: Intoxicated Parents

It may be hard to imagine that parents could actually arrive to pick up their children while intoxicated with alcohol or drugs. Yet it does happen, and educators must know how to handle such situations for the safety of the child and parent. Educators have a number of concerns:

- releasing the child to a parent whom they consider to be incompetent to care for the child
- the safety of parent and child on the way home

- the safety of others if the intoxicated parent is driving
- the child's safety and well-being once at home, especially if there is no second adult in the home
- the potential liability of the program if staff knowingly allow an intoxicated parent to drive and a motor vehicle mishap occurs

From both an ethical and a legal perspective, educators cannot release a child to someone who could cause the child harm. Each situation is different. Each depends on the age of the child, the staff's relationship with the parent, whether the problem is a recurring one, and so on, and as such it is a subjective decision on the part of the staff. The situation could be difficult to handle. Educators should

- offer the parent coffee and calmly talk about safety concerns for the child and parent (the child should not be present);
- ask the parent whether someone could come and pick them up and ensure that the child is cared for when they arrive home, such as
  - the other parent, if he or she is active in the child's daily life, or
  - another authorized adult;
- in extreme cases, call the child protection agency and discuss the situation with them; and
- if the parent is belligerent or confrontational, or wants to or has already taken the child from the program and is driving away, call the police and tell them that a drunk driver is leaving the program with a child. If possible, providing the police with the make, model, and colour of the car, as well as the licence plate number, would be helpful.

When No One Arrives

What happens if half an hour after closing the program, the parents have not yet arrived and cannot be reached by phone? Staff should try contacting the following people:

- the alternate adults listed in the emergency information
- people on the authorized list
- as a last resort, the child protection agency, who will provide staff with guidance in handling the situation

REVISITING THE HEALTH PROMOTION ACTION PLAN

With reference to the Action Plan for Health Promotion introduced in Unit 1, the following are examples of what we can do to reduce exposure to and production of environmental contaminants.

Individual Problem Solving and Self-Reliance

- Install and maintain carbon monoxide monitors as well as smoke detectors.
- Pay attention to air-quality advisories and the air-quality index.

- Limit activities that contribute to air pollution.
- Minimize contact between food and plastics (e.g., use glass containers in microwave ovens).
- Minimize the use of plastic mouthing toys.
- Run the water taps (or water fountain) for a few minutes each morning to reduce the contaminant load, including lead.
- Eat pesticide-free foods (e.g., organic fruits and vegetables) when possible.
- Use non-toxic repellents to control pests (e.g., dab white vinegar behind ears, knees, and wrists; spray a hot-pepper and water mix on leaves to deter caterpillars).
- Minimize the ingestion of toxic chemicals through routine hand washing.
- See resources such as *Hidden Exposures* for further suggestions (see Resource Materials, page 334).

Collective Self-Help
- Insist on nonsmoking environments.
- Test for lead in paint, soil, dust, solder, and drinking water (see Abotex Enterprises under Resource Materials, page 334). Share your findings with others in your neighbourhood.
- Demand full disclosure if pesticides are used in public places (school yards, parks, roadsides).

Community Action
- Interested citizens can meet with the local supermarket manager to request organic produce, or start a "fresh food box" program. A number of communities in Canada have started programs in which affordable locally grown produce (both organic and non-organic) is made available on a weekly or monthly basis.
- Find out if your community is or is in the process of becoming a pesticide-free zone. If it is not, find out how to advocate for this.
- Join or start a group to learn about environmental contaminants and how to reduce them.

Societal Change
- Join a national organization that advocates for children's environmental health. The Canadian Institute of Child Health is at the forefront of this important movement.
- Advocacy that results in legislated changes benefits everyone. Support the campaign for a clean environment and health protection laws in Canada. The public is encouraged to send messages to key federal officials to continue improving standards through the *Canadian Environmental Protection Act.*

CONCLUSION

Since 1980, the rate of hospitalization due to injury has been decreasing. We must remain vigilant and act on behalf of children to decrease the injury rate further in the coming decades. One senseless death of a child is too many. "As long as the design of our technology and our physical and socio-legislative environments does not account for their specific safety needs, children and youth will incur injuries that could otherwise have been avoided" (Health Canada 1997, 7). Air bags in cars, for example, are a preventive measure that can be detrimental to young children. Parents and educators have an integral role in helping children to learn lifelong safety behaviour. As children grow and develop, the educators' role moves from one of protecting children to one of enhancing their understanding of safety, identifying potential risks, and preventing injuries. Our communities and society have an important role in safety promotion through research, education, and legislation based on children's needs.

What's Your Opinion?

TO CLIMB OR NOT TO CLIMB?

If there is a tree to be climbed, there will be children wanting to climb it. Tree climbing in program playgrounds continues to be a controversial issue among educators, parents, and health professionals. For a class debate, remember to consider the different age groups and types and sizes of trees.

ASSESS YOUR LEARNING

Define terms or describe concepts used in this unit.

- the who, why, where, when, and what of children's injuries
- injury prevention strategies
- serious occurrences
- Canadian Standards Association
- protective surfaces
- encroachment area
- safety checks
- sun protection factor
- UV index
- frostbite
- wind-chill factor
- considerations for field trips
- emergency preparations
- unauthorized persons

Evaluate your options in each situation.

1. The daily routine usually ends with outdoor play, and parents pick up their children from the playground. Children need active supervision on equipment, but parents also need the opportunity to speak with an educator about their child's day.

2. School-agers on the playground are inundated with a long list of rules and often feel that they have no control. Many children are trying to feel more powerful by deliberately breaking rules when educators' backs are turned.

3. The winter has been extremely cold and windy, yet a number of the school-agers are not wearing their boots and hats because "it's just not the thing to do." Before and after school, the children have a choice between staying in and going out to the playground. These same children choose to stay indoors. Some haven't played outside all month.

4. You are on a long summer walk with the preschoolers before lunch and suddenly you remember that none of you is wearing sunscreen.

RESOURCE MATERIALS

Organizations

Abotex Enterprises Ltd., 3031 Wildwood Drive, Windsor, ON N8R 1S7. Tel. (519) 735-8645 or 1-800-268-5323 for nearest retail location. (Suppliers of lead test kits.) www.leadinspector.com

Canadian Hospitals Injury Reporting and Prevention Program (CHIRPP), Health Canada, 0904A Brooke Claxton Building, Tunney's Pasture, Ottawa, ON K1A 0K9. Tel. (613) 957-2991; fax (613) 941-5366. www.hc-sc.gc.ca/pphb-dgspsp/injury-bles/chirpp/index.html

Canadian Institute of Child Health, 384 Bank Street, Suite 300, Ottawa, ON K2P 1Y4. Tel. (613) 230-8838; fax (613) 230-6654. www.cich.ca

Canadian Standards Association (CSA), 5060 Spectrum Way, Mississauga, ON L4W 5N6. Tel. (416) 747-4000 or national toll-free 1-800-463-6727; fax (416) 747-2473. www.csa.ca

Safe Kids Canada, 180 Dundas Street West, Toronto, ON M5G 1Z8. Tel. (416) 813-6766 or national toll-free 1-888-723-3847; fax (416) 813-4986. (Monitors children's injuries and develops prevention programs; Safe Kids coalitions are located across Canada.) www.safekidscanada.ca

Other Websites of Interest

Canada Safety Council: www.safety-council.org

Canadian Toy Testing Council: www.toy-testing.org

The Toy Report (annual): www.toy-testing.org/contents/reports/treport.htm

Child Safety in Vehicles, Canadian Automobile Association: www.caa.ca/e/news-issues/child-safety/contacts.shtml

Is Your Child Safe?, Consumer Product Safety, Health Canada: www.hc-sc.gc.ca/hecs-sesc/cps/child_safe.htm

Elmer, The Safety Elephant, Canada Safety Council: www.elmer.ca/english/index.htm

Health Protection, Health Canada, Consumer Products: www.hc-sc.gc.ca/english/protection/consumer.html

Environmental Health: www.hc-sc.gc.ca/english/protection/environment.html

Healthy Spaces, Canadian Child Care Federation: www.cfc-efc.ca/healthy-spaces/home_en.php

Pest Management Regulatory Agency, Health Canada: www.hc-sc.gc.ca/pmra-arla/english/index-e.html

The War Amps, PLAYSAFE: www.waramps.ca/playsafe/home.html
   Safety Walk Program: www.waramps.ca/playsafe/walk.html
Water Safety Services, Canadian Red Cross:
   www.redcross.ca/article.asp?id=000881&tid=001

Printed Matter

Children's Playspaces and Equipment (2003), by the Canadian Standards Association,
   1-800-463-6727 or www.csa.ca.

*Hidden Exposures: A Practical Guide for Creating a Healthier Environment for You and
   Your Children* (2003), by South Riverdale Community Health Centre (send cheque or
   money order for $10—this includes postage and taxes—to Programs Assistant, 955
   Queen Street East, Toronto, ON M4M 3P3).

Lead in Your Home (1997), by Canada Mortgage and Housing Corporation. www.
   hc-sc.gc.ca/ehp/ehd/catalogue/bch_pubs/leadhome/booklet.pdf.

Let's Go Outside!: Designing the Early Childhood Playground (1999), by Tracey Theemes
   (High Scope Educational Research Foundation).

Videos

Child's Play: A Playground Safety Guide for Daycares, Schools and Communities (1997),
   by Safe Kids Canada (video and booklet are available from CSA. Tel. 416-747-4000,
   or national toll-free 1-800-463-6727, or e-mail: sales@CSA.ca).

Cutting the Risk, Keeping the Magic (1997), by Metro Toronto Community Services.

BIBLIOGRAPHY

Canadian Child Care Federation and Association of Canadian Community Colleges
   (1998). "Linking Research to Practice: A Canadian Forum," Proceedings report,
   October 25–27. Ottawa: Canadian Child Care Federation.

Canadian Dermatology Association (2003). *Sun Facts*. Ottawa: Canadian Dermatology
   Association.

Canadian Foundation for the Study of Infant Deaths, Canadian Institute of Child
   Health, Canadian Paediatric Society, Health Canada (1993). *Joint Statement:
   Reducing the Risk of Sudden Infant Death Syndrome in Canada*. Ottawa: Health
   Canada.

Canadian Hospitals Injury Reporting and Prevention Program (2000). "Injuries Associated
   with ... Inline Skating." CHIRPP Database: Summary Data for 1998. <www.hc-sc.gc.ca/
   pphb-dgspsp/injury-bles/chirpp/injrep-rapbles/inline_e.html> (July 2003).

Canadian Institute of Child Health (2002). "Fact Sheet: Air Pollution."
   <www.cich.ca/EnvironmentHealth_ClimateFactSheets.html#AirPollution> (July 2003).

———— (2000). *The Health of Canada's Children: A CICH Profile*, 3rd ed. Ottawa:
   Canadian Institute of Child Health.

Canadian Paediatric Society (1996). *Well Beings: A Guide to Promote the Physical Health,
   Safety and Emotional Well-Being of Children in Child Care Centres and Family Day
   Care Homes*. Ottawa: Canadian Paediatric Society.

Canadian Standards Association [CSA] (2003). *Children's Playspaces and Equipment*.
   Mississauga: Canadian Standards Association.

——— (2003). *Children's Playspaces and Equipment.* Mississauga: Canadian Standards Association.

Chance, G., and E. Harmsen (1998). "Children Are Different: Environmental Contaminants and Children's Health." *Canadian Journal of Public Health* 89 (supplement 1): S9–S13.

Chaudhuri, N. (1998). "The Case for Child Development as a Determinant of Health." *Canadian Journal of Public Health* 89 (supplement 1): S26–S30.

Children's Environmental Health Network (2003). "An Introduction to Children's Environmental Health." <www.cehn.org/cehn/WhatisPEH.html> (July 2003).

Cooper, K., et al. (2000). "Environmental Standard Setting and Children's Health." Report by the Children's Health Project. Toronto: Canadian Environmental Law Association and Ontario College of Family Physicians.

Environment Canada (2002a). "Canada's New Wind Chill Index." <www.mb.ec.gc.ca/air/wintersevere/windchill.en.html>(July 2003).

——— (2002b). "Living with Ultraviolet." Ottawa: Supply and Services Canada. <www.ns.ec.gc.ca/udo/uv/uvandyou.html> (July 2003).

——— (2002c). "Guarding Our Earth Ozone." Ottawa: Environment Canada. <www.ec.gc.ca/ozone/DOCS/KIDZONE/EN/guardearth.cfm> (July 2003).

Harvey, R. (2003). "A Silent Danger Still Unheeded." *The Toronto Star*, April 13.

Health Canada (2003). "West Nile Virus." <www.hc-sc.gc.ca/english/westnile/general.html> (July 2003).

——— (1999). "A Parent's Guide to Sun Protection." <www.hc-sc.gc.ca/hecs-sesc/ccrpb/fiction_fact.htm (July 2003).

——— (1997). *For the Safety of Canadian Children and Youth: From Injury Data to Preventive Measures.* Ottawa: Supply and Services Canada.

Ministry of Community and Social Services (March 2000). Serious Occurrence Reporting Procedures for Service Providers. Toronto.

Pest Management Regulatory Agency (2003). "Safety Tips on Using Personal Insect Repellents." <www.hc-sc.gc.ca/pmra-arla/english/pdf/pnotes/deet-e.pdf> (July 2003).

Raizenne, M., R. Dales, and R. Burnett (1998). "Air Pollution Exposures and Children's Health." *Canadian Journal of Public Health* 89 (supplement 1): S26–S30.

Safe Kids Canada (2003). "Safe Kids Canada's Position Statement to Ban Baby Walkers." <www.safekidscanada.ca/ENGLISH/IP_PROFESSIONALS/Advocacy/BabyWalkersPositionStatement.document> (July 2003).

——— (2002). "New Survey Reveals Kids Are Not Wearing Helmets." Media release, June 3. <www.safekidscanada.ca/ENGLISH/Media/Media_PressRelease5.html> (July 2003).

——— (2001). *Majority of Canadian Parents Don't Know Biggest Burn Hazard.* Media release, May 29. <www.safekidscanada.ca/ENGLISH/Media/mediarelease_skweek2001.html> (July 2003).

——— (1997). *Child's Play: A Playground Safety Guide for Daycares, Schools and Communities.* Toronto: Safe Kids Canada.

South Riverdale Community Health Centre (2003). *Hidden Exposures: A Practical Guide for Creating a Healthier Environment for You and Your Children.* Toronto: South Riverdale Community Health Centre.

Stanwick, R. (1993). "Preventing Childhood Injuries in Day Care Settings." *Interaction* Summer: 23–24.

Theemes, T. (1999). *Let's Go Outside! Designing the Early Childhood Playground.* Ypsilanti, MI: High Scope Educational Research Foundation.

Transport Canada, Transportation Development Centre (2001). "Doing Our Homework on School Bus Safety." *R&D Updates* 11(4). <www.tc.gc.ca/tdc/publication/updates/v11n4.htm> (July 2003).

World Wildlife Foundation (1998). "Global Toxics Initiative." <www.worldwildlife.org> (January 1999).

Young, N. (1994). *Caring for Play: The School and Child Care Connection.* Toronto: Direction 2000.

Weekly Safety Checklist

Name of Person Performing Inspection: _____

Date of Inspection: _____

INDOORS	OK	ACTION REQUIRED			
	X	X	Please Specify	Date Completed	Comments

PLAY AND SLEEPING AREAS

	OK	Action			
There are no long paths that encourage running.	❏	❏			
All exits are clearly marked and free of any obstacles or clutter.	❏	❏			
There is easy access to emergency phones.	❏	❏			
Electrical cords are not within children's reach. Cords do not run under carpeting or in traffic paths or doorways.	❏	❏			
Unused extension cords are unplugged and out of reach.	❏	❏			
Unused electrical outlets have plastic outlet covers.	❏	❏			
Drawers and cupboards are kept closed.	❏	❏			
Matches, lighters, medicines, cleaning agents, and tools are inaccessible to children.	❏	❏			
Staff and visitors' belongings, purses, and medications are inaccessible to children.	❏	❏			

(appendix continues on next page)

INDOORS	OK	ACTION REQUIRED			
	X	X	Please Specify	Date Completed	Comments
Locks on doors can be opened by an adult without difficulty, but not by children.	❏	❏			
Garbage containers have tightly fitting lids, preferably operated by foot pedals. (Lids should not be left up after use.) Garbage containers are emptied daily.	❏	❏			
Soiled diapers are disposed of in securely tied plastic bag(s). Soiled diapers and diaper pails must be stored away from children.	❏	❏			
Cat litter boxes are not accessible to children.	❏	❏			
There are no precariously placed small, sharp, or otherwise hazardous objects.	❏	❏			
Furnishings are in good repair and free of sharp edges, splinters, pinch points, and crush points.	❏	❏			
Drapery and blind cords are tied up and secured with safety hooks.	❏	❏			
All storage units are well constructed and stable. Units are anchored to the wall or flooring to prevent sliding, collapsing, or tipping over.	❏	❏			
All TVs, VCRs, computers, projectors, etc., are secured on stands that ensure no tipping or collapsing.	❏	❏			
Supervision					
Children are never unattended and always supervised by enough well-trained staff who can evacuate children in an emergency.	❏	❏			
There is no bottle propping.	❏	❏			
Toddlers are not permitted to walk with bottles or food.	❏	❏			
Running is not allowed inside the space.	❏	❏			
Equipment					
Baby carriers are never used as car seats.	❏	❏			
Toys are in good repair and free of sharp edges, pinch points, and splinters.	❏	❏			
No toys accessible to young children have strings or cords longer than 15 cm (6 in.) that can encircle the neck.	❏	❏			
Toys are stored when not being used. (Open shelving is desirable for easy selection.)	❏	❏			

(appendix continues on next page)

INDOORS	OK	ACTION REQUIRED			
	X	X	Please Specify	Date Completed	Comments
Toys are age appropriate and suited to the abilities of the children using them.	❑	❑			
Toys for different ages are stored separately.	❑	❑			
Art materials are properly stored in labelled containers.	❑	❑			
HALLWAYS AND STAIRS					
Stairways are well lit.	❑	❑			
Stairs and stairways are free of stored items.	❑	❑			
Safety gates are at the top and bottom of the stairs, if appropriate.	❑	❑			
Exits are clearly marked.	❑	❑			
Electrical cords are out of children's reach and kept out of doorways and from under carpets. Unused extension cords are unplugged.	❑	❑			
Unused electrical outlets have plastic outlet covers.	❑	❑			
Locks on doors can be opened by an adult without difficulty, but not by children.	❑	❑			
KITCHEN					
Pot handles are always turned toward the back of the stove.	❑	❑			
Appliance cords are rolled up when not in use. No cords hang over the counter where they could be caught in a cupboard or drawer or be within children's reach.	❑	❑			
Dishes are in good condition and not cracked or chipped.	❑	❑			
Sharp, pointed, or otherwise dangerous cooking utensils (such as knives or glass) are not within the children's reach.	❑	❑			
Garbage containers have tightly fitting lids, preferably operated by foot pedals. (Lids should not be left up after use.) Containers are not near a furnace or hot water heater (fire hazard).	❑	❑			
Cleaning agents are stored in original containers. The only exception is bleach, which is often added to water in properly labelled spray bottles. All cleaning agents are kept in a locked cupboard (along with any tools, matches or lighters, and plastic bags) away from any food.	❑	❑			

(appendix continues on next page)

INDOORS	OK	ACTION REQUIRED			
	X	X	Please Specify	Date Completed	Comments
All medication is stored out of the reach of children (a locked cupboard or container may be required).	❏	❏			

Supervision

Children are never left unattended in the kitchen.	❏	❏			

WASHROOMS

Step stools are provided where appropriate for sink and toilet.	❏	❏			
Small toilet seats, which fit on top of the toilet, are flush with the toilet's seat. (Seats that elevate the child high off the floor are not recommended.)	❏	❏			
Cleaning agents are stored in original containers and kept in a locked cupboard out of children's reach.	❏	❏			
Garbage containers have tightly fitting lids, preferably operated by foot pedals. (Lids should not be left up after use.) Garbage containers are emptied daily.	❏	❏			
Plastic bags are stored in a locked cupboard out of children's reach.	❏	❏			
Soiled diapers are stored in securely tied plastic bag(s). Soiled diapers and diaper pails must be stored away from children.	❏	❏			
Locks on any doors can be opened by an adult without difficulty, but not by children.	❏	❏			

Supervision

Young children are never left unattended in the washroom.	❏	❏			

OUTDOORS

TRAFFIC/FIELD TRIPS/VEHICLES

Staff are aware of who can take a child out of the facility.	❏	❏			
Staff are trained in what to do in an emergency; a written plan or procedure is available.	❏	❏			

Supervision

Children proceed directly from vehicle to building and vice versa with no playing allowed in the passenger loading area.	❏	❏			

(appendix continues on next page)

INDOORS	OK	ACTION REQUIRED			
	X	X	Please Specify	Date Completed	Comments
Equipment					
Vehicles are well maintained and lights are working.	❏	❏			
No sharp or heavy objects are stored on the back cargo shelf. (They could become missiles in a sudden stop or collision.)	❏	❏			
Each vehicle contains a first-aid kit and the emergency record of every child on board.	❏	❏			
Each vehicle has a list of emergency phone numbers, such as police, fire, hospital.	❏	❏			
PLAYGROUND					
The area is free of litter and sharp objects.	❏	❏			
Furnishings are not broken or overturned.	❏	❏			
There are no stagnant ponds of water.	❏	❏			
Paths are clear.	❏	❏			
Garbage containers are provided. They are anchored and away from equipment and play areas.	❏	❏			
Poisonous plants are removed from the play area.	❏	❏			
Staff provide clean drinking water in the play area.	❏	❏			
Shady areas are provided.	❏	❏			
The entire playground is structured for quick and easy inspection for good supervision.	❏	❏			
Supervision					
Equipment is age appropriate and does not exceed the abilities of the children using it.	❏	❏			
Protective, Energy-Absorbing Surfaces					
All play equipment more than 30 cm (12 in.) above ground has at least 25–30 cm (10–12 in.) of cushioning material beneath the structure (more if tall structure). The material extends 1.8 m (6 ft.) beyond the piece of equipment. The material may be sand, pea gravel (.32 cm [1/8 in.] diameter round stones), bark chips, or manufactured surfaces approved by the CSA. (Pea gravel and wood should be avoided in infant/toddler areas.)	❏	❏			
Protective cushioning surface are checked daily to remove foreign objects and materials (e.g., animal feces, garbage, sharp objects).	❏	❏			

(appendix continues on next page)

INDOORS	OK	ACTION REQUIRED			
	X	X	Please Specify	Date Completed	Comments
Rake weekly to prevent surfaces from becoming compacted and hard.	❏	❏			
No standing water is on protective surfaces or within play structures.	❏	❏			
Drains are checked for plugging and debris. Plant growth is removed from drains.	❏	❏			
All Equipment					
No splinters, cracks, or breaks appear in wooden equipment.	❏	❏			
Equipment is free of sharp edges, protrusions, and cracks.	❏	❏			
No equipment is bent or inadequately anchored. No parts of the equipment are missing.	❏	❏			
All pinch and crush points are securely covered.	❏	❏			
All moving parts function smoothly and are well lubricated. There is no excessive motion or noise and no protective pieces are missing.	❏	❏			
Slides					
If the slide is made of several sections, there are no gaps, pinch points, or rough edges in the sliding surface.	❏	❏			
Tunnels					
The tunnel material is securely anchored to the ground.	❏	❏			

Sources: Developed in part from *Health in Day Care: A Manual for Health Professionals, American Academy of Pediatrics* (Elk Grove Village: American Academy of Pediatrics, 1987) and *Healthy Young Children: A Manual for Programs* (Washington, DC: National Association for the Education of Young Children, 1988). Courtesy of the Canadian Paediatric Society, *Well Beings: A Guide to Promote the Physical Health, Safety and Emotional Well-Being of Children in Child Care Centres and Family Day Care Homes* (Ottawa: Canadian Paediatric Society, 1996), 982–91.

Injury Report

Name of child: _____   Date of birth: _____

Date and time of injury: _____

Parent(s) notified: _____

Describe the injury (you may also use the line drawing of the child to indicate where the injuries are located on the child's body):

_____

_____

Describe how the injury occurred:

_____

_____

Where did the injury occur? _____

If any equipment or product was involved, please describe it:

_____

_____

Was first aid administered? Yes ❏   No ❏ (If yes, specify)

_____

_____

Who administered first aid? _____

Was any further action taken (e.g., child sent to hospital, to physician, taken home)?

_____

_____

If the child remained at the facility, what was the child's level of participation?

_____

_____

Other comments:

_____

_____

What corrective action should be taken to prevent further injuries of this type?

_____

When was the director notified about the injury?   Time: _____   Date: _____

Names of staff who witnessed the injury: _____

_____

_____   _____   _____   _____
Reporting educator's signature   Date   Parent's signature   Date

(Please use the attached diagram, when applicable.)

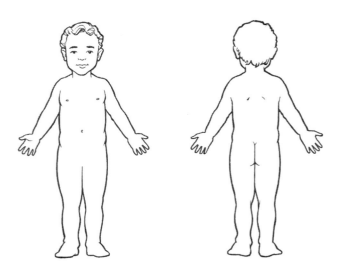

Indicate site of injury with an "X."

Name of educator _____   Date : _____

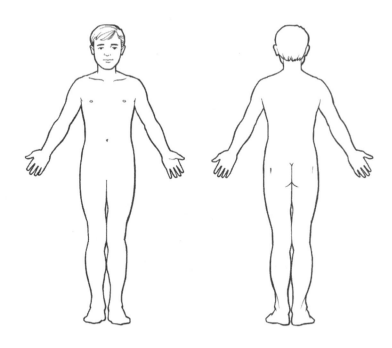

Indicate site of injury with an "X."

Source: Courtesy of the Canadian Paediatric Society, *Well Beings: A Guide to Promote the Physical Health, Safety and Emotional Well-Being of Children in Child Care Centres and Family Day Care Homes* (Ottawa: Canadian Paediatric Society, 1996), 867–69.

UNIT
7

Child Abuse Prevention

CONTENTS

Exploring Your Feelings 350
    ABOUT CHILD ABUSE 350
    ABOUT FAMILY DIVERSITY 351

Child Abuse 352
    TYPES OF ABUSE 352
    BEHAVIOURAL INDICATORS OF ABUSE 363
    CONSEQUENCES OF ABUSE 364
    CAUSES OF CHILD ABUSE 367

Preventing Child Abuse 368
    CHILD PROTECTION AGENCIES 368
    PRIMARY CHILD ABUSE PREVENTION 369
    SECONDARY CHILD ABUSE PREVENTION 377
    TERTIARY CHILD ABUSE PREVENTION 391

Revisiting the Health Promotion Action Plan 395

Conclusion 396

What's Your Opinion? TO REPORT OR NOT TO REPORT? *396*

Assess Your Learning 397

Resource Materials 398

Bibliography 399

TABLES

TABLE 7.1   CONSEQUENCES OF ABUSE 365
TABLE 7.2   STRATEGIES TO ENHANCE POSITIVE RELATIONSHIPS 375
TABLE 7.3   WHEN A PARENT DISCLOSES AN ABUSIVE DOMESTIC SITUATION: FOR THOSE ENTERING EARLY CHILDHOOD EDUCATION 380
TABLE 7.4   WHEN A PARENT DISCLOSES AN ABUSIVE DOMESTIC SITUATION: FOR THOSE WITH EXPERIENCE IN EARLY CHILDHOOD EDUCATION 380

FIGURES

FIGURE 7.1   CHILDREN'S BRUISES 353

Many trained and experienced educators identify child abuse as an area in which they need further education. Although it is impossible to know the true extent of child abuse, because much goes unreported, even conservative estimates of the number of reported cases make it likely that educators will come in contact with children who are victims of abuse. Participating in continuing education opportunities combined with work experience and collaboration with professionals and agencies enhances your understanding and skills in the area of child abuse.

Since educators are frontline professionals and work closely with children, they are in a position to identify children whom they suspect are being abused, and are able to activate primary, secondary, and tertiary prevention. In other words, early childhood programs can contribute to the prevention of child abuse in three ways:

- by modelling positive child guidance (primary prevention)
- by early identification of suspected child abuse and by reporting suspected abuse, if warranted, to the child protection agency (secondary prevention)
- by supporting both children and their families when child abuse has been confirmed (tertiary prevention)

As professionals, educators are required by law to report their suspicions of child abuse. Their relationship with children and their families also creates an ethical responsibility to report. These reports make it possible for child protection agencies to provide protection for children who are at either immediate or future risk and to assist the children and their families in recovery.

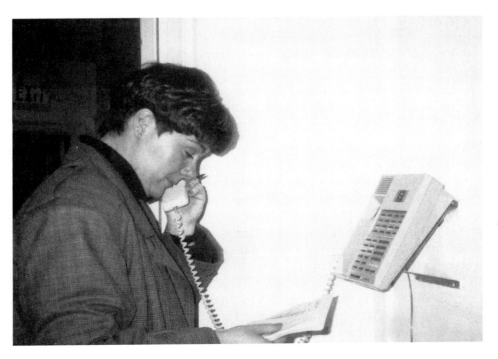

Failure to recognize and to help stop child abuse can result in serious consequences for children, including long-term emotional and physical problems, and, in extreme cases, death. Another devastating consequence is that adults who were abused as children may themselves become abusers or be further victimized (e.g., spousal abuse), so the cycle of abuse continues.

OBJECTIVES

To identify your feelings about child abuse and how you can deal with them.

To identify your level of openness to family diversity.

EXPLORING YOUR FEELINGS

As individuals, we need to understand our own feelings about this sensitive and emotional subject. Working with families involves a wide range of philosophies, parenting practices, and lifestyles. Educators' openness to diversity in values and customs contributes to their sensitivity and effectiveness on a personal as well as a professional level.

About Child Abuse

Each of us brings different life experiences and spiritual and cultural beliefs to the program. Some people find it incomprehensible that someone could inflict emotional and physical pain on a child, or they may feel anger and hatred for abusers. Others are themselves survivors of child abuse. Even if you were not abused as a child, you probably know someone who was. For survivors, the realm of emotional and physical reaction to child abuse may be overwhelming. Attempting to understand child abuse from a professional rather than personal perspective is challenging. Even if we have only read or heard about child abuse, we may still have strong feelings about abuse.

What do we do with all these emotions and responses? You may feel the need to acknowledge and work through your feelings to deal effectively with this issue in your work.

- You are so angry at the thought of a parent hurting a child that you question your ability to provide further support to the child and family.

- As an adult survivor of child abuse, you may feel that this course is the motivation you need to work through the abuse.

Sexual abuse can generate a range of intense emotional reactions. We all experience some reaction when faced with disturbing behaviour. When you read a newspaper article or hear a story on the television or radio about sexual abuse, how do you feel? Perhaps you feel disbelief that anyone could do such a thing to a child. Perhaps you feel anger at the child for not telling someone when it started. It is important for anyone caring for children to explore her or his feelings about sexual abuse. Our reactions can affect our understanding of sexual abuse and the way we respond to children who have been sexually abused (Institute for the Prevention of Child Abuse 1995, 50).

Obviously, not everyone responds to child abuse in a dramatic or emotional way. However, those who have concerns about their confused feelings or about approaching issues that may not have been dealt with since childhood may find it necessary to talk with a trusted friend or a counsellor. The college's counsellors and instructors can provide students with names of referrals (social workers, counsellors, or psychologists) and community services.

About Family Diversity

The region of Canada we live in and, more specifically, the location of the program we work in may determine the diversity of families' structures, living styles, social and economic situations, ethno-cultural backgrounds, religions, and so on. It is important to realize that you don't have to adopt someone else's values and beliefs but you do need to develop a level of understanding and respect for others' values and beliefs.

> While helping preschoolers with their bathing suits for the wading pool, you notice that Khoa has small circular bruises over his chest and back. When you ask, "How did you get these bruises?" the four-year-old replies, "Mommy used a spoon to make me better." The child is not upset, and is generally a content child who is always happy to see his mother at the end of the day.
>
> *A manifestation of bad wind (a notion derived from Chinese medicine) such as a cough can be released by creating small bruises on the body, commonly effected by rubbing the body with a coin or a spoon or by cupping—that is, by placing a hot cup on the body and letting it cool until the air contracts and draws the skin upward. When bruise lines appear the bad wind has come to the surface and left the body* (Dinh et al. 1990, 194).
>
> In this example, the educator may suspect child abuse. Yet by talking with the child and the parent at the end of the day, the educator learns more about the family's traditional health practices, and learns that the practice was done in the best interests of the child and with the best intentions. However, every situation is unique. There may be times when educators must pursue their suspicions further.

e.g.

Learning to work effectively with diverse families requires an open attitude and skills. These skills can be developed from

- the family, in a respectful manner,
- coworkers,
- post-diploma courses and anti-bias workshops,
- relevant agencies in the community, and
- literature and videos.

To summarize, you must ask yourself two important questions before you can manage suspicions of child abuse in a practical way in early childhood programs:

1. What are some of the feelings I have about child abuse—such as fear, anger, frustration, sadness—and how can I deal with these in a way that enables me to work effectively with families?

2. How open am I to living styles, values, and parenting practices that are different from my own? In other words, am I able not to assume automatically that different practices are wrong or abusive?

OBJECTIVES

To define and describe each category of abuse: physical abuse, emotional abuse, sexual abuse, and neglect.

To develop a heightened awareness of the complex consequences of abuse on children.

CHILD ABUSE

The definition of child abuse has evolved over time and will continue to do so. Thirty years ago, child abuse was thought to concern mainly children who were severely physically abused. Since then, we have become aware of the high incidence of child sexual abuse, especially when considering the far-reaching consequences of child pornography on the Internet. We are also more aware of the damaging consequences for children who have been abused emotionally, including issues such as children witnessing the abuse of their mother and, in rare situations, the abuse of their father (domestic violence).

Child abuse is always a misuse of power—a person with greater physical, intellectual, or emotional power and authority controls a child in a way that does not contribute to the child's health, growth, and development. Abuse or neglect of children can occur within the home, in institutions, and even at the community or societal level:

- parents or other individuals may physically or sexually abuse children
- institutional practices may be abusive to children, such as the inappropriate use of physical restraints
- the physical, emotional, and social consequences can be devastating for the more than one million children in Canada who live in poverty

Types of Abuse

Generally, child abuse is categorized into four types: physical abuse, emotional abuse, sexual abuse, and neglect. While this categorization can be useful, it implies distinctions that don't always exist. In reality, the four types of abuse do not operate exclusively of one another. In fact, it is common to find that categories of child abuse coexist.

Gemma is being physically abused, and is also abused emotionally or at least suffers emotionally as a result of pain inflicted on her. A child is being emotionally abused when she or he is witness to violence against a parent. This child may also be the victim of physical abuse through injury intended for that parent, such as cut by shards of glass from a bottle thrown across the room.

Physical Abuse

Children who have suffered injuries that were inflicted by parents, older siblings, extended family members, or others have been physically abused. In some cases, abuse occurs only once, but in most situations the child is abused over a period of time. The physical abuse usually becomes more severe over time; the abuser often justifies his or her actions in terms of discipline and may not have initially intended to hurt the child. There are as many types of injuries as there are ways and objects with which someone can physically abuse. Physical injuries that result from physical abuse can be grouped into four categories (Ayoub et al. 1990, 239–42):

1. Injuries to the skin and soft tissue underneath include bruises, abrasions (e.g., cuts, scrapes), hematomas (swellings containing blood), bites, and burns. Bruises or abrasions can be caused by being hit by hands or blunt instruments (e.g., belts, hairbrushes, or rope), or by being kicked. Severe bruising, especially on the buttocks or legs, often results from excessive discipline involving objects such as fly swatters or wooden spoons. Bruises often take on the shape of the object used. Tying children's arms or legs together or to a chair or bed can cause burn marks or cuts to wrists or ankles. Dunking children in hot water can cause burns. "Isolated burns on the buttocks, palms of the hands, or soles of the feet are particularly suspicious. Another kind of contact burn is from cigarettes" (Ayoub et al. 1990, 241) (see Figure 7.1).

FIGURE 7.1 **Children's Bruises**

Areas of Bruising

Common (over bony prominences)

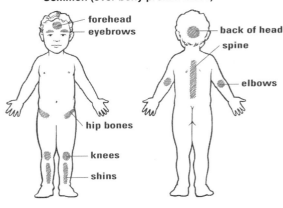

forehead
eyebrows
back of head
spine
elbows
hip bones
knees
shins

Questionable (over soft, fleshy areas)

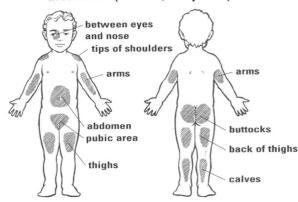

between eyes and nose
tips of shoulders
arms
arms
abdomen
pubic area
buttocks
back of thighs
thighs
calves

2. Injuries to the head and central nervous system include bleeding inside the eyes or brain tissue (often from being violently shaken), spinal injuries, and asphyxia (from choking or suffocating). Shaking a young child, especially an infant, is a common cause of serious injury or death. Adults may not realize that the use of force in a moment of anger can lead to a lifetime of ill effects.

3. Internal (abdominal) injuries are serious and can lead to death. Internal organs such as the spleen and pancreas can be crushed or ruptured. A punch or kick to the abdomen can rupture the child's stomach. If a child is thrown, the impact could tear the liver or spleen.

4. Injuries to the skeletal system can result from shaking, squeezing, or a direct blow. Actions such as pushing the child down the stairs can result in fractures of the arms, legs, or skull. An infant's skull is thin and pliable, so a blow to the head by a hand or foot can easily cause a fracture.

Shaken Baby Syndrome

Shaken baby syndrome occurs when an infant or young child (including preschoolers) is shaken violently, usually by a parent or caregiver. It is believed that the demands of caring for an infant, especially a baby's crying, may trigger a frustrated parent or caregiver to shake the infant (Canadian Paediatric Society 2001, 664).

Although it can happen with small children, shaken baby syndrome is so named because infants under the age of one are the most common victims. They are particularly susceptible to injury because of their large head, heavy brain, and weak neck muscles, coupled with the fact that the perpetrator is much larger and stronger than the infant.

This is a very serious form of child abuse and is never acceptable. After a child has been shaken, usually there are no signs of trauma visible on the outside of the head, even if the shaking occurred against something (it is often something soft, such as a mattress), but the damage to the brain can be very serious (Canadian Paediatric Society 2001, 663). The shaking causes the head to undergo rotational forces, cutting off blood vessels around the brain. This leads to hemorrhage (bleeding) and subdural hematoma (bleeding in the lining around the brain), which results in swelling of the brain and a possible lack of blood and oxygen to the brain tissue, which in turn causes further damage. A head injury may not be diagnosed, depending on the severity of the symptoms. For example, a physician may observe a baby who is mildly shaking or trembling and be experiencing some vomiting. This could be explained by the flu. On the other hand, the baby's symptoms could include seizures or loss of consciousness, or the baby could die. According to the Canadian Paediatric Society (2001, 665), recent Canadian data on children hospitalized for shaken baby syndrome show that

- 59% had neurological deficits, visual impairments, or other health impairments,

- 22% appeared well at discharge, although they may show evidence of cognitive or behavioural difficulties later on, and

- 19% died.

Experts suspect that the incidence of shaken baby syndrome is substantially underestimated due to missed diagnoses. The Canadian Paediatric Society, together with other organizations, endorsed the Joint Statement on Shaken Baby Syndrome to contribute to public awareness and promote policies and strategies to alleviate this problem. Many prevention resources are available from agencies at the community and federal levels.

Female Genital Mutilation

Female genital mutilation (FGM) is an extreme form of physical abuse that has come to the attention of the general public in Canada over the past decade. The severity of the mutilation is usually classified into three categories:

1. Clitoridectomy: Removal of all or part of the clitoris.

2. Excision: Clitoridectomy and the removal of all or part of the labia minora. Excision is performed on most girls who undergo FGM.

3. Infibulation: Removal of the clitoris, the labia minora, and at least two thirds of the labia majora. The edges of the remaining tissue of the vulva are sewn together. This very severe form of mutilation leaves only a tiny opening for urinating and menstruating that is later cut open for intercourse and childbirth.

The short- and long-term health effects of this practice can be physically, emotionally, and socially devastating to the girls and women, causing excruciating pain and sometimes death. According to the World Health Organization, approximately 100 to 140 million girls and women worldwide have been subjected to this violence. Each year, approximately 2 million girls are at risk of undergoing FGM. Most live in 28 African countries, although some live in Asia, the Middle East, and increasingly are immigrants to the West, including Canada (World Health Organization 2000). It is usually done when girls are between the ages of 4 and 10 years old, without anesthetic and under unsterile conditions (Clement 1994). The usual rationale for the practice is that it will reduce the girl's sexual response after puberty, allegedly preventing promiscuity, and thereby increasing her marriage prospects (i.e., larger monetary price for virgin brides) (Save the Children Canada 2002).

There has been global action to prevent further incidents of FGM, and an acknowledgment that it is a violation of human rights.

. . . .

- FGM is against the law in Britain, France, Sweden, Switzerland, the United States, and Canada.   **e.g.**

- In Canada, FGM violates several Criminal Code provisions and any person performing the mutilation, as well as the girl's parents, could be charged and tried for assault causing bodily harm.

. . . .

Culture, tradition, and religion are used as the rationale to justify this violent abuse. FGM is practised predominantly in countries in which the religion is Islam. However, the Koran, the sacred book of Islam, holds no requirement for this practice. Therefore, using religion as a rationale for violence is insupportable.

FGM is done traditionally for men to maintain control over women's lives, including their sexual lives.

Many girls and women who come to Canada are victims of FGM. A range of issues may emerge for these girls and women and they must be treated with sensitivity. If you have had this procedure, seek out caring and enlightened physicians and other professionals who will be supportive to your physical, emotional, and social well-being.

Child protection agencies, particularly those in large Canadian cities, have developed (or are developing) a policy to respond to victims of FGM. These policies acknowledge that girls who have already undergone the practice need compassion and support—particularly culturally relevant support. Child protection agencies aim to protect young girls where there is risk of this physical abuse. Canada's Criminal Code prohibits citizens and landed immigrants from being removed from the country and subjected to FGM. Parents who insist on continuing this practice do so illegally, using untrained persons in unhygienic conditions, and putting their daughter at substantial risk. Contact the agency in your community that will be helpful with your concerns.

Discipline versus Punishment

The practice of corporal punishment, often a hotly debated issue in parenting, illustrates how difficult it is to define child abuse. Violence in our society is not only accepted but is often also revered. Some of the most popular movies of our time depict extreme violence. At the same time, the media bombard us with images of war and political unrest, institutional and parental child abuse, date rape, murders of young women, spousal abuse, and elder abuse. "Our society is so used to seeing and accepting violence that it is not uncommon to excuse the violence or blame the victim. We say, 'It was the alcohol,' or 'He had a bad day.' We may even ask, 'What did she do to provoke the violence?'" (Caring Communities Project 1994, Book 1, 12).

Federal and provincial/territorial governments have finally acknowledged the prevalence of child and spousal abuse, and have begun to take a stronger stand against violence in the home. Children are not their parents' property, nor is a wife owned by her husband. It may be hard to believe that only in the last 20 years was the Criminal Code amended to state that husbands have no legal right to force their wives to have sex.

Corporal punishment is the use of physical force to discipline children. It is not against the law in Canada, but it is illegal in a growing number of countries (e.g., Sweden, Austria, Denmark). The Criminal Code of Canada defines assault as the use of physical force on an individual without consent. Assault charges can be laid any time an adult strikes, shakes, or kicks another adult. However, section 43 of the Code gives adults permission to use physical force on children. Children are the only people in Canada who can be legally "assaulted." Their assailants need not fear legal reprisal unless the force is deemed to be unreasonable. This difference between the way the Criminal Code deals with hitting children and hitting adults reflects a lack of societal respect for the child.

The child welfare laws across Canada define the degree to which corporal punishment is legal, beyond which it is excessive and is considered child abuse.

"Excessive" is sometimes difficult to distinguish from "not excessive," and the difficulty can lead to a vast range of interpretations. Excessive punishment results when the strikes leave marks, shapes, bruises, cuts, or scrapes; when the skin is burned; when bones are broken; when hair is pulled out in clumps; when retinas are detached; or when the brain hemorrhages.

Many parents who adhere more closely to authoritarian discipline believe that corporal punishment in the form of slapping, spanking, or even beating is an appropriate form of discipline. These parents may use the familiar refrain "spare the rod and spoil the child" or insist that their own parents spanked them as children and they've turned out fine. Much of raising children has been subtly or overtly concerned with being master over them—controlling children or breaking their spirit. Even when parents or educators have some understanding of child development, they may feel an overriding need to exert authoritarian control over children. In some early childhood programs, we hear phrases such as "Can the teacher control the children?" or "Does she have control over the group?" This is not surprising, because many adults have been raised with these principles. No one is implying that children shouldn't learn respect for others, but we must be aware of methods and motivations in guiding children if our goals are to promote self-esteem and model self-control. Children benefit when parents learn to guide their children with positive discipline, instead of viewing corporal punishment as an option.

> The primary objective of discipline is to help children learn—to help them develop the ability to use their own judgment and to cultivate self-control. With discipline, the adult has control, but the child's needs, wishes, and abilities are respected in light of his or her development and personality. Positive relationships between children and parents, as well as other caring adults, play a significant role in a child's self-esteem. (Canadian Institute of Child Health 1997, 82)

Corporal punishment often results from an adult's failure at self-control—as a means to relieve their anger, stress, and frustration. Who benefits? What are children learning from being slapped, spanked, shaken, beaten, constantly yelled at, or told hurtful things? Anti-spanking advocates believe that children learn that

- it's permissible to hurt and humiliate someone, especially someone smaller than you ("My parents do it to me, so it's acceptable"),
- the reason they need to obey rules is to avoid being hit,
- when they get bigger, they will have power over others, and
- violence is an acceptable way of expressing anger and solving problems.

Parents who believe that spanking is acceptable and appropriate may justify their actions in the following ways:

- "We are teaching them right from wrong." In reality, spanking teaches children only what is not acceptable. They will not learn right from wrong without being taught what they should be doing; spanking may also communicate to children that they are "bad" persons.
- "It is an act of love." This is a confusing message for children, who learn that people who love them also hurt them. It's not surprising, then, that so many women choose husbands and boyfriends who abuse them, since traditional gender socialization teaches girls to be submissive and boys to dominate.

- "It's a cultural practice." Hitting children is a widespread practice throughout Canada. Many adults today, regardless of culture or race, were hit as children and believe that it is an acceptable parenting practice.

- "I don't want them to become spoiled." Children who are "spoiled" learn disrespectful behaviour from inconsistent parenting, insufficient provision of necessary structure, and neglect of children's needs, not from lack of spanking.

In 1999, a large population survey study linked slapping and spanking in childhood with psychiatric disorders in adulthood (MacMillan et al. 1999). It found that although being spanked as a child didn't necessarily result in having later psychiatric disorders, compared to the general adult population children who were spanked were twice as likely to develop drug and alcohol problems in adulthood. They also had increased rates of anxiety disorders, antisocial behaviour, and depression. According to the study, "spanking remains one of the most hotly debated issues among professionals working with children and families and among the general public" (806).

The debate over spanking becomes relevant when we discuss child abuse. Corporal punishment by parents is not, in itself, against the law, but child advocates agree that it is not a positive way to discipline children. Many cases of physical abuse in Canada have involved the child protection agency's difficulty in distinguishing between corporal punishment and physical abuse (Trocmé 2002, 4–5). The distinction must be made before charges of abuse can be laid (see The Educator's Role in Primary Prevention, page 369). Built into the use of corporal punishment is a lack of societal respect for the child. This is evident in the legal ambiguity. Assault charges can be laid whenever an adult strikes, shakes, or kicks another adult. There is no ambiguity here. It is important to realize that children benefit when parents, rather than viewing corporal punishment as an option, learn to guide their children with positive discipline, not punishment.

The many good reasons not to use corporal punishment for the long-term well-being of Canada's children should motivate policymakers, educators, and parents to put much effort into alternatives. Several national and regional groups concerned with children's rights are advocating for the repeal of section 43 of the Criminal Code, to make corporal punishment of any kind illegal, including spanking. To date section 43 has been successfully used by some parents as a defence for injuring their children. Repealing this law would send a strong message to the community that this method of child rearing is no longer condoned.

> Two essential components of effective parenting skills are responsiveness and discipline. Appropriate discipline is firm but not excessively restrictive, and does not involve bullying or shaming. There are clear limits and expectations on children's actions, children are encouraged to take responsibility for their actions, and learn from the consequences of their behaviour. When confrontation becomes necessary, parents should encourage children to find acceptable alternatives to actions which are not acceptable. The parenting style that combines a high level of caring and involvement with high but reasonable expectations is most likely to help children develop the confidence, and coping skills needed to maintain competence and the sense of perspective that shapes how they react to stress. The interaction of these factors contributes to the achievement of resiliency.

Data from the National Longitudinal Survey of Children and Youth showed that positive parenting practices, which included positive interactions and consistent supervision, help children get along with others. Positive parenting practices make a real difference, especially in families where there are challenges and difficulties for children. (Guy 1977, 75–76. Reprinted with permission.)

Emotional Abuse

Emotional abuse is the most widespread type of abuse, yet it is also the most difficult to prove. Children can't escape emotional harm when they are physically or sexually abused or neglected. Although the physical injuries may heal, the scars of emotional abuse last forever. A parent or educator can be emotionally abusive to a child in many ways, by frequently using the following behaviour (Toronto Child Abuse Centre 1997–98):

- rejecting (e.g., saying "I wish you were never born")
- criticizing (e.g., saying "Why can't you do anything right?")
- insulting (e.g., saying "I can't believe you would be so stupid")
- humiliating (e.g., embarrassing a child in front of other people)
- isolating (e.g., not allowing a child to play with friends)
- terrorizing (e.g., scaring a child by saying "The police will come and take you away")
- corrupting (e.g., always swearing in front of the child, or getting the child to participate in things against the law)
- not responding emotionally
- punishing a child for exploring the environment

Emotional abuse can occur without children being abused in any other way. Parents who never use physical discipline may not realize that they are being abusive when they ridicule children, frequently use sarcasm or harsh criticism, or make inappropriate demands. This ongoing rejection is harmful to children's self-esteem. "Emotional abuse derails the child's sense of mastery and competence. The push to conquer the environment is fueled by curiosity, autonomy, and a positive sense of self, all of which are often damaged in these children" (Ayoub et al. 1990, 235).

For some parents, particular times create situations that trigger feelings of anger, disapproval, frustration, etc. Perhaps it is at a time of a developmental milestone (e.g., learning to use the toilet) or the time of the day (e.g., bedtime). In some family situations, one child is singled out as the scapegoat—the target at which the parent's anger is inappropriately directed.

Domestic Violence

We would like to preface the discussion that follows here and in the section Identifying Suspected Domestic Violence. Both women and men are victims of such violence although women make up the majority of cases. We will be referring to women as the victims in these discussions; however, this in no way should be interpreted as negating the abuse of men in domestic situations.

The witnessing of domestic violence by children is now recognized as a form of emotional abuse. The vast majority are cases in which the child's mother is being abused emotionally or physically by her partner (e.g., the child's father or stepfather, the mother's boyfriend). In 2000, victims of spousal violence represented 18% of all victims of violent offences in Canada, and 64% of family violence victims. Of the victims of spousal violence reported in that year, 85% were women (Canadian Centre for Justice Statistics 2002, 1). Today we are much more aware of exposure to domestic violence as a form of emotional child abuse. In Ontario alone, the number of suspected cases went up from approximately 1000 in 1993 to 8700 in 1998, mostly driven by investigations into domestic violence (Trocmé et al. 2002, 10).

Children exposed to domestic violence experience a variety of problems similar to those caused by other forms of abuse (Baker et al. 2001a, 15). They live in an atmosphere of threat and fear, even though they themselves may not be assaulted (Canadian Institute of Child Health 1997, 55), and are in physical, emotional, and psychological danger. They are caught up in a complex dynamic of violence where they feel powerless. Their needs are also not likely to be met. In addition, if they escape violence in the home by leaving with their abused parent, children often continue to live in another form of abuse—poverty. Children under age five make up the largest proportion of children living in women's shelters in Canada (Baker et al. 2001b, 10). Violence often escalates after leaving home, so the fear continues. Because so many incidents of spousal abuse are unreported, the estimate that 1 in 10 women is abused is conservative, and the number of children who witness violence in their home is substantial.

Sexual Abuse

There is no one definition of child sexual abuse; however, it is generally defined as the involvement of children in sexual activity in which the offender uses power over the child. The offender seeks sexual gratification from the child, who may or may not be of the same gender. Sexual abuse includes oral, anal, genital, buttock, and breast contact, or the use of the penis, fingers, or objects for vaginal or anal penetration, fondling, or sexual stimulation. Although vaginal or anal intercourse doesn't occur in most incidents of sexual abuse, either is a possibility.

Exploitation of the child for pornographic purposes and making a child available to others as a child prostitute are also forms of sexual abuse. Inappropriate solicitation, exhibitionism, and exposure to erotic material for the purpose of sexually arousing a child, or for adults to use to stimulate themselves, are further forms of sexual abuse.

Sexual abuse is never the child's fault. Some offenders use the excuse that the child or adolescent initiated the contact ("She came onto me") or were willing participants. This assumes incorrectly that the child had the choice to refuse. The offender is in a position of power and must exercise self-control. Children are vulnerable not only because of their physical size but also because they depend emotionally and economically on adults and are easily manipulated due to their limited understanding of adult sexuality (Caring Communities Project 1994, Book 1, 12). "Seductive sexualized behaviour and/or sexual promiscuity in children should be understood to be the result of sexual abuse, not the cause of it" (8).

When children are examined by a physician, fewer than half of children who have been sexually abused show any physical changes (e.g., bruises on the breasts, tears in or bleeding from the vaginal wall or the anus and rectum). If there are physical signs, the physician may not be able to confirm that the changes are due to sexual abuse. However, any evidence of a sexually transmitted disease is clear evidence. Other common indicators of sexual abuse are complaints by the child that suggest that the genitals have been injured, irritated, traumatized, or infected, including genital discomfort, pain on passing urine, blood in the diaper or underwear, the presence of infection, and so on. Children may also complain about headaches and stomachaches, which are related to the stress of sexual abuse.

The report of the Committee on Sexual Offences against Children and Youths made the Canadian public realize that sexual abuse is not rare and that young children are frequently victims (Badgley 1994). "Drawing on the information from the Badgley Report and on the other research, current estimates are that one in four girls and one in eight boys will be sexually abused before the age of eighteen" (Caring Communities Project 1994, Book 1, 8).

The National Clearinghouse on Family Violence (1997) reports that the vast majority of sexual abuse offenders are men. Yet women too can be offenders. A small unknown percentage of offenders are pedophiles who are sexually excited only by children. Pedophiles are more likely to abuse a large number of children, and in these cases the victims are more likely to be boys than girls. However, most sexual offenders are heterosexual males who have sexual relationships with adult women as well as the children they sexually abuse.

In most cases the offenders are well-known to their victims. Approximately 25% of the offenders are adolescent, but offenders can be found among all ages, ethno-cultural communities, and social classes. Most sexual abuse takes place in the context of an ongoing relationship between the abuser and the child. This longer term relationship provides the offender with the opportunity to manipulate the child's desires and fears to exploit the relationship.

Due to the nature of these relationships, the abuse can go on for years. Even in cases in which sexual abuse happened only once, children may experience an enormous degree of emotional turmoil. The sooner children are able to seek professional help, the better.

Children often feel confused, especially because in many cases the sexual abuse is not painful and may even feel somewhat pleasurable. For some children, this contact may be the only physical affection they receive. When children realize that a trusted adult has betrayed them, children may feel guilt about "causing" the abuse, or shame that it felt good sometimes. Children with high self-esteem and strong communication skills may be less likely to be sexually abused, but it is clear that the abuse is never the child's fault. It is almost impossible for the child to resist the abuse; offenders put a great deal of thought into how they will manipulate children.

Neglect

Neglect occurs when parents do not meet their children's physical, emotional, and social needs. Neglect can be acute or chronic. In acute neglect, the care usually improves when the crisis has passed. Chronic neglect, though, usually results from the parents' incompetence to respond to children's needs. However, neglect is not based simply on monetary standards. Families who live in poverty and are doing the best with what they have must not be unjustly suspected of neglect. "Standards of neglect are culturally derived. Some situations have little ambiguity. Many others leave families vulnerable to standards that may speak more to an ideal than to essential components of child care" (Ayoub et al. 1990, 236).

The consequences of neglect can be extreme, especially for infants and young children. Inadequate emotional and physical stimulation and malnutrition cause a condition known as "failure to thrive." Infants who suffer from this condition gain little weight with no medical explanation and experience delays in development, particularly in language, during the second year of life.

The Canadian Incidence Study of Reported Child Abuse and Neglect (Trocmé et al. 2001, 35–37) outlines eight forms of neglect:

- Failure to supervise or protect leading to physical harm. For example, the caregiver drove drunk with the child in the vehicle or engaged in criminal activities with a child.

- Failure to supervise or protect a child from possible sexual abuse. For example, the caregiver failed to protect a child at risk of being sexually exploited.

- Physical neglect. For example, the caregiver failed to care for the child adequately. This includes at least partial responsibility for inadequate nutrition or clothing and unhygienic or dangerous living conditions.

- Medical neglect. For example, the caregiver refused to allow medical treatment or to alleviate physical harm or suffering.

- Failure to provide treatment for mental, emotional, or developmental problems. For example, the caregiver did not provide treatment for a child suffering from severe anxiety, depression, withdrawal, self-destructive or aggressive behaviour, or from a condition that could seriously impair his or her development.

- Permit maladaptive or criminal behaviour. For example, a child has committed a criminal offence with the caregiver's encouragement, or because of the caregiver's failure to supervise the child adequately.

- Abandonment or refusal of custody. For example, the caregiver has died, without making adequate provisions for care and custody, or caregiver refused to take custody of a child.

- Educational neglect. For example, a caregiver knowingly allowed a child to miss school regularly or repeatedly kept the child at home (at least five days a month) or failed to enroll the child in school.

Child neglect was the most frequently investigated category of maltreatment in Canada in 1998 (Trocmé et al. 2001). The most common form of investigated neglect was failure to supervise.

Behavioural Indicators of Abuse

This section examines some of the behavioural and emotional indicators that educators may observe in children who suffer from any type of abuse or neglect. What are behavioural or emotional indicators? They are signs, symptoms, or clues seen in a child, or in the adult in the child's life, that lead educators to suspect that the child is being abused. Unless we actually witness abuse, or a physician diagnoses physical injuries or symptoms consistent with abuse, we must remember that no single behaviour confirms child abuse. We should never make assumptions based on indicators alone until we have justification to be suspicious. A cluster of indicators should lead the educator to pursue her or his suspicions further.

. . . .

Lars, usually a cheerful, sociable child, now acts withdrawn. To suspect abuse immediately in his case is making a big leap. We must know more about what is happening in Lars's life and family. Perhaps his whole family is anxious about his mother's loss of her job. Maybe Lars is afraid of being bullied on the school playground.

e.g.

. . . .

Abuse or neglect leads to serious emotional distress in children and damages their self-esteem. Almost any behaviour indicating emotional distress can be a symptom of child abuse. Behavioural indicators differ depending on the child's personality and temperament.

The following short list focuses only on general behavioural indicators that may be exhibited in children who are being abused in any way. An abused child may

- either be overly compliant or overly aggressive;
- either resist physical contact or not hesitate to go to strangers for affection;
- either be overanxious to please or resist all limits and react with temper tantrums or rage;
- be afraid to go home or fearful when a parent or a particular adult arrives at pickup;
- experience delays in development, particularly in language and occasionally in gross and fine motor development or in the development of age-appropriate social relationships with peers;
- be overwhelmed with sadness, anger, or apathy;
- lack confidence in his or her abilities and have low self-esteem;
- not be emotionally attached to anyone;
- demonstrate regressive behaviour, for example a five-year-old who wets his or her pants or reverts to constant crying, rather than using words;
- lack curiosity and interest in the surroundings (e.g., not interested in play); or
- disclose to educators that someone, for example, has caused an injury (physical abuse), constantly puts down the child (emotional abuse), has had sexual activity with the child (sexual abuse), or has left the young child without supervision or other basic needs for periods of time (neglect).

These behavioural indicators can apply to any of the four types of abuse. However, because of the individual nature of the different types of abuse, some indicators tend to be more relevant to one type of abuse than another.

- In physical abuse, the child is often absent, and returns with signs of an injury that is healing (e.g., bruises that have changed from red-purple to greenish).
- In emotional abuse, the child sets unreasonably high expectations for self and refuses to try again if he or she doesn't succeed the first time.
- In sexual abuse, the child has an unusual level of sexual knowledge, sexual play, or excessive self-stimulation (masturbation) for his or her age and developmental level.
- In neglect, the child seems hungry, tired, or dirty all the time.

Educators observe not only children but also the relationships they have with their parents. No list of possible indicators for a suspected offending parent is given here, to avoid stereotyping. An educator's role is to objectively and carefully document his or her observations (which aids the child protection agency in their investigation), not to identify the abuser. Remember that as a professional you are legally and ethically obliged to report your suspicions of child abuse. If you are unsure of whether your observations are reportable, call your local child protection agency to consult.

Consequences of Abuse

> Child abuse can have devastating consequences for victims. Depending on its form(s), duration and severity, abuse may affect every aspect of a child's life; it may have consequences that are psychological, physical, behavioural, academic, sexual, interpersonal, self-perceptual or spiritual. (Department of Justice Canada 2003)

Each individual child is unique in terms of development, personality, temperament, and so on. It is impossible to make generalizations about all children or about children who are survivors of abuse. The effects of abuse may appear at the time of the abuse, or surface only in adolescence or adulthood. No one can predict the outcomes that children will experience as a result of having been abused. We don't understand why one child who experienced one incident of abuse may suffer far more than another who had been abused for a number of years. Resilience has been defined as "the individual's capacity for adapting successfully and functioning competently despite experiencing chronic stress or adversity, or following exposure to prolonged or severe trauma" (Cicchetti and Rogosch 1997, 797). One study of 6 to 11 year olds found that the maltreated children who were resilient exhibited self-reliance and self-confidence, along with positive future expectations (Cicchetti and Rogosch 1997). Resilient children usually have the capacity to find allies outside their family and to identify that things should be different than they are in their family. However, the concept of resiliency can also minimize the impact of children's suffering, because it's impossible to know the full potential that has been lost to abuse even though the child appears to be resilient and develops coping strategies (Sundelin 1994, 715).

Many studies continue to refer to consequences of child abuse, which can be numerous and wide ranging. Table 7.1, adapted from "The Consequences of Child Maltreatment: A Reference Guide for Health Practitioners" by Jeff Latimer (1998), provides just some of the possible short- and long-term consequences experienced by children and adults of abuse. You are encouraged to refer to this paper for a comprehensive discussion and to review the supporting literature (see Resource Materials, page 398).

TABLE 7.1	Consequences of Abuse

Note: The following are overall conclusions drawn by various researchers. Don't assume that 100% of children who are abused behave in any one certain way, but be aware that a statistically significant number of children display similar characteristics.

Psychological Consequences

- extreme and repetitive nightmares
- anxiety or depressive symptoms, long bouts of sadness, social withdrawal
- sudden phobias, such as a fear of darkness or water
- psychosomatic complaints, including stomach aches, headaches, hypochondria, excessive blinking

Physical Consequences

(in addition to the obvious physical injuries related to the abuse)

- small body size and low weight
- permanent neurological damage (e.g., as a result of shaken baby syndrome, head trauma abuse)
- stress-related symptoms (e.g., gastrointestinal problems, migraine headaches, difficulty breathing, aches, pains, rashes that are not easily diagnosed or treated)

Interpersonal Consequences

- insecure attachments to parents and caregivers
- difficulty in trusting others
- relationship problems, such as overly sexualized or overly conflicted relationships

Self-perceptual Consequences

- extremely low levels of self-esteem
- inaccurate body images, which often lead to eating disorders
- overwhelming sense of guilt or self-blame for the abuse

TABLE 7.1   **Consequences of Abuse (continued)**

Behavioural Consequences

- developmental delays, including language delay

- clinging behaviour, extreme shyness and fear of strangers

- troubled socialization with peers (constant fighting, bullying, teasing)

- poor school adjustment and disruptive classroom behaviour

- self-destructive behaviours, such as self-mutilation or burning

- early use of drugs or alcohol and substance abuse or dependence

- suicide and suicide attempts

Academic Consequences

- low overall school performance test scores and low language, reading, and math scores

- weak orientation to future vocational and educational goals compared to non-maltreated children

Sexual Consequences

- engaging in open or excessive masturbation, excessive sexual curiosity, and frequent exposure of genitals

- premature sexual knowledge, sexualized kissing in friendships and with parents

Spiritual Consequences

- loss of a sense of faith, in a divine being as well as in themselves, other people, or the world around them, sometimes referred to as a "shattered soul"

- can become further victimized as adolescents and adults, and may become violent themselves toward their own children and in intimate relations

Source: Adapted from Jeff Latimer, "The Consequences of Child Maltreatment: A Reference Guide for Health Practitioners" (Ottawa: Family Violence Prevention Unit, 1998).

Emotional and social difficulties affect children in the areas of attachment, security, trust, confidence, motivation, social sensitivity, and play behaviour, and result in low self-esteem. Frustrated by their limited social skills, by their lack of achievement, and by difficulties in their home environments, these children are frequently aggressive or withdrawn. Girls and boys tend to be affected differently by abuse. Girls are more likely to internalize their response to abuse, resulting in psychological disorders, including eating disorders, low self-esteem, and thoughts of suicide. Boys, however, are more likely to externalize their response through aggression, delinquency, and later spousal abuse (Alliance of Five Research Centres on Violence 1999, 5–7). Research supports focusing treatment on socio-emotional problems, because an increased belief in oneself, trust in others, and positive social skills are springboards to developing other competencies. Research also reinforces the importance of ECE training for educators. Because much of what educators do daily is promote each child's self-esteem, this is even more crucial for children who have been abused or have experienced other trauma (see Providing a Secure Environment, page 393).

Causes of Child Abuse

Child abuse occurs for a variety of complex reasons that cannot be explained by any one theory. Many factors are involved in causing and perpetuating child abuse. Society consists of a number of interacting components, including economic, social, educational, cultural, individual, familial, and religious ones. Inevitably, some interactions create stress.

Although there are many stress factors that can affect parents' lives, not all parents under stress abuse their children. Just because parents are separating, for example, doesn't mean that you should look for signs of abuse. If you have developed a relationship with the family, you probably know how they have coped with stress in the past. If a family is experiencing several life events at the same time, the increased stress may be more than they are able to cope with, which can contribute to child abuse. Some families are under ongoing stress, such as those living in poverty or those in which one or more members has a chronic debilitating illness. Again, these families do not necessarily abuse their children. Similarly, a family's financial stability does not necessarily mean that a child cannot possibly be suffering abuse within the family.

We live in a mobile society, and one consequence of this is that many adults live far from their parents, siblings, or extended family. Our social environment can either contribute to or prevent incidents of child abuse. As a society, as a community, and as individuals, we can help parents to raise children in abuse-free environments by reducing stressors and helping them cope. Some parents are fortunate enough to have a network of friends or extended family members that provide emotional support or help (sometimes in the form of respite) when they need it. Those families who are isolated, with no one to turn to in times of extreme stress, can be at higher risk for abuse. When the early childhood program is a support system for families, it reduces the sense of isolation. Families are then more likely to seek help if they are at risk of abusing.

OBJECTIVES

To describe the function of child protection agencies with regard to child abuse.

To define primary prevention and outline the educators' role in the early childhood education environment and beyond.

To define secondary prevention and discuss the educators' role in identifying suspected child abuse, and in documenting and reporting it to the child protection agency.

To define tertiary prevention and discuss the educators' role in working with children, families, and agencies.

PREVENTING CHILD ABUSE

Everyone in the community has a role to play in preventing child abuse. Educators are professional advocates for children and they can make a significant contribution in preventing the abuse of children. Educators' roles can be divided into three levels of prevention: primary, secondary, and tertiary. We begin this section with a brief introduction to child protection agencies that are involved in prevention.

Child Protection Agencies

Child welfare legislation and services are under provincial or territorial jurisdiction, as are health, education, and early childhood education. As a result, the delivery system varies not only across Canada but between regions within a province or territory. Because of these inconsistencies, and for the sake of clarity, we use the term "child protection agency" throughout this unit. Each agency office operates autonomously and may differ in the way documentation, reporting procedures, investigations, and treatments are carried out. Despite these variations, the primary goal remains the same: prevention and community support services. Child protection agencies are required by law to investigate all reports of suspected child abuse and to take steps to protect children from further abuse. This discussion touches on the broad responsibilities of the agencies.

The job titles of the personnel working in an agency's office vary. We use "child protection workers" to describe the people who take the calls from directors or educators, teachers, and other members of the public, and who are assigned to the child's case. They are usually social workers trained to assess situations in which children may be at risk. As it relates to early childhood programs, the child protection worker talks with the director or educator and advises how to proceed. The staff may be asked to continue to observe the child and document observations in the child's file or to make a formal report to the agency. Based on this report, a child protection worker is assigned to the child's case, and an investigation begins. In the section Secondary Child Abuse Prevention, you will read more about this process. There will be situations in which the worker and director believe that the child is at immediate risk and the worker, perhaps with the police, may apprehend the child.

The agency's priority is to maintain the family unit while preventing further abuse to the child. There is recognition that in Canada today, significant changes to child welfare legislation are required to ensure that children's health and safety are the first priority. With that in mind, the agency's investigation determines that child and offender are best served by

- appropriate community services that meet the needs of the child and the family, or
- temporarily removing the child from the home while the offender seeks treatment.

Criminal charges are laid when the offender is found guilty of abuse, which happens only in a small number of cases.

Primary Child Abuse Prevention

Primary prevention refers to early childhood programs' policies and practices that support relationships with children and families so that child abuse doesn't happen. Educators are not immune to abusing children. For this reason, programs' policies address child abuse, child guidance, child-centred programming, nutrition, and health, and establish procedures that are implemented by staff. These policies and practices, combined with training, enhance educators' ability to provide and model quality care.

The Educator's Role in Primary Prevention

Educators have a unique opportunity to demonstrate that abuse can be prevented. Prevention begins within early childhood programs by

- supporting each child in developing positive self-esteem and confidence,
- providing a positive role model for parents, and
- supporting parents in their parenting rights and responsibilities.

Creating a Positive Early Childhood Environment

High-quality early childhood education environments are caring and nurturing and respect children and their families. Parents see how educators interact with their child and other children, and how they guide behaviour and provide a safe, suitable physical environment for children. Knowing that their child is well cared for in their absence alleviates stress for parents.

In terms of the children, a high-quality early childhood education program promotes children's health—and helps prevent child abuse. The most obvious example is the promotion of self-esteem as an essential part of all practices and curricula. Children who feel good about themselves may be better protected from child abuse than those who don't. They may be more aware of their rights and those of others. A high-quality program also helps prevent sexual abuse by integrating children's awareness of their bodies, healthy sexuality, and personal safety (see Sexuality, page 414).

Enrollment interviews are ideal opportunities for directors (or educators) and parents to begin getting to know one another. Over time, educators develop meaningful partnerships with families. Often these result in parents sharing more personal information, such as their views on discipline, their support systems, or their relationship with a spouse or partner. Educators combine this information with observations of parents and children interacting to help them understand the parent-child relationship. Some parents do not feel comfortable sharing personal details about their family. This is perfectly acceptable and they deserve the same respect as other parents. Educators need to be careful not to pry or make judgments based on the family's wish for privacy. They shouldn't assume that parents are trying to hide something. Providing parents with nonjudgmental support is a positive primary strategy.

. . . .

e.g. A parent rushes into the program at the end of each day. She seems to be in a never-ending battle with her three-year-old. He doesn't want to go home and often has a tantrum. This is an upsetting way to begin the evening. As the educator, you have two options. You can either do nothing, which in some ways contributes to the tension—the tired, frustrated, rushed mother may yell at or slap her child—or you can recognize the stress she is under as she tries to leave work on time and travel across town to pick up her son. By acknowledging how difficult this is for her, by talking about how the two of you can work together, you can make the stress more manageable. Perhaps the mother could call the program when she is leaving work or try to arrive at the same time each day so that you can have her son prepared for the transition. As well, spending 10 minutes together in the play area before getting ready to leave, or sitting down and relaxing together over a snack before the commute home, may be options that the parent and child like.

. . . .

Educators often establish closer, more personal relationships with some children than with others. These relationships are essential for children if they are going to trust an educator enough to disclose abuse. There may be times when you have concerns about a child, though he or she hasn't said anything to you or any other educator. In this situation, the educator with the closest relationship with the child is probably best positioned to talk with the child. Discuss your observations of the child's behaviour. You might say, "I have noticed lately that you are getting angry with your friends and storming off a lot. Is something bothering you?" The child may actually have something to talk about that has nothing to do with child abuse. Opening the door in this way may help her or him to feel comfortable enough to talk. Children often want to protect offenders, especially if they are significant in their lives. Children may not want to talk at first but may approach you at another time when they know that an educator will listen and is concerned about them. However, if a child does not disclose abuse to you, even though your observations lead you to suspect abuse, follow the steps in your program's child abuse protocol. For a number of reasons, a child may not disclose abuse or may recant—say it didn't really happen after disclosing earlier (see Secondary Child Abuse Prevention, page 377).

Educators can contribute to reducing the incidence of parental spanking and other forms of punishment by

- modelling positive guidance with children;
- being open to discussion with individual parents about discipline issues and avoiding being judgmental or prescriptive, which undermines a parent's authority;
- providing access to resources on discipline and parenting such as articles, books, and videos for parents;

- providing opportunities for group discussions such as parent meetings or workshops (e.g., see "Nobody's Perfect" in the Resources Section) and ensuring that the facilitators are flexible, able to suspend judgment, and trained to recognize suspected child abuse;

- collecting community resources that may be of assistance to parents, including ethno-culturally relevant resources, if available; and

- becoming involved in organizations that are committed to reducing violence in society and, in particular, advocating for positive environments for children.

Personal Safety Programs for Children

Caring adults want children to be safe. Personal safety programs seem, on the surface, an obvious way to help protect children from harm. However, ongoing research has shown that the issue is not as simple as it seems. Before deciding to evaluate a specific personal safety program for children, please consider the following concerns about such programs:

- The main challenge of primary prevention is that it is a socialization process as well as an educative one—child abuse, and particularly sexual abuse, occurs in a society that fosters the sexualization of children and the absolute power of adults. Protecting young children is the responsibility of adults, who are in charge of creating the environment. This is a huge, never-ending task, but it helps keep in perspective who has the major responsibility and the focus that must be maintained (Institute for the Prevention of Child Abuse 1995, 53). We want children to have tools that can help them in a potentially abusive situation, but we don't want them to feel responsible for protecting themselves, or to believe that they failed in any way if they were unable to protect themselves from an offender.

- Prevention programs may be presenting concepts that make sense to adults but are beyond the young child's cognitive capacities. All children relate to prevention strategies on different emotional and cognitive levels, and respond in accordance with their developmental stage (see Table 8.1, page 429). Evaluation of prevention programs has not as yet given us specific recommendations for program development.

- Young children can acquire skills and concepts, but the issue is whether they can retain the information over time (Institute for the Prevention of Child Abuse 1995, 54). Interactive and comprehensive programs in which children can role-play and practise skills are likely helpful, although children won't necessarily be able to apply the skills in real-life situations. Programs that include relevant information and resource materials for parents and educators likely reinforce the learning as well as involve the adults in a meaningful way. This potentially reduces the burden of responsibility that children feel.

- The inclusion of self-defence strategies is controversial. They may help the child develop self-esteem and skills to escape, but their use could potentially place the child in greater danger. The program must stress that the goal of using self-defence is flight, not fight.

- A child's disclosure of abuse already suffered is the most tangible result of these programs, which performs a secondary prevention function (Finkelhor and Strapko 1992). It is important for educators to be both aware of and prepared for this possibility.

- Educators must be committed to critically examining the assumptions behind a particular personal safety program, as well as the specific content. Many assumptions are implicit in child sexual abuse prevention programs and criteria for evaluating these programs (see *Reaching Out: Working Together to Identify and Respond to Child Victims of Abuse*, Rimer and Prager 1998, 146).

Networking with Community Resources

Every program has access to professionals and printed resources on child abuse. Access to parenting consultants and parenting courses may be limited to larger urban communities. Programs must have the name and phone number of the child protection agency and a clear understanding of the program's role in reporting and documenting suspected abuse. In-service training for staff on child abuse is always beneficial. Educators are also in a position to respond to parents' requests for information or consultation with a specific agency related to parenting, health, housing, or finances. Programs should make it a priority to ensure that their staff are aware of ethno-culturally and language-sensitive resources.

➤ PROFILE: TORONTO CHILD ABUSE CENTRE

Toronto Child Abuse Centre believes that all children have the right to a safe, nurturing environment in which to grow to their full potential, free from trauma related to violence, abuse, and neglect. Working collaboratively with the community, the agency helps coordinate efforts to improve prevention, detection, reporting, investigation, and treatment of child abuse.

Making a Difference: A Child Care Community Response to Child Abuse and *Making a Difference: The Community Response to Child Abuse* are programs designed to train individuals who provide frontline services to children and families in early identification of child

continued

---

abuse and effective intervention in situations where children are at risk of being abused. More than 8,000 people have participated in the training program, and hundreds more are using the program's manual in the workplace to support staff who work with children every day.

The centre offers crisis support programs for children and their families, individual trauma assessments for children and youth who have been abused, coping skills groups and relationship violence programs for adolescent and teen girls, as well as court preparation for children and youth who have experienced or witnessed violence and who will be testifying in court. In addition to these direct services, the agency has developed an innovative *Primary Prevention* program for children between the ages of 4 and 12. The *I'm a Great Kid!* and *I'm a Great Little Kid!* programs introduce children to six basic concepts (self-esteem, communication, making choices, respect, touch, how and where to get help) that help them to develop and strengthen healthy relationships, and acquire skills and attributes that lessen their vulnerability to abuse and bullying.

For information about these programs and other services of Toronto Child Abuse Centre, call (416) 515-1100 or visit their website at www.tcac.on.ca.

Source: Adapted with permission from the Toronto Child Abuse Centre.

Preventing Child Abuse by Educators

The primary focus of this unit is the prevention of child abuse within families. Abuse can happen anywhere and by any persons of authority, including educators in early childhood programs. Factors that contribute to abuse in families are not unlike those that may lead to abuse within programs. Abuse is always a violation of power. Feelings of frustration or of being trapped lead to short tempers and striking out physically or emotionally as a way of regaining a sense of control and power. Although it is rare that educators hit or spank a child, they might shake or excessively restrain, threaten, use sarcasm, or yell at a child. Work environments that contribute to educators' physical, emotional, and social health are vital in providing educators with a true sense of autonomy, job satisfaction, and improved overall well-being.

Sexual abuse in programs is rare, yet it is understandably alarming for parents to realize that this, and other forms of abuse, can happen when they entrust their child's care to others. This realization has had both positive and negative effects on early childhood programs. On the positive side, parents demand that programs have an open-door policy for parents. Parents may want to be more closely involved in the program to understand what the children are doing all day, and to ensure that all policies and procedures are respectful of children. On the negative side, some parents may become suspicious of educators, leading to allegations of child abuse that, in many cases, are retracted or prove to be unfounded. However, the process is a difficult emotional experience for educators. Educators may be overly cautious about the physical affection they give to children. They may feel inhibited because of the possibility that parents will misconstrue appropriate behaviour as inappropriate. This is particularly the case for male educators, who may feel that they are suspect because of their gender (see Men Working in Early Childhood Settings, page 74). Although it is not common practice, there are programs where staff are, unfortunately, discouraged from reciprocating children's hugs or having children sit on educators' laps. Policies and practices must provide checks and balances, combining warm, sensitive caregiving with ways to ensure that educators' behaviour is verifiable.

TABLE 7.2	Strategies to Enhance Positive Relationships

The following strategies can create an early childhood environment that supports high-quality relationships among educators, children, and their families. The intent is to reduce situations that may either place children at risk of being abused by educators or make educators vulnerable to false allegations.

Hiring and Employment Probation Policies

- Each successful candidate must sign a consent form that permits the employer to have the police check for criminal convictions. Depending on your jurisidiction's regulations, this may be voluntary or a hiring requirement, and a standard consent form may be provided by the licensing office.

- Check employment and personal references thoroughly and regard them as important information when evaluating job candidates.

- Hire staff with formal training in ECE.

- Familiarize new staff and volunteers with the program's policies and procedures, particularly those that involve child guidance and child abuse. Review these policies regularly with all staff.

Staff Supervision

- Work toward exceeding the minimum educator–child ratio required in your jurisdiction's regulations. This demonstrates the program's commitment to provide the best environment for children and counters any charge of inadequate supervision resulting in negligence, in the event of an investigation of suspected abuse by an educator.

- Provide supervision to staff on employment probationary period throughout their shift, and do not give them full responsibility for opening and closing duties.

- Maintain adequate educator–child ratios throughout the day.

- Provide regular, consistent supervision for all staff.

- At all times, keep co-workers informed of what each person is doing with children and where.

- Never leave volunteers, visitors, or students alone with children.

- Minimize hard-to-supervise areas wherever possible. Place equipment so that it ensures easy supervision and install windows or doors in secluded spaces.

- Minimize, as much as possible, staff working in isolation from other adults in private areas such as in the nap room, or diapering or toileting areas.

- Provide staff with effective guidelines for field trips.

continued

| TABLE 7.2 | Strategies to Enhance Positive Relationships (continued) |

Observation and Child Guidance

- Observe children as they arrive at the program, and follow the program's procedure for documentation and reporting to the child protection agency.

- Make sure staff follow the child guidance policy. If an interaction between a child and educator goes out of control, call a co-worker for assistance.

- Provide and make available personal care and safety kits and training opportunities on child abuse for staff and parents.

- Provide guidelines for staff on how and when to intervene appropriately in child sexual play.

- Provide developmentally appropriate personal safety teaching for children in the program.

- Use the correct terminology for body parts with children.

- Exercise good judgment in the choice of language used with children. Adjectives such as "sexy," "babe," "little bugger," and "brat" are unacceptable and disrespectful.

Involvement of Parents

- Inform parents of all parent policies at registration. It is recommended that parents be provided with a copy of the policies. At the very least, child guidance policies must, according to early childhood regulation, be posted.

- Invite and welcome parents to observe in the program at any time of the day.

- Inform parents how to report concerns they have, with respect to the program, to the early childhood office.

- Provide opportunities for parents to network with one another.

- Inform parents of any change in program practices and procedures and the rationale for changes.

Source: Adapted with permission from Manitoba Child Care Association, *Human Resource Management Guide for Early Childhood Programs* (Winnipeg: Manitoba Child Care Association, 1999).

Assessing the situation:

After half an hour, Shelly is still unable to comfort a toddler. She is becoming increasingly frustrated and has said, "I just want to leave him in the crib until he stops crying." You can see that she is handling the child less and less gently. How could you manage this situation to reduce Shelly's stress, and the stress experienced by the child, and reduce the risk of abuse?

Training in early childhood education is extremely important in all aspects of working with groups of children. Working with children is hard work, both physically and emotionally, and the difficulty can be compounded by educators' low status and wages. Trained staff should have the knowledge and confidence to create programs that are caring, interesting, varied, stimulating, and rewarding for both children and themselves. Those with little or no formal early childhood training often lack the knowledge and skills necessary to manage the everyday stresses of the work.

Teamwork is a crucial component of working effectively in early childhood. Of course, new graduates want to focus their efforts on a high-quality team approach to their work and learn from their more experienced educators. This is ideal when educators are positive models, but not if a coworker is abusive in any way to children. In worst-case scenarios, new graduates begin to take on some of the negative behaviour, such as belittling children, using sarcasm, or grabbing, shaking, or restraining children. As trained educators, they should recognize that this behaviour is unacceptable and ask the director for assistance.

Secondary Child Abuse Prevention

Secondary prevention encompasses

- identifying children who may be victims of abuse,
- documenting observations and possible indicators, and
- reporting to the child protection agency.

This is a balancing act for educators whose role in secondary prevention is complex. First, educators are not "child abuse police." They must not be suspicious every time a child comes in with a bruise or in dirty clothes or yells at a doll in dramatic play. Second, educators make numerous observations about dramatic changes in a child's behaviour, emotional state, or physical appearance. Using these indicators, the educator attempts to find out why the child's behaviour has changed. Third, educators must understand that it is the child protection agency's responsibility to respond to suspicions, investigate the abuse, and identify the offender. It is not your job to prove that abuse has occurred.

Identifying Suspected Child Abuse

The identification of suspected child abuse and the subsequent intervention with children and families are complex and difficult issues. Because educators spend so much time with children and because of their observation skills, they are often the first people in children's lives to suspect the possibility of abuse. They are also in a position to provide support to the family. This can often create a conflict for the educator. Stopping abuse now can have long-term positive effects for children and often for their whole family.

Educators who suspect a child in their care is being abused may have the following reactions:

- They may refuse to believe that this parent would do this to the child. This may be especially difficult if they've known the parent for a while and have established a relationship.
- They may be afraid
  - of the parent's anger, and as a result fear for the child's safety or their own safety,
  - of having falsely suspected the parent, or
  - that the child will be removed from the home or withdrawn from the program.

Ultimately, the child's welfare is your overriding concern. Most parents love their children and don't want to continue to hurt them once they understand the negative effects of abuse on children. Even after parents have been made aware of the educators' suspicions of abuse, educators need to ensure that the parents still feel welcome in the program—otherwise staff are not fulfilling their role as child advocates. It's important for educators to support positive change within the family and not to expect miracles to happen overnight. Educators are a part of the child's life for only a few years, whereas the parent is involved for a lifetime.

Educators know each child's temperament, personality, and family. They observe children achieving developmental milestones and the normal range of behaviour. Educators draw on this experience in making judgments about children's behaviour and observing physical injuries. By asking themselves questions, educators rule out other possible explanations such as illness, usual locations of bruises, vision or hearing problems, anxiety about specific stressors (e.g., a grandmother's recent death), developmentally appropriate fears, or developmental delays unrelated to abuse. Educators discuss concerns among themselves as well as ask parents questions (e.g., "How did Sam get the bruise on his back?"). However, it is important not to talk to the parent about your suspicion of child abuse. It can be useful to call the child protection agency and discuss concerns before formally reporting. Such consultation may lead to a resolution that works in the child's best interests (e.g., feedback to the family, referral for counselling, a change in your program that may help the child during a crisis period). For school-agers, it may also be appropriate to speak with the child's school teacher to verify whether she or he has made similar observations.

Identifying Suspected Domestic Violence

Several (but not all) provinces and territories have mandated reporting to the child protection agency when there is knowledge that a child is witnessing (a better term may be "exposed to") domestic violence. Those that do not have mandated reporting nonetheless expect that reporting would ensue if there was concern that the child is in danger or that circumstances have changed that justify the involvement of the child protection agency (and possibly the police). Find out what the legal requirements are in your province or territory. When in doubt, call the child protection agency for direction.

Mandated reporting acknowledges the position that being exposed to domestic violence is a form of child abuse, whether the child actually sees or hears the violence, witnesses the aftermath of the violence (e.g., non-offending parent's injuries or emotional upset, police intervention), or is an unintentional victim of the violence (e.g., child hurt while in mother's arms). Also, due to the power and control tactics that are used by the offender, the child may be used as a pawn in the violence. For example, the offender may claim that the child's "bad behaviour" is the reason for the assaults against the non-offending parent, may engage the child in the abuse of the other parent, or may hold the child hostage or abduct him or her to punish the victim or to gain compliance (Baker et al. 2001b, 4).

Some examples of indicators that would justify calling the child protection agency when domestic violence is known or suspected (Toronto Child Abuse Centre 1999, 1–3):

- The child has been hurt (whether accidentally or intentionally) in the cross-fire of a violent episode (e.g., hurt by a thrown object, walked on broken glass, hurt while trying to protect sibling or another family member, or hurt while in mother's arms).
- The child has been threatened with harm.
- The child believes that he or she is responsible for the abuse or can stop it.
- The child is exhibiting symptoms of emotional distress. There is a range of possible symptoms depending on age of child, degree of trauma, child's temperament, etc.
- There is a change in the family situation that may increase risk, such as the victim tries to leave, returns to an abusive partner, or increased danger such as the purchase of a gun.
- Legal conditions have been violated (e.g., custody of or access to child, restraining order) that have not been reported to authorities.
- There is a change in capacity to look after the child, such as the result of substance abuse, mental health issues, or parental hospitalization, and no suitable arrangement for safe care of the child.
- The child is denied necessities of life due to offender's control over victim (e.g., financial, social isolation).

This list is not exhaustive, but relays the important message that there are many indicators that children exposed to domestic violence are in need of protection. What is also true is that the non-offending parent most often is very concerned about the well-being of her children and will act in ways to protect them to the best of her ability. We are not usually fully aware of the many steps non-offending parents take in the best interests of the children.

. . . .

The next-door neighbour who notices that the children are playing outdoors without coats on in cold weather does not realize that the mother has sent them outside to prevent them from witnessing her impending assault. This example is not meant to underplay the children's needs for proper clothing, but to highlight the mother's assessment of risk and her strategy to protect her children from the greater risk. It also highlights the importance for us to suspend judgment.

e.g.

. . . .

It is very important to support the non-offending parent when she takes steps to disclose domestic violence. Although you may not feel ready or equipped to handle this type of disclosure, your level of acceptance and support for the victim is most important. Early childhood programs can display information that acknowledges domestic violence and a willingness to help (e.g., a poster from the local or regional women's shelter that includes a phone number).

The parent may decide to call the help line or may decide to talk to an educator or the director, believing that this must be a safe environment to talk about it. Remember that her safety and that of her children are paramount, so you must be very sensitive. Although you may believe that she should leave the abusive situation immediately, remember that the woman knows her reality and you don't.

Violence often escalates when women leave, or try to, and afterward—sometimes resulting in murder.

Tables 7.3 and 7.4 list suggestions to consider if a non-offending parent approaches you about her situation. The first table is aimed at people entering the field of early childhood education and the second lists additional considerations for those staff with more experience and additional training or workshops in domestic violence.

Domestic violence is a very complex issue with many other considerations in addition to those highlighted here. Graduates of an ECE program require further knowledge and understanding of their role in

TABLE 7.3	When a Parent Discloses an Abusive Domestic Situation: For Those Entering Early Childhood Education

- Try to stay calm, and ensure that it is safe for her to talk (e.g., if she is on the telephone).

- Acknowledge her feelings and reality, and avoid a judgmental tone or comments. For example, don't sound disappointed if she is unable to take action right away. Remember, the victim knows her situation, you don't. Victims often try leaving many times; it can take several attempts, and the reality may be that she is not able to leave.

- Acknowledge steps that she has already taken, including talking with you.

- Recognize the importance of her cultural values and beliefs in her choices and decisions.

- Reinforce the fact that domestic violence is a crime and that it does not stop without outside help.

- Express your concern for her and her child(ren) and strongly suggest medical treatment if she has injuries.

- Refer her to a local women's shelter; offer to make the call for her if she prefers. Even if she decides not to go to the shelter, the workers will be able to offer her other information to help.

Source: Adapted from *What Is Family Violence?* (Toronto: Toronto Child Abuse Centre, 1999), 1–2.

TABLE 7.4	When a Parent Discloses an Abusive Domestic Situation: For Those with Experience in Early Childhood Education

- Remember you are there as a support and to offer information, not to give advice or take over. The victim's relationship with the offender is all about power and control. She needs to feel in control. Ask her what she wants to have happen and what you can do to help.

- Help her know her options. If you do not have this information, ensure her that you will either find out and share it with her as soon as possible or, if she agrees, connect her with someone who does.

- Help her develop a safety plan for both staying and leaving (or ensure that she gets connected with someone else who can help her with this).

Source: Adapted from *What Is Family Violence?* (Toronto: Toronto Child Abuse Centre, 1999), 1–2.

supporting families in these situations—particularly in supporting children exposed to domestic violence.

Suspecting Child Abuse

Educators' suspicions of physical abuse are based on

- the severity of the marks or injuries that can't be explained by a mishap during play, and
- the type, number, size, and shape of the trauma to the skin.

Whenever a child is hurt, you must ask yourself, "How did this happen?" and "Did adults fail to protect the child?" Just as in programs, injuries that occur at home are understandable: bumps and bruises are a normal part of every child's life. Figure 7.1 (see page 353) illustrates the parts of the body on which educators are most likely to see bruises due to everyday activities as well as the locations where bruises may be cause for concern. Even though it is not your role to determine which bruises are suspicious or to interpret their origins, some markings do have identifiable shapes. Ask the child for explanations for burns, scalds, and fractures. Suspicious physical marks should be seen as soon as possible by your director. This should be done respectfully and with as little commotion as possible. If it is appropriate, you and the director may gently question the child about the nature and circumstances of the injury. Use non-leading questions such as "What happened to your arm?" followed by "What happened next?" Leading questions such as "Who did this to you?" or "Why did your mother hurt you like that?" not only put ideas or answers into the child's mouth but may also result in an unjustified accusation. It is important to stay within your role boundaries and to remember that you could potentially jeopardize the investigation if you seem to ask leading questions. Confirmation of trauma is made by child protection workers, often in consultation with physicians. One of the strongest indicators of suspected physical abuse is a delay in seeking medical treatment for extensive and serious injuries. Although some children are more injury prone, children who repeatedly injure themselves raise serious concerns about the possibility of physical abuse or the level of supervision and guidance at home.

Purposeful Disclosures of Abuse or Witnessing Domestic Violence

When children decide to disclose, it is a call for help. When they approach educators, educators must not only listen to their story but also support them. It is difficult for children to disclose abuse for a host of reasons. Here are a few:

- The child has only started to realize that something "not right" is happening to him or her.
- The child has been threatened with physical or emotional consequences if she or he tells.
- The child feels it is his or her fault and will be blamed.
- The child feels vulnerable or powerless, and does not think she or he will be believed.

Do's and Don'ts When There Is a Disclosure

If you have seen or heard something that leads you to suspect child abuse, remember to:

1. Control your emotions.
    - Try to be calm and relaxed.
    - Do not look shocked, disgusted, or say nasty things about who you think may have abused the child.
    - If you feel that you cannot control your feelings, call your director or a trusted friend to talk.

2. Offer comfort.
    - Support children by letting them know that:
        - they were very brave to tell,
        - you are glad they are telling you about this,
        - you are sorry that this has happened to them,
        - they are not alone—this happens to other children too,
        - you will do everything you can to help, and
        - you are there to love and support them.
    - Do not say things like:
        - "How can you say those things about…?"
        - "Liar."
        - "That horrible man has ruined you forever!"
        - "How could you let him do those things to you?"
        - "Why didn't you tell me this before?"
    - Children may "take back" (recant) what they have said. These children continue to need your love and support.

3. Be aware of the child's age and skills.
    - Accept the words a child uses (including slang or offensive words) to describe what happened. Some children do not know the right words for body parts or sexual behaviour. Do not correct or change the words the child uses—it is extremely important for the investigation that the child's words are used when telling what happened.
    - Do not use words that may frighten the child—for example, rape, incest, child abuse, wife assault, or jail.

4. Let the child tell the story in his or her own words.
    - Ask questions such as:
        - "Can you tell me what happened?"
        - "What happened next?"
        - "How did you get that bruise?"
    - Avoid asking questions that might lead a child to provide a story different from the one he or she actually wanted to tell.

- Do not ask leading questions—questions that suggest what happened or who did what—for example, "Did you get that bruise because mommy hit you with a brush?"

- Do not question what the child tells you by asking, for example, "Are you sure it was Uncle Ted?"

- Do not interrupt or add your own words when the child stops talking.

- Do not ask the child why something may have happened. Children may think you are blaming them for what happened.

- Do not try to change the mind of a child who has recanted or changed his or her story.

- Do not keep on asking questions because you want to prove child abuse.

5. Respect the child who discloses.

- Listen.

- Do not force a child to talk.

- Do not use force to undress a child to see injuries.

- Do not show off the child's injuries to others.

6. Tell the child what will happen next.

- Do not make promises you cannot keep. For example, do not agree to keep what the child called a "secret." It is important to explain to the child that some secrets must be shared in order to get help, or to keep people from being hurt. Tell the child the information will be shared only with people who will try to help.

- Answer the child's questions as simply and honestly as possible. Do not make up answers. For example, if a child asks, "Will Daddy have to go to jail now?" you can only say "I don't know. Other people decide that."

- Do not tell the child to keep any of your discussions with him or her secret.

Source: Adapted with permission from P. Rimer and B. Prager, *Reaching Out: Working Together to Identify and Respond to Child Victims of Abuse* (ITP Nelson, 1998), 75–79.

Clarifying Your Concerns with Parents

Even when there are concerns about suspected child abuse, ongoing communication with parents is of utmost importance in promoting children's well-being. When approaching parents, your goal is to clarify a situation, not to suggest that they are the offenders.

....

Start with your observation and follow with a question:

e.g.

- "Jacob has a black eye. Do you know how it happened?"

- "Josie has seemed very sad for the past week and hasn't been interested in playing. Have you found that she is behaving this way at home too?"

....

Additional observations or questions depend on the parents' responses to your initial observation and question.

- You may ask Jacob's mother, "Did he see the doctor? Were there any special instructions to care for him or concerns about his eyesight?"

- Josie's dad has noticed her lack of interest too. And you respond by saying, "Do you have any idea why Josie seems so sad?"

Take the parents' lead while being careful not to put them on the defensive. Questions starting with "Why did you…?" or "Why weren't you…?" are inappropriate, and most parents, whether or not they are guilty of the abuse, will feel they are being judged. In most instances, the parents' explanation is sufficient and your questions and concerns are resolved. The parents appreciate your concern, and your positive relationship with them is maintained. Even in cases in which you are no longer concerned, it is important to document your initial concerns and the conversation in the child's file. Jacob may have recurring black eyes or other injuries that may begin to form a pattern that is of concern later on.

There are times when the parents' response reinforces your suspicion of child abuse. If the explanation for the black eye seems unusual, the parent seems nervous in her or his response, and perhaps the child looks fearful, you will likely question the validity of the explanation. After the parent leaves, express your concern to the director.

Educators are strongly discouraged from approaching parents in the following situations:

- Whenever sexual abuse is suspected. There are a number of reasons for this. If the offender is the mother's husband or boyfriend and he talks with the child's mother before the child protection worker or police do, he may convince her that he could never have done such a thing. After all, who would want to believe that her partner is capable of sexually abusing her own child? It is even more devastating for children if their mother does not believe them.

- When you are concerned that the child may be abused again as a result of your conversation with the parents.

- When you fear the family would disappear, making follow-up impossible. You may base this decision on the family's history of moving frequently.

In fact, child protection agencies prefer that any action beyond clarifying a situation be checked with them first. In other words, contact the child protection agency for direction. The child protection worker may indicate that they or the police will contact the parents. Or the child protection agency may advise the director to call the parents and ask them to come in for a meeting. A director with at least one other person present (e.g., an educator or staff person from the early childhood office) would then talk to the parents about the report. It is important to follow the direction of the child protection agency.

Documenting Suspicions

Educators may hesitate to document their suspicions in children's files for the following reasons:

- They don't fully understand the importance of documentation in proving a case of child abuse.
- They believe that they don't have time to document suspicions.
- They are concerned that their report may be made public.

Documentation is an important part of the administrative responsibilities of educators for a range of health care concerns. Every program's work schedule needs to provide staff with the time to write relevant notations in children's files concerning illness, observations on their development, or suspected child abuse. Because of the serious legal implications of child abuse, documenting your observations, concerns, and questions is critical in that it provides evidence for the child protection agency. Although the child's file and the educators involved may be called to testify in court, this is the exception rather than the rule. This is why the quality of your documentation is so important.

Documentation serves two main purposes:

1. It provides a guide for educators and the director in determining their next step. If, after talking with the parents, your concerns are resolved, your documentation supports your decision not to proceed further. If you are still concerned after your discussion with the parent, documentation is critical. Remember that you must report your suspicions rather than waiting until you believe there is "proof."

2. All the documentation on the child is used by the child protection agency, and possibly the police, in the investigation of the alleged abuse. The more complete and comprehensive the information is, the more able the agency is to fulfil its important role in protecting children. Verbal accounts based on your memory are not as reliable as documentation written at the time. Child protection agency staff view educators who document well as conducting themselves as professionals, and will respond to you and your report accordingly.

Documentation: What Is Involved?

What makes a document objective, clear, concise, and complete? Every time you document, observe the following guidelines:

- Include the full name of the child, the date and time of recording, and the date and time of your observations.
- Describe clearly whatever you observed—the child's physical injury or behaviour—that is of concern. Note the type of injury (i.e., burn, bruise, cut, fracture), the shape, size, colour, and number. A form that has a line diagram of a child's body makes it easier for educators to indicate where the mark(s) appeared on the body than to write, "It was three inches (6 cm) to the left of the belly button and maybe two inches (4 cm) above." In terms of behaviour, document any patterns that contribute to your suspicions (e.g., aggressive behaviour toward others, unexplainable fears) and direct quotations (if possible) of comments the child made during play (e.g., dramatic play).

- In chronological order and using direct quotations, write down anything that was said by the child, by the parents, and by you. This will assure the agency staff that you did not ask the child leading questions, such as "When did your dad hit you so hard?"
- List the names, time, and date when you told others about your suspicions.
- Sign and date your form in ink and have the director do the same.
- Record everything in your own handwriting.
- Use a new form if you have concerns on another day.
- Document objectively. Do not include how you feel about the incident or ideas about what you think might have happened.

Unless otherwise instructed by your child protection agency, put one copy in the child's file (in a sealed envelope) and give a second copy to the director. Your early childhood office may require a call or a copy whenever child abuse is suspected, or both. Documentation should be completed as soon as possible after you become aware of the physical or behavioural indicators or after a child's disclosure.

Remember, frequently you'll find that once you've talked with the parents about the child's injury or change in behaviour, your concerns will be resolved. After you've documented the incident and talked with your director, no further steps need to be taken. In the remainder of cases, you will call the child protection agency, with the director's support.

Reporting to the Child Protection Agency

Program staff are included in provincial/territorial child welfare legislation's list of professionals working with children who are legally obliged to report to the local child protection agency when they have reasonable grounds to suspect child abuse. You are expected to become familiar with the child welfare legislation in your province or territory and to read the section that covers children in need of protection.

The staff member who initially suspects abuse is expected to call the child protection agency, with the support of the director, if possible. When telephone contact is made with a child protection worker,

- the person reporting is asked a number of questions, many of which are answered by the documentation in the child's file;
- the agency may recommend that the director refer the family to resources that are appropriate for the situation in order to prevent further abuse; and
- the child protection worker advises the caller on whether further evidence is required. If it is, the educators are required to continue monitoring the child before a formal report is submitted. Otherwise, the child protection worker proceeds with the case and instructs the caller about who should contact the parents: child protection staff or early childhood program staff.

When the child protection agency decides that a formal report is required, the agency usually follows a set of guidelines, which it shares with the staff. The style of these guidelines varies from agency to agency within a region.

As you are probably aware, reports can be made anonymously, and by educators. However, anonymous reports may be taken less seriously than reports by someone who identifies herself or himself. Staff are professionals, have specialized skills and knowledge, and have a relationship with the child in question. They are able to work effectively with other groups of professionals. The agency's staff often incorporate educators into the child's treatment plan, but if they don't know who is calling, this obviously can't be done. The agency is not obligated to reveal who made the report; however, the parent will likely suspect that it came from the program. If a parent approaches you angrily after a report is made, it is important that you explain that you are legally obligated to report any suspicion of child abuse, so that the concern can be investigated by the proper authority. You are fulfilling your responsibilities under the law and are not making any accusations.

Even if the abuse cannot be proved, someone who reports suspected abuse is not vulnerable to any consequences unless the report was made maliciously or without reasonable grounds. For educators, it is evident that they have opportunities to get to know children, to know what is "normal" for individuals, and to have a positive impact on the child's life when abuse is stopped early on. It is rare for educators' reports to be considered malicious. Malicious reporting comes into question at times during a custody battle, when one parent has wrongly accused the other of child abuse to prevent him or her from having access to the children.

Hesitations in Reporting

Educators and directors may hesitate to take the final step and make the formal report even when they have reasonable grounds to suspect child abuse. Here are some reasons why:

- Reporting is a difficult emotional experience for anyone. Staff benefit from discussing their reactions and feelings with appropriate professionals, such as someone from the child protection agency, the early childhood office, or their regional public health unit or social service office.

- The child or parent may request that the staff keep the abuse a secret. No one benefits from keeping it secret, and it is against the law. Not reporting may bring further harm to the child.

- Staff may be uncertain about what information is required, so they are discouraged from reporting. If they are uncertain about what to report, discuss the general situation with the child protection agency or the consultant from the early childhood office and ask for advice.

- Individual educators may not be aware that it is their professional and legal obligation to report suspected abuse, if for some reason the program's child abuse protocol is not comprehensive or the educator did not learn about reporting responsibilities while in training.

- Staff may not believe that the child protection agency will act on their report. Remember that it is the child protection agency's responsibility to investigate. The child protection agency acts according to its assessed risk of the case.

What Happens during Investigations

The child protection worker decides whether the reported concerns require an investigative response based on the conditions set out in the provincial or territorial child protection legislation. If the case doesn't meet at least one of the conditions, the agency does not have legal grounds to intervene. If a decision is made by the child protection agency not to intervene, your report and the information obtained in the investigation is retained and filed for future reference. Unfortunately, the agency may not always inform the director of this decision. This often leads educators to feel that making the report was a waste of time. Every situation is unique, so the response depends on the circumstances.

- Where there are visible injuries, someone from the agency will probably see the child on the day the report is made. If there are concerns of physical abuse but no visible trauma, the child protection worker may not proceed any further that day. Remember that the agency must assess each case and decide which cases require immediate attention.

- Investigations of sexual abuse almost always start immediately when the alleged offender lives with the child. Occasionally, the child protection worker waits a day or two, if the wait improves the quality of the investigation and the agency's ultimate ability to protect the child.

- Investigating neglect requires the collection of documentation from all agencies and professionals involved with the family, including the family physician or pediatrician, the public health nurse, educators, teachers, and any social agencies involved with the family. Because of this consultation, the investigation takes time.

- For reports that children are left unsupervised or refuse to go home, or when parents call the agency and demand that they remove their children from the home, child protection workers respond immediately. If reasonable time has lapsed with no response from the child protection agency, it is appropriate for the staff who reported or for the director to phone again. Once a decision is reached by the child protection worker, and if the staff or director believe that their concerns have not been adequately addressed, a follow-up call may be placed to the worker's supervisor.

Child protection workers may not conduct the investigation on their own but may include others on the team. Some communities have put protocols in place that determine how investigations are responded to and conducted, and by whom. As mentioned above, cases of sexual abuse are usually investigated jointly with the police. For other types of abuse, police may be consulted. If there is concern for the child protection worker's safety, a police officer may accompany her or him when going to the child's or alleged offender's home. The agency staff often consult with other social service and health professionals during the investigation, calling on them to assess the child and the alleged offender. Investigative interviews are analyzed according to specific criteria, findings of medical exams are gathered, and a thorough assessment of the circumstances surrounding the allegations is conducted. Family dynamics and the presence or absence of indicators of abuse are taken into account.

There are four possible outcomes of an investigation:

- unfounded, because the evidence leads authorities to conclude that the child has not been abused;
- unsubstantiated, because adequate evidence is lacking to establish proof of abuse;
- suspected, because there is enough evidence to suspect but not to prove abuse; or
- verified, because there is adequate evidence to establish proof of abuse.

When we report suspected child abuse, children who are being abused learn that someone significant in their life is telling them that this should not be happening to them. This information can be instrumental for children in the long term. We send important messages to children that they are not to blame for the abuse, that it should stop, and that someone cares enough to try to stop it. Even if the abuse doesn't stop after authorities are involved, the offenders get the message that someone in authority is aware of their suspected abusive behaviour and is watching for opportunities to prove abuse and stop it.

Role in Assisting Investigations

As stated repeatedly in this unit, staff in early childhood education programs are not responsible for investigating suspected child abuse. However, their assistance to the authorities in the investigation can be summarized as follows (Rimer and Prager 1998, 94–95):

- Be attentive to physical and behavioural indicators of child abuse and your role if a child discloses (see Purposeful Disclosures of Abuse or Witnessing Domestic Violence, page 381).
- Document effectively (see Documentation: What Is Involved?, page 385).
- Know your legal responsibilities and your program's internal policies and procedures regarding suspected abuse.
- Be aware of your emotional responses to the situation and deal with them effectively.
- Provide clear and complete information to the authorities, and document any advice or direction provided by the child protection agency, police, or other involved agency.
- Consult with the child protection agency or police to determine whether the child would benefit from your presence during an interview.
- Find out whom to contact at the child protection agency to follow up or ask further questions.
- Continue to monitor the child, document, and report further, if appropriate.
- Respect the confidentiality of the information related to the case.

Refer to Rimer and Prager (1998) for an in-depth look into all aspects of the child abuse response process.

Dealing with Your Emotions

It is a very emotional experience to deal with a case of suspected child abuse. Most educators experience a range of conflicting emotions, including anger, frustration, concern, sadness, denial, and disbelief. It is important, for your own well-being, to acknowledge your feelings and find ways to cope constructively with them. If you are fortunate, you will be working in a supportive environment where you can speak with your coworkers or the director about your feelings. Perhaps a counsellor would be helpful. You may find that your usual ways to relieve stress (e.g., physical activity, deep breathing, tai chi) are good coping mechanisms, too. In any case, you need to find ways to care for yourself and your own health as well as to ensure that you are in control of your emotions. This is important so that you have an effective response to the entire situation (e.g., the anger must not come through to the child or the frustration to the parent).

Preventing Abuse by Educators

The line between child abuse and excessive discipline may be blurred at times—when observing both parents' and educators' behaviour. Remember that corporal punishment and emotional putdowns are never to be tolerated in early childhood programs. Suspicions that a coworker is maltreating children physically, emotionally, or sexually, or is neglecting their needs, are stressful, to say the least.

Any allegation must be responded to immediately. Not responding quickly creates the feeling that the program is not prepared to deal with the situation, and that there must be something to hide. Document any concerns, questions, or suspicions about educators abusing children. If you witness physical or sexual abuse, your actions are much more clear-cut. Because emotional abuse is more subjective than other types of abuse, you must carefully document what was said and by whom, what was going on at the time (e.g., the activity), and the child's behaviour in response to the educator. Commonly, an educator is emotionally abusive to certain children, perhaps only one or two from the group. Often, when talking with this educator about the group, you will find that she or he shows hostility toward those children. Comments like the child "never listens" or "does things just to annoy me" or "is basically a bad kid" are objective clues that may support your suspicion.

An educator who has suspicions should talk with the immediate supervisor about the observations. The individual who suspects the abuse, whether it is an educator, a parent, or someone else, should call the child protection agency for advice and be assured that the matter will be kept confidential until the initial investigation is complete. The children's parents or other people involved will be notified according to the child protection agency's recommendations.

Another difficult situation arises when staff suspect the director of child abuse. The educator documents the concerns and contacts the president or chairperson of the board of directors (or owner, if applicable). The staff who suspects abuse must also call the child protection agency to report. As with any suspicions of abuse, remember that you are legally bound to report, even if another party (e.g., board member or owner) tries to dissuade you from calling against your better judgment. The board member or owner must call the early childhood office and speak with the consultant responsible for the program and inform that person of the situation. This individual advises about sending the letter to their office.

Incidents of Sexual Abuse

Staff may suspect the child is being abused but not realize that it is happening in the program, or staff may suspect an educator. Sexual abuse by educators may be identified through the child's disclosure or by parents who approach the director with their concerns and perhaps their suspicion of a particular educator. Regardless of how the director is made aware of the alleged abuse, the director notifies the child protection agency and proceeds accordingly. As in the case of suspected sexual abuse of children in the home, the educator is not confronted. In the interim, if the alleged offender is known, the director takes the following action:

- removes the educator from any possibility of being alone with children
- notifies the early childhood office
- informs the program's board of directors immediately. It may be appropriate to remove the accused staff from the program until the investigation has been completed or to assign that person to administrative duties.

Tertiary Child Abuse Prevention

Investigations into child abuse may confirm that a child has suffered abuse. The offender may be identified and criminal charges may be laid. In tertiary prevention, there are a number of objectives. For the child, it means preventing further abuse and developing a care plan for the individual child's recovery. For the family, the objective is to work toward short- and long-term change. Beyond any criminal charges for the offenders, treatment must be explored to prevent abuse from recurring.

Educator's Role in Tertiary Prevention

The role of educators in tertiary prevention is threefold:

- They maintain ongoing communication with the child protection and other agencies' staff involved with the child and family, and work as part of the team.
- They provide a secure and developmentally stimulating environment for the child.
- They support change in parents who have been abusive by providing good role-modelling and resources.

Communicating with Child Protection Agencies

High-quality early childhood education and care programs recognize that staff can't be all things to all people. This is why directors establish connections with relevant professionals in their community and collect materials for the program's resource library and for distribution among parents. Depending on the issue, educators are called on to work collaboratively with other professionals—for example, the public health nurse during an outbreak of diarrhea. In the case of child abuse, educators are team members with a child protection worker and possibly other specialists assigned to an individual child.

....

e.g.

The director has already established a working relationship with someone at the child protection agency during the reporting and investigation process. Now the director and educators are requested to participate in the child's recovery process along with the child protection worker. Following the director's assessment of the child, she may determine that play therapy is a valuable tool. However, this aspect of the child's therapy must be conducted and supervised by trained play therapists. The child's play therapist and behavioural therapist may have particular recommendations for the educators to incorporate into the child's everyday program. Whether these are specific guidelines for play or for all the educators to manage a child's inappropriate behaviour consistently (i.e., the six-year-old's temper tantrums), the recommendations are an important aspect of the child's care.

....

Because children's situations and types of abuse vary so greatly, it is impossible to discuss fully the range of professionals and therapies that may be part of an individual child's recovery.

As part of the child's care plan, educators may be asked to observe, document, or complete developmental checklists to aid these professionals in assessing the child's progress. Educators are encouraged to call on the child protection worker when they are uncertain about a particular behaviour (e.g., self-mutilation), and for guidance in supporting children and families that are going through the court process.

There are times when a child who has been abused is enrolled in a program for the first time by the child protection agency or another agency as part of the care strategy. Social workers recognize that trained professionals in high-quality early childhood programs enhance the child's well-being. Usually, the goals for enrolling a child who has been abused into a program include building positive relationships, overcoming developmental delays, and increasing self-esteem, as well as providing modelling and support for parents. The decision to accept this added responsibility should not be taken lightly. It will not be in anyone's best interest, including the child's, if the educators can't cope with the challenges and stresses of the situation. Educators will not yet have an ongoing relationship with the new child and may therefore need increased support.

Reaching Out: Working Together to Identify and Respond to Child Victims of Abuse (Rimer and Prager 1998, 120–25) lists the following strategies in working with children identified as victims of abuse. Professionals, which includes educators, help the child to

- develop a positive self-image and self-esteem,
- trust,
- identify and express emotions,

- learn to communicate,
- identify and solve problem situations,
- get through the mourning process,
- overcome developmental lags, and
- develop a personal safety plan.

High-quality early childhood programs strive to provide most of these things for all children in their program. You are already participating in the child's recovery regardless of the specific therapies carried out by other professionals. If you refer back to the discussion on the consequences of being abused, you will see just how they interconnect with these strategies.

Providing a Secure Environment

Beyond the essentials included in the preceding list, certain aspects of your everyday work come into play when caring for children who have been abused:

- Provide predictability and security in the day's routine (e.g., bringing a transition object such as a toy back and forth between home and the program). Routines and rituals are important coping mechanisms for children, especially if their lives have been stressful or disorganized.

- Help children learn appropriate ways to have their needs met, even when that means learning to delay gratification (e.g., an educator explains to the preschooler that he will be able to use the swing as soon as the next swing is free).

- Provide clear and firm, but kind and reasonable, limits as an important part of the early childhood environment. Since they suffer from injuries and pain, or fear that someone will hurt them again, children who have been abused often feel unsafe. As a result, they may take risks even though they may know, or have been told, that an action can result in an injury. Or they may intentionally hurt others, since they have learned that others have hurt them.

- Guide children to help them learn age-appropriate behaviour. Abuse may result in children having developmentally inappropriate behaviour.

- Be an active listener. Children can sense when they can trust an educator and express worries, fears, and concerns related to their family. This is not a counselling relationship but one in which an educator can help the child deal with stress.

- A family's situation rarely changes from inadequate to wonderful overnight. The child probably feels frustrated and worried about the family, or has fears and concerns about social services or a legal proceeding that he or she is involved in.

- Recognize that children's behaviour can have many different meanings. Consider a child with a short attention span. Although it may be a developmental stage, perhaps it is a learned behaviour that is used as a survival tool (e.g., he or she expects that any activity will be interrupted with yelling or a smack, and so is overly attuned to every movement or conversation in the room, always ready to move quickly).

Supporting Change in Parents

> Communicate respect for the parent and the parent's own ways of coping and adapting to his or her unique realities. When supported and respected as a person, a parent is more likely to use the day care setting as a resource to develop the confidence and skills needed to interact successfully with other persons and institutions in his or her life. (Ayoub et al. 1990, 244)

All parents bring strengths and weaknesses, past experiences, and expectations to parenting. Most parents who abuse their children love them and want to stop. One of the child protection agency's roles is to identify the offender, whenever possible, and assess what form of treatment would be most appropriate. A range of treatments have been developed for parents and other adults who abuse children, many based on the various theories on what has caused the abuse. The success of the treatment depends in part on two variables:

- the offender's willingness to accept the fact that he or she has abused children
- the offender's potential and desire for change

As was the case for children who are abused, educators' communication with the child protection worker is important in providing consistency and support to parents who are abusive. Here are just three ways educators can play a role in the treatment of these parents.

1. Provide respite for parents. Parents may need to work on managing or eliminating stress factors or problems that directly or indirectly relate to their parenting (e.g., counselling or treatment sessions, resolution of marital, housing, education, or employment issues). Programs can provide high-quality care for the child during this time. The child protection worker may request that these parents enroll their children in a program for the first time. This may not only benefit the parents but also encourage the development and recovery of the children.

2. Provide modelling of positive ways to interact with children (e.g., talking, playing) and guide their behaviour. As part of their treatment, parents may be expected to spend a certain period each week in the early childhood program.

3. Supervise the non-custodial parent during supervised access visits with his or her child as part of the treatment. Some programs and parent-child drop-in programs have established agreements with the child protection agency.

Ultimately, the child's rights must be at the forefront of our concerns. In recent years, tragic stories of children who have suffered further abuse or who have been killed while in the care of known offenders have been terrible reminders that not all parents have the support or possibly the will to change their abusive behaviour. Educators who continue to have concerns about the well-being of a child whose report has already been filed must report any new information. In the big picture, re-evaluating existing child welfare legislation, policies, and protocols is part of the solution to this important social problem.

REVISITING THE HEALTH PROMOTION ACTION PLAN

Child abuse is a major social problem that requires a multidimensional approach by all members and levels of society. With reference to the Action Plan for Health Promotion introduced in Unit 1, the following examples demonstrate how the plan incorporates child abuse prevention.

Individual Problem Solving and Self-Reliance

Increase our awareness of the factors that contribute to child abuse and try to eliminate them or at least lessen their effect. Organize staff training on child abuse and invite a child protection worker to speak at a parent night (see Profile, page 373). Or offer interested parents the "Nobody's Perfect" program with a trained facilitator. Of course, you as an educator can play a significant role in primary, secondary, and tertiary child abuse prevention, as this unit has shown.

Collective Self-Help

After talking with single parents from the program, one educator who is also a single parent organized a support group. The group set up a baby-sitting exchange that allows a parent to go to the laundromat without the children. Besides making these errands less stressful, this arrangement provides the parent with respite time. They also exchange clothing and toys. This group provides valuable and enjoyable opportunities for the parents to establish friendships and also reduce feelings of isolation. Time is allotted in staff meetings to discuss program issues and solve problems as a group. Policies and procedures are regularly evaluated to maintain focus on supporting children and families.

Community Action

Within some communities, professionals who work in the area or have an interest in child abuse form a child protection team (e.g., professionals working in the fields of education, medicine, public health, mental health, social work, law enforcement, law). These teams improve communication among professionals, and they coordinate more effective prevention programs, training, and child abuse response in the community. Educators and parents should be encouraged to become involved as participants. Another possible way to contribute is to serve on the board at a women's shelter (or family shelter), often affiliated with a range of services. Educators contribute valuable knowledge and skills.

From the grassroots, community action can include the establishment of parent resource centres; book, toy, and clothing exchanges; and telephone help lines (e.g., Kids Help Phone). Recognition of the importance of parent–child attachment is resulting in community attention on home visiting programs for the first three years (some with public health nurses based on Olds' Prenatal and Early Infancy Project; others with paraprofessionals based on the Hawaii Healthy Start Project). These are all examples of services developed by concerned people at the community level, and often by those who actually use the services. Through their network of community resources, educators can explore potential sources of funding, start-up grants, and so on, which are essential in the development and maintenance of these services.

Societal Change

As child advocates, educators can be involved in organizations that work to reduce the acceptance of violence in our society, which is a root cause of abuse. Child advocacy associations, for example, are working toward laws against any type of corporal punishment of children. Changes in legislation would lead to tighter restrictions on, and greater penalties for, persons responsible for child abuse, spousal abuse, elder abuse, rape, child prostitution, violence portrayed in the media, children being portrayed as sexual objects in the media, and pornography. An important focus is to help support parents in raising their children. Social policy that reduces poverty would lower stress for families. To address the many other stressors for families, governments should have adequate child welfare budgets for prevention and quality services (Canadian Institute of Child Health 1997, 135). Understanding why individuals abuse children is only part of prevention. As a society, we must move from focusing on individuals to addressing the root causes of abuse, which will take a multifaceted approach.

CONCLUSION

Whether we are referring to primary, secondary, or tertiary prevention, the prevention of child abuse has a lot to do with working collaboratively. This issue, more than any other in the early childhood program, illustrates that promoting children's health is not done in isolation.

The safety and well-being of every child in Canada should be a priority for each adult and each level of government. Regrettably, this is not the case. As part of a process of public education, we need to persuade the community to begin to look at children as the Europeans do—as a shared natural resource that represents society's future—rather than as most North Americans do—as solely the responsibility of their parents (Steinhauer 1998, 91).

What's Your Opinion?

TO REPORT OR NOT TO REPORT?

You have a good relationship with one child's mother and have become friends over the last two years. You know that she is in the midst of a nasty separation and has been taking work home at night to do after her three children go to bed. Through all of this, she seems to have been handling the situation fairly well. This morning, though, she comes to you in tears and tells you that she slapped her toddler across the face and left a bruise on his cheek. Would you document this parent's disclosure in the child's file and call the child protection agency?

ASSESS YOUR LEARNING

Define terms or describe concepts used in this unit.

- child abuse
- physical abuse
- shaken baby syndrome
- female genital mutilation
- emotional abuse
- domestic violence
- sexual abuse
- neglect
- behavioural indicators

- parenting approaches
- corporal punishment
- child protection agency
- documentation
- reporting
- primary child abuse prevention
- secondary child abuse prevention
- tertiary child abuse prevention

Evaluate your options in each situation.

1. A coworker remarks that there are probably a lot of children in your program who are abused, because most are part of single-parent families.

2. A month after you reported a case of suspected abuse to the child protection agency, there has been no news. The child continues to come to the program each day, and is demonstrating the same behaviour that led you to make the report in the first place. You are angry and confused by the lack of response from the agency.

3. A coworker who spanks her children starts a conversation at lunch time about repealing section 43 of the Criminal Code. She suggests that doing so would mean parents would be charged for "a little slap."

4. Lily, one of the five-year-old children who attends the program in the mornings and school kindergarten in the afternoon, is quiet and listless this morning. When you sit with her for a while, she tells you that she's scared to go home tonight. Lily says that last night her dad was really mad and hit her mom. She comments that she is going to be a good girl tonight so it won't happen again.

5. The director meets with the educators to inform everyone that the child protection agency has requested that a child who has been abused be enrolled in your program as part of his treatment. He requires a caring, consistent environment to help reduce developmental delays and build self-confidence. While you are flattered, and the director obviously wants to say yes, you are concerned because you and the other educators are already feeling stretched meeting the needs of the present children.

RESOURCE MATERIALS

Organizations

Canadian Council on Social Development (CCSD), 309 Cooper Street, 5th floor, Ottawa, ON K2P 0G5. Tel. (613) 236-8977; fax (613) 236-2750. www.ccsd.ca

Canadian Institute of Child Health, 384 Bank Street, Suite 300, Ottawa, ON K2P 1Y4. Tel. (613) 230-8838; fax (613) 230-6654. www.cich.ca

Canadian Society for the Prevention of Cruelty to Children, 356 First Street, Box 700, Midland, ON L4R 4P4. Tel. (705) 526-5647; fax (705) 526-0214. www.empathicparenting.org

Child Welfare League of Canada (CWLC), 75 Albert Street, Suite 209, Ottawa, ON K1P 5E7. Tel. (613) 235-4412; fax (613) 235-7616. (Has downloadable pamphlets such as "Discipline Without Hurting.") www.cwlc.ca

Family Violence Initiative, Department of Justice Canada, 284 Wellington Street, Ottawa, ON K1A 0H8. Tel. (613) 946-2222 or national toll-free 1-888-373-2222; fax (613) 946-2211. Child Abuse: www.canada.justice.gc.ca/en/ps/fm/childafs.html; Family Violence: www.canada.justice.gc.ca/en/ps/fm/index.html

Kids Help Phone, 439 University Avenue, Suite 300, Toronto ON M5G 1Y8. Tel. (416) 586-5437 or national toll-free for children 1-800-668-6868; fax (416) 586-0651 (or contact regional office). www.kidshelp.sympatico.ca

National Clearinghouse on Family Violence, Population and Public Health Branch, Health Canada, 1907D1 Jeanne Mance Building, Tunney's Pasture, Ottawa, ON K1A 1B4. Tel. (613) 957-2938 or national toll-free 1-800-267-1291; fax (613) 941-8930. www.hc-sc.gc.ca/hppb/familyviolence/index.html (excellent website for resources)

Toronto Child Abuse Centre, 890 Yonge Street, 11th Floor, Toronto, ON M4W 3P4. Tel. (416) 515-1100; fax; (416) 515-1227. www.tcac.on.ca

Vanier Institute of the Family, 94 Centrepointe Drive, Nepean, ON K2G 6B1. Tel. (613) 228-8500; fax (613) 228-8007. www.vifamily.ca

Other Websites of Interest

Canadian Society for the Investigation of Child Abuse (CSICA): www.csica.zener.com

Child Welfare Resource Centre: www.childwelfare.ca

Department of Justice Canada (excellent site for resources): www.canada.justice.gc.ca

Education Wife Assault (excellent site for resources): www.womanabuseprevention.com

Suspected Child Abuse and Neglect Program (SCAN) (Hospital for Sick Children): www.sickkids.on.ca/scan/default.asp

Printed Matter

Canadian Incidence Study of Reported Child Abuse and Neglect – Final Report (2001), by Nico Trocmé et al. (Minister of Public Works and Government Services). www.hc-sc.gc.ca/pphb-dgspsp/publicat/cisfr-ecirf/index.html.

"The Consequences of Child Maltreatment: A Reference Guide for Health Practitioners" (1998), by Jeff Latimer (Family Violence Unit, Health Canada). www.hc-sc.gc.ca/hppb/familyviolence/html/98p057e0.html.

"Dispelling the Myths, Fact Sheets" (2001), by Education Wife Assault. www.womanabuseprevention.com

Family Violence: A Canadian Introduction (1997), by Ann Duffy and J. Momirov (James Lorimer and Company).

"Family Violence in Canada: A Statistical Profile" (2001), by Canadian Centre for Justice Statistics (Statistics Canada). Cat. No 85-224-XPE. Tel. 1-800-263-1136 or www.statcan.ca/english/freepub/85-224-XIE/85-224-XIE00002.pdf.

Family Violence Newsletter (bi-annual), by the National Clearinghouse on Family Violence, Family Violence Prevention Unit (Health Canada). (For contact information, see Organizations.)

High-Risk Caregiver Behaviours (2002), by the Toronto Child Abuse Centre. (For contact information, see Organizations.)

National Clearinghouse Fact Sheets on Family Violence (series), by the National Clearinghouse on Family Violence, Family Violence Prevention Unit (Health Canada). (For contact information, see Organizations.)

"Nobody's Perfect," by the Family and Child Health Unit (Health Canada, 467 Jeanne Mance Building, Ottawa, ON K1A 1B4). Tel. (613) 957-7804; fax (613) 990-7097.

Reaching Out: Working Together to Identify and Respond to Child Victims of Abuse (1998), by P. Rimer and B. Prager (ITP Nelson).

Restoring Dignity: Responding to Child Abuse in Canadian Institutions (2000), by the Law Commission of Canada (Minister of Public Works and Government Canada).

"Spanking: Do We Need Alternatives?" (1994), by N. Burns. *Interaction* (Fall) 8(3): 6–7.

"Spanking: Should I or Shouldn't I?" (1995), by J. Durant and L. Rose-Krasnor. To obtain a copy of the brochure, fax Dr. J. Durant at (204) 275-5299.

Understanding the Effects of Domestic Violence: A Handbook for Early Childhood Educators (2001), by Linda Baker, Peter Jaffe, and Kathy Moore. Ontario Women's Directorate. For copies contact the Centre for Children & Families in the Justice System, tel. (519) 679-7250, ext. 206, or www.lfcc.on.ca.

BIBLIOGRAPHY

Alliance of Five Research Centres on Violence (1999). *Violence Prevention and the Girl Child: Final Report*. Ottawa: Status of Women Canada.

Ayoub, C., et al. (1990). "Working with Maltreated Children and Families in Day Care Settings." In S.S. Chehrazi (ed.), *Psychosocial Issues in Day Care*. Washington, DC: American Psychiatric Press.

Badgley, R. (1994). *Report of the Committee on Sexual Offenses against Children and Youths*, Vol. 1. Ottawa: Minister of Supply and Services.

Baker, L., P. Jaffe, and K. Moore (2001a). *Understanding the Effects of Domestic Violence: A Training Manual for Early Childhood Educators*. London, ON: Centre for Children and Families in the Justice System.

——— (2001b). *Understanding the Effects of Domestic Violence: A Handbook for Early Childhood Educators*. London, ON: Centre for Children and Families in the Justice System.

Canadian Centre for Justice Statistics (2002). *Family Violence in Canada: A Statistical Profile 2002*. Catalogue No. 85-224-XIE. Ottawa: National Clearinghouse on Family Violence. <www.statcan.ca/english/freepub/85-224-XIE/85-224-XIE00002.pdf> (July 2003).

Canadian Institute of Child Health (1997). *Our Promise to Children.* Ottawa: Health Canada.

Canadian Paediatric Society (2001). "Joint Statement on Shaken Baby Syndrome." *Paediatrics & Child Health* 6(9): 663–67.

Caring Communities Project (1994). *Child Sexual Abuse Prevention: A Resource Kit.* Ottawa: Canadian Institute of Child Health.

Cicchetti, D., and F.A. Rogosch (1997). "The Role of Self-Organization in the Promotion of Resilience in Maltreated Children." *Development and Psychopathology* 9(4): 797–816.

Clement, M. (1994). "Mutilation in Canada." *The Toronto Sun*, October 10.

Department of Justice Canada (2003). "Child Abuse: A Fact Sheet." Ottawa: Department of Justice Canada. <www.canada.justice.gc.ca/en/ps/fm/childafs.html> (July 2003).

Dinh, D.-K., et al. (1990). "The Vietnamese." In N. Waxler-Morrison et al. (eds.), *Cross-Cultural Caring: A Handbook for Health Professionals in Western Canada.* Vancouver: University of British Columbia Press.

Finkelhor, D., and N. Strapko (1992). "Sexual Abuse Prevention Education: A Review of Evaluation Studies." In D.J. Willis, E.W. Holden and M. Rosenberg (eds.), *Prevention of Child Maltreatment: Developmental Ecological Perspectives.* New York: John Wiley.

Guy, K. ed., (1997). *Our Promise to Children.* Ottawa: Health Canada.

Institute for the Prevention of Child Abuse (1995). *Getting It Right: Responding to the Sexual Abuse of Young Children.* Toronto: IPCA Conference Services.

King, W.J., et al. (2003). "Shaken Baby Syndrome in Canada: Clinical Characteristics and Outcomes of Hospital Cases." *Canadian Medical Association Journal* 168(2): 155–65.

Klass, C.S. (1999). *The Child Care Provider, Promoting Young Children's Development.* Baltimore: Paul H. Brookes.

Latimer, J. (1998). "The Consequences of Child Maltreatment: A Reference Guide for Health Practitioners." Ottawa: Family Violence Prevention Unit. <www.hc-sc.gc.ca/hppb/familyviolence/html/98p057e0.html> (July 2003).

MacMillan, H., et al. (1999). "Slapping and Spanking in Childhood and Its Association with Lifetime Prevalence of Psychiatric Disorders in a General Population Sample." *Canadian Medical Association Journal* 161(7): 805–17.

Manitoba Child Care Association (1999). *Human Resource Management Guide for Early Childhood Programs.* Winnipeg: Manitoba Child Care Association.

National Clearinghouse on Family Violence (1997). "Child Sexual Abuse." Ottawa: Health Canada. <www.hc-sc.gc.ca/hppb/familyviolence/html/nfntsxagrsex_e.html> (July 2003).

Rimer, P., and B. Prager (1998). *Reaching Out: Working Together to Identify and Respond to Child Victims of Abuse.* Toronto: ITP Nelson.

Save the Children Canada (2002). "Female Genital Mutilation Fact Sheet." Toronto: Save the Children Canada. <www.savethechildren.ca/en/whatwedo/isfemgen.html> (July 2003).

Steinhauer, P. (1998). *Developing Resiliency in Children from Disadvantaged Populations: Canada's Health Action, Building on the Legacy,* Vol. 1 (Children and Youth). Ottawa: Health Canada.

Sundelin, W. (1994). "Developmental and Survival: A Study of Children at Risk Living in Adverse Psychological Milieu." *Child Abuse and Neglect* 18(9): 715–23.

Toronto Child Abuse Centre (1999). *What Is Family Violence?* Toronto: Toronto Child Abuse Centre.

——— (1997–98). "Information Packages and Sheets." Toronto: Toronto Child Abuse Centre.

Trocmé, N. (2002). "Responding to Changes in Reported Child Maltreatment: Federal Program and Policy Implications." OIS 1993/1998. Ottawa: Health Canada Policy Forum on the Canadian Incidence Study of Reported Child Abuse and Neglect.

Trocmé, N., B. Fallon, B. MacLaurin, and B. Copp (2002). "The Changing Face of Child Welfare Investigations in Ontario." OIS 1993/1998. Toronto: Centre of Excellence for Child Welfare. <www.cecw-cepb.ca/Pubs/PubsOIS.html> (July 2003).

——— (2001). *Canadian Incidence Study of Reported Child Abuse and Neglect*. Ottawa: Health Canada. <www.hc-sc.gc.ca/pphb-dgspsp/publicat/cisfr-ecirf/index.html> (July 2003).

World Health Organization (2000). "Female Genital Mutilation: Fact Sheet No. 241." <www.who.int/inf-fs/en/fact241.html> (July 2003).

Supporting Children's Development

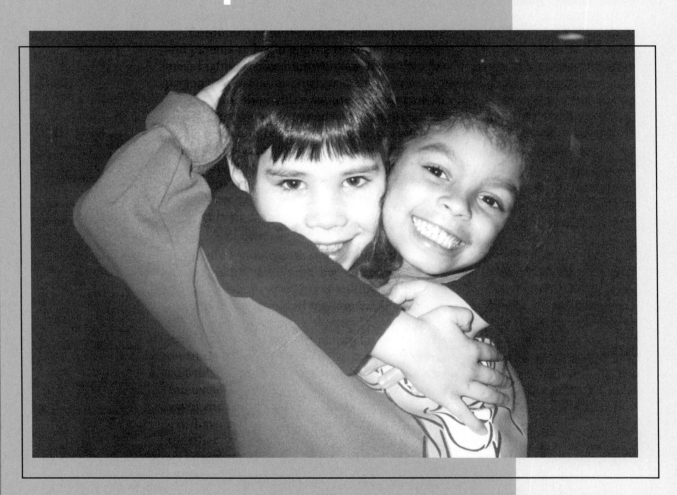

CONTENTS

Healthy Brain Development   *404*
        SELF-REGULATION   405
        RELATING TO OTHERS   405
        HELPING CHILDREN COPE WITH STRESS   408
        SEXUALITY   414

Rhythm of the Program   *421*
        THE NEED FOR REST AND RELAXATION   422
        THE NEED FOR PHYSICAL ACTIVITY   423

Health Curriculum   *428*
        CHILDREN'S UNDERSTANDING OF HEALTH   428
        DEVELOPING AND IMPLEMENTING A HEALTH CURRICULUM   433
        HEALTH NEEDS AND INTERESTS OF CHILDREN   433
        GETTING DOWN TO THE HEALTH CURRICULUM   438

Revisiting the Health Promotion Action Plan   *454*

Conclusion   *456*

What's Your Opinion? TO BRUSH OR NOT TO BRUSH?   *457*

Assess Your Learning   *457*

Resource Materials   *458*

Bibliography   *459*

TABLES

TABLE 8.1   COGNITIVE UNDERSTANDING OF HEALTH   429
TABLE 8.2   DEVELOPING A HEALTH CURRICULUM: GUIDELINES   434
TABLE 8.3   SNACKS CHILDREN CAN MAKE   444

FIGURE

FIGURE 8.1   BRUSHING PATTERN   451

APPENDIXES

APPENDIX 8.1 *CANADA'S PHYSICAL ACTIVITY GUIDE FOR CHILDREN*   462
APPENDIX 8.2 BREAD   464

High-quality early childhood education and care programs strive to support children's growth and development in all areas. Educators think about each child holistically to achieve a balance in their physical, emotional, and social health. This is particularly important as our further understanding of health and illness makes the interconnections between the mind and body obvious, such as the physical wear and tear of stress on the body.

Students and, ultimately, graduates integrate their knowledge of health, illness, safety, and nutrition with what they learn about child development, curriculum, families, diversity, and inclusion to create early childhood programs that meet the needs of both the group and each individual child. Recent research confirms that the brain is the key to our overall health and well-being, including our abilities and coping skills. Prolonged exposure to stress will have a negative effect on a child's brain development. Children enrolled in high-quality early childhood programs have been found to have lower stress hormone levels than those children enrolled in poor-quality programs (Canadian Child Care Federation 2001, 1). Although many elements influence development, there is general agreement that human development follows predictable sequences in all areas—cognitive, emotional, social, physical—but that individuals have unique "timing." Children learn through interacting with people, objects, and the environment.

Children's growth and development is an ECE course in itself, and you will have taken it before you graduate. This textbook examines certain issues relating to children's well-being that readers can integrate with their knowledge of child development, psychology, and sociology. The topics covered here will add to your understanding and ability to support children's well-being. Educators are in an ideal position to support children in their learning of lifelong healthy habits and positive attitudes. The latter portion of this unit is devoted to the health curriculum for children in early childhood programs.

HEALTHY BRAIN DEVELOPMENT

Brain research is continuing to help inform parents and educators about the types of relationships, environments, and experiences that support optimal brain development. The brain, as master control of our health and well-being, is paramount in all aspects of cognition and emotion (Bertrand 2001, 8).

The importance of our emotional and social well-being and how these relate to physical well-being cannot be overstated. How you feel about yourself and the effectiveness of your relationships with others profoundly affect your health. For example, several longitudinal studies have documented that between half and two-thirds of children who have undergone adversity have overcome the odds and manifest resilience, the term often used to describe a set of qualities that include successful adaptation in the face of risk (Benard 1995, 1). "We are all born with an innate capacity for resilience, by which we are able to develop social competence, problem-solving skills, a critical consciousness, autonomy, and a sense of purpose" (1). Two aspects of long-term emotional-social health—self-regulation and relating to others—are discussed below.

Self-Regulation

Self-regulation and our ability to relate to others are two complex and recurring emotional and social tasks that are themes in our lives from birth. Self-regulation refers to the ability to focus attention, control emotional energy, and initiate and recover from anger, disappointment, joy, or other emotions, as well as manage facial and body movement. How well a child (or adult) can self-regulate has a dramatic effect on that individual's quality of daily life. To adapt, the child must be capable of flexible regulation because life requires action and reflection, intensity and calm, concentration and split attention.

Responsive relationships are the cornerstone of emotional development and self-regulation. A newborn needs the educator to regulate his or her state. As the child grows, regulation becomes dyadic—child and educator work together. During the preschool years, the child begins to self-regulate. The child learns to tolerate strong emotions and recover from arousal in secure, responsive relationships that support regulation. Self-regulation develops when children are exposed to manageable levels of stimulation and are protected from over-arousal. Differences exist among children in their ability to regulate and tolerate stress. Children use a variety of sensory and motor skills to regulate. Temperament also accounts for individual differences in a child's emotional arousal and reactivity. But it is through the relationship that the child learns to recover from arousal and stress. When educators remain emotionally available, and are sensitive and responsive to individual differences, children learn to regulate. When children anticipate the empathy and understanding of their educator, they are more likely to cope with distress.

Children need to experience a full range of emotions and feel that it is safe to express them. When they do, they learn to regulate emotions and practise the culturally determined display rules for expressing emotions. For example, they learn when to make eye contact and how to show gratitude. They must know how to regulate emotions and behaviour in order to choose actions that will achieve their goals when exploring and relating to others. A child who wants to play with peers needs to regulate the impulse to take all the toys. Self-regulation is therefore central to the child's social, cognitive, and emotional development. Focusing on self-regulation means understanding individual capacities for stimulation and patterns of recovery from arousal. Educators need to use this information to create a safe environment and relationship for exploration and the development of self-regulation. As the child develops new language and cognitive and social skills, they are used for regulation. These new skills are practised and sorted out in the context of secure educator-child relationships.

Relating to Others

Relating to others refers to children's ability to build relationships, which begins at birth with their parents and develops with other significant people. In addition to relationships with adults, peer relationships are very important. The three major tasks of early childhood relationships are peer group entry, conflict resolution, and maintaining play (Guralnick and Littmann 1992). Children need to regulate their emotional energy in order to accomplish all three tasks. Individual

Educators support self-regulation when they

- initiate and maintain communication with parents and staff that increases sensitivity to the individual child's security and exploration;
- create an environment that is safe for exploration and the expression of impulses;
- observe and record individual sensory and motor skills that are used to regulate;
- are responsive to the child's signals and intentions;
- remain emotionally available;
- pair novel stimulation with familiar experience;
- remain sensitive to individual differences in coping and relating;
- expose the child to stimulation that matches the individual's ability to cope and, when the child is over-stimulated, support recovery within the relationship;
- avoid the following measures that violate the relationship: emotional withdrawal, punishment, imposition of educator control, intense expression of the educator's negative emotion;
- create optimal individual stimulation, taking into consideration the type of stimulation, its form, intensity, and variations in presentation;
- increase stimulation over time in small increments that are responsive to the individual's ability to cope;
- respond to the child's signals and intentions (signals can be bids for regulation, requests for assistance to deal with feelings; signals are not only an expression of an internal state but an outward show of feelings);
- ensure that the child's voice is heard and that the child is able to participate meaningfully in matters that directly affect him or her (as per the UN Convention on the Rights of the Child);
- observe the child's behaviour and figure out the meaning that his or her experience has for that individual;
- create spaces in the playroom with reduced stimulation;
- create stimulus shelters and comfort zones in the playroom;
- create spaces for one-to-one interaction in the playroom.

Source: Adapted from M. Goulet and R. Schroeder, *How Caring Relationships Support Self-Regulation: Video Guide* (Toronto: National Association for the Education of Young Children, 1998), 37–45.

differences exist in the speed, intensity, and duration of emotional responses. Educators must know each child's emotional reactions to promote regulation and recovery before the child can make progress.

To support achievement, the educator must understand all developmental areas. He or she must observe the children to determine how each individual regulates emotional energy, preferences for other children, the familiar play situations chosen, the types of toys, and the pretend themes in which the child engages. When these things are known, educators can design environments that maximize the child's interactions with other children.

Making friends during the early years forms the basis for children's future relationships (Guralnick and Littmann 1992). Educators can enhance children's opportunities to make friends through social play by

- providing equipment and activities that help children learn social rules and roles, and practise taking turns and ownership as they are developmentally ready;

- observing children's individual strengths and interests, and using these to involve the child with others;

- actively guiding children to initiate play with one another when an educator observes an opportunity to foster a friendship. Insisting, however, that children play together, or that "we are all friends," is artificial and does not help children make friends. The reality is that although we all need to show respect for one another, children choose friends;

- choosing and arranging furniture to promote social interaction;

- providing equipment that provides the child with the opportunity to release emotional energy; and

- recognizing those school-agers who are having difficulty making friends and using observation to determine how educators can foster these skills. This may also mean making changes in the program (Musson 1994).

Helping Children Cope with Stress

We have heard many times that stress is one of life's realities, and that a certain degree of stress is important and positive; it challenges the individual to learn and grow. We also know that the causes of stress are varied. Some stressors are situational and short-lived, such as an upcoming birthday party, breaking an arm, or planning a wedding, and some are chronic and long-term, such as living in an abusive home environment, the death of a loved one, or working at a high-pressure job. In addition, stress factors are unique to individuals: adults should be sensitive to each child's stress factors, realizing that they have meaning for the child. Urging a child to stop worrying, or suggesting that he or she shouldn't be upset, trivializes a child's concerns, causing more stress. Almost anything can cause stress. Regardless of the cause, however, stress management is crucial for a child. In some ways, children can be very resilient, but emotional vulnerability that begins in childhood can affect someone for a lifetime. How?

As complex and dynamic research on brain development is, one piece of evidence stands out clearly: "The neural pathways involved with how we respond to stressors and new information seem to be particularly powerful in shaping brain development and learning, behaviour and health" (Bertrand 2001, 11). Stressors arouse pathways in the brain, and very early in life individuals establish physiological stress responses that either contribute to lifelong health or detract from it. You are encouraged to look at other references for descriptions of what is known about these physiological stress responses (e.g., Bertrand 2001). A dramatic example involves cortisol, a chemical produced to respond to the stress. Higher cortisol levels are produced in response to stress, and repeated or prolonged elevated cortisol levels can damage organs, including the brain, or body systems. In other words, lifelong health can be affected by the patterns of stress response established early, and this response is highly influenced by early experiences interacting with the brain. The most critical early experiences involve the quality of interactions with primary caregivers.

Although infants, toddlers, and younger preschoolers have personality strengths, they don't yet have the cognitive skills to develop optimal coping on their own. They need adults to create environments that are low in stress and to help them find ways to cope with stress. Young children hear about things that relate to the outside of their bodies (e.g., changing a diaper, putting a coat on because it's cold outside, tying shoes), but beginning in the preschool years, their awareness of how they are affected by stress involves the inside as much as the outside of their body (e.g., heart beats faster, mouth becomes dry, and butterflies in her tummy). When children become aware of their internal body cues, they can recognize when they are experiencing stress. This leads to adults helping children to learn to regulate their internal responses and acquire coping strategies, such as relaxation techniques (e.g., taking slow, deep breaths) or moving away from the situation that is causing the stress. Coping skills are usually more developed in older children, because they have developed the sequential and logical thinking skills to be able to think about their problems and anticipate consequences.

Most children can cope with the usual stress factors arising from growth and development and everyday living, especially with the support of adults. "Separation protest is a healthy and normal reaction in young children, because these children lack a sense of control or ability to have an effect on their environment; despite the child's protest, the parent can leave anyway" (Kalmanson 1990, 163). An individual's control or perceived control reduces elevations in cortisol. Children who are more certain about their ability to control their distress, and who develop strategies to do so, exhibit less stress and have lower levels of cortisol. Educators must support the development of children's personal control over the environment and over their own internal body state to reduce stress and regulate the production of cortisol (Stansbury and Gunnar 1994).

Children's Stress Factors

It can be difficult to categorize stress factors into those that are less serious and usually of short duration and those that are not, because a stressor is defined by how the individual perceives it. Generally, the following stress factors are often less serious or short-term:

- those related to developmental milestones with no other mediating forces (e.g., toilet learning, separation anxiety, new baby in the house, making friends, learning to read, most fears)
- those related to everyday frustrations, such as too many choices, no choices, or no or little control over decisions that affect their life
- common but often anxiety-inducing experiences, such as visits to the doctor (e.g., for immunization shots or blood tests), dentist, or hospital emergency room; short stays in the hospital for minor ailments; short separations from family; moving; transition to an early childhood education program; leaving that program to attend school; transitions within a program or school (e.g., from infant to toddler room); rejection from a peer

The following stress factors are often more traumatic or long term:

- parents' separation or divorce; death of a family member
- everyday life in poverty; homelessness
- living with violence in the family
- bias (e.g., racism or a home culture very different from that of the early childhood program or school)
- extreme fears or phobias
- repeated hospitalizations or a long stay in a hospital, particularly between the ages of six months and four years, especially when separated from parents
- refugee experiences (e.g., war, the witnessing of torture or death, the separation or loss of family members, different climate or weather, different language)
- witnessing a catastrophe or disaster (e.g., hurricane, tornado, fire, kidnapping, terrorist attack)

Although these lists are incomplete, they convey the idea that children can have a range of stress factors, some of which they resolve or cope with over time or with experience. Others are overwhelming, or begin as something relatively minor and then escalate, resulting in a major negative effect on how the child functions every day.

Identifying Children Who Are Experiencing Stress

Many people assume that signs of stress are easy to pinpoint in children. However, with the exception of some very obvious signs, identification relies on educators' observation skills and sensitivity to individual children. Identifying that the child is experiencing stress is only the beginning. Effective communication with parents is critical in determining the stress factors and deciding how you can work together to support the child. Possible signs are endless, but these are some common ones:

- The child seems sad, has a vacant expression, whines a lot, or has frequent temper tantrums.
- The child clings to educators, although he or she has been in the program for an extended period, or hasn't connected with at least one educator.
- The child is constantly worried.
- The child complains about physical symptoms (e.g., headaches or tummy aches, especially for school-agers).
- The child seems to be tired and rundown, and gets sick a lot (e.g., has frequent colds).
- The child has nightmares.
- Bodily functions are not working properly—the child may have trouble with feeding, be constipated, have diarrhea, be unable to sleep or relax, or want to sleep all the time.
- The child self-stimulates constantly (e.g., rocking back and forth, thumb-sucking, self-pleasuring).
- The child's overall behaviour suddenly changes drastically (e.g., becomes very aggressive or withdrawn).
- The child's development regresses.
- The child is hyper-vigilant, and lives in a state of anxious readiness.

Suggestions for Reducing Children's Stress

Supporting children in their coping with their stress—helping them develop healthy ways to cope with what is usually normal stress—is one of the educators' roles in promoting the child's emotional well-being. Developing coping skills contributes to children's self-control and self-esteem. Although we tend to think of stress as primarily affecting emotional health, educators should help children become aware of the mind-body-emotion interconnection whenever possible.

· ·

Help children develop coping skills by responding to needs and cues (e.g., comfort a distressed infant as promptly as possible, respect a toddler's need to try it independently, offer a preschooler a choice whenever possible, provide a school-ager with opportunities for decision making without adult interference).

Asking a school-ager who has started biting his or her nails lately what the child is thinking and feeling at that moment can help make this connection.

· ·

In order to reduce overall stress for the children in their program, educators can implement a number of strategies to create a "stress-aware" environment. Here are some of those strategies:

- Provide a secure, calm environment where schedules, routines, and transitions contribute to stability, not to heightened stress. Do what you can behind the scenes to reduce stress.
- Maintain an emotional climate of trust. Children will feel that they can express a range of emotions and be supported.
- Be calm and provide security for children.
- Recognize and respond to children's feelings, taking your cues from the child.
- Create a curriculum that supports the development of children's learning about self—feelings, rights, responsibilities.
- Honour children's right to participate. Ensure that each child's voice is being heard so children can express their views according to their developing capacities. This supports the UN Convention on the Rights of the Child. Equally important, it helps reduce stress for the child because it contributes to a sense of control.
- Create developmentally appropriate stimulus shelters where a child can choose to be away from the group (e.g., pillows in a cozy corner for infants and toddlers, lofts or tents for preschoolers and school-agers).
- Evaluate the level of stimulation. Remember that some children are very much affected by sensory stimulation. For example:
  - Is the environment too busy and disordered, which can contribute to unfocused play, or uncluttered and organized, to help children feel in control?
  - Is the noise level conducive to focused play? Are there quiet times during the day to encourage calmness?
  - Is there music playing and, when it's playing, does the music fit the mood of the room?
  - Is the lighting natural and adequate or artificial and inadequate?

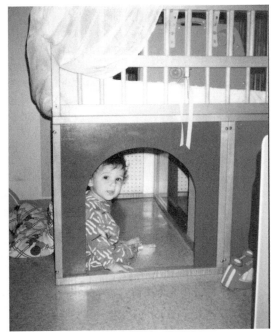

Helping infants and toddlers start to learn they can reduce their own stress levels usually means comforting them, but it also means helping them find ways to comfort themselves, identifying for them what they are experiencing, and guiding them to activities that help them work out some of their anger or frustration (e.g., large motor activities, water and sand play). With preschool and school-age children, educators can help them to identify the "inside and outside" body cues for their stressful feelings, and suggest ways they can alleviate those feelings now and in the future. As children learn about what makes them feel stressed and how they react, they learn a lot about themselves that will be beneficial in the long term.

Some older children may express their fears about terrorist attacks or armed conflicts (i.e., war).The following list of suggestions may help children process these fears. These strategies are similar to those used by parents and educators when helping children deal with other types of fears:

- Reassure children that they are safe, that you will protect them from danger, and that you will continue to help them when they feel afraid, sad, etc.
- Know that reactions are usually short-term.
- Take the time to listen actively.
- Answer questions as well as you can, but don't make promises you can't keep.
- Take their fears seriously; never ridicule or belittle children's fears.
- Be a role model. Share feelings and appropriate ways that you cope with feelings.

Here are some examples of coping strategies that educators can help children to develop:

- deep, slow breathing to help slow down the body
- stretching exercises (e.g., tensing and relaxing muscles), which can be incorporated into a creative movement activity for preschoolers (e.g., jungle animals), or relaxation exercises, which use imagery (e.g., the children lie down with eyes closed and an educator takes them on an imaginary journey)
- discussions in small groups, in which the children are asked what they would do if a big dog came up to them, if they got lost, if they smelled smoke in their bedroom. Helping children think of options encourages them to participate in overcoming fears. Note that such discussions would be inappropriate if any child in the group had an intense fear of dogs or fire; in that case a one-to-one conversation with that child would help gauge her or his reactions.
- helping individual children identify what is a stress release for them. Some need vigorous physical activity, others prefer time alone looking at books or listening to music, others may need to pound clay.
- asking children to identify what causes their stress and what they can do to prevent a reaction (e.g., remove themselves from a stressful situation if possible, think about something else)
- resolving conflict—much of school-agers' stress, in particular, is related to interaction with peers

Terry Orlick's *Feeling Great: Teaching Children to Excel at Living* has more than 100 activities designed to help children cope effectively with stress (see Resource Materials, page 458).

Helping Specific Children

Educators create a stress-aware environment for all the children, but there are times when an individual child needs extra support because stress is affecting her or him significantly. Educators use their observation skills to identify signs and possibly stress factors. The director may also be involved, and certainly parents are fully involved, unless there is a strong suspicion of child abuse.

When children's stress reactions are developmentally based, educators and parents are often able to support children through this process in a positive way. Here is an example of a preschooler who expresses his fear of doctors and hospitals, and how educators offer support along with his family.

- Desmond is four years old. He has always been afraid of the doctor's office, mainly because of the immunization shots that he hates so much. Next month, he is to be hospitalized to have minor surgery. His mother, Lorna, tells you that he is terrified. His stress is evident in the program as well as at home. He is not sleeping well and is having recurring nightmares. At the program, he can't lie still to rest, although he is obviously tired and irritable. Desmond is usually quite involved in play—able to concentrate for periods of time at the blocks and in dramatic play. Lately he flits around aimlessly, unless an educator spends one-to-one time with him.

Lorna and Desmond's educators have decided to try to help Desmond in the weeks leading up to the surgery in a number of ways:

- Desmond and Lorna are scheduled to take the guided tour of the hospital, which is designed for children about to have surgery. The goal of these tours is to decrease children's anxiety about the unknown, including the operating room, the playroom, and their own room.

- Educators will be particularly sensitive to providing Desmond with one-to-one time whenever possible, reading books and encouraging him to discuss his feelings when he is comfortable.

- Because Desmond enjoys dramatic play, the educators have set up this area as a hospital. The setting encourages him to act out his feelings and experiences. Since children tend to play about what they already know, the educators realize that his most meaningful play will be after the surgery. However, it is helpful for Desmond to handle the medical instruments and for educators to listen to his fears. He hasn't been able to articulate those fears when asked, but he does in the context of play with dolls.

continued

Desmond is worried that when he is in the hospital the doctor will remove a leg or arm rather than just performing the minor surgery. He's afraid that the doctor is mad at him because he always cries when he gets his shots. He's afraid he is going to be punished. This is helpful information to share with Lorna, because until now she thought his only fear was that she was going to leave him in the hospital. During the hospital tour, Lorna focuses her questions on issues that help reduce Desmond's fears.

- She finds out that she can stay in the hospital room with him.
- In the children's playroom, Desmond talks with two children who had minor surgeries and sees that they have both arms and legs.

After the visit, Desmond is more focused at the program. Although he is still stressed, he's playing with other children again and isn't as hesitant to voice his fears. He isn't crying as much or talking about cutting off arms during play in the hospital play area. Lorna says that Desmond is sleeping better and has had only two nightmares.

The day of surgery arrives. When the doctor comes in to see Desmond, she assures him that she will only fix what she said she would and that he has done nothing wrong. When Clarissa, an educator, comes to visit with two of Desmond's friends from the early childhood program the day after surgery, he is happy to see them and shows them his room and the playroom. Within a week of his return to the program, Desmond seems to be back to his old self, proudly showing the pictures that his mother took at the hospital. Lorna isn't anticipating that he will love the doctor from now on, but she believes that the preparation and positive hospital experience alleviated Desmond's stress and fear. Educators observe a change in his dramatic play, which reflects Desmond's positive experience and ability to cope with this fear.

This example highlights the benefits of program involvement with parents in managing children's stress factors that may be developmentally based and, it is hoped, short-term.

When children's stress is due to a very serious or long-term factor such as child abuse, the death of a parent, or an experience as a refugee, educators will likely need to collaborate with others in ensuring that the child receives consistent support. Other agencies may be involved, and educators may be given recommendations from play therapists or other developmental specialists and counselling services.

Sexuality

Sexuality is part of us all, regardless of our age. Yet this topic often makes adults feel uncomfortable because they may be hesitant to acknowledge young children's sexuality. Young children's sexual feelings provide sensory pleasure, but without the erotic overtones that develop during and after puberty. Children's sexuality is an integral part of growth and development.

Stimulating our genitals in some way is called masturbating or self-pleasuring. Masturbation is an act of stimulating oneself to reach orgasm. Touching oneself for pleasure is normal and a natural behaviour, and in keeping with this positive view, we use the term "self-pleasuring" in this textbook. In fact, self-pleasuring more closely describes the child's intent. The word "masturbation" may evoke negative feelings for some adults, due to taboos or messages learned as they were growing up. Self-pleasuring is a healthy behaviour for children unless it becomes the focus and interferes with the child's involvement in activities. When you observe children self-pleasuring, your reaction should be to help children to learn social parameters, as with all behaviour. Acknowledge the child's pleasure, and help him or her to regard it as private, to be performed when alone. If children feel shame or embarrassment for normal, curious, or stimulating behaviour, this negativity about sexual matters may stay with them.

Developing Human Sexuality

With an understanding of development, educators are able to predict the normal patterns of sexual behaviour and are prepared for and respond calmly to them.

Infants:
- Early experiences with sucking and being held, rocked, and cradled provide a foundation that fosters positive feelings toward self and relationships.
- Touching or fondling the genitals when the diaper is off is normal, as infants explore all parts of their body.
- Activities such as bouncing, swinging, and jumping may produce sexual pleasure; boys may have an erection, and girls, although it is less noticeable, may have vaginal secretions (Maguire 1993, 33).

Toddlers:
In addition to the experiences and activities listed above for infants:
- They learn words for private body parts and toileting.
- They have increased interest in others' genitals, an interest heightened by learning to use the toilet.

Preschoolers:
- They have concerns about their genitals. Boys might worry about their penis falling off, or girls wonder why they don't have a penis. If they tell an educator of their concern, children must be reassured and not teased. Boys need to know that their penis won't fall off, and girls need to know that they have all their sexual parts, some of which are inside their body and not as obvious as boys' genitals.
- They self-pleasure or explore their genitals.
- They observe each other during washroom routines.
- They sex-play, including You Show Me and I'll Show You, Doctor, and so on.
- They question educators about how their body works, where babies come from, why those two dogs in the park are stuck together (i.e., mating), why girls and boys are different, and so on.

School-Agers:

■ They sex-play.

■ They possibly self-pleasure in public, though most school-agers understand privacy rules.

■ They use slang or swearwords for private parts, sexual acts, or sexual orientation.

■ They ask educators questions similar to those that preschoolers ask, but are somewhat more sophisticated (e.g., "How do babies get into a uterus?" or "What are those animals doing?"). Questions such as "What does homosexual mean?" and "How do people get AIDS?" or those related to puberty (e.g., "When will I get hair down there?") are common. ECE students and educators should also be prepared for personal questions from school-age children, such as "Do you have sex with your boyfriend?" These questions are personal. You should feel confident in responding respectfully by saying that this is a personal question, and that you will not answer a question that is private. By asking questions, children learn which questions are private and which we will answer. Here again, educators help children to learn social skills.

Knowledge Promotes Healthy Attitudes

Knowing about sex does not encourage children to become sexually active too early. The World Health Organization (1983) states that it is a lack of knowledge that leads to early sexual adventures. Of course, this doesn't mean that four- or five-year-olds are interested in sexual intercourse, or should be taught about it. A five-year-old may have an idea that a man and a woman rub bodies (and may even play this out with a partner in dramatic play with clothes on). However, the child probably does not understand the specifics of intercourse, and if he or she does, the educators should explore the possibility of sexual abuse. Educators should be prepared to discuss anatomical facts related to gender identity and sexual differences. Adults' comfort level concerning sexuality may reduce children's anxiety about this topic. However, developing a common approach to this topic is difficult because of differences in opinion (American Public Health Association and American Academy of Pediatrics 1992, 61).

. . . .

e.g. Educators should not offer their opinion on sexual intercourse outside of marriage. It is the family's right to convey their moral beliefs. Educators must try not to be judgmental about family beliefs and teachings. However, if there is concern that the child is being physically, emotionally, or sexually abused as a result of the family's sexual mores, educators cannot ignore this possibility and must explore it further.

. . . .

Around two years of age, children begin to be interested in parts of the body—both theirs and those of the opposite sex. Giving nicknames to genitals rather than the anatomically correct term, or discouraging children from mentioning these body parts, leads to confusion later. When they hear another child or adult call a penis a "wee-wee," they begin to assume that there is something wrong with using the word "penis," though it's acceptable to use the correct names for other body parts. The same confusing message is learned by infants. Adults smile at them when they play with their toes but slap them or say no when they touch their genitals. If these messages are reinforced as children grow, they will view self-pleasuring and their genitals as bad or dirty.

Preschoolers and young school-agers between the ages of three and eight may be eager to explore similarities and differences in their bodies with peers. Sexual games like Doctor or You Show Me and I'll Show You, often while playing House, are motivated by natural curiosity, not by erotic drive. Although these games are predictable and part of development, adults often overreact to them.

For preschoolers, one of the important aspects of their emerging sense of self is awareness of their gender. Around age four or five, many focus on gender stereotypes, much to the chagrin of parents and educators who foster less rigid roles for males and females. When children reach the school-age years, many are naturally drawn to stereotypes in clothing, hairstyles, toys, and play behaviour. They also observe and experience gender stereotypes around them. Without devaluing individual children's interests and inclinations, educators must give the same kind of care and attention to girls as to boys, and continue to offer them the same range of choices. Ongoing commitment to a nonsexist approach in the program helps to counteract the gender stereotypes that children face in society. Adapting to a stereotype is harmful because it replaces behaving in accordance with your own personal identity with behaving in accordance with expectations of how you should behave.

. . . .

A relatively common stereotype is that boys should not cry. This may result in a boy's reluctance to talk to anyone about what is worrying him for fear that he will cry. This can negatively affect his long-term emotional health.

e.g.

. . . .

Parents' Perspectives on Children's Sexuality

We have made some strong comments in this textbook on the advantages of direct communication about children's sexuality. Just as it is important to acknowledge parents' views on issues such as guidance, illness, and safety, the same principle applies to sexuality. Some parents may not agree with this open approach, and educators must respect their position. So how do educators handle situations in which a child's sexual question or behaviour is one that you know the parent discourages or forbids?

First, educators need to come to an agreement among themselves on how they approach sexual questions and behaviour. This type of discussion provides opportunities for staff to talk about differences of opinion. Staff may benefit from additional post-diploma training (in-service) or consultation with a sexual health educator, often affiliated with the local public health agency. Libraries, too, provide educational materials. Some adults grew up with negative feelings or attitudes about bodies and sexuality. Some have values based on religious or ethno-cultural beliefs about sexuality or sex roles. Although you must respect these views, it is inappropriate for a professional working with children to impart them to children.

■ John believes that children should not explore or stimulate their genitals under any circumstances. He recognizes that he needs to explore why he feels this way. Meanwhile, he knows that he must avoid reacting negatively to children's self-pleasuring.

■ A child asks how babies are born. Madeline is tempted to answer, "They are found in a cabbage patch." Madeline must recognize that giving children false information is not helpful. The child will eventually find out that she wasn't telling the truth. Older children already have some idea, and may be testing their educator's honesty.

Second, programs' policies on child guidance and curriculum should clarify staffs' commitment to answering children's questions, including ones of a sexual nature. Written information that educators develop for parents should mention that children's awareness of self, others, and the world is part of the ongoing curriculum. To avoid misunderstanding, include examples such as "We use anatomically correct names for all parts of the body," and "A preschooler who is exploring his or her genitals is redirected if this occurs in a social situation. The child is reminded that this is a private activity, which is acceptable at nap time."

Third, meeting with the parents at the time of enrollment allows the director to raise this issue and discuss the parents' views, and how they wish to handle their child's questions. Differences of opinion may arise, and in those cases a workable and practical compromise can be reached. In the future, if a sexuality issue arises that is relevant to all parents, it would be beneficial to have a parent meeting facilitated by a sexual health educator (or other expert).

Some children have shown a keen interest in playing Doctor, and parents have concerns that individual children may be hurt either physically or emotionally. At a parent meeting, a staff person outlines how educators manage these situations in the program:

■ The children are clearly told that their individual rights are to be respected and that no one has a right to touch them in a way that makes them feel uncomfortable. They are also not permitted to touch another person against that person's wishes. This rule applies at all times, whether it concerns aggressive behaviour (e.g., hitting, pushing) or sexual behaviour (e.g., kissing, touching private body parts).

■ No child is permitted under any circumstances to insert parts of the body (e.g., fingers) or other objects into any part of another child's body.

■ If one child is being forced to play Doctor against her or his wishes, the children are reminded of individual rights and the importance of respecting those rights. If children are discovered playing Doctor (e.g., with clothes off), the educator responds by calmly instructing children to put their clothes on and redirecting their play to another area (i.e., the rule is that children keep their clothes on at the program).

The sexual health educator facilitates a discussion to identify concerns and issues that need to be addressed. Changes in a program's policy or practices may be required.

Assessing the situation:

A mother asks you to tell her four-year-old son that it is "bad" whenever you see him touch his penis. She tells you that the behaviour is morally wrong. How would your conversation with her proceed?

Role of Educators as Sex Educators

Parents are the primary sexual health educators in children's lives. But educators too have a significant role to play as sex educators, whether they are aware of it or not. How? Children are constantly learning about their sexuality by

- listening to adults and other children,
- observing the way adults interact with each other and react to events and comments,
- absorbing attitudes that are communicated in adult conversation and action, and
- interacting with adults and other children.

In other words, educators are teaching about sexuality simply by the way they act, what they say, and what they don't say.

. . . .

A school-age girl is looking at a magazine that has a picture of a girl about the same age as she posed in a way that looks seductive. The educator who remarks, "Isn't she gorgeous?" is teaching something different from the educator who asks, "What do you think of this advertisement?" The question may initiate a conversation between the girl and the educator about how advertisers use children in inappropriate ways and how they affect the way that girls and boys view females.

e.g.

. . . .

Educators contribute to children's sexual learning in a number of ways:

- They contribute to children's self-esteem and positive body image, by helping them to feel proud and in control of their body.
- They help children to value themselves as female or male, by using implicit and explicit messages about real similarities and differences, and celebrating these similarities and differences.
- They encourage knowledgeable and responsible behaviour, by being informed about sexuality, answering questions simply and honestly, and responding gently to normal, curious sexual behaviour—while at the same time setting clear limits that help children to learn about boundaries.
- They serve as role models, by helping children understand acceptable and unacceptable private and public behaviour.

- They help to protect children from exploitation or sexual abuse, by teaching preschool and school-age children about the idea of privacy and about private body parts, and by teaching that sexual touching between children and adults is inappropriate (Brick et al. 1989, 2).

Children's Questions about Sex

Questions about sexuality emerge from children as they become interested. Sexuality, like any other aspect of what is going on inside and around children, is something they naturally want to know about—their body, how it works, and sex. Be sensitive and follow the child's lead. Remember, the story unfolds for children over many years along with their cognitive development. It is inappropriate to provide a long, detailed explanation that holds more information than the child wants or needs. Even for many older school-agers, the whole idea of sex can sound disgusting (Greenspan 1993, 240). Many children ask questions when you least expect them. Don't be surprised when at times you feel uncomfortable with a question or panicky at the prospect of answering it. Many educators feel this way. Part of this reaction stems from the fact that you aren't the child's parent and want to avoid saying anything that contradicts what the parents have told, or will tell, their child.

Often a simple answer is all the younger child wants or needs. If he asks, "What are those two dogs doing?" you could answer, "The dogs are making puppies." Remember three key points when answering children's questions at any age:

1. Be sure you understand what it is the child wants to know. For example, when Chantal asks, "Where did I come from?" she might not be interested in the sexual act but rather what city or country she originated from, or that she came from her mother's uterus.

2. Find out what the child already knows. For example, ask Chantal, "Where do you think you came from?" This will help you clarify what she is actually asking and what she already knows.

3. If you can't answer immediately, be sure to get back to the child soon.

Assessing the situation:

An ECE student who is pregnant is approached by an eight-year-old boy who asks: "How did you get pregnant? Were you raped?" The student responds angrily, "That's not a very nice question. Do you know you could hurt someone's feelings by asking that?" How would you respond?

Sexual orientation, like race, gender, class, and religion, is part of an individual's identity and must be respected as such. When children ask what the words "gay," "homosexual," or "lesbian" mean, or when they use derogatory names for sexual orientation to name-call, this is a very important learning moment. Some children may be part of a family with gay parents or be friends with someone who has gay parents. However, even these children may use negative remarks or stereotypes based on lack of knowledge or misconceptions due to overwhelming stereotypes.

· ·

A seven-year-old is angry at his friend on the playground and shouts, "You fag!" When the educator asks him whether he knows what the word means, he replies, "It means stupid." After reminding the child that name-calling is unacceptable, she must clarify this child's confusion.

· ·

For most children, it is not the homosexual or heterosexual sex act that they generally want to know about but the importance of different kinds of families and relationships. What is important for adults to focus on is the caring part of the relationship (Tony Gambini, cited in Brown 1994, C1, C3).

Gay families are the same as any other family! The legalization of same-sex marriages in Canada supports this fact. It is commonly believed, although it is not possible to substantiate, that approximately 10% of the adult population is lesbian or gay (Corbett 1993, 30). Consequently, there will be parents or co-workers who are lesbian or gay. There will also be children that we are caring for now in programs who will become aware of their lesbian or gay sexual orientation as they get older. Most individuals who are homosexual were raised by heterosexual parents, and the children of most lesbian and gay parents grow up to have heterosexual orientation (30). Perhaps this reality helps to highlight the importance of educators' attitudes in acknowledging families with same-sex parents as we do single parents, stepparents, and so on. This is as integral a part of a child's identity as his or her race, religion, and socioeconomic level.

Older children are bombarded by stereotypes from the media and possibly from adults in their lives. They may repeat some of what they've heard. They may ask more direct questions such as "How do you get to be gay?" To respond appropriately to children's questions, comments, and behaviour, educators need to explore their attitudes and knowledge about homosexuality. People who hold negative attitudes about a sexual orientation that is different from their own must recognize that this bias is discriminatory. Discrimination perpetuates unjust treatment of individuals based on their identity. Though educators may not agree with someone's sexual practice (just as they may disagree with some religious beliefs), they must tolerate diversity. Children and parents need to be accepted and supported as families, and if educators are either subtly or overtly disapproving they are not contributing to emotional health. Educators can seek out community resources to help them understand more about homosexuality and gay families.

RHYTHM OF THE PROGRAM

OBJECTIVE

The rhythm of a program refers to the pace of daily routines and activities. Establishing a rhythm that respects and responds to the children is an educator's daily role, beginning with greeting and talking with parents and children at drop-off. The rhythm is influenced by the ages of the children and other factors such as group size, ratios, interests of the children, time of day, weather, space available,

To describe essential principles in planning and carrying through with a program that recognizes children's needs for rest and physical activity.

UNIT 8 SUPPORTING CHILDREN'S DEVELOPMENT

mood of the group, and individual children. Adequate opportunities for physical activity, cognitive stimulation, and nutrition must be balanced with opportunities for rest and relaxation. Children of all ages need opportunities to reduce stimulation and stress. Respect for individual children is paramount in planning and carrying out the day's activities, as there are some children more than others who need more opportunity for down time.

The Need for Rest and Relaxation

Napping or resting is an issue that arises in every program and with every age group. Educators balance the needs of the group with those of the individual. This requires acknowledging the limitations of group care while recognizing and carrying through with practices and routines that endorse the child's uniqueness. When this is not done, children may be negatively affected. For example,

- they may not get the rest they need,
- they may be forced to comply with rigid rules, such as lying on a cot for over an hour even if they don't need to nap,
- they may be involved in a lose-lose situation, with child and educator developing unhappy relationships around routines such as napping or resting.

It is evident, then, that even with a physical need such as rest, emotional and social needs are interrelated.

Opportunities for rest and relaxation take into account the developmental and individual needs of children in the group:

- Infants follow their own individual nap schedules, which should be somewhat consistent with nap times at home.
- Some toddlers may need only one nap while others need two. While the latter group naps, the other will need physical areas and opportunities to do quiet, relaxing, less stimulating things (e.g., being read to, working at puzzles).
- Preschoolers, especially older ones, don't require a nap any longer but still need to slow down and rest. They are only expected to lie on cots for a half-hour and then they can get up and do quiet activities. However, even some older preschoolers need nap time, and provisions should be made for this.
- School-agers are provided with comfortable furniture or spaces where they can wind down or do quiet activities, if they would like to, after school.

Massage has gained recognition as an effective relaxation technique. But there are differing opinions on the appropriateness of infant massage in programs. Some people believe that massage can be soothing or stimulating for infants, and involves caring touch. Others believe that infant massage is an intimate practice that should be done only by parents (if they choose). Some infants enjoy being massaged. Others are not comfortable with a tactile approach and show signs of distress. When an infant is obviously not relaxing or enjoying it, the educator must stop the massage. Not stopping indicates a lack of respect for the infant's physical and emotional needs. Educators who practise infant massage recognize the importance of following infants' cues, and should seek training from appropriate resources in the community and obtain the parents' permission.

The Need for Physical Activity

The need for rest and relaxation must be balanced with the need for physical activity. *Canada's Physical Activity Guide for Children* calls parents, educators, physicians, and community leaders to action to support children's daily active time (see Appendix 8.1, page 462). The reasons behind this call to action won't likely surprise you. As we discussed in Unit 5, rates of childhood obesity in Canada have tripled in less than 20 years, from 5% of 7- to 13-year-olds in 1981 to 17% of boys and 15% of girls in 1996 (Tremblay and Willms 2000, 1429). A study in Quebec indicated that almost 25% of 9-year-olds and half of 16-year-olds in Quebec were at risk of developing heart disease later, due to lifestyle factors such as obesity, physical activity, or smoking (Spurgeon 2002, 1416). In order to derive all the benefits of physical activity, *Canada's Physical Activity Guide for Children* highlights the importance of including all three types of physical activity:

- endurance
- flexibility
- strength

Physical activity enables children and adults to release tension, have fun, learn social skills, and feel good about themselves as they develop skills. A body that is physically fit works better. Physical activity should be part of everyday life for everyone. It is common knowledge that exercise builds a healthy heart and contributes to increased energy and better eating and sleeping habits. A six-year study in Quebec found that children who exercised regularly had "better concentration, memory, creativity, problem-solving ability and overall mood for up to two hours following exercise" (Barker 1994, 25).

Depending on life circumstances, children of all ages may have many or few opportunities outside the program to be physically active. Children may live in urban dwellings (e.g., high-rise buildings) where there is no back yard or safe area to run and play in either indoors or outdoors. Parents may have neither the time nor place available to take their children for regular physical activity. In towns and cities where the population is growing, trees and grass are often replaced with malls and subdivisions. In most communities, parents are concerned about their children's safety outdoors when they are not actively supervised. In addition, parents' lives are so busy that preparing dinner, doing laundry, or finishing work from the office seems easier if their child is safely indoors, watching television, reading, or doing other passive activities. Studies have found that the body's metabolism slows significantly during television watching (Barker 1994, 25).

The number of hours that most school-agers sit in class each day emphasizes the importance of providing physically active school-age programs. With the growing number of children who are overweight or unfit, the need to encourage children to be physically active is essential. Some school-agers are involved in after-school physical activities such as basketball, soccer, hockey, gymnastics, dance, or karate. Yet other extracurricular activities are sedentary: music lessons, choir, chess, computer clubs. All these activities are valuable to the child, but daily physical activity needs to be fitted into the schedule.

It is important to recognize the benefits of physical activity for all children in your program, regardless of body type, size, or physical agility. Educators should plan a program that integrates physical activity in ways that invite children to become involved. The goal is not to produce Olympic athletes but to contribute to lifelong attitudes that value regular physical activity. Most children want to be active, especially when offered a range of possibilities. The child who is reluctant to join active games or activities may need more encouragement. However, children should never be singled out or embarrassed into physical activity. Instead, educators can use their observation skills to identify clues to explain the reluctance and then find ways to encourage that child's involvement.

· ·

Nine-year-old Roberto, whose peers are more physically skilled and better coordinated than he is, is embarrassed to play ball games with the group. He always strikes out, highlighting his lack of batting skills, and his peers are impatient because he runs more slowly than they do.

· ·

You can find a range of issues in this example:

- Roberto's lack of confidence
- his reluctance to join group games and sports
- his lack of interest in physical activity (which increases neither his skill nor his fitness level)
- his peers' intolerance and focus on competition

The last issue is a difficult one to counterbalance when we consider the school-ager's developmental level and interest in rules, and the constant messages about winning that bombard us in our society. Focusing on skill competence is developmentally important. Most children of this age have been playing cooperative games since their early preschool days. Educators can do their best to adapt competitive games to be more cooperative (i.e., by moving the emphasis away from winning and losing and toward participation, playing together, and having fun). Educators recognize in Roberto his need for long-term physical fitness and to be part of a social group. First, he is willing to practise ball skills with a trusted educator. As he progresses, one of his peers becomes interested in playing ball with him. Eventually, the group plays their ball game cooperatively (any game can be adjusted with minimal changes) part of the time, so that all children can be involved.

Educators' sensitivity, creativity, and determination to support children's physical involvement encourage children like Roberto to build the interest, skill, and confidence they need to join in. This example is not meant to provide a "recipe for success," because obviously every child is unique and every group has its own social dynamics. However, educators can be confident that the effort they put into children's physical involvement is worth the long-term benefits.

For all ages, educators who model a physically active lifestyle contribute to the children's interest in activity. When educators participate with children and observe them in active play, they use their observations to design the environment and to facilitate so that children can challenge themselves in play.

Active Infants and Toddlers

Educators set up the environment to enhance each child's physical development. Taking cues from the child, educators engage in one-to-one interaction when the child is alert and interested. This provides an opportunity to focus on the child's needs and interests (e.g., action songs).

Infants' need for physical activity changes dramatically in the first year—from rolling over, to pulling themselves up, to creeping, crawling, and walking. Educators are continually responding to these needs by providing an environment that is developmentally appropriate, challenging, and safe.

Toddlers are at a stage of motor development where they often need to run more than walk. They need an adequate amount of open space, small climbing equipment, and slides to go up, down, around, into, and out of. Ramps and steps need to be the right size to encourage toddlers' exploration, not to frustrate them or make them prone to falls. Creative movement can be enhanced when the toddlers are in smaller groups. Opportunities to dance to music or move like animals minimize educators' expectations for sit-down time and maximize opportunities to move. Passive activities such as reading a book and singing quiet songs are more appropriate with one or two toddlers, who join and leave the activity as they wish. Of course, toddlers should always be allowed to come and go with group activities, unless supervision and safety is an issue (e.g., walking to the park).

Most infants and toddlers go for daily walks in strollers or wagons, which provides them with fresh air and stimulation and sometimes rest. They also need plenty of opportunity to move around freely, out of strollers and wagons, with a minimum of restrictions.

Active Preschoolers and School-Agers

Preschool and school-age children need plenty of indoor and outdoor space in which to play in order to practise their locomotor skills, such as running, jumping, galloping, balancing, riding bikes, and ball skills. Though programs must meet the space requirements in the early childhood regulations, remember that those are minimum requirements. Staff are often called on to be creative in finding additional space to use. Community facilities such as schools, recreation agencies with gyms, pools, skating rinks, and neighbourhood parks often cooperate by offering space at times when a facility isn't in use.

Children need a variety of play equipment and activities to develop the three types of physical activity that we have already named. They don't need large, expensive pieces of equipment. Car tires can be used for many activities, and scarves, ribbons, hoops, beanbags, and balls can be used for creative movement. Early childhood programs can offer a range in the physical activity curriculum, including

- total child-directed outdoor use of playground equipment and free space to run around in;

- outdoor organized games such as ball games, obstacle courses, cooperative games, and games that children, parents, and staff teach each other (e.g., a game that originates from their ethno-cultural background);

- indoor or outdoor creative movement or dance, with as many open-ended challenges as possible. This encourages children to use and move their bodies in different ways;

....

Ask children to crawl with a beanbag balancing on one body part or move across the room with one body part leading the way. Children will use their imagination, physical skills, interests, and problem-solving skills to rise to the challenge—resulting in all sorts of possibilities.

....

e.g.

- organized activities run by local agencies that teach lessons, such as the YMCA/YWCA, Kindergym, Boys' and Girls' Club, karate club. Or programs can invite a qualified instructor (e.g., in creative movement, movement and music, yoga for children) to the early childhood program. This service depends on availability and the program's or parents' ability to pay for the service. Programs may be able to use parent or volunteer talents or skills.

Physical Activity Checklist

An integral part of the early childhood curriculum is physical activity. By evaluating the variety of opportunities for physical activity in the program, educators can determine to what degree the children are provided with opportunities to be active and the essential components of activities. The following are implementation strategies of a quality early childhood physical activity program:

- Educators demonstrate attitudes and behaviour that show their commitment to physical fitness, ensuring that their indoor and outdoor curriculum planning and implementation for physical activity is an integral part of the program.
- Children's development is the basis for planning the curriculum.
- Educators offer a wide variety of physical activities, with opportunities to develop endurance, flexibility and strength.
- Activities are child-directed to provide children with problem-solving opportunities. This does not eliminate the need for children to learn when to stop and listen to the person leading the activity.
- Educators promote equal opportunities for all children, respecting individual skills and abilities, energy, and interest level, and encouraging and celebrating each child's attempts and successes.
- Educators downplay competition, focusing instead on individual competence and cooperating together with group activities.
- Educators emphasize fun, socialization, and active living.
- Educators provide various types of equipment in quantities that do not overwhelm children with choices or result in children being left out or fighting over the few pieces of equipment.
- Educators offer planning that includes active alternatives when the weather doesn't permit outdoor play.

- Activities incorporate music when possible, fitting the tempo of the activity-promoting rhythm.
- Educators provide music and activities that reflect a range in musical styles (e.g., jazz, R & B, folk, classical, reggae) and ethno-cultural diversity.
- Educators use clear, simple, and minimal directions to promote maximum child-directed involvement in the activity, encouraging children to challenge themselves.
- Educators maintain safety in all aspects of the physical activity program (i.e., supervision, equipment, children's level of involvement). The child isn't expected to go beyond his or her skill level or energy level.
- Educators invite parents, older siblings, and extended family members, and encourage them to provide input and be involved whenever possible (e.g., share active games from their childhood).

Refer to Appendix 8.1, page 462.

Refer to Appendix 8.1, page 462.

HEALTH CURRICULUM

OBJECTIVES

To identify and describe four factors that influence children's understanding of health.

To discuss the guidelines in developing an appropriate health curriculum and identifying inappropriate practices.

To identify developmental health needs and interests for each age group.

To offer suggestions for integrating the health curriculum in each age group on topics such as environmental education, dental health education, and hand washing and germs.

To identify the who, what, when, where, and why of cooking with children.

To discuss how educators promote dental health with each age group.

As with all aspects of the curriculum, the health curriculum should be designed using this principle: curriculum design requires that teachers identify the play and learning priorities for the young children in the program. In this step, teachers rely on information about individual children based on their observation and assessment of children's developmental levels and needs (Shipley 2002, 410).

In other words, children's health education should be integrated into the program in ways that relate to their developmental needs and interests.

Children's Understanding of Health

Children's understanding of health is influenced by the interaction of a number of factors:

- stage of cognitive development and temperament
- family connection; i.e., cultural identity, socioeconomic circumstances, parenting styles
- peers, their community, and the media

Cognitive Development

Young children's growing cognitive abilities affect what and how they think about health, prevention, and health promotion. Combining Piaget's theory of cognitive development and Natapoff's research on children's understanding of health, Table 8.1 provides examples of how children perceive concepts of health and prevention at each level. The term "prevention," for example, assumes an understanding of future and causality—actions that you take today can affect your health in 20 years. Does a three-, five-, or seven-year-old understand this concept? No. To fully understand and talk about these and other concepts, we have to reach Piaget's formal operational level in our cognitive development (at about age 12).

TABLE 8.1

Cognitive Understanding of Health

CONCEPT	SENSORIMOTOR: BIRTH TO 2 YEARS	PREOPERATIONAL: 2 TO 7 YEARS	CONCRETE OPERATIONAL: 7 TO 11 YEARS
Health	• Concept too abstract for a pre-symbolic child. Groundwork is laid for later cognitive stages through child's experiences of healthy environments.	• Only the physical dimension of health • Egocentric (e.g., if candy makes me feel good, it must be good for me) • Can't focus on the whole and the part at the same time; e.g., child believes that someone with a Band-Aid on the knee is not healthy (the physical signs of injury or illness are less of an abstract concept)	• Beginning awareness of health as more than a physical dimension (e.g., understanding that emotional stress can cause physical symptoms) • Has conservation—believes it's possible to be partly healthy and partly not healthy (e.g., realizes that the child is still healthy even with a sprained ankle)
Causality	• Too abstract—repeated experiences with cause and effect will contribute to development in this realm	• Has "magical thinking" and is intuitive rather than logical—sometimes unrelated practices are thought to affect health or illness (e.g., child believes that getting sick must have been a result of misbehaviour—"Why did Rena give me chickenpox? I wasn't mean to her")	• Has cause-and-effect reasoning—understands that certain actions or inactions can affect health (e.g., eating breakfast helps you concentrate at school)
Time	• Too abstract—consistent daily routines provide some predictability in their day (e.g., toddlers know that after lunch they will have a nap; they understand sequence)	• Present oriented—here-and-now orientation; does not have an understanding of the future	• Still present oriented • Has reversibility, enabling child to think through a chain of events and back—important in beginning to see more long-term orientation to health
Body	• Beginning awareness of body parts will contribute to later stages	• Has some body awareness but not a holistic view of how systems interrelate • Perceptually bound • Developing an awareness of body cues	• More aware of the body and mind and how they work together • Beginning awareness of body cues (e.g., child with asthma recognizes early symptoms of an episode and by acting on these cues takes medication)

Does that mean that teaching young children about health is pointless? No. It means that the health curriculum, in order to be relevant, should be based on children's cognitive abilities. Content that fits their ability to process information is more likely to have a positive effect on long-term health behaviour (Natapoff 1982).

Appropriate health education focuses on what children want and need now, not on what they'll need in future.

Explaining to Jamie, a preschooler, that if he brushes his teeth every day they will be healthy in 20 years is too abstract.

Memorizing rules is fairly easy for children. Yet we can't assume that when Jamie repeats "Brushing my teeth every day will keep them healthy in 20 years" he fully understands what he has said. For him, 20 years from now holds no meaning. It makes more sense to Jamie if we relate health education to his everyday life.

Brushing your teeth takes all the sticky food off your teeth so you won't get cavities (or a hole in the tooth). Brushing cleans your mouth and makes it smell good too.

Cognitive development is a natural process. We can no more speed up its progress than we can speed up physical development and get a two-month-old to sit up. Learning is an interactive process and children's exploration and interaction enhance their development. Using the concept of the body as an example, educators can provide experiences, materials, and questions that promote children's learning. Children build on their experiences. During diaper changes, educators can talk to infants about their tummy, knees, and toes, and ask them to help lift their bottom to take the diaper off. Toddlers are learning names and locations of body parts and beginning to identify feelings. Educators help preschoolers progress in their understanding of the body by asking them questions such as "How do you know when you are tired (or hungry, afraid, sick, happy)?" Educators can thus encourage children to become more aware of concrete body cues. School-agers begin to understand how the internal circulatory, digestive, and other systems work.

Temperament

The sequence of development is similar for children, though temperaments are unique. Temperament is generally considered to refer to characteristic patterns of emotional reactions and emotional self-regulation. Biological characteristics influence behaviour very early in life. Renowned psychologist Jerome Kagan has studied shyness in children for many years. He believes that approximately 20% of infants are born with an inhibited temperament. By two months old, these infants show sensitivity to unfamiliar stimuli, such as strangers and loud noises. Their anxiety is apparent in louder crying and a faster heart rate (Kagan 2001, 25). Often, such behaviour begins to be labelled as shyness as the child grows older. Shyness doesn't always mean that the child is more anxious than a more outgoing child. However, anxiety in a child is an important consideration because temperament has an effect on the child's understanding and view of health.

. . . .

Irena's parents let her walk to the corner store by herself. She feels proud, excited, and independent. On the other hand, her older sister Thea is relieved now that Irena can go to the store when the family needs milk or bread. She has always felt anxious about going because she worries about all the things that could go wrong (e.g., she could trip and fall, not have enough money, be hit by a car, be approached by a stranger).

e.g.

. . . .

Thea has an inhibited temperament compared with her sister. She views many of life's challenges as risky and threatening, while Irena sees challenges as positive and exciting. People's temperaments are on a continuum, with those more fearful on one end and those who believe they are invincible on the other. Of course, feeling invincible can also be influenced by development. As we noted in Unit 6, young children may not as yet understand the risks involved in their activity. A preschool child cannot estimate how long it will take a moving vehicle to reach the child's location, and therefore may take undue risks. When developing and implementing a health curriculum, educators need to consider the range of temperaments in their group. Remember that increasing children's anxiety or feelings of vulnerability to encourage them to take positive health action has serious ethical questions. We must be careful not to raise anxiety levels in children, because increased stress for children does not mean increased health, as discussed earlier.

. . . .

Educators are planning to teach children to be cautious about crossing streets, ingesting poisons, or approaching animals by focusing on all the dangers. Educators are concerned about some of the children who feel invincible. While their approach may have a positive effect on the safety behaviour of some children, it may have a negative effect on those who worry. Their fears about crossing streets, exploring new things, or approaching animals are intensified. This negates children's confidence in striving toward self-care.

e.g.

. . . .

The Family Connection

Family is an essential connection to children's identity. The connection between children and their families is a powerful one that has a significant effect on their understanding of health. Members of various ethno-cultural groups connect the cause of disease, to varying degrees, to certain theories such as the imbalance of hot and cold in the body, spiritual or supernatural powers, or magic (e.g., the evil eye causing fever, vomiting, or diarrhea). Illness may be viewed as an invasion of body, mind, soul, and spirit (Waxler-Morrison et al. 1990). A family's health beliefs and practices may be effective in maintaining the health of an individual and his or her family, even if these practices are not based on contemporary medical theories. In fact, traditional remedies may at times help someone feel better when conventional medicine has failed or has no recommendation.

It is critical that the early childhood program "respect the dignity and worth of each family's cultural beliefs and practices" (La Grange et al. 1994, 31). Of course, this statement must be qualified with regard to concerns that children are being mistreated, malnourished, or neglected in any way by a particular family practice. Other influences that may stem from ethno-culture are beliefs about health care professionals (e.g., conventional versus complementary practitioners) and types of treatment (e.g., prescription medicine versus herbs). Clearly, a practice that is unfamiliar to an educator is just that—unfamiliar. In their work with families, educators learn about health beliefs and practices other than those learned in their own families or at school, and use this knowledge and experience in health curriculum development. The differences in cultural practices can be overshadowed by socioeconomic factors.

> There may be more similarities between the health beliefs or practices of different ethno-cultural groups at the same socio-economic level than there are among the people within the same ethno-cultural groups who are from different socio-economic levels. (Masi et al. 1993, 8)

In other words, if you are wealthy you probably have more in common with others who are wealthy than you do with people who are poor and from your ethno-cultural background. The reverse is true also.

Socioeconomic Factors Affecting Well-Being

The socioeconomic gradient in health status has been a pattern for over a century in all industrialized, wealthy societies. This pattern can be stated simply: "From birth to death, higher socio-economic status is related to better academic achievement, lower rates of illness and even lower rates of accidents and suicides" (Bertrand 2001, 4). Children who are poor are likely to be living in unhealthy environments that are beyond their ability to change. Poverty usually means food insecurity, substandard housing (e.g., cold, damp, drafty, crowded) in unsafe areas, inadequate clothing, and no access to safe play and recreation opportunities. These living conditions result in a higher incidence of disease, hospitalization, and deaths due to injuries. Families in poverty rarely see reason to hope for improvement in their situation.

It is difficult for children to develop a future-oriented attitude toward health (e.g., health prevention) when the world they live in is filled with daily crises (e.g., uncertainty over when they will have food). Children who live in families that are comfortable financially have more reason to believe that they have control over and can affect their health.

Peers, Community, and the Media

As children grow older, the influence of their peers, community, and the media can have either a positive or negative effect on their health. Sam was eating a variety of nutritious foods until he was six years old; then he told his mom that he could bring in only those foods that his friends approved. Similarly, Olivia stopped washing her hands because it wasn't "cool" with her friends. On the other hand, if peers are excited about healthy habits or have positive views of health, they tend to influence one another positively. Children's willingness to try new foods that peers, possibly from different ethno-cultural backgrounds, bring in fosters an openness that promotes health. Friends who are willing to wait while their peers wash their hands are making a statement about health.

The community—neighbourhood, early childhood program, school, recreation centre—in which children live also affects their overall well-being and influences their view of health.

Every morning the program's playground is strewn with broken glass and discarded needles, syringes, and condoms from the night before. To date, nothing proactive has been done to change this and the children are getting the impression that we have to accept the situation.

Children, educators, parents, and the police work together to develop a plan of action that results in changing the situation. Children see firsthand that it is possible to have an impact on our health.

The media influence children's understanding of health and perceptions of what is healthy. This varies with the age of children and how much television they watch. Children who watch a lot of television and use the Internet regularly are inundated with themes and messages, some of which have negative influences on their understanding of physical, emotional, and social well-being. Parents must take an active role in selecting the types of TV programs, videos, and computer games that their children are exposed to. Whenever possible, parents should interact with them to answer questions, clarify, and ensure that they are getting positive, health-promoting messages.

Developing and Implementing a Health Curriculum

Many of the programs' healthy practices are important for all of us in our everyday lives—hand washing, dental care, healthy eating, physical activity, stress management. The hygiene practices described in Unit 3 are not of particular educational interest to children, even though they have a direct impact on their health (e.g., food storage, sanitation of mouthing toys). Providing a health curriculum in a program is more than occasionally reading a children's book about a health-related issue. Table 8.2 consists of guidelines for appropriate and inappropriate health curricula for children that educators can refer to in evaluating their curriculum.

Health Needs and Interests of Children

Certain health education topics or behaviour are more appropriate to introduce at particular ages and developmental stages. Beginning to learn about germs, for example, makes much more sense to preschoolers than it does to infants. The following discussion is by no means exhaustive, but it indicates typical health areas of need or interest for each age group. Of course, each group of young children in early childhood programs is unique, and these general ideas must be tailored to the group.

Infants and Toddlers

The focus in a health curriculum for infants and toddlers is on adults caring for children's health needs and modelling healthy attitudes and behaviour.

TABLE 8.2   **Developing a Health Curriculum Guidelines**

APPROPRIATE HEALTH CURRICULUM

GUIDELINES	EXAMPLES
focuses on the children's developmental needs, interests, and level of understanding	Preschooler's interest and readiness to learn simple safety rules that can be practised, such as "stay away from matches" or "stop, drop, and roll" if clothes catch fire.
is interactive—children learn best when they interact with people and materials in their environment (play-based or fit into their daily lives)	Toddlers are encouraged, but not forced, to try new foods (e.g., pineapple). They can see peers and educators eating the food, hear its name, observe it with their other senses, and have opportunities in the home living centre to play with lifelike fruits and vegetables. They are learning about the food and therefore more likely to try it.
acknowledges children's rights through participation	The educator supports the children's ideas for incorporating a safety rule for a new activity according to their developing capacities.
has clear and reasonable objectives for children's learning based on developmental areas (cognitive, physical, emotional, social)	The primary objective for the preschool cooking experience is to encourage the child to follow a sequence. Secondary objectives include sensory exploration, cause and effect, promoting turn taking, and small-motor skills.
is organized so that much of the health curriculum happens as part of the program's routines—hand washing, rest and relaxation, physical activity, healthy eating, and so on	Infants' hands are washed by the educator after diapering and before eating; school-agers are encouraged to respond to their body cues, such as needing to rest or drink water after vigorous physical activity.
includes practices modelled by educators	Children see educators washing their hands after helping a child in the washroom and before eating with the children.
fits into the natural daily, weekly, monthly, and seasonal rhythm of the program	From the spring to the fall harvest is an ideal time to learn about growing vegetables and flowers from seeds.
is integrated into all curriculum areas—music, movement, science, literature, and so on	Preschooler body awareness: <ul><li>art—body tracing on paper; children paint in body parts</li><li>music—songs about bodies</li><li>creative movement—body games, challenging children to explore their bodies with questions such as "How tall/small can you be?" "How high can you jump?" "How angry/happy can you look?"</li><li>science—use a magnifying glass to look at skin</li><li>literature—many children's books (e.g., *The Bare Naked Book*)</li><li>numeracy—graph particular body characteristics (e.g., skin, hair and eye colour, "inny" or "outy" bellybuttons) by printing names or placing photos of children on paper</li><li>dramatic play—a full-length mirror</li></ul>

| TABLE 8.2 | Developing a Health Curriculum: Guidelines (continued) |

APPROPRIATE HEALTH CURRICULUM

GUIDELINES	EXAMPLES
is flexible so that educators can take advantage of teachable moments or one-to-one interactions	Answer a preschooler's question during a food experience (e.g., "Why are vegetables good for me?"); show a toddler how to sneeze into the sleeve after the child has sneezed without covering his or her mouth.
builds self-esteem and competence, moving from simple to complex	Use simple three-step recipe cards for "ants on a log" (celery, cream cheese, raisins), allowing children to feel accomplishment in completing a task independently.
is respectful and inclusive of family beliefs, practices, and situations	A parent regularly comes in and teaches tai chi to the school-age children and educators and discusses its advantages to reduce stress in mind and body.
focuses on the concrete rather than the abstract, and on present rather than future health	Say "Physical activity helps your body work better" rather than "Physical activity now lowers your risk of heart disease when you are an adult."
emphasizes all aspects of health, so that children begin to develop an awareness of holistic health involving physical, emotional, and social well-being	Healthy eating is viewed not only in terms of its effect on growth and physical well-being but also on mental alertness: if you eat well, you learn better and you have opportunities to spend enjoyable, relaxed social time with your friends while eating.
moves toward increased understanding and responsibility for their own health with knowledge about what aspects of their health are in their control	Emphasize to preschoolers that making hand washing a habit before eating and after toileting is something they can take responsibility for, something that helps them take control over how often they get sick; let preschoolers know that they have no control over how safely an adult drives a car, but they do have control over putting on their seat belts to protect themselves.

INAPPROPRIATE HEALTH CURRICULUM

PRACTICES	EXAMPLES
a series of lessons are formally taught to children	Talking (or lecturing) to children about do's and don'ts of hygiene without hands-on practice does not allow interaction with children; reading a book about sexuality in group time is inappropriate.
is based on themes, so a health area is highlighted for a week but is not a priority for the rest of the year	Peacemaking is introduced as a week's theme in the school-agers' room, when a conflict is in the news. For the remainder of the year, the principles of peacemaking are ignored by educators, and children are not developing the skills to put peacemaking into practice.
is based on the adults' health interests rather than the children's interests	An educator who does aerobics every day conducts daily instructional exercises and loses patience with the toddlers when they don't seem interested in the activity.
is designed or implemented in a way that instills fear, an inappropriate sense of responsibility, or groundless vulnerability in the child	An educator pressures preschoolers to eat everything on their plate because children elsewhere are starving; an educator cautions children to never talk to strangers because they may hurt them.

Environments that support infants' and toddlers' emotional health and development are ones in which children feel safe and secure and trust that adults will meet their physical, emotional, and social needs and respond to their cues. In order to achieve such environments, early childhood programs need to

- establish effective ongoing communication with parents (e.g., practices around separation for child and parent that promote trust)
- implement good hygiene practice, ensure safety, and actively involve children in routines. This would include as many one-to-one or small group experiences as possible. The very young child learns about health by experiencing healthy environments and by educators' actions. For example:
  - responding to infants' and toddlers' verbalization, and talking about the activity's process, including naming parts of the body while diapering, while toileting, and during other routines
  - encouraging the child's involvement in undressing (e.g., diapering, getting into sleeper for nap after outdoor play) and older toddlers' involvement with dressing
  - hand washing with children, who become increasingly involved as time goes on
- provide opportunities for children's bodies moving in space, minimizing restriction except for safety reasons
- relate physical activities to growth and development, such as short flexible tunnels for budding crawlers and large foam blocks for climbers
- ensure that infants are given a spoon and are encouraged to be as involved as they would like to be in self-feeding. Be patient with toddlers' learning table behaviour and respectful of cultural practices in eating that differ from yours (e.g., using hands to eat, or an adult feeding a child). Establish basic limits: Food is not to be thrown, for example
- offer opportunities for various sensory experiences, including foods with interesting natural colours and textures, as appropriate
- serve nutritious food, encouraging preference for whole foods without a lot of processing and added sugar, salt, and additives
- monitor and control sudden loud noises in the program because of young children's fears. When adults who are unfamiliar to the children visit the program, or when the children are outside, be sensitive to the children's responses. Support children in daily separation from parents.

Toilet learning often begins somewhere between 18 and 36 months. The term "learning" highlights children's active role in this process. As with most aspects of working with children, educators should follow the child's lead. Readiness for using the toilet is demonstrated when all three of the following are observed in a child:

- physical maturity—stays dry for several hours, can get to the toilet, pulls down loose-fitting pants

- awareness—of a full bladder or bowel; the child understands that she or he has wet or soiled diapers
- desire—to use the toilet (or potty) and to have a dry diaper

When all three aspects of readiness are in place, toilet learning is usually a positive process. Educators in toddler (or preschool) rooms often find that children's desire is high when peers are using the toilet. Children's feelings of self-esteem are paramount in the approach to toilet learning. In the best interests of the child, together parents and educators work to provide support through this period. When there is a difference of opinion on timing or approach to toilet learning, educators and parents work together to reach a compromise.

Preschoolers

This group of children is particularly interested in learning about

- cleanliness, toilet learning and toileting, good grooming, dressing themselves;
- germs and sickness;
- health and safety rules (e.g., cover your mouth when you cough and sneeze, look both ways before crossing street);
- safety and injury prevention, at least on an early-awareness level, and especially using simple rules;
- personal safety, again on an early-awareness level, and following child-centred guidelines (see Personal Safety Programs for Children, page 372);
- community helpers (e.g., role of firefighters, police officers, doctors, nurses, dentists), and especially what happens in a hospital if the child or a friend has been a patient;
- some common fears: fear of the dark, monsters, loud noises (e.g., thunder, truck backfiring), abandonment (especially if divorce, death, hospitalization, or other trauma has occurred);
- food and good nutrition, how and where foods are grown or are eaten, different foods eaten by people and animals;
- the role of sleep and relaxation; and
- the role of physical activity and movement.

The following are usually of more interest and more appropriate developmentally for older preschoolers:

- body awareness, interest in more complex body parts and systems (e.g., internal organs, respiratory system)
- brushing, primary teeth coming out, new teeth coming in
- emotions, own feelings, awareness of similarities and differences (e.g., gender, race), manners, own family and others' families, having babies
- beginning awareness of conflict resolution and peacemaking
- basic understanding of importance of caring for the environment

School-Agers

School-agers are interested in more complex issues and want more details, but they still haven't developed abstract reasoning. The following are some examples that particularly interest them:

- illnesses
- loss of primary teeth, emergence of permanent teeth
- body awareness that is more complex than when younger (e.g., interest in body secretions and body noises, changes with puberty)
- consumer health, especially as reflected in advertisements in television commercials, magazines, product labels, prices
- environmental health issues, particularly issues around landfill sites, over-packaging, air quality, depletion of the ozone layer, animal extinction, and actions we take such as observing the three R's (reduce, reuse, recycle), composting, returning bottles and can, and renewing and refinishing
- personal feelings, making friends, family dynamics, getting along with others (e.g., bullies, peacemaking)
- human rights: racism, sexism, classism, homophobia, and concern for those whose rights have not been respected
- safety and injury prevention (e.g., bicycle, pedestrian, playground, home safety, first-aid treatments)
- awareness of own stressors and positive ways to deal with stress
- how the body works (e.g., how nutrition, rest, and physical activity interrelate)
- physical fitness
- foods friends eat that may be different from theirs, and nutrients in foods
- self-care, as in learning to make snacks and meals independently, knowing what to do in an emergency, finding out about personal safety and street-proofing
- community awareness, and with support from adults work with others to affect health in the community (e.g., neighbourhood, school, early childhood program)

Younger school-agers might also be afraid of ghosts and other supernatural beings. As they get older, they may have more concrete fears such as being lost or kidnapped, being disliked, or real-life catastrophes (e.g., floods, fires, armed conflicts).

Older school-agers may be afraid of being humiliated in front of their friends, being the victim of physical violence, family breakup or changes, looking or acting strange, news reports of war on television (some children arriving in Canada have firsthand experience), or terrorist attacks.

Getting Down to the Health Curriculum

When health is viewed holistically, countless topics and issues can be included in a program's health curriculum. Although this section does not include a multitude of ready-to-use activities for different age groups, it does offer suggestions for implementing health curricula in a selected number of health-related topics (see Resource Materials, page 458). From here, students will be able to take what they learn from the entire discussion on health curricula and develop a curriculum on topics of their choice. Of course, any specific curriculum must always be based on the needs and interests of the particular group of children as they emerge. The following topics are discussed in more detail in connection with the guidelines for the various age groups:

- environmental health
- nutrition education
- dental health
- hand washing and germs

Environmental Health Education

Over the past decade, concern about the health of our planet, which ultimately affects all life, has been a major educational focus for everyone. Lots of resources are available that encourage public involvement in environmental health. Of course, increased knowledge is essential for changes in public and personal attitudes and behaviour that will positively affect the earth.

Children can learn good helping habits and may even be involved in community action to improve the environment. However, we must never imply or state that children are solely responsible for the future of the planet. Because children have reached only the early stages of cognitive and moral development, they are liable to take this message seriously. Feelings of guilt (e.g., whenever a child uses a paper product), fear or hopelessness for the future, and other feelings will contribute to children's stress levels. They may begin to view the onerous task of saving the planet as theirs alone and become consumed by it.

Environmental health education can be a part of the everyday life at home and in programs. Adults who "live gently"—a term used to refer to a way of living that respects life, uses resources without wasting, and causes minimal harm to the planet—are helping children to learn about environmental health. Programs model these practices by

- participating in recycling programs, where available. The most common recycling programs are community-wide and accept glass, plastics, cardboard, and newspapers. Recycling can also include clothing, winter boots and coats, skates, and toy swaps in early childhood programs and between early childhood programs;
- composting. Some local waste management programs also accept food waste for composting;
- choosing products that are safer for the environment (e.g., cloth diapers or use of a recycling system for disposable diapers, biodegradable products). Refer to *Hidden Exposures: A Practical Guide to Creating a Healthy Environment For You and Your Children* in Resource Materials, page 459;
- using energy efficiently;

- repairing, remodeling, and reusing, when possible;
- respecting ecosystems.

Refer to Healthy Spaces, the interactive website hosted by the Canadian Institute for Child Health and the Canadian Child Care Federation that provides information on healthy indoor and outdoor child care and home environments (see Resource Materials, page 458).

Within programs, educators need to be aware of the messages they are sending to children about their role in saving the earth. Our goal is for children to develop a positive attitude and belief that they can make change happen, and to incorporate actions that contribute to that change, but not to be overwhelmed with a sense of personal responsibility.

Infants and Toddlers

Environmental education for infants and toddlers should focus on role modelling. Children observing educators who respect plants, trees, animals, and insects on walks, and children guided by gentle reminders when handling nature inappropriately (e.g., plucking flower petals, stomping on earthworms), are on their way to becoming environmental advocates. However, it is important to remember that, developmentally, these very young children are egocentric and that going beyond this level of environmental education would not be good practice.

Preschoolers

As with all learning, preschoolers build on what they have already experienced with the environment. For preschoolers to develop respect for the environment, they first need to learn about it. However, environmental concepts and issues are complex. Since children learn from the simple to the complex, educators begin with simpler versions of relevant concepts for preschoolers. They learn best when they interact with people and objects.

The environmental concept of life cycles can be introduced at the preschool level in a number of ways. Planting and harvesting, composting, and observing trees change with the seasons are ways that help preschool children begin to understand nature. Ideally, a respect for nature is a part of everyone's value system. "The world needs people who may not necessarily love earthworms or spiders, but who respect the role they play in the environment" (Lewis-Webber 1993, 3). Educators need to provide experiences through the seasons that serve as springboards for observing, investigating, discovering, and learning about the environment through nature. Adults, including ECE students and educators, sometimes feel that they do not know enough about nature, but they can learn along with children. Adults who demonstrate a quest for learning, rather than pretending to know everything, actually provide very good role modelling.

Children can express their interest in the environment in all areas of the program's curriculum:

- *Art.* Use easels outdoors to inspire children to paint their representation of trees or their feelings about trees; make leaf rubbings.
- *Music.* Sing songs about nature or create chants; identify sounds of nature.
- *Creative movement.* Express the rhythms of the earth or move like wind, water, and so on.
- *Science.* Care for a living thing through planting and gardening; adopt a tree in the park and see how it changes with the seasons.
- *Literature.* Read and discuss books about nature or about legends that involve nature, possibly stories from the children's backgrounds (e.g., Native Canadian legends embody nature).
- *Numeracy.* Compare sizes and shapes of plants, seriate, classify.
- *Dramatic play.* Add a small recycling box in the home living centre; play jungle animals; transform the play area into a forest with trees and animals.
- *Field trips.* Walk in your neighbourhood in the different seasons; visit a botanical garden, recycling plant, community playground, garden centre, farm, orchard, bird sanctuary, pond.

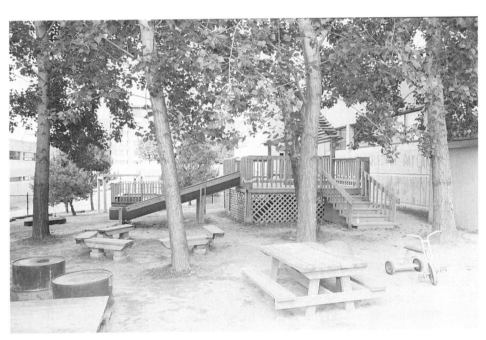

Though they are still young, preschoolers could become involved at a simple level with community action, along with their parents or educators.

City developers were planning to cut down trees in the program's neighbourhood to build a parking lot. Educators and concerned parents involved the children in a walk of support for the park, the trees, and the play area. The event got media attention. As well, pictures the children drew of the park and trees were enclosed in a letter to the mayor.

Educators must be careful to ensure that participation of this kind does not instill fear, that children understand the purpose of what they are doing, and that they are not being exploited to gain public support for adults' issues. Many complex environmental issues are beyond a preschooler's cognitive level of understanding (e.g., animal extinction).

Today's preschoolers will become the adults who make major environmental decisions in the future. The interest in, knowledge of, and concern for the environment that begin in their preschool years will eventually benefit everyone.

School-Agers

In our community, this age group is already targeted more than any other with regard to environmental education resources. School-agers, especially those who have reached a concrete-operational level of thinking, can have a fuller understanding of environmental issues, particularly if they have had environmental experiences earlier in life. Children are becoming interested in the democratic process. Those who have been developing decision-making and coping skills may have been involved in some social action. Any number of approaches and activities can be part of school-age early childhood programs. Through a discovery approach supported by educators who believe in the importance of living gently, school-agers can get involved in meaningful and practical experiences. For example, two books by Larraine Roulston, *Pee Wee and the Magical Compost Heap* and *Pee Wee's Great Adventure: A Guide to Vermicomposting,* were designed to teach 5- to 10-year-olds the facts and process of composting (see Resource Materials, page 459). Through their experiences, school-agers acquire the knowledge and life skills to develop their confidence as change agents. They may also be interested in becoming involved in community action with such activities as writing letters to policymakers about environmental issues that affect them, such as residential pesticide use.

. . . .

e.g. When children put their energy into contributing to change, a health promotion philosophy is put into practice.

. . . .

By planning and networking with teachers in the children's school, ideally the educators and teachers can coordinate their environmental health policies and practices. As well, they can find out how much time is spent on the environment in the classroom. Your efforts will be in vain if children become turned off environmental education rather than motivated and excited by it.

Nutrition Education

Nutrition is the easiest health area to integrate throughout the curriculum and from infancy to school age. The possibilities for learning are endless but usually centre on some general concepts. The following nutrition concepts can be appropriately incorporated into children's nutrition experiences:

- Everyone needs food in order to grow, feel good, and have energy to do things.
- A wide variety of foods is available and it is best for our body if we have variety every day.

- Foods have unique colours, flavours, textures, smells, sizes, shapes, and sounds.
- Foods that are unfamiliar to you are enjoyed by other people. Trying new foods helps you to learn about yourself and the world, and to gain respect for and insight into other ethno-cultural backgrounds.
- Everyone has individual food likes and dislikes.
- Food should be respected for its role in fulfilling needs—and should not be used for art activities.
- Foods have different sources (e.g., some grow on trees or in the ground, some come from animals).
- Foods are made up of nutrients, and the foods that have more nutrients are better for our body.
- The way that food is handled and cooked affects the amount of nutrients in it, its safety, and its taste.
- Food provides the opportunity for social time, and the rights of self and others are considered through the sharing of food.

Nutrition experiences help children to develop cognitively, physically, emotionally, and socially. Here are some examples of how food can be incorporated into all areas of the program's curriculum:

- *Art.* Use magazines and grocery store fliers to create collages of various foods; food cartons to be recycled after use can be painted or used in box sculpture; draw pictures of how you feel eating different foods (e.g., puckered face after eating a lemon). Using food that will not be eaten in art and craft activities is unacceptable and disrespectful of food and of those who do not have enough to eat.
- *Music.* Sing songs about foods; the words to familiar children's songs can be modified to include nutrition messages.
- *Creative movement.* Pretend to be fruits or vegetables planted, picked, harvested, falling to the ground.
- *Science.* Design activities using one or more senses (e.g., discovery box with foods inside to touch and describe before eating). Grow foods (e.g., gardening in plots or boxes). Compare fruits and vegetables (e.g., fresh, frozen, canned, dried).
- *Literature.* Read books about food, cooking, gardening (e.g., *The Sandwich* or *Everyone Eats Rice* to support issues of diversity).
- *Numeracy.* Use scales and measures to compare weights of foods.
- *Social studies.* Share foods and eating customs with others—activities particularly relevant for older preschool and school-age children. Examples are foods eaten for Dwali, harvest foods, haggis, foods for Kwanza celebrations, the origin or invention of certain foods and eating implements, cooking equipment, utensils).
- *Dramatic play.* Set up a grocery store (e.g., empty cracker and cereal boxes), restaurant, or pizzeria, and provide lifelike food. Use cooking and eating utensils that reflect ethno-cultural diversity.

- *Field trips.* Visit a grocery store, market, bakery, farm, local garden, or health food store, or invite a child's family member to come and cook a traditional dish.

Cooking with Children

Cooking with children is an ideal way to begin their nutrition education. Snacks provide an opportunity each day for children to have food experiences. Food preparation calls on children to use their five senses, to learn about colours, shapes, and textures, and to use simple kitchen utensils. Children can begin to learn the basic principles of hygiene and food safety, and of course take pride in their accomplishments and eat the "fruits" of their labour. Even older infants love to squeeze bananas or help mash potatoes. When children enjoy cooking and eating nutritious foods, and develop food preparation skills, they may be inclined to have a more balanced lifestyle as they get older. Current public health concerns about the mass consumption of unhealthy food, particularly convenience foods with high contents of trans fats, salt, and sugar, require changes in eating habits. Table 8.3 offers suggestions for snacks that children can make.

TABLE 8.3	Snacks Children Can Make
AGE GROUP	**SNACK IDEAS**
Infants	simple fruit salad, mashed banana, applesauce, blended mango pudding, cottage cheese with a face made with Cheerios, frozen fruit juice on sticks, finger gelatin made with fruit juice and plain gelatin, well-cooked carrot sticks with yogurt dip,* smoothed avocado on crackers, fruit and yogurt blender drinks
Toddlers	devilled eggs using yogurt instead of mayonnaise, cottage cheese salad with crushed pineapple, porridge for a teddy bear picnic, ants on a log (e.g., bread sticks with apple butter and Rice Crispies), fruit or vegetable and cheese kabobs using Popsicle sticks, frozen bananas on sticks served with yogurt or applesauce dips, banana coins in orange juice, nutritious milk shakes
Preschoolers	English muffin pizzas, dippidy-doo and vegetables too*, guacamole and corn tortilla chips, pita sandwiches, unidentified frying objects (i.e., cut circle out of slice of bread and fry with an egg in the hole), homemade butter (shake cream) for sandwiches or crackers, vegetable ("stone") soup, yogurt and fruit sundaes, "people" sandwiches (e.g., hummus on circles of bread with grated carrots, alfalfa sprouts, apple smiles, sunflower seeds, banana coins, etc., to make faces)
School-Agers	tacos, three-bean salad, muffins, baked apples, rice pudding, Waldorf salad, banana-egg pancakes, chop suey, stir-fried vegetables, pretzels, fondue, stuffed pita, hummus with crackers, sticky rice

* Provide children with individual dishes of dip. Double dipping in a communal dish spreads germs.

The Five W's of Cooking with Children

Who?

The ideal educator–child ratios:

- infants 1:1
- toddlers 1:2
- preschoolers 1:3
- school-agers 1:4 maximum

The worst situation:
A large group of children with one educator.

These ratios promote safe cooking practices and allow for individual participation.

What?

Two ways of cooking with children:

- small group with an educator, usually using a recipe that makes enough food for a number of children (e.g., baking)
- individual children following the recipe, often called "production-line cooking," usually using a recipe that makes individual portions

Select nutritious foods that are developmentally appropriate and do not pose a risk for choking. Ensure that allergies and food restrictions (religious, ethno-cultural) are considered in planning any food experience.

Children learn from following recipes:

1. the names of food and food mixtures
2. sequential learning: recipes that are based on developmental appropriateness, for example
   - two steps for infants
   - three to four steps for toddlers
   - four to six steps for preschoolers
   - eight steps maximum for school-agers
3. measuring ingredients

Pictorial and written recipe cards are particularly useful for preschoolers and school-agers. They incorporate sequencing and pre-reading skills (or reading, for older children) into the experience, and children learn that a lot of food preparation involves recipes. For pre-readers, there should be many illustrations with just a few words. It is possible to use one recipe card listing all the steps (e.g., on a piece of construction paper). For individual portion cooking, a set of recipe cards (one card for each step) makes it easier for children to do one step and then move to the next station.

Tips in making recipe cards:

- Cut out pictures or drawings of food, cooking equipment, and utensils used in each step.

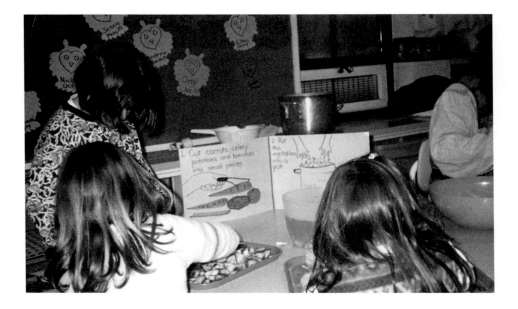

- Use a dot system rather than numbers to indicate each step, particularly for pre-schoolers (e.g., one dot on the first card, two dots on the second).
- Laminate for durability with repeated use.

As children become more familiar with the printed word, you may want to create recipe cards that combine pictures and words (e.g., have a picture of the apple, and print the word apple, or use the dots and symbol for the number two). For readers, the recipe's steps can be presented in a chart format.

When?

The ideal time is during play time, as one choice among several activities. This way, you may be able to work with smaller groups at a time and repeat the recipe until all children who want to can do it. With the ideal number of children (or close to it), you are able to focus on each child's questions, reactions, and so on, and each child is truly involved in the process. Your role as facilitator is very important. If children are independently doing a production-line recipe, ensure that other children are not waiting in line. This creates an antisocial climate. Instead, children can sign up and come at their turn.

The worst time is during a circle time or other large group times. It is not realistic to expect a large number of children to work together at something that needs only a few. Passing a bowl around while each child has one stir is not learning—it creates frustration and your role is focused on crowd control rather than on facilitating.

Where?

The ideal place:
In a low-traffic area located close to running water and an electrical outlet, if needed.

The worst place:
In a noisy, busy area.

Why?

Food experiences (or cooking) with children can be positive in many ways:

- Everyone needs to eat!
- When children are involved in food preparation, they are more likely to try the food.
- Cooking is usually an enjoyable experience for children. They are proud of their accomplishments, which builds self-esteem.

Any well-planned food experience has many advantages for children:

1. Cognitive opportunities are made available and facilitated through foods.
   - Children can see similarities and differences (classification).
   - They can experience temporal relations (sense of time and sequence).
   - They can develop a sense of quantity and measurement.
   - They can problem-solve (e.g., What will happen if…?).
   - They can take part in matching (one-to-one correspondence).
   - They can learn about growing plants.
   - They can learn about the origins of foods, such as eggs from chickens, milk from cows and goats.
   - They can see the effect of temperature on substances (e.g., freezing fruit juice, frying potato pancakes, baking muffins).

2. Educators use opportunities to build language skills through food routines and nutritional learning experiences (e.g., by using the correct terms for foods, equipment, cooking processes, discussions about foods, and by following recipe cards).

3. Children regularly have the opportunity to participate in food preparation. This can be integrated into the everyday curriculum. In addition to viewing meal and snack preparation as important aspects of everyday life, children build their cooking skills and have opportunities for cooperation and for appreciating a wider repertoire of foods, enhancing their ethno-cultural learning. Appendix 8.2 (page 464) has a list of breads and some recipes. Most ethno-cultural groups have particular breads that are either staples or are familiar to them.

4. Food experiences involve both girls and boys, promoting an atmosphere of equity in both food preparation and cleanup.

To enhance the cooking experience, educators should follow these recommendations.

1. Prepare for the activity:
   - try out the recipe before using it with the children.
   - Ensure that all ingredients and equipment are available and in working order.
   - Check carefully for any food allergies or restrictions.

2. Promote safety:
   ■ Have all necessary equipment and ingredients set out in a safe location before beginning the activity (involve school-agers in this aspect).
   ■ Explain and demonstrate all safety aspects to the children before starting (e.g., using knives) and practise these precautions during the activity.
   ■ Follow food safety tips:
      – The table is cleaned and sanitized before you begin.
      – Everyone, including you, washes hands before setting up the ingredients, utensils, and equipment.
      – Consider using an apron or some type of cover-up.
      – If the snack is not to be eaten immediately, it is stored safely (e.g., blender drinks in the fridge).
      – The utensils, equipment, and table are cleaned and sanitized when finished.

3. Facilitate the activity:
   ■ Encourage every child to participate.
   ■ Be receptive to the questions and feelings of each child.
   ■ Show interest and enjoyment in the activity through facial expression, tone of voice, body language, flexibility, and positive interactions with children.
   ■ Ask questions that encourage problem solving.
   ■ Use positive guidance throughout the activity.

4. Evaluate the activity after it is over:
   ■ Were the expectations appropriate for children's learning?

- Did each child have opportunities to actively participate?
- Was the time frame appropriate?
- What follow-up experiences would be meaningful?

It is important to involve families in your nutritional education curriculum. Some family members may be available to come in and make a favourite recipe with the children; others may send in a recipe or a food that has special meaning in ethno-cultural or religious events. Programs may also find ways to share families' favourite recipes through newsletters, bulletin boards, cookbook projects (possible fundraiser), and potluck events throughout the year.

Dental Health Education

Dental health education is a good example of children learning through a daily routine. Dental care is a lifelong health habit. Educators are in an ideal position to take an active role in ensuring that children's teeth are protected and to help children learn good dental health practices. Taking good care of teeth and gums is important in maintaining dental health, and so are regular dental checkups, to respond to problems early. For families who are financially comfortable, professional dental care is usually not a problem. Many of these parents have dental benefits through their employers. Families with a low income but not on social assistance are often in a position where they do not have dental benefits, and the family budget may not be able to include the costs of a dentist.

By around age two, children have 20 primary (or baby) teeth. Between ages 5 and 13, primary teeth start to loosen and fall out as the permanent teeth underneath begin pushing through the gums. Most children start by losing the lower two front teeth and then the top two, creating the classic gap-toothed smile. The back four molars are some of the first permanent teeth to come in, around age six; special care is needed in brushing and flossing these back teeth.

Everyone gets plaque. This thick, sticky bacterial layer is constantly on our teeth. The bacteria in the plaque mix with food in our mouth to produce an acid that begins eroding the enamel layer of our teeth. While saliva helps to neutralize the acid and rinse food out of our mouth, it can't do it all. Brushing and flossing are needed to remove food and plaque; if the plaque stays there, it hardens and causes tartar, which leads to tooth decay. Brushing our teeth before going to sleep is a good practice. When we are asleep we don't produce as much saliva, so the bacteria and food left in our mouth produces acid that eats at enamel.

Do not prop baby bottles or put children to sleep with a bottle. It is not advisable for the following reasons.

- These practices allow formula or milk (which contain natural sugars) to pool in the mouth for a long period of time. Babies' teeth are soft and very susceptible to acid and decay. Nursing bottle syndrome can happen very quickly, leading to the painful decay of primary teeth. Dull white spots or lines can appear on newly erupted teeth seemingly overnight. Parents are encouraged to see a dentist as soon as possible if this happens.

- Children should not be put to bed even with a bottle of water. This practice increases the child's risk of choking. Children who need the extra comfort of sucking for sleeping could be offered a soother.

- Sucking is a natural and normal developmental need in young children. Although parents and physicians have different opinions about the use of bottles and soothers, dentists are concerned about the child's teeth when usage continues after age five. If an older child (aged four or five) still derives comfort and security from soothers or thumb sucking, adults must take care to help the child find a replacement. This is important for children's emotional well-being.

- Children's eustachian tubes are shorter and straighter than adults'. When children lie on their back with a bottle in their mouth, the liquid and saliva may run back into the middle ear and cause an ear infection.

How Do We Promote Dental Health?

Fluoride is a mineral that strengthens tooth enamel. People who live in communities in which the drinking water is supplied through a water treatment plant probably haven't given much thought to fluoride. In many places, fluoride is added to the drinking water before it reaches our homes, which is a decision made by each community's public health agency. Other sources of fluoride are toothpaste, fluoride drops prescribed by physicians, and fluoride treatments by dentists.

Limit the amounts of high-sugar foods offered, particularly sticky ones (e.g., raisins, granola bars, pop, hard candies) or foods with cooked starch (e.g., potato chips, bread, potatoes). Sugars mix with the bacteria to quickly produce acid. Choose nutritious foods, especially fresh fruit and vegetables, plain yogurts, cheese, and milk. Frequent snacking (or grazing) is discouraged because food is in our mouth so often that acid production is frequent.

Ideally, we should brush our teeth after every meal and snack, and floss at least once a day. When this is not possible, we should at least try to rinse our mouth with water. The Canadian Dental Association recommends that parents thoroughly brush their young children's teeth once a day. This is in addition to the children learning how to brush their teeth themselves. Parents should also floss their child's teeth once a day until the child has the skill to floss his or her own teeth.

In programs, educators are encouraged to have children brush their teeth at least once during the day. For many programs, this follows lunch time as children begin the transition to a nap or quiet activity. On field trips, children can rinse their mouth with water. Flossing is difficult in programs because of the extra time and demands involved.

Tips for brushing:
- Use a soft toothbrush.
- Add toothpaste. Use a small dab for infants and toddlers; preschoolers need an amount only about the size of a pea. Be careful that the tip of the tube doesn't touch the brush. An educator will need to help younger children to

put on the paste, especially if one tube is used for everyone. Some programs find that it is easier and that it promotes independence if each child has his or her own tube of toothpaste.

- Follow the three-step method (see Figure 8.1) and brush or supervise the child's brushing. Start at the far lower-back teeth, using a "wiggling," not a scrubbing, motion. Move around the mouth, wiggling the brush on all the surfaces. Don't forget to brush the tongue to fight bacteria and freshen the breath.
- Teach children not to swallow the toothpaste; rinse with water and spit.
- Rinse the brushes well.

| FIGURE 8.1 | **Brushing Pattern** |

Tips for toothbrushes:

- Use a baby toothbrush for infants and toddlers and a child-sized one for children up to 12 years old.
- Each child must have his or her own brush and must never share it.
- Label each child's toothbrush and store it to dry where air will circulate around it and where it doesn't touch other toothbrushes. Educators often have to be very creative in designing a convenient, hygienic storage method.
- Keep out of reach of children to ensure that brushes are not used by different children and as a safety precaution. Children must learn not to run or walk around with a toothbrush in their mouth.
- Replace brushes when the bristles begin to flatten, after the child has been ill with a cold or the flu, or at least twice a year.

Infants and toddlers:

When toddlers are able to stand at the sink, they are able to participate more in brushing. Standing behind the toddler and facing the mirror tends to be a convenient position. Educators may either do the brushing for the child or hold the brush with the toddler. For older toddlers, the educator carefully supervises.

Preschoolers and school-agers:

With experience, preschoolers become skilled at brushing, and the educator eventually needs only to supervise rather than be actively involved. Most school-agers are able to brush their teeth without supervision and have gained more responsibility and independence in self-care. Although some children simply don't like brushing their teeth or don't like one more routine, most children appreciate the immediate results: brighter teeth and a clean-tasting mouth. Involve children in planning and preparing dentally healthy snacks. Educators can also encourage children to be aware of healthy food choices and explain how some foods promote dental health.

e.g. The program has the children brush their teeth after lunch. However, for afternoon snack a child's birthday cake is served. Because there is sugar and sticky icing on the cake, the children brush their teeth again after snack that day.

Learning about dental health can be incorporated into all areas of the program's curriculum:

- *Art.* Paint and draw pictures of food; create a big set of teeth with egg cartons.
- *Creative movement.* Children can wiggle their bodies like they wiggle the toothbrush, an activity more appropriate for younger preschoolers.
- *Music.* Sing songs (e.g., about smiles: Raffi's "You Brush Your Teeth").
- *Science.* Place a hard-boiled egg in vinegar, which helps to show how enamel dissolves.
- *Literature.* Read books about keeping teeth, losing teeth (e.g., tooth fairy stories such as *Where Do the Fairies Keep All the Teeth?*), and dental health.
- *Numeracy.* Count teeth (e.g., how many molars); classify pictures of foods that are good and bad for your teeth.
- *Lunch time/snacks.* Discuss the importance of our teeth in crunching carrots and biting into apples.
- *Dramatic play.* Set up a dentist's office and provide a variety of real props, including flashlight, mirror, and lab coat.
- *Field trips.* Tour a dentist's office; invite a dental hygienist to talk about dental health.

Hand Washing and Germs

As we discussed in Unit 3, hand washing is the most important routine that we do every day to prevent infections. It is a health practice that children need to learn in order for it to become a lifelong health habit. Like dental health, education about hand washing is based on an ongoing routine in the program, and there are many opportunities to reinforce it.

Infants and Toddlers

The hand-washing routine begins in infancy as part of diapering and feeding routines. Educators talk with infants about what they are doing as they are doing it, making comments like "The water is warm" or "The cloth feels soft and wet." Infants are aware of their hands being washed, and feel that it is part of caring.

Once toddlers are physically able to stand at the sink, educators can help them learn to wash their own hands. It is easier for children to learn the proper way and to make it a habit with practice than it is to change poor habits once they are formed. Educators may make the routine enjoyable for children by singing action songs like "This Is The Way We Wash Our Hands."

Preschoolers

Preschool children are ready for basic information about germs and what hand washing does to germs. During the preschool years, children become skilled at hand washing when adults provide consistent support built on earlier experience. By the time they are independently washing their hands, with educators now only supervising, they can learn some basic information about germs (e.g., germs are on our hands even when they look clean and they hide between fingers and under nails).

How can preschoolers learn about germs when germs can't be seen on hands? As with all aspects of the curriculum, it is essential to encourage active involvement and introduce concepts in a concrete way. Educators reinforce that we are trying to prevent as many germs as we can from entering our bodies. Because our hands touch many things, there are a lot of germs on them. Most children don't walk around with facial tissue in a pocket; rather than not covering their mouth when they sneeze, and rather than sneeze into their hands, they can put their arm in front of their mouth. This prevents germs from getting on their hands.

Since we can't see germs, educators can show preschoolers something to compare to germs. Use a spray bottle to spray water into the air; the water droplets seem to disappear in the air and fall onto objects. Germs in the water now float in the air, and can land anywhere—including on someone else. When we cough and sneeze, droplets of saliva that carry germs spray out. This helps children to understand why covering their mouth before sneezing is a good way to cut down on germs going from one person to another.

Learning about hand washing can be incorporated into different curriculum areas:

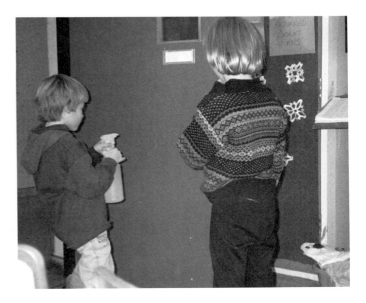

- Art. Draw what they think germs would look like if they could see them.
- Music. Sing songs (e.g., to the tune of "Row, Row, Row Your Boat," "Scrub, scrub, scrub your hands, put the soap between, wash the germs right down the drain, make them nice and clean").
- Science. Put a piece of bread in a jar, and over the next several days invite the children to watch mould grow.
- Literature. Read books (e.g., William! Won't You Wash Your Hands?).
- Dramatic play. Use the water table to wash dolls, including the hands.

■ *Nutrition*. Show how food can be shared without spreading germs (e.g., serving spoons, cutting a sandwich in half rather than taking turns having a bite).

School-Agers

School-age children will be hand washing without supervision, although many need to be reminded. Developmentally, these children are at an age when discussions about germs and the role of hand washing can be more complex.

. . . .

e.g.

Germs are everywhere and some of them help keep us healthy (e.g., penicillin, yogurt). Skin and nose hairs stop some germs from getting into our bodies. Our body has other ways to defend us: tears, saliva, and stomach juices kill some germs when they get into our body.

. . . .

Activities such as growing moulds on foods (e.g., apple core in a jar) or growing germs from fingers on agar in petri dishes are appropriate (contact your local hospital or make an agar mixture with the children.) Children in the concrete operational stage of development can understand that the mouldy apple is the same apple a week later, and the same with the petri dish.

REVISITING THE HEALTH PROMOTION ACTION PLAN

Children need to be consulted and participate meaningfully in the decisions and activities that affect them. The skills that children develop in this process include expressing views, decision making, coping, and public participation. These skills don't happen overnight. It takes practice and confidence to develop them. As children get older, they need experiences that encourage them to see themselves as participants, helpers, or agents of change in their communities. Educators and parents assist children in finding a balance between having confidence in their own skills and abilities and knowing when to depend on adults, the community, and society.

Health promotion is based on the philosophy that individuals can have both personal and public control over their lives, and can improve their own health. Through our awareness, we can make change happen from the individual level to the societal level. Using the four components of the Health Promotion Action Plan presented in Unit 1, the following example highlights this philosophy.

The children and their families who attend a community after-school program are frustrated because safety issues in their playground meant their equipment was removed. To top it off, the municipally funded recreation programs, such as tai chi and basketball, that the educators took the children to each week for no charge instituted user fees as a cost-cutting strategy. At the same time, the municipal medical officer of health was dismayed to learn from a recent Health Canada survey that the citizens in her city were found to be the least physically active in the province. This prompted her to declare physical activity a priority public health issue for the city, with a strategic plan to improve population fitness levels by 2010.

The children, parents and staff talked about their frustration at the mixed messages and barriers in their way, but decided to make their own call to action. Following two group discussions in which the school-agers participated actively and competently, the following outlines their action plan.

Individual Problem Solving and Self-Reliance

The children identified after-school computer use as one of their most powerful distractions from active play, and agreed as a group on a system to limit each child's weekly computer use to two hours.

Educators evaluated how they are incorporating the three types of physical activity (i.e., endurance, flexibility, and strength) into the daily program. Weaker areas of programming (e.g., flexibility) are now receiving attention (e.g., a grandparent is running tai chi classes for the interested children and adults). They ensure, with the children's input, that every program includes play, creative expression, and skills.

In the spirit of *Canada's Physical Activity Guide for Children* (see Appendix 8.1, page 462), over the next six months, the children are helping each other add an additional 10 minutes to their daily physical activity, one month at a time, to incorporate daily active time as part of a healthy lifestyle. They are helping each other by

- suggesting games and encouraging peers to join them;
- helping educators keep large bags of small equipment appealing for the children, sorting out unused or broken equipment on a regular basis, and suggesting new pieces of equipment; and
- encouraging peers to reduce their allotted computer time further, or deciding as a group to reduce it in increments.

Educators have approached the local high-school physical education department with a idea that is a mutually beneficial activity. High-school students under the direction of their teacher are teaching the school-agers team skills in basketball, soccer, and other sports. Students use this experience as co-op placement hours or volunteer hours, while developing employability and life skills.

Community Action

A subcommittee of educators, parents, and children was formed to represent the community centre's interests at community meetings that were held to discuss needs and suggestions. The three goals in the strategic plan are

1. child and youth development,
2. lifelong health and wellness for all, and
3. environmental stewardship.

The subcommittee put together a successful grant proposal for funding to build an adventure playground under the direction of a university urban planning committee with an environmentally sound focus. Although safety (including standards set by the Canadian Standards Association) will be a cornerstone of the project, meaningful ways to involve children and families will be incorporated.

Societal Change

The school-agers, parents, and educators are involved in a letter-writing campaign to their city counsellors highlighting important directions that the policy-makers and funders need to take (Toronto Parks and Recreation Department 2003):

- Restore (or continue) public availability of swimming pools, ice arenas, soccer fields, baseball diamonds, cricket fields, tennis courts, etc.
- Develop standards for providing no-charge recreation programs.
- Reduce barriers to participation by addressing support needs, including transportation, child care, program supplies, and equipment.
- Strive to make all parks and recreation facilities barrier-free.
- Increase the number of youth leadership development programs.
- Target high-needs communities when setting geographic priorities for program and service development.
- Create community capacity by working with community organizations to deliver a wide range of programs reflecting the diverse nature of each community.
- Move beyond indoor facilities to increase the range and number of recreational opportunities in parks and natural areas.
- Help maintain continuous enjoyment of activity throughout life.

CONCLUSION

A holistic view of children's health is based on the premise that the whole child must always be considered. This view is particularly important when discussing issues that at first glance seem to relate to only one dimension of well-being, such as stress (emotional) or rest (physical). We quickly realize that there are physical, emotional, and social considerations for all health issues. Health policies and procedures based on the program's philosophy are written and reviewed regularly to ensure that this holistic view of health is put into practice on an ongoing basis.

A health curriculum is determined by the developmental needs and interests of the children. It is integrated into everyday life at the program. The relevance of the health curriculum to the children's lives as well as viewing children as partners are paramount in planning, implementing, and evaluating a health curriculum.

TO BRUSH OR NOT TO BRUSH?

You and the other preschool educators at your program are pleased that your brushing routine after lunch seems to be working well for the children. Most of the preschoolers independently follow the routine and sometimes make comments like "My mouth feels clean" or "Brushing takes the food out of my teeth."

It is quite challenging to ensure that each child's toothbrush does not touch the next one stored in the container, and a few times the container has toppled to the floor, requiring disinfecting all around. During the annual visit, the public health inspector was concerned about the risk of contamination, particularly because the name labels were coming off the wet brushes.

You and your colleagues now need to decide: can you arrive at a more stringent procedure and storage arrangement, or should you discontinue the routine at the program while encouraging the children to brush at home at least twice a day?

ASSESS YOUR LEARNING

Define terms or describe concepts used in this unit.

- self-regulation
- sexuality
- self-pleasuring
- common, short-term stress factors
- traumatic, long-term stress factors
- coping strategies for stress
- stress-aware environment
- rhythm of the program
- physical activity
- children's understanding of health
- temperament
- health curriculum
- health needs and interests
- 5 W's of cooking with children
- dental health
- nursing bottle syndrome
- bottle-propping

Evaluate your options in each situation.

1. You overhear an ECE student say to a three-year-old, "You have to play with Daniel. We are all friends at day care."

2. While you are on a field trip, a four-year-old boy points to a pregnant woman and asks, "Why is that woman's tummy so big?"

3. A few preschoolers have recently moved to Canada from countries that are much warmer year-round. They are having a difficult time adjusting to winter. The parents have asked you to let them stay inside with another group of children rather than taking them outside to play.

4. You and a classmate have been asked to plan a curriculum to help preschoolers learn about poison prevention. You agree that it would be a good idea to bring in real objects. Next day, your colleague arrives with a bag of potentially hazardous products, including oven, window, and toilet cleaners used at home.

5. The program where you are doing a placement does not promote good nutrition. You are responsible for the weekly after-school cooking club and have submitted your plan to the educator. You would like to begin with simple recipes such as "dippidy-doo and vegetables too" and move to more complex recipes such as soups and breads. The educator discourages you with the comment, "This will never work. The children only want to make cookies and cakes."

RESOURCE MATERIALS

Organizations

Division of Childhood and Adolescence, Population and Public Health Branch, Health Canada, Tunney's Pasture, 1909C2, Ottawa, ON K1A 1B4. Tel (613) 952-1220; fax (613) 952-1556. www.hc-sc.gc.ca/dca-dea/main_e.html

Other Websites of Interest

Canadian Association for Health, Physical Education and Recreation: www.cahperd.ca

Canadian Dental Association: www.cda-adc.ca

Canadian Nature Federation: www.cnf.ca

Healthy Spaces, Canadian Institute of Child Health and Canadian Child Care Federation: www.cfc-efc.ca/healthy-spaces

Kids Have Stress Too!: www.kidshavestresstoo.org

Pollution Probe: www.pollutionprobe.org

Sierra Club of Canada: www.sierraclub.ca

Printed Matter

The ABCs of Caring for Your Child's Teeth (1999), by the Canadian Dental Association. Contact: Canadian Dental Service Plans Inc., 155 Lesmill Road, Toronto, ON M3B 2T8. National toll-free 1-800-561-9401; fax (416) 296-9299.

Earthcycles: Environmental Education with Preschool Children (1993), by M. Lewis-Webber (Winnipeg: Mavis Lewis-Webber).

Feeling Great: Teaching Children to Excel at Living (1998), by Terry Orlick (Creative Bound Publishers).

Growing Up: What It Means for Your Child's Dental Health (1999), by the Canadian Dental Association. Contact: Canadian Dental Service Plans Inc., 155 Lesmill Road, Toronto, ON M3B 2T8. National toll-free 1-800-561-9401; fax (416) 296-9299.

A Guide to School Ground Naturalization: Welcoming the Wilderness (1994), by Evergreen Foundation, 24 Mercer Street, Toronto, ON M5V 1H3. Tel. (416) 596-1495 (Prentice-Hall Canada).

Healthy Foundations: Developing Positive Policies and Programs Regarding Young Children's Learning About Sexuality (1993), by P. Brick (Center for Family Life Education, Planned Parenthood of Greater Northern New Jersey, 575 Main Street, Hackensack, NJ 07601. Tel. [201] 489-1265).

Healthy Habits for Healthy Happy Kids (1991), by Canadian Institute of Child Health (Canadian Institute of Child Health).

Here We Go...Watch Me Grow!: A Preschool Health Curriculum (1991), by C. Hendricks (Network Publications).

Hidden Exposures: A Practical Guide to Creating a Healthy Environment for You and Your Children (2000), by the South Riverdale Community Health Centre (Toronto).

Ideas: The Journal of Emotional Well-Being in Child Care (IDEAS Alliance and George Brown College, Early Childhood Development Department, George Brown College at Ryerson University, P.O. Box 1015, Station B, Toronto, ON M5T 2T9. Tel. [416] 415-5000, ext. 2566).

Keepers of Life: Discovering Plants through Native Stories and Earth Activities for Children (1994), by M.J. Caduto and J. Bruchac (Fifth House).

Keepers of the Animals: Native Stories and Wildlife Activities for Children (1991), by M.J. Caduto and J. Bruchac (Fifth House).

Keepers of the Earth: Native Stories and Environmental Activities for Children (1989), by M.J. Caduto and J. Bruchac (Fifth House).

The Kids' Around the World Cookbook (1994), by D. Robins (Kingfisher).

Moving and Growing: Exercises and Activities for Fives and Sixes (1987), by J. Hansen (Fitness Canada and the Canadian Institute of Child Health).

Moving and Growing: Exercises and Activities for the First Two Years (1983), by M. Dalley (Fitness Canada and the Canadian Institute of Child Health).

Moving and Growing: Exercises and Activities for Twos, Threes and Fours (1984), by M. Dalley (Fitness Canada and the Canadian Institute of Child Health).

Owl (for school-agers) and *Chickadee* (for preschoolers and younger school-agers), two Canadian magazines on nature and environmental topics. For subscriptions: The OWL Group, 49 Front Street East, Suite 200, Toronto, ON M5E 1B3. Tel. (416) 340-2700 or national toll-free 1-800-551-6957; fax (416) 340-9769. www.owlkids.com/chickadee.

Pee Wee and the Magical Compost Heap and *Pee Wee's Great Adventure: A Guide to Vermicomposting,* by Larraine Roulston. Contact Recycling Resource Services at (905) 420-5625 or roulstonlp@sympatico.ca.

Revisting Children's Outdoor Environment: A Focus on Design, Play, and Safety (1999), by Anne Gillian Maufette et al. (Gauvin Presses).

Starbright: Meditations for Children (1991), by M. Garth (HarperCollins Publishers).

Teaching Snacks: Snacktime Learning Opportunities (1994), by G. Bittinger (Warren Publishing).

Zero to Three [journal], National Center for Infants, Toddlers and Families, Suite 200, 2000 M Street NW, Washington, DC 20036. Tel. (202) 638-1144. www.zerotothree.org/index.html.

BIBLIOGRAPHY

American Public Health Association and American Academy of Pediatrics (1992). *Caring for Our Children: National Health and Safety Performance Standards—Guidelines for Out-of-Home Child Care Programs.* Washington, DC: American Public Health Association.

Avery, M. (1994). "Preschool Physical Education: A Practical Approach." *Journal of Physical Education, Research and Development* August: 37–39.

Barker, G. (1994). "The Facts about Fitness: Why Exercise Is Important for Kids." *Today's Parents* 11(7): 25–27.

Benard, B. (1995). "Fostering Resilience in Children." ERIC Clearinghouse on Elementary and Early Childhood Education (ED386327). <www.ericfacility.net/ericdigests/ed386327.html> (July 2003).

Bertrand, J. (2001). *Summary of Research Findings on Children's Developmental Health.* Ottawa: Canadian Child Care Federation/Canadian Institute of Child Health.

Brick, P., N. Davis, M. Fischel, T. Lupo, A. MacVicar, and J. Marshall (1989). *Bodies, Birth and Babies: Sexuality Education in Early Childhood Programs.* Hackensack, NJ: Center for Family Life Education, Planned Parenthood of Greater Northern New Jersey.

Brown, L. (1994). "When Kids Ask about Homosexuality." *The Toronto Star*, 20 September, C1, C3.

Canadian Child Care Federation (2001). *Child Care and Children's Health: Quality Is Vital.* Ottawa: Canadian Health Network.

Cech, M. (1990). *Globalchild: Multicultural Resources for Young Children.* Ottawa: Health and Welfare Canada.

Corbett, S. (1993). "A Complicated Bias." *Young Children* 48(3): 29–31.

Goulet, M., and R. Schroeder (1998). *How Caring Relationships Support Self-Regulation: Video Guide.* Toronto: National Association for the Education of Young Children.

Greenspan, S.I. (1993). *Playground Politics: Understanding the Emotional Life of Your School-Age Child.* Don Mills, ON: Addison-Wesley Publishing.

Guralnick, K.M., and E. Littmann (1992). *Making Friends: A Guide to Using the Assessment of Peer Relations and Planning Interventions.* [Video and guide.] Ottawa: Department of National Health and Welfare.

Kagan, J. (2001). "Born to Be Shy?" In R. Conlon (ed.), *States of Mind: New Discoveries About How Our Brains Make Us Who We Are.* Toronto: John Wiley & Sons.

Kalmanson, B. (1990). "Understanding Children's Responses to Separation." In S.S. Chehrazi (ed.), *Psychosocial Issues in Day Care.* Washington, DC: American Psychiatric Press.

Keating, D.P., and C. Hertzman, eds. (1999). *Developmental Health and the Wealth of Nations: Social, Biological, and Educational Dynamics.* New York: Guildford Press.

La Grange, A., et al. (1994). "Culturally Sensitive Child Care: The Alberta Study." *Interaction* 8(3): 29–32.

Lewis-Webber, M. (1993). *Earthcycles: Environmental Education with Preschool Children.* Winnipeg: Mavis Lewis-Webber.

Maguire, J. (1993). *Your Child's Emotional Health.* Toronto: Macmillan Canada.

Masi, R., L.L. Mensah, and K.A. McLeod, eds. (1993). *Health and Cultures: Exploring the Relationships—Policies, Professional Practice and Education*, vol. 1. Oakville, ON: Mosaic Press.

Musson, S. (1994). *School-Age Care: Theory and Practice.* Don Mills, ON: Addison-Wesley Publishers.

Natapoff, N.J. (1982). "A Developmental Analysis of Children's Ideas of Health." *Health Education Quarterly* 9(2, 3): 34–45.

Shipley, C.D. (2002). *Empowering Children: Play-Based Curriculum for Lifelong Learning*, 3rd ed. Scarborough, ON: Nelson Canada.

Spurgeon, D. (2002). "Childhood Obesity in Canada Has Tripled in Past 20 Years." *British Medical Journal* 324: 1416.

Stansbury, K., and M.R. Gunnar (1994). "Adrenocortical Activity and Emotion Regulation." Monograph: Social Resiliency. *Child Development* 59: 108–34.

Toronto Parks and Recreation Department (2003). *Toward a Healthy, Active Future: Toronto Parks and Recreation in 2010—A Strategic Plan.* Toronto: City of Toronto.

Tremblay, M.S., and J.D. Willms (2000). "Secular Trends in the Body Mass Index of Canadian Children." *Canadian Medical Association Journal* 163(11): 1429–31.

Waxler-Morrison, N., J. Anderson, and G. Richardson, eds. (1990). *Cross-Cultural Caring: A Handbook for Health Professionals in Western Canada.* Vancouver: University of British Columbia Press.

World Health Organization (1983). *Survey of 35 Studies.* Press release. Geneva: WHO Global Program on AIDS.

Canada's Physical Activity Guide for Children

(continues on next page)

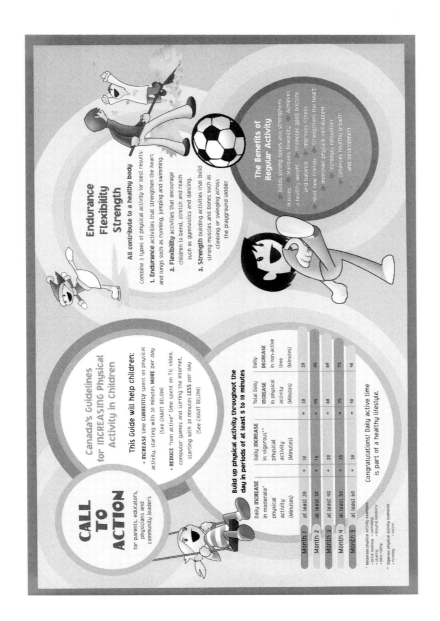

Canada's Physical Activity Guide for Children, Cat. no. H39-611/2002-2E/(2002), Health Canada. Reproduced with the permission of the Minister of Public Works and Government Services Canada, 2003.

Bread

Multicultural snacks need not be exotic and expensive food bought at specialty shops. Start with a very basic food such as bread. Avoid the butter-and-cracker trap and put a variety of breads on your snack plate instead. Slice them, stuff them, spread them, dip them, toast them, or cut them with cookie cutters to make interesting shapes. Some of the breads you may want to use are listed below.

Bagels (Jewish)
Baguette (French)
Bannock bread (early Canadian)
Bran bread
Bread sticks, cheese sticks
Buns
Buttermilk biscuits
Challah (Jewish)
Chapati (Indian)
Christonomo (Italian)
Corn bread
Corn tortillas (Central American)
Croissants (French)
Date bread
Fry bread (Navajo)
Gingerbread
Injera (Ethiopian)
Irish soda bread

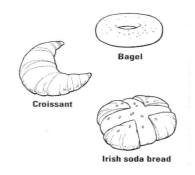

Bagel

Croissant

Irish soda bread

Kamaj (Palestinian)
Klaben (German)
Knackbrod (German)
Laufabrod (Icelandic)
Matzot (Jewish)
Muffins
Nan (Indian)
Pita (Middle Eastern)
Popovers
Potato bread
Pumpernickel
Pumpkin bread
Raisin bread
Roti (Caribbean/East Indian)
Rye bread
Scones
Steamed buns (Chinese)
Taboun (Palestinian)
Whole-wheat bread

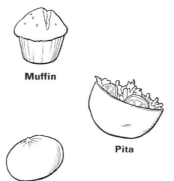

Muffin

Pita

Steamed bun

Show the children photographs of people baking bread. Use Ann Morris's book *Bread, Bread, Bread* (published by Lothrop, Lee, and Shepard, 1989) to give a photo tour of world cultures and the breads native to each. Then buy the bread or try your hand at making some. Unleavened bread or bread leavened by an agent other than yeast is best to make with young children because it is so quick. Try these recipes, adjusting quantities to suit the group. Each recipe serves about 20 children.

Bannock (early Canadian, originally Scottish)

Ingredients:

750 mL flour	30 mL water
dash of salt	10 mL oil
40 mL baking powder	

Method:
1. Use a fork to mix all the dry ingredients.
2. Make a well in the dry ingredients, then pour in the water.
3. Mix the dough by hand, kneading it, then pound it flat.
4. Fry on an oiled griddle until puffy and golden on both sides.

Chapatis (Indian)

Ingredients:

500 mL whole-wheat flour	175 mL water
2 mL salt	

Method:
1. Mix whole-wheat flour, salt, and water to form a stiff dough. Add more water if necessary.
2. Let the dough rest for half an hour, then roll into small balls.
3. Flatten the balls, then fry them on a very hot griddle until brown spots appear on the dough.
4. Take them off the griddle and brush with butter or serve plain.

Tortillas (Mexican)

Ingredients:

625 mL corn flour	10 mL oil
250 mL water	10 mL butter
rolling pin or tortilla press	

Method:
1. Mix corn flour with enough water to make a stiff dough.
2. Roll into small balls, then flatten with a rolling pin or tortilla press.
3. Fry in a lightly oiled pan, turning until cooked.
4. Brush with butter and serve.

Source: Reprinted with permission from M. Cech, *Globalchild: Multicultural Resources for Young Children* (Ottawa, 1990), 43–44.

INDEX

Abuse. *See* Child abuse

Accidents. *See* Injuries

Action plan, health promotion, 22–26
    collective self-help, 23–24
    community action, 24–25
    in early childhood programs, 26
    individual problem-solving and self-reliance, 23
    revisiting the, 83–84, 129–30, 177–78, 250, 331–32, 395–96, 454–56
    societal change, 25–26

Additives. *See* Food processing

Adrenalin, medication, 168, 171–72, 173

AIDS. *See* Human immunodeficiency virus (HIV)

Air quality
    in facilities, 68
    pollution, 323–24

Allergies
    adrenalin, use of, 168, 171–72
    anaphylactic shock, 171
    common allergens, 171
    communication with parents, 172–73
    defined, 170
    managing food allergies in the facility, 173–74
    preventing reactions, 172–74

Alternative care arrangements, 149

Alternative medicine. *See* Complementary medicine

Anaphylactic shock, 171

Antibiotic resistance, 162–65

Arts and crafts, safer products, 66

Aspartame, 212–13

Asthma
    communication with parents, 176–77
    defined, 174–75
    episodes, 175, 177
    managing in the facility, 176–77
    medication for, 175–76

Baby bottle syndrome, 449

Back care. *See* Educators

Basal metabolic rate, 191

Biting
    blood-borne disease transmission, 105–6

Bleach, use of, 125–26

Blood spills, clean-up of, 127–28

Body image
    society's standard of, 21–22, 51–54, 196–98
    school-agers and, 230–31
    self-esteem and, 235

Body Mass Index (BMI), 52

Body weight, 233–35

Bottle feeding, 222–23

bottle propping, 222, 449
    juice, and dental caries, 225
    warming bottles, 249

Botulism, 243–44

Brain development, 404
    stress and, 408

Breast milk, 221–22

Bruises, related to child abuse, 353

Burns
    childhood deaths, 277
    prevention strategies for, 274
    risks of, 276, 277

Canada's Food Guide to Healthy Eating, 201–7, 259–60
    body image, 196–98
    children and, 204–6
    child-sized servings, 204–6
    create your own, 52
    five principles of, 51
    food groups, 202
    key nutrients, 202
    multicultural foods and, 206–7
    other foods, 203
Canadian Standards Association (CSA), 286,
        287–96, 298
Carbohydrates. See Nutrients
Cardiopulmonary resuscitation (CPR)
    training, 281
Caregivers. See Educators
Centres. See Facility
Chickenpox
    children with, 160
    during pregnancy, 60
    immunization for, 110–11
Child abuse
    behavioural indicators of, 363–64
    consequences of, 364–67
    disclosures of, 381–82
    documentation of suspicions, 384–86, 390
    female genital mutilation (FGM), 355–56
    identifying suspicions of, 377–79
    sexual offenders, 360–61
    shaken baby syndrome, 354–55
    working with abused children, 392–93
    working with abusive parents, 394
    working with child protection agency, 391–93
Child abuse by educators
    acting on suspicions of, 390–91
    primary prevention, 374–77
Child abuse, causes, 367–68
Child abuse, defined, 352
    emotional, defined, 359–60
    neglect, defined, 361–62
    physical, defined, 352–59
    sexual, defined, 360–61

Child abuse prevention
    communication with parents, 369–72, 383–84,
        394
    personal safety programs, 372–73
    primary, educators' role, 369–77
    providing a secure facility environment, 370–72,
        375–76, 393
    role of child protection agency, 368–69
    secondary, educators' role, 377–91
    tertiary, educators' role, 391–94
Child abuse, reporting
    educators' legal responsibility, 386–87
    hesitation in reporting, 387
    reporting suspicions of, 386–87
Child care. See Early childhood education and care
Child protection agency, 368–69
    investigative process, 388–87
    programs' involvement with, 391–93
    reporting to, 386–87
Choking, suffocating, and strangling
    bottle propping, 449
    childhood deaths, 277
    clothing, 273, 275, 277
    defined, 277
    food, 243
    prevention strategies for, 273, 275
    risks of, 243, 273, 275, 277, 449
Cleaning
    defined, 123
    gloves for, 128
    products, environmentally friendly, 67, 164
    products, safe use, 66–68, 127–28
    rationale for, 123–24
    steps to, 126
    toys, 124
    See also Sanitizing
Climbing equipment. See Indoor play;
        Outdoor play
CMV. See Cytomegalovirus
Colds, 156–57
    vehicle of transmission, air, 106
Communicable diseases. See Infectious diseases
Communication
    health documentation, 143–46, 152–55
    literacy, 11–13
    role of directors, 71–72
    skills, 11–13, 80–81

with parents, 32–33, 136–37, 328–31
with physicians, 146, 148–49
See also Documentation
Community
    health centres, 17
    networking with the, 36, 37, 373
    role in health promotion, 4–5
Complementary medicine, 18–19, 61
    See also Medication
Complementary protein, 208
Conjunctivitis (pinkeye), 159–60
Conventional medicine, 16
Convulsions, febrile, 141
Cooking with children, 444–49
Crib safety, 284
    table, 285
Cross-contamination, food safety practices, 243–46
CSA. *See* Canadian Standards Association
Culture
    communication with parents, 34–35
    defined, 34
    health beliefs, 34–35, 351–52, 431–32
    resolving cultural conflicts, 34–35
    See also Ethno-culture
Curriculum, health. *See* Health curriculum, planning
    considerations
Cytomegalovirus
    during pregnancy, 60–61

DEET, 314
Defence mechanisms, 101–2
Dehydration
    diarrhea, risk of, 158–59
    summer, risk of, 310–11
Dental health, 449–52
    bottle propping, 449
    curriculum, 452
    juice in bottles, 225
    nursing bottle syndrome, 449
    plaque, defined, 449
    promotion, 450–52
    toothbrushing, 450–52
    tooth decay, 449
Determinants of health. *See* Health
Development, child
    brain, 404
    healthy, 9–10

self-regulation, 405, 406
sexuality, 414–16
social, 403–7
understanding of health, 428–30
Diapers
    types of, 118
Diapering, 118–22
    contamination of facility, 118–21
    disposable gloves for, 121–22
    rationale for routine, 120–21
    sanitizing change table, 121
    steps to, 119
    use of ointments, 120
    vehicle of transmission, stool, 106
Diarrhea, 158–59
Dieting, 196–98
Directors
    role of, 71–72
Discipline, 356–59
    objective of, 357
Discrimination
    determinants of health, 10–11
    persons who are HIV positive, 32
    poverty and, 11
    race and, 10–11
    sexual orientation and, 420–21
    toward male caregivers, 76–77
    See also Culture
Disinfecting. *See* Sanitizing
Diversity, family, 32–35, 195–96, 232–33,
    351–52
Doctor's notes. *See* Communication
Documentation
    administering medications, 167–70
    allergies, 172–74
    asthma, 176–77
    caregivers' injuries, 69–70, 344–46
    children's injuries, 327, 344–45
    health observations, 143–46, 150–55
    infant and toddler, form, 150–51
    suspicions of child abuse, 384–86, 390
    See also Communication
Domestic violence
    children witnessing, 359–60, 378–81
    identifying suspected, 378–81
    disclosures of, 380, 381
    educators living with, 58–59

Drowning
    childhood deaths, 372
    prevention strategies for, 275–76
    risks of, 372, 375

Ear infections (otitis media), 157–58
Early childhood education and care
    advocating for quality, 29–30
    elements of quality, 28–29
    environment, supportive, 70–77
    partnership with parents in, 32–33
    policies, 30–32
    regulations, 26–27
    See also Community
Eating concerns
    body weight, 233–35
    communication with parents, 232–33
    developmental, 231
    ethno-culture, 232–33
    food insecurity, 232
    personal preferences, 232
Eating, developmental considerations
    infants, 220–27
    preschoolers, 229–30
    school-agers, 230–31
    table, 217–19
    toddlers, 227–29
Eating environment, positive, 216, 219, 220
Eating habits, factors affecting
    body image, 21–22, 151, 191–99
    developmental, 216, 217–19
    economics, 198–99
    emotional, 193–94
    food meanings, 194
    physical, 191–93
    social and cultural, 195–96
Educators
    back care and, 61–66, 92
    balanced lifestyle and, 50–59
    child abuse and, 374–77, 390–91
    facility environment, supportive of, 70–80
    feelings about child abuse, 350–52
    healthy practices, self-assessment for, 95–97
    leisure and, 56–57
    infectious diseases and, 59–61, 93–94
    male, 74–77
    musculoskeletal, preventing injuries of, 61–66, 92

nutrition, 50–54
physical activity and, 54–56, 90–91
professionalism, 70, 71, 78–79, 80–82
reducing risk factors of, 57–59
rest and, 56–57
risks of workplace physical injury, 63–70
role of, 72–74
stress factors of, 77–80
turnover, 48
wellness, dimensions of, 49–50, 89
Emergencies, 326
    training for, 281, 326
Emotional abuse. *See* Child abuse, defined
Encroachment area, defined, 287, 289
    table, 290–95
Environmental health issues
    air pollution, 323–24
    children's vulnerability, 322–23
    environmental health concerns, 323–26
    lead, 324
    pesticides, 325
    pressure-treated wood, 287
    PVCs, 325–26
    workplace, 68–69
Environmentally friendly cleaning products, table, 67
Environmental health education, 439–42
Ethno-culture
    defined, 34
    eating habits, 193, 194, 195–96
    foods and, 206–7, 232–33
    variety of breads, 464–65
    See also Culture
Exclusion
    alternative care arrangements, 149
    children, 146–49
    parents understanding of, 147–48
    staff, 59, 93–94
    table, 182–87
Exercise. *See* Physical activity

Facility
    building/structural features, 68–69
    environment checklist, healthy work, 95–97
    layout and furnishings, 63–66
    policies, 30–32
Failure to thrive, 362

Falls
    childhood injuries, 277–78
    prevention strategies for, 273
    risks of, 275
Fat, children and, 204–5
    dietary, 203–4
    food labels, 209–10, 215
    function of, table, 200
Female genital mutilation, 355–56
Fever, 141–43
Field trips, 318–21
    identification of children on, 320
    planning, 319–20
    supervision on, 320
First aid
    frostbite, 317
    tongue frozen to metal, 317
    training, 281, 326
Fluoride, 450
Food-borne illness, 242–48
Food groups. *See* Canada's Food Guide to Healthy
        Eating
Food irradiation, 213–14
Food insecurity. *See* Poverty
Food jags
    defined, 229
    development, table, 217, 218
Food meanings, 193–94
Food processing
    additives, 211–14
    aspartame, 212–13
    food irradiation, 213–14
    genetically modified organisms, 213–14
    nitrates and nitrites, 212
    pesticides, 213
Food safety practices, 242–48
    cooking equipment and surfaces, 245
    danger zone, 245
    handling, 201, 245–46
    microwave ovens, 248–49
    personal hygiene, 244–45
    spoilage, 246–47
    storage, 247
    vehicle of transmission, food, 106
Formula, infant, 250
    bottle feeding, 222–23
    warming bottles, 249

Frostbite, 315–17
    defined, 317
    first aid for, 317
Furniture, 63, 65–66, 283–84

Garbage containers, 248
Gastrointestinal infections. *See* Diarrhea
Genetically modified organisms, 213–14
German measles. *See* Rubella
Germs, defined, 103
    curriculum and, 452–54
    life of viruses, 104
    spread by insects and rodents, 247–48
Gloves
    disposable, 121–22
    during cleaning and sanitizing, 128
    rubber, 123
Group size, quality ECE programs, 27, 69, 298

Hand washing, 113–17
    curriculum and, 452–54
    steps to, 116
    steps to, infants and toddlers, 117–18
    supplies, 114–16
    when, 114
Head lice, 161–62
Health
    care systems, 13–15
    defined, 3–4
    determinants of, 4–13
    prevention, 19–22
    prevention, defined, 19
    promotion, 20–22
    promotion defined, 20
    See also Health care system, Canada
Health care, children
    alternative care arrangements, 149
    communication with parents, 136–37,
        143–46
    educators' role in, 136–37
    exclusion, 146–49, 182–87
    medical examinations of, 137–38, 146
    observations, 138–41, 143–45
    See also Infectious diseases
Health care, community
    conventional, 16
    alternative or complementary, 18–19, 61

Health care system, Canada, 13–15
    changing attitudes toward, 15–19
    medicare, 13
    personal, 14–15
    public, 15
Health, caregivers. *See* Educators
Health curriculum, planning considerations
    children's cognitive development, 428–30
    children's family health beliefs, 431–32
    guidelines, table, 434–35
    interests of infants and toddlers, 433,
        436–37
    interests of preschoolers, 437
    interests of school-agers, 438
    socio-economic factors, 432
    social influences, 432–33
    temperament, 430–31
Health curriculum, topics
    dental health, 449–52
    environmental health, 439–42
    hand washing and germs, 452–54
    nutrition, 442–49
Health promotion, 19–22
    action plan, 22–26, 36–37
    community's role in, 4–13
    defined, 20
    individual's role in, 4–13
    integrating prevention into, 20–22
    public health's role in, 68
    quality ECE programs and, 26–37
    See also Action Plan; Health
Health records. *See* Documentation
Hepatitis B
    adults, prevention of, 57, 59–60, 106–7
    immunization for, 110, 111
    transmission of, 105, 106–7
Heredity, as health determinant, 4
High-chair safety, table, 285
Host, defined, 104
    new, defined, 107
Human immunodeficiency virus (HIV)
    adults, prevention of, 57, 106–7
    breast milk and, 222
    confidentiality and, 105
    policy discussion about, 32
    testing for, 105
    transmission of, 105, 106–7

Humidex, 312–13
Hygiene personal, defined, 140
Hygiene practices. *See* Diapering; Food safety prac-
        tices; Hand washing; Infection control;
        Toileting

Illness. *See* Infectious diseases
Immunity, 102
    See also Immunization
Immunization, 109–13
    adults and, 110
    adverse reactions, 113
    immune globulin, 105, 113
    records, 112
    schedule, table, 111
Income. *See* Poverty
Indoor play
    equipment, 284, 286
    supervision, 299
Infection control, 107–28
    cleaning and sanitizing routines, 123–28, 164
    how germs spread, understanding, 102–8
    hygiene practices and, 113–23
    implementing routines, 127
    universal precautions, 127–28
    See also Cleaning; Diapering; Hand washing;
        Sanitizing; Toileting
Infectious diseases
common childhood, 156–62
    during pregnancy, 60–61
    exclusion of educators, table, 93–94
    exclusion of children, 146–49,163–64
    exclusion table, 182–87
    risks to educators, 59–61
Infestation, insects and rodents, 247–48
Injuries
    background of children's, 266–79
    child development and, 267–69
    educators', 61–66, 71
    learning from serious occurrences, 281–82
    program-related, 269–71
    reports for educators', 69–70
    reports for children's, 327
    report form, 344–46
    types of, 266, 271–79
    See also Safety, prevention strategies; Child
        abuse, defined

Insects
    infestation, 247–48
    stings, allergies, 171
    using repellent, 314
Isolation. *See* Exclusion

Kitchens. *See* Food safety practices

Lead, 324
Leisure. *See* Rest and leisure
Lice, head, 161–62
Life skills, 11–13
Lighting, in facilities, 68

Massage, infant, 422–23
Masturbation, defined, 414–15
Meals. *See* Eating environment, positive; Menu planning
Medical examinations, children, 137–38, 146
Medicare
    five principles of, 13
Medication, 165–70
    adrenalin, 168, 171–72, 173
    asthma, 175–76
    fevers and, 143
    naturopathic and homeopathic, 166
    over-the-counter, 165–67
    parents' written consent for, 167
    prescription, 165–66
    preventing errors, 169–70
    safe administration of, 167–69
    See also Antibiotic resistance
Menu planning, 239–42
    checklist, table, 242
    rotation, 240
    samples of, 161, 162
    snacks, 237–38
    steps in, 240–41
Microwave ovens, 248–49
Milk
    breast milk and formula, 221–23
    recommendations for children, 204
Minerals. *See* Nutrients
Motor vehicle collisions
    childhood injuries, 272
    prevention strategies for, 276
    risks of, 274
Multicultural foods. *See* Ethno-culture

Naps
    need for, 422
    supervision during, 298–99
Neglect. *See* Child abuse, defined
Networking. *See* Community
Nitrates and nitrites, 212
Noise levels, in facilities, 68–69
Nursing bottle syndrome, 449
Nutrients
    defined, 200
    functions and sources of, tables, 200, 256–58
    key, 202
    role of, 200–1
Nutrition
    community action, example of, 23–26
    concerns about over- and undereating, 231–35
    curriculum, 442–49
    defined, 190
    educators, personal, 50–54
    introducing new foods, 223–27
    labels, 209–11, 215
    programs for children, 238–39
    providing food in programs, 235–39
    vegetarianism, 207–9
    See also Canada's Food Guide to Healthy Eating;
        Eating environments, positive; Eating habits,
        factors affecting
Nutrition, infants, 220–27
    bottle feeding, 222–23
    breast milk and formula, 221–22
    communication with parents, 225
    first foods for, 223–24
    juice, dental caries, 225
    serving sizes, table, 227
    warming bottles, 249
Nutrition, preschoolers, 229–30
Nutrition, school-agers, 230–31
Nutrition, toddlers, 227–29
    food jags, 229
    new foods, 228

Obesity
    concerns about overeating, 231–35
    physical activity and, 423
    See also Body image
Observations, health
    baseline, 138–41

documentation of, 143–46, 152–55

forms, 150–51, 152, 153, 154–55

sharing with parents, 144–45

sharing with physicians, 146

signs and symptoms, 139–41

throughout the day, 139

Observations, nutrition

developmental characteristics, related to eating, table, 217–18

over- and undereating, 231–35

Observations, occupational health

risks and recommendations, table, 64

Observations, safety

identifying risks through, 279–80

implementing prevention strategies, table, 273–76

Occupational health. *See* Educators; Facility

Oral hygiene. *See* Dental health

Oral rehydration solution (ORS), 158

Otitis media. *See* Ear infections

Outdoor play

equipment, 286–97

suggested facilities and equipment, tables, 288–89, 290–96

supervision, 300–1

See also Protective surfaces

Overeating, 231–35

See also Body image

Parents

cultural diversity, 10–11, 34–35

educators supporting, related to child abuse, 392–94

family diversity, 351–52

gay families, 421

intoxicated, 330–31

non-custodial, 330, 394

partnerships with, 32–33

Pesticides, 213, 325

Physical abuse. *See* Child abuse, defined

Physical activity

active living, guide, 90–91

checklist, 427–28

children's need for, 423–28

educators' need for, 54–56

educators' role for infants' and toddlers', 425–26

educators' role for preschoolers' and school-agers', 426–27

nutrition and, 191–92

summer and, 308–14

winter and, 314–18

Piaget, J., 428

Pinkeye (conjunctivitis), 159–60

Play. *See* Indoor play; Outdoor play

Playground. *See* Outdoor play

Playpen safety, table, 285

Poison-proofing, defined, 279

Poisoning

childhood injuries, 278–79

food, 243–47

insect repellents and, 314

risks of, 274

prevention strategies for, 276

See also Environmental health issues

Policies, program, 30–32

allergies, 172–74

asthma, 176–77

authorized persons, 329–30

child abuse, table, 375–76

children's sexuality, 418

effective health, 30–32, 136–37

exclusion of educators, 59, 93–94

exclusion of children, 146–49, 182–87

manual, 31

nutrition, 236

occupational health, 71–72

quality ECE program, 30–32

riding toys and bicycles, 277–78

walks and field trips, 318

Pollution. *See* Air quality; Environmental health issues

Poverty

affecting nutrition, 198–99

environmental risks, 323

health determinants, 5–9, 432

risk for child abuse, 367

Pressure-treated wood, 287

Professionalism, 70, 71, 78–79, 80–82

Protective surfaces, 286–97

related to falls, 277

table, 290–96

Protein. *See* Nutrients; Vegetarianism

Public health

agency, 15, 68

medical officer of health's responsibilities to facilities, 15, 148–49

system, role of, 15
Punishment, corporal, 356–59
    defined, 356
PVC, 325–26

Quality ECE programs. *See* Early childhood
    education and care

Racism. *See* Discrimination
Ratios, educator–child
    cooking with children, 445
    quality care, related to, 27–28
    supervision, 298
Record-keeping. *See* Documentation
Rest and leisure
    caregivers, need for, 56–57
    children, need for, 422
    infant massage, 422–23
    relaxation techniques, 56–57, 422
Rubella
    during pregnancy, 60
    exclusion for, table, 187
Rules, safety, 302–8
    examples of, 306–8
    guidelines for, 304–6

Safety, prevention strategies
    at pickup times, 328–31
    class A, B, and C hazards, 298
    checks, 297–98, 338–43
    indoor play equipment, 284, 286
    infant and toddler equipment, 284, 285
    outdoor play equipment, 286–97
    rules, 302–8
    summer, 308–14
    table, 273–76
    winter, 314–18
    See also Safety, supervision
Safety promotion
    physical environment, 282–97
    reviewing injury reports, 281–82, 327
    role of training, 281–82, 326
Safety, supervision, 335–39
    communication with parents, 328–31
    during nap time, 298–99
    indoor play and, 299
    intermittent supervision, defined, 328
    outdoor play and, 300–1

preventing missing children and, 301–2
school-age children, 328–29
See also Field trips
Salmonella, 244, 247
Salt, food labels, 215
Sanitizing
    bleach for, 125–26
    blood spills, 127–28
    defined, 124
    gloves for, 128
    products, safe use, 127–28
    steps to, 126
    toys, 124
    universal precautions, 127–28
    water tables, 124–25
    See also Cleaning
Seizures, febrile, 141
Self-pleasuring, defined, 414–15
Self-regulation, 405, 406
Semi-solid food. *See* Nutrition, infants
Separation anxiety for children, 408–9
Serious occurrences
    learning from, 281–82
Sexual abuse. *See* Child abuse, defined
Sexuality, 414–21
    communication with parents, 417–19
    development of children's, 414–16
    educators' role as sex educators, 419–20
Shaken baby syndrome, 354–55
Sickness. *See* Infectious diseases
Signs and symptoms. *See* Health care, children;
    Observations, health
Skin cancer, 309
Sleep. *See* Naps; Rest and leisure
Smoking
    health risk, 19, 21, 57–58
Snacks
    children preparing, table, 444
    dentally healthy choices, 450
    morning, 237–38
    See also Menu planning
Soap, hand-washing, 114–15
Soothers
    dental health, 450
    strings, risk of strangling, 273, 275
Spanking, 358–59
    reducing incidence of, 371–72
Spousal abuse. *See* Domestic Violence

Staff. *See* Caregivers

Strangling. *See* Choking, suffocating, and strangling

Stress-aware environment, strategies for, 410–12

Stress, educators
    balanced lifestyle and, 50–59, 77–79
    preventing child abuse, 374–77
    stress factors, 77–80

Stress, defined, 77
    coping, defined, 77

Stress, children, 408–14
    factors of, 409
    helping them cope, 410–12, 412–14
    signs of, 410

Stress, parental
    risk factor for child abuse, 367–68
    supportive educators during, 371–72, 394

Stroller safety, table, 285

Sudden infant death syndrome (SIDS), 299

Sugar, food labels, 215

Summer safety, 308–14

Sunburn, 311

Sun protection factor (SPF), 309

Sunscreen, 309–10
    PABA, 309–10

Temperament, 430–31

Temperature, body. *See* Fever

Teeth. *See* Dental health

Toileting, 122–23
    steps to, 122

Toothbrushing, 450–52

Towels, hand-washing, 115–16

Toys
    mouthing, cleaning and sanitizing, 124
    risk of choking, 273, 275

Transitions, program, 411

Transmission of germs
    blood-borne infections, 105, 106–7
    insects and rodents, 247–48
    vehicles of, 104–7

Turnover, caregiver, 48

Unauthorized persons, 329

Undereating, 231–35
    See also Body image

Universal precautions, 127–28

UV index, 309, 310, 312–13

Vaccination. *See* Immunization

Vegetarianism, 207–9

Violence
    child witnessing domestic, 359–60, 378–81
    corporal punishment, 356–59
    educators living with domestic, 58–59

Vitamins. *See* Nutrients

Walks
    discouraging the use of ropes on, 320–21
    planning, 318–21

Walkers, 284

Water, drinking. *See* Nutrients

Water tables
    hygiene practices for, 125
    infants and toddlers, 124–25

West Nile virus, 314

Weight. *See* Body image; Overeating; Undereating

Wind chill factor, 316

Winter, safety, 314–18

Workplace hazards. *See* Caregivers; Facility; Injuries

Workplaces hazardous materials information system
    (WHMIS), 67–68